LTE and the Evolution to 4G Wireless

Design and Measurement Challenges

Printed in China

ISBN 978-988-17935-1-5

Credits

Publisher : Agilent Technologies

Editor-in-Chief : Moray Rumney

Program Manager : Jan Whitacre

Managing Editor : Mary Jane Pahls

Technical Editors : Dr. Michael Leung, Phil Lorch

Cover Design : Dr. Michael Leung

Compositor : Vivian Lee

Foreword

The introduction of any new access technology into the current mobile telecommunication network is going to be filled with challenges, and not all of them can be anticipated. For network operators, convincing tech-savvy customers that new is better will need more than a marketing effort; it will need demonstrable results. The one thing that connects a customer to the network operator is the mobile device or handset. If that device does not appear to work in a variety of situations, then inevitably good reputations will be lost, customers may leave, and ultimately revenue and profits will suffer. No matter how big the investment in the new technology, mastering the physics of the mobile device and its supporting network is the foundation of success.

Expectations are high for Long Term Evolution, or LTE as it commonly called. But these expectations are based on the premise of fault-free performance. Therefore, LTE's initial success will be determined by the ability of handset and radio infrastructure manufacturers to deliver products that conform to 3GPP standards and are robust enough to allow operators to introduce improved services without disruption. Product testing is essential, but it can also be expensive and time-consuming. Manufacturers of new LTE products will have to make difficult decisions regarding what elements require rigorous procedures such as conformance testing and what can be safely left to testing in the field. The bottom line is that compromised quality or outright failure is unacceptable, costing more in the long run if it affects thousands or even millions of users.

Whatever the strategy a manufacturer adopts, the telecommunications test industry will once again play the important (but often unenviable) role of providing the equipment necessary to protect the huge investments made by LTE equipment manufacturers so that they, in turn, can fulfil the demands of the operators.

The reality is that operators, manufacturers and the test industry need to work together closely as they try to establish competitive advantage. The scale of investment required to introduce LTE is likely to be the factor that brings about its success, as all players realise the common goal of making the new technology work. In this respect I have seen cooperation between competitors at all levels, whether it is in a 3GPP Standards meeting room with the sharing of work or consensus building, or even at the commercial level where compromises often have to be made to adapt to shifting moods in the market place.

Standards for new technology are essential, but proving adherence to those standards is a serious and expensive task. One approach to managing risk during LTE introduction can be found in the work of the Global Certification Forum (GCF). In March 2008, GCF initiated a process to define the criteria against which the first LTE devices can be certified; this will ensure GCF is well placed to assume market requirements prior to full scale development of conformance test cases. Here is an example of cross-industry commitment and cooperation. To start with, much consensus building was required between operators and manufacturers to select and prioritise the conformance tests being developed by 3GPP TSG RAN WG5. With that selection came the increased confidence needed to invest resources into developing the most relevant test specifications and test platforms in a timely manner. The GCF processes, along with the benefits to be gained by the industry, are explained in this book.

Leading test companies such as Agilent understand the technical challenges ahead. This working knowledge, coupled with an appreciation of market requirements such as device certification and a sensitivity to the needs of their manufacturer customers, qualifies Agilent to weigh in on the complexities and test challenges of LTE. Although no one person or one company can fully comprehend all aspects of LTE, this book sets out to give practical information to practicing engineers who are or will be working with LTE technology. In so doing, the authors are helping prepare the way for successful LTE deployment.

Phil Brown
Chair of 3GPP TSG RAN WG5
Chair of the Global Certification Forum Steering Group 2008

Preface

The next generation of cellular technology will dramatically alter the communications landscape, changing the way people access information and interact with one another. At the forefront of the new technology is LTE, the Long-Term Evolution of UMTS, developed by the Third Generation Partnership Project (3GPP). LTE promises consumers a new level of mobile broadband access while ensuring that network operators achieve greater operational efficiencies and reduced cost of service. The further evolution of LTE through the LTE-Advanced project will become 3GPP's submission to the ITU-R IMT-Advanced (4G) program.

While the idea of a new technology is exciting, turning it into reality takes thousands of hours of engineering development. This book is intended to help make the task easier. The engineers at Agilent have contributed their insights to provide readers with an understanding of LTE that comes from working with the technology on a daily basis, both in the lab and on the committees that are defining the LTE standards. As Agilent engineers, they also have a unique measurement perspective to offer. The authors have shared the best, most current information from Agilent and its partner Anite to help ensure the success of LTE and future generations of cellular technology. The book is not intended, however, to substitute for reading the standards.

Chapter 1 introduces LTE with an overview of the technology's objectives, services and architecture. The chapter covers the standards process and status of the LTE/SAE Trial Initiative (LSTI).

Chapter 2 discusses air interface concepts, including the OFDMA modulation scheme used for the downlink, the new SC-FDMA uplink modulation scheme and multiple antenna techniques such as MIMO.

Chapter 3 gives more detail about the air interface design. The chapter describes the downlink and uplink frame structures and defines the physical signals and channels. Multiplexing, channel coding and physical layer measurements are covered. The procedures for the physical layer and radio access are explained along with radio resource management.

Chapter 4 covers upper layer signalling including the specifications for access stratum signalling and non-access stratum protocol states and transitions.

Chapter 5 introduces the System Architecture Evolution (SAE), which is the evolution of the core network towards an all-IP system. The SAE is being developed concurrently with the LTE air interface.

Chapter 6 turns to the challenges of system design and testing. The chapter begins by exploring how to use LTE simulation tools to design a system and translate simulations into real signals for testing. This leads to a discussion of testing the new DigRF standard that provides a digital interface between the baseband and RF integrated circuits. Considerable time is spent discussing likely design issues and the challenges of testing LTE receivers and transmitters at the physical and transport channel layers. MIMO test challenges are also addressed in detail. Other sections cover signalling protocol development and network monitoring and troubleshooting.

Chapter 7 covers RF and signalling conformance testing and the role of the Global Certification Forum (GCF) and PCS Type Certification Review Board (PTCRB).

Chapter 8 concludes with a forward look at how LTE will be developed further into LTE-Advanced, in anticipation of being adopted as a 4G standard by the ITU-R.

Acknowledgements

The management team of Agilent's Global LTE Initiative would like to recognize the valuable insights and hard work of the many contributors to this book.

Moray Rumney has done an outstanding job of defining the book's focus and the content. He spent many hours writing, working with other authors and editing to give the book its final shape.

Dr. Michael Leung's enthusiasm was instrumental in getting this project started and his encouragement and support kept it going over many months.

Many experts provided valuable input and comments on the content. We would like to recognize Jinbiao Xu, Mike Hurst, Yuqin Shen, Andrea Leonardi, Dan Aubertin, Bob Cutler, Phil Lorch, Jing Ya, Hongwei Kong, Dan Jaeger and Juergen Placht for their contributions.

Our special thanks go to Mary Jane Pahls for all her hard work. Without her dedication to the project, it would never have happened. The editors also wish to thank our compositor, Vivian Lee, of Agilent. We thank Agilent and our managers for providing their support and encouragement in the book's creation.

The 3GPP standardization process involves people from all over the world. We wish to acknowledge the work of our colleagues in creating the LTE standards documents. Without these documents, this book would not be possible.

Finally, we are grateful for our families who provided understanding and support during our long hours to complete this work.

Jan Whitacre
LTE Program Lead and Project Director
Agilent Technologies

April 2009

Author Biographies

Randy Becker

Randy Becker obtained his BSE with a major in Electrical Engineering from Walla Walla College in 1997 and an MSEE from the University in Nebraska in 1999. He then joined Hewlett-Packard/Agilent Technologies where he has worked for 10 years in a variety of technical marketing roles. Randy started as a marketing engineer in the Spectrum Analysis Division; two years later he moved to the Signal Sources Division where he stayed for eight years. Randy is currently a senior application engineer supporting various cellular technologies with a focus in W-CDMA and LTE.

Peter Cain

Peter Cain is a wireless solution planner working for Agilent's Wireless Business Unit near Edinburgh, Scotland. Since joining Hewlett-Packard/Agilent Technologies in 1985, Peter has had a variety of roles as an RF engineer, project manager and marketing specialist. Over the last decade he has directed solution plans and written application notes for Bluetooth, Wireless LAN, Ultra Wideband and Mobile WiMAX™. Most recently he has applied his knowledge of MIMO to LTE. Peter obtained a first class degree in Electronic Engineering at Southampton University in 1981.

Steve Charlton

Steve Charlton is currently working for Anite Telecoms Ltd. as part of their LTE Layer 2 development team. An engineer for more than 30 years, Steve has been primarily involved in real-time embedded systems, mostly in the telecoms arena.

Niranjan Das

Niranjan Kumar Das is currently working with Anite Telecoms Ltd. and has primary responsibility for the development of the MME protocols for Anite's test system. After graduating in 1999 with a BE in Computer Science from Dibrugarh University, India, Niranjan has been mainly involved with 3GPP Layer 3 protocol development in UMTS and LTE.

Sandy Fraser

Sandy Fraser is a 25-year veteran of the RF and microwave industry with expertise spanning DC to 100 GHz applied to such diverse technologies as space and military products and Infrared. Sandy's career includes over 15 years' experience with a cellular radio focus. During the last nine years with Agilent Technologies, Sandy has focused on base station emulators for manufacturing test instruments, including the 8922 and the E5515B/C. Today he is the product manager for GSM and EGPRS R&D test solutions and a leader in LTE technology awareness and training, specializing in LTE protocol and signalling. Sandy is a well-published author and his papers and presentations are appreciated by a global audience. He holds a BSc in Mechanical Engineering from Glasgow University.

Peter Goldsack

Peter Goldsack is an R&D engineer at Agilent Technologies. He has a BS in Mathematics from Edinburgh University, Scotland, and an MS in Electronics from Napier University, also in Edinburgh. Peter has worked at Hewlett-Packard/Agilent Technologies for the past 14 years in a variety of roles within R&D and marketing. He has developed protocol stacks for GSM, GPRS, EGPRS and LTE and worked in a technical marketing role on GSM, GPRS, EGPRS, W-CDMA, HSDPA, HSUPA and WiMAX™. Currently his primary responsibility is developing LTE solutions for cellular R&D customers.

Jean-Philippe Gregoire

Jean-Philippe Gregoire received a Masters in Electrical Engineering (microelectronics) from the Université de Liège, Belgium, in 2001. He joined Agilent Technologies the same year. Since then Jean-Philippe has contributed significantly to various projects — from specification to implementation — focusing on baseband digital with a specific interest in MIMO. As member of Agilent Labs, he currently leads a research program on closed loop MIMO and multichannel fading in a European collaborative framework. Jean-Philippe is the author of several patent applications and technical papers in the field of signal processing, MIMO and OFDM systems.

Craig Grimley

Craig Grimley joined Hewlett-Packard/Agilent Technologies in 1993 after completing a BEng (Hons) in Electrical and Electronic Engineering from Edinburgh's Heriot-Watt University. Craig initially spent a few years in manufacturing engineering before moving to his current product development research and design role in Agilent's Signal Analysis Division. Over the years Craig has gained measurement experience in many wireless communication signal formats including GSM, EDGE, W-CDMA, DVB-T/C, Bluetooth, WLAN, cdma2000 and 1xEVDO, as well as other general purpose measurement applications including AM/FM and noise figure. His current technology focus is the development of signal analysis measurement capabilities for LTE within the Agilent 89600 VSA product.

Pankaj Gupta

Pankaj Gupta obtained his Bachelor of Technology in Electronics and Communications from Cochin University, India, in 2000. He has worked with SASKEN/Anite for more than eight years. During this time Pankaj has been involved with design and development of 3G conformance test cases. He started attending the 3GPP testing standardization group RAN5 (formerly known as T1) in 2004. Since then he has contributed to the development of R99, HSDPA, HSUPA and now LTE conformance signalling test cases. In addition to working on the standards, Pankaj is the test case lead manager within Anite's Conformance Business Unit and is responsible for the Anite Conformance Test product for 3G and LTE test cases.

Bob Irvine

Bob Irvine is a senior product manager with Agilent Technologies. He graduated from the University of Glasgow in 1991 with a Masters in Electronic Engineering. He then joined Hewlett-Packard/Agilent Technologies and has handled a variety of technical marketing roles for the last 17 years. During his early career, Bob worked on the launch and support of test equipment for mobile cellular R&D and manufacturing. For the last 10 years Bob has been working on leading-edge RF test products for the deployment and optimization of wireless cellular networks, including GSM, GPRS, UMTS, HSPA and now LTE.

Peter Jones

Peter Jones is the Technical Authority/System Architect for the Development Toolset Business Unit at Anite Telecoms Ltd. and is part of the DT Business Unit Management Team. He is responsible for the overall technical direction of LTE development in terms of the Development Toolset product. Peter, who has worked at Anite since 1998, has been personally involved in the development of the network side EGPRS protocol stack for UE testing, conformance testing solutions and interoperability testing solutions. Additionally he has been responsible for overall project management of new product development for UTRAN, in particular for HSPA and GERAN. Peter received his HND, with distinction, in Information Technology from Hertfordshire University in 1989.

Greg Jue

Greg Jue is an applications development engineer/scientist with Agilent EEsof Electronic Design Automation (EDA). As a product manager for the ADS 3GPP LTE and Mobile WiMAX Wireless Libraries, Greg has pioneered combining design and test solutions at Agilent Technologies. He has also authored numerous articles, presentations and application notes, including the popular Connected Simulation and Test Solutions Using the Advanced Design System (Application Note 1394) and Agilent Technologies RF/IF-Digital Connected Solutions Bit Error Rate using the Advanced Design System (Application Note 1471). Greg developed the ADS 3GPP W-CDMA and ADS Communications System Design courses, and he has taught numerous RF circuit design, communication system design and 3GPP W-CDMA simulation design courses. Before joining Agilent in 1995, he worked on system design for the Deep Space Network at the Jet Propulsion Laboratory, Caltech University.

Per Kangru

Per Kangru is currently the world wide Business Development Manager for Agilent's Networks Solutions Division in the areas of LTE and SAE. Per has been with Agilent since 2001 working mainly in the area of mobile protocol testing but with MPLS and IP routing conformance testing as well. Over the years at Agilent Per has contributed to more than 20 patent applications and he is the sole inventor of several pending patents. Per is Agilent's lead representative in the LTE & SAE Trial Initiative (LSTI) and has been an invited speaker at several industry conferences. Per has a background in basic research in atomic and laser physics from Uppsala University in Sweden.

Eng Wei Koo

Eng Wei Koo has extensive experience in 3GPP and cdma2000 wireless system technologies both as a cdma2000 BTS developer at Motorola and as a lead engineer at Agilent Technologies for protocol test and monitoring solutions. Eng Wei joined Agilent in 2002 and has worked on UTRAN and E-UTRAN protocol monitoring solutions, pioneering the development of new and innovative approaches to data analysis. Eng Wei is currently the lead engineer for network protocol test for LTE and legacy UTRAN. Eng Wei received a Bachelor of Engineering from the University of Queensland, Australia, in 1999.

Dr. Michael Leung

Dr. Michael Leung is an applications program manager for Agilent Technologies' Asia Electronic Measurement Group. Michael plays a significant role in Agilent's wireless technology development for 3G (W-CDMA), 3.5G (HSPA) and 3.9G (LTE), protocol research and testing development in Asia. During his 12 years at Agilent, Michael has received five Agilent technical invention awards, contributed more than 20 Agilent technical conference papers, and authored 10 research papers for various international journals and conferences. He received a Master of Science and Doctor of Engineering from Hong Kong Polytechnic University in 1998 and 2005 respectively. Michael is a chartered engineer, a member of IET, and a senior member of IEEE.

Zach Lovell

Zach Lovell is a product planner for network protocol test focusing on protocol diagnostics solutions for evolving 3G and LTE in Agilent Technologies' Next Generation Wireless business. He graduated from the Georgia Institute of Technology with a BS in Electrical Engineering in 1998. During his 10-year career, Zach has worked with network equipment manufacturers and wireless service providers focusing on active and passive testing of CDMA, GSM, GPRS, UMTS and NGN networks. Zach has been engaged in all aspects of protocol tests, including consultative assistance in troubleshooting live network problems and providing training in leading wireless technologies.

Masatoshi Obara

Masatoshi Obara obtained his BSc in Acoustics Design Engineering from Kyushu Institute of Design (a part of Kyushu University today), Japan, in 1979. He then joined Matsushita Intertechno in Tokyo, which represented test equipment companies such as B&K and DISA in Denmark and Leuven Measurements Systems in Belgium. Starting as a sales engineer, he later became a system engineer to design and develop automated acoustic and vibration test systems. Obara moved to Hewlett-Packard/Agilent Technologies in 1985. During the past 23 years he has developed many RF and microwave test systems for RF and microwave component test, radar and antenna test, satellite receiver test, and analog and digital cellular mobile and base station test. His roles have included system engineer, project manager and engineering manager. Today he is responsible for product planning of an LTE RF design verification and conformance test system. He regularly attends GCF meetings as an Agilent delegate.

Mary Jane Pahls

Mary Jane Pahls is the owner of Eikonal Communications, a firm serving the engineering community. She has worked as a writer and editor in the test and measurement and telecommunication industries for more than 20 years, including eight years at Hewlett-Packard Company in Santa Rosa, California. Mary Jane's recent projects, in addition to those for Agilent, include work for engineering standards groups and for companies in the semiconductor industry. She holds BA and MA degrees from Kent State University.

Venkata Ratnakar Rayavarapu

Venkata Ratnakar Rayavarapu is currently working with Anite Telecoms Ltd. as a member of their Layer 3 protocol development team for LTE. He holds a Masters in Telecommunication Systems from IIT, Kharagpur, India. Over the past eight years Venkata has worked on various mobile technologies including GSM, GPRS, W-CDMA, HSDPA and HSUPA. He was previously with Hellosoft and Samsung.

Moray Rumney

Moray Rumney joined Hewlett-Packard/Agilent Technologies in 1984, after completing a BSc in Electronics from Edinburgh's Heriot-Watt University. Since then, Moray has enjoyed a varied career path, spanning manufacturing engineering, product development, applications engineering, and most recently technical marketing. His main focus has been the development and system design of base station emulators used in the development and testing of cellular phones. Moray joined ETSI in 1991 and 3GPP in 1999 where he was a significant contributor to the development of type approval tests for GSM and UMTS. He currently represents Agilent at RAN WG4, developing the air interface for HSPA+ and LTE. Moray has published many technical articles in the field of cellular communications and is a regular speaker and chairman at industry conferences. He is a member of IET and a chartered engineer.

Darshpreet Sabharwal

Darshpreet Sabharwal is currently working as a Senior Software Engineer at Anite Telecoms Ltd. and is responsible for the development of the Medium Access Control layer for LTE. He has developed protocol stacks for GPRS, EGPRS and LTE and has worked with various generations of ETSI and 3GPP technologies including 2G, 2.5G, 3G and LTE. Previously he was a technical leader with Aricent, India. He received his BE in Computer Science with distinction from Guru Nanak Dev Engineering College, India, and holds a postgraduate diploma in Business Administration from Symbiosis, India.

Sarabjit Singh

Sarabjit Singh is a Technical Architect at Anite Telecoms Ltd, UK, where his main responsibility involves shaping Anite LTE solutions for cellular R&D customers. Previously, Sarabjit worked with Tata Consultancy Services Ltd as a Technical Consultant and was a Subject Matter Expert on various mobile technologies from both 3GPP and 3GPP2. He is currently involved in LTE and HSPA+, and previously worked on UMTS (Release 99, HSDPA, HSUPA) and CDMA (IS 95 B, cdma2000®, 1xEV-DO). He received a BE in Computer Science with distinction from Guru Nanak Dev Engineering College, India, in 1996.

Mark Stambaugh

Mark Stambaugh has a BS in Electrical Engineering from the University of Cincinnati, an MEE from Rice University and an MS in Computer Science from National Technological University. He joined Hewlett-Packard/Agilent Technologies in 1987 and began his career developing signal generators. Throughout most of his 21 years with Agilent, Mark has been part of Agilent's R&D team developing base station emulator products and has implemented all the major digital cellular protocols that these instruments support since GSM. Concentrating on the physical layer, his roles span implementation, system engineering and technical leadership. Mark has nine patents.

Dr. K. F. Tsang

Dr. K. F. Tsang obtained a PhD from the University of Wales, College of Cardiff, UK. K. F. is now the Chairman and Managing Director of Citycom Technology Ltd., as well as an associate professor in the Department of Electronic Engineering, City University of Hong Kong. K. F., who has published more than 80 technical papers, is actively engaged in various professional activities. His achievements include receiving the City University of Hong Kong's Applied Research Excellence Award and the Certificate of Merit in both the first Hong Kong Science & Product Innovation Competition in 1998 and the World Chinese Invention Exposition'98. In addition, he has won the EDN Asia Innovator Award, the Ericsson Super-Wireless Application Award and the Freescale Semiconductor Ltd. Best Award.

Chris Van Woerkom

Chris Van Woerkom obtained his BSEE from the University of California at Davis in 1977 and his MBA from the University of Colorado in 1996. He has worked at Hewlett-Packard/Agilent Technologies for 31 years in a wide variety of positions in marketing and technical marketing. Chris is presently managing the marketing activities for the DigRF program to assure that the digital and RF tools work together seamlessly. He is also responsible for efforts within Agilent to ensure that instrument connectivity and test system automation are simplified for the end user. This includes coordinating activities within Agilent for the LAN Extensions for Instrumentation (LXI) program. Chris has published a number of articles and application notes about building test systems.

Hiroshi Yanagawa

Hiroshi Yanagawa obtained his BSc in Communication Engineering from Shibaura Institute of Technology, Japan, in 1985. He then joined Hewlett-Packard/Agilent Technologies and has worked in various engineering positions over the last 23 years. Hiroshi worked as a marketing engineer for impedance measuring instruments for five years and then moved to custom solution engineering. During this time he developed analog and digital cellular mobile and base station test systems as a system engineer. He is now designing an LTE design verification test system.

Bai Ying

Before joining Agilent Technologies, Bai Ying received his Masters in Communication and Information systems from the Institute of Electronics, Chinese Academy of Sciences, in 2006. Starting at Agilent as an application support engineer for the Signal Sources Division, Bai Ying was initially responsible for offering in-depth technical support to application engineers and customers worldwide, including TD-SCDMA products. In 2008, as an application expert, Bai Ying took on the responsibility of planning the LTE TDD version of Agilent's Signal Studio software. He now has product planning, product marketing and technical support roles for TD-SCDMA and LTE TDD applications.

Mitsuru Yokoyama

Mitsuru Yokoyama is a lead technologist for wireless applications at Signal Analysis Division, Agilent Technologies, in Kobe, Japan. He joined Hewlett-Packard/Agilent Technologies in 1982 after graduating with a BE and ME in Electrical Engineering from Kyoto University. Mitsuru worked initially on software design and development for Agilent's semiconductor test systems, moving to project management of PDC/PHS test products in 1992. Mitsuru represented Agilent at 3GPP committee T1 from its formation in 1999, and was the first chair of T1's RF sub-group where the UE RF conformance tests were developed. Mitsuru is now engaged in application design and implementation for HSPA, EDGE Evolution, LTE and other wireless applications.

Ryo Yonezawa

Ryo Yonezawa is currently an R&D engineer at the Signal Source Division, Agilent Technologies, in Kobe, Japan. He has a BS in Electrical Engineering from Hosei University and joined Hewlett-Packard/Agilent Technologies in 1997. He started as a system development engineer and since then has developed RF verification/conformance test systems that support GSM, GPRS, EGPRS, W-CDMA, HSDPA, C2K and EVDO. He currently develops LTE signal generation software.

Ben Zarlingo

Ben Zarlingo is a product manager for communications test with Agilent Technologies' Signal Analysis Division. He received a BS in Electrical Engineering from Colorado State University in 1980 and has worked for Hewlett-Packard/Agilent Technologies in the areas of spectrum, network and vector signal analysis, with a primary focus on techniques for the design and troubleshooting of emerging communications technologies.

Contents

Chapter 1

LTE Introduction

1.1 Introduction

The challenge for any book tackling a subject as broad and deep as a completely new cellular radio standard is one of focus. The process of just creating the Long Term Evolution (LTE) specifications alone has taken several years and involves tens of thousands of temporary documents, thousands of hours of meetings and hundreds of engineers. The result will be several thousand pages of specifications. Then the hard work begins, turning those specifications into real products that deliver real services to real people willing to pay real money. A single book of this length must therefore choose its subject wisely if it is to do more than just scratch the surface of such a complex problem.

The focus that Agilent has chosen for this book is a practical one: to explain design and measurement tools and techniques that engineering teams can use to accelerate turning the LTE specifications into a working system.

The first half of the book provides an overview of the specifications starting in Chapter 2 with RF aspects and moving through the physical layer and upper layer signalling to the System Architecture Evolution (SAE) in Chapter 5. Due to limited space, the material in Chapters 2 through 5 should be viewed as an introduction to the technology rather than a deep exposition. For many, this level of detail will be sufficient but anyone tasked with designing or testing parts of the system will always need to refer directly to the specifications. The emphasis in the opening chapters is often on visual rather than mathematical explanations of the concepts. The latter can always be found in the specifications and should be considered sufficient information to build the system. However, the former approach of providing an alternative, more accessible explanation is often helpful prior to gaining a more detailed understanding directly from the specifications.

Having set the context for LTE in the opening chapters, the bulk of the remainder of the book provides a more detailed study of the extensive range of design and measurement tools and techniques that are available to help bring LTE from theory to deployment.

1.2 LTE System Overview

Before describing the system overview it is useful to explain some of the terminology surrounding LTE since the history and naming of the technology is not intuitive. Some guidance can be found in the Vocabulary of 3GPP Specifications 21.905 [1], although this document is not comprehensive. The term LTE is actually a project name of the Third Generation Partnership Project (3GPP). The goal of the project, which started in November 2004, was to determine the long-term evolution of 3GPP's Universal Mobile Telephone System (UMTS). UMTS was also a 3GPP project that studied several candidate technologies before choosing Wideband Code Division Multiple Access (W-CDMA) for the Radio Access Network (RAN). The terms UMTS and W-CDMA are now interchangeable, although that was not the case before the technology was selected.

In a similar way, the project name LTE is now inextricably linked with the underlying technology, which is described as an evolution of UMTS although LTE and UMTS actually have very little in common. The UMTS RAN has two major components: (1) the UMTS Terrestrial Radio Access (UTRA), which is the air interface including the User Equipment (UE) or mobile phone, and (2) the UMTS Terrestrial Radio Access Network (UTRAN), which includes the Radio Network Controller (RNC) and the base station, which is also known as the Node B (NB).

Because LTE is the evolution of UMTS, LTE's equivalent components are thus named Evolved UTRA (E-UTRA) and Evolved UTRAN (E-UTRAN). These are the formal terms used to describe the RAN. The system, however, is more than just the RAN since there is also a parallel 3GPP project called System Architecture Evolution (SAE), which is defining a new all-IP packet-only Core Network (CN) known as the Evolved Packet Core (EPC). The combination of the EPC and the evolved RAN (E-UTRA plus E-UTRAN) is the Evolved Packet System (EPS). Depending on the context, any of the terms LTE, E-UTRA, E-UTRAN, SAE, EPC and EPS may get used to describe some or all of the system. Although EPS is the only correct term for the overall system, the name of the system will often be written as LTE/SAE or even simply LTE, as in the title of this book.

Figure 1.2-1 shows a high level view of how the evolved RAN and EPC interact with legacy radio access technologies.

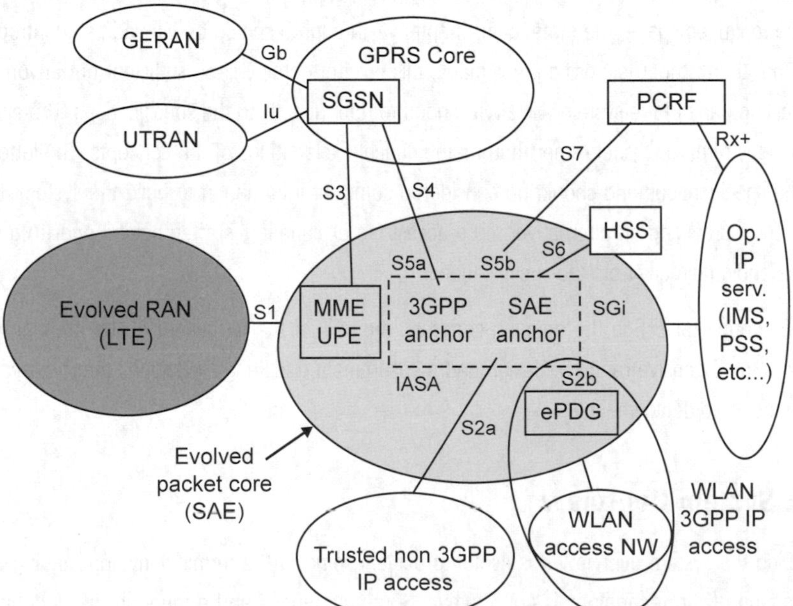

Figure 1.2-1. Logical high-level architecture for the evolved system (from 23.882 [2] Figure 4.2-1)

3GPP's drive to simplify the existing hybrid circuit-switched/packet-switched core network is behind the SAE project to define an all-IP core network. This new architecture is a flatter, packet-only core network that is an essential part of delivering the higher throughput, lower cost and lower latency that is the goal of the LTE evolved RAN. The EPC is also designed to provide seamless interworking with existing 3GPP and non-3GPP radio access technologies. The overall requirements for the System Architecture Evolution are summarized in 22.278 [3]. A detailed description of the EPC is given in Chapter 5.

1.3 The Evolution from UMTS to LTE

The LTE specifications are being written by 3GPP, which is a partnership of Standards Development Organizations (SDOs). The work of 3GPP is public and, as will be described in Section 1.6, it is possible to gain access to all meeting reports, working documents and published specifications from the 3GPP website: www.3gpp.org. The organizational partners that make up 3GPP are the Japanese Association of Radio Industries and Businesses (ARIB), the USA Alliance for Telecommunications Industry Solutions (ATIS), the China Communications Standards Association (CCSA), the European Telecommunications Standards Institute (ETSI), the Korean Telecommunications Technology Association (TTA) and the Japanese Telecommunications Technology Committee (TTC).

Table 1.3-1. Evolution of the UMTS specifications

Release	Functional freeze	Main UMTS feature of release
Rel-99	March 2000	Basic 3.84 Mcps W-CDMA (FDD & TDD)
Rel-4	March 2001	1.28 Mcps TDD (TD-SCDMA)
Rel-5	June 2002	HSDPA
Rel-6	March 2005	HSUPA (E-DCH)
Rel-7	Dec 2007	HSPA+ (64QAM downlink, MIMO, 16QAM uplink) LTE and SAE feasibility study
Rel-8	Dec 2008	LTE work item — OFDMA/SC-FDMA air interface SAE work item — new IP core network Further HSPA improvements

Table 1.3-1 summarizes the evolution of the 3GPP UMTS specifications towards LTE. Each release of the 3GPP specifications represents a defined set of features. A convenient summary of the contents of any release can be found at www.3gpp.org/releases. The date given for the functional freeze relates to the date when no further new items can be added to the release. After this point any further changes to the specifications are restricted to essential corrections. The commercial launch date of a release depends on the period of time following the functional freeze before the specifications are considered stable and then implemented into commercial systems. For the first release of UMTS the delay between functional freeze and commercial launch was several years, although the delay for subsequent releases was progressively shorter. With LTE/SAE being a completely new system, the delay before commercial launch is likely to increase again to perhaps two years. This period includes the time taken to develop and implement the conformance test cases, which requires significant work that cannot begin until the feature set of the release is frozen.

After Release 99, 3GPP stopped naming releases after the year and opted for a new scheme starting with Release 4. This choice was driven by the document version numbering scheme explained in Section 1.6. Release 4 introduced the 1.28 Mcps narrow band version of W-CDMA, also known as Time Domain Synchronous Code Division Multiple Access (TD-SCDMA). Following this was Release 5, in which High Speed Downlink Packet Access (HSDPA) introduced packet-based data services to UMTS in the same way that the General Packet Radio Service (GPRS) did for GSM in Release 97 (1998). The completion of packet data for UMTS was achieved in Release 6 with the addition of High Speed Uplink Packet Access (HSUPA), although the official term for this technology is Enhanced Dedicated Channel (E-DCH). HSDPA and HSUPA are now known collectively as High Speed Packet Access (HSPA). Release 7 contained the first work on LTE/SAE with the completion of feasibility studies, and further improvements were made to HSPA such as downlink Multiple Input-Multiple Output (MIMO), 64QAM on the downlink and 16QAM on the uplink. In Release 8, HSPA continues to evolve with the addition of numerous smaller features such as dual carrier HSDPA and 64QAM with MIMO.

The main work in Release 8, however, is the specification of LTE and SAE, which is the main focus of this book. Work beyond Release 8 is also in progress and will be covered briefly in Chapter 8, which describes the process whereby LTE will be enhanced and put forward as a candidate technology for 4G. Within 3GPP there are further standardization activities not shown in Table 1.3-1 such as those for the GSM Enhanced RAN (GERAN) and Internet Protocol Multimedia Subsystem (IMS).

1.4 LTE/SAE Requirements

The high level requirements for LTE/SAE include reduced cost per bit, better service provisioning, flexible use of new and existing frequency bands, simplified network architecture with open interfaces, and an allowance for reasonable power consumption by terminals. These are detailed in the LTE feasibility study 25.912 [4] and in the LTE requirements document 25.913 [5].

To meet the requirements for LTE outlined in 25.913 [5], LTE/SAE has been specified to achieve the following:

- Increased downlink and uplink peak data rates, as shown in Table 1.4-1. Note that the downlink is specified for Single Input-Single Output (SISO) and MIMO antenna configurations at a fixed 64QAM modulation depth, whereas the uplink is specified only for SISO but at different modulation depths. These figures represent the physical limitation of the FDD air interface in ideal radio conditions with allowance for signalling overheads. Lower peak rates are specified for specific UE categories, and performance requirements under non-ideal radio conditions have also been developed. Comparable figures exist in [4] for TDD operation.
- Scalable channel bandwidths of 1.4 MHz, 3.0 MHz, 5 MHz, 10 MHz, 15 MHz and 20 MHz in both the uplink and the downlink.
- Spectral efficiency improvements over Release 6 HSPA of 3 to 4 times in the downlink and 2 to 3 times in the uplink.
- Sub-5 ms latency for small Internet Protocol (IP) packets.
- Performance optimized for low mobile speeds from 0 to 15 km/h supported with high performance from 15 to 120 km/h; functional support from 120 to 350 km/h. Support for 350 to 500 km/h is under consideration.
- Co-existence with legacy standards while evolving toward an all-IP network.

Table 1.4-1. LTE (FDD) downlink and uplink peak data rates (from 25.912 [4] Tables 13.1 & 13.1a)

FDD Downlink Peak Data Rates (64QAM)			
Antenna configuration	SISO	2x2 MIMO	4x4 MIMO
Peak data rate Mbps	100	172.8	326.4
FDD Uplink Peak Data Rates (single antenna)			
Modulation depth	QPSK	16QAM	64QAM
Peak data rate Mbps	50	57.6	86.4

The headline data rates in Table 1.4-1 represent the corner case of what can be achieved with the LTE RAN in perfect radio conditions; however, it is necessary for practical reasons to introduce lower levels of performance to enable a range of implementation choices for system deployment. This is achieved through the introduction of UE categories as specified in 36.306 [6] and shown in Table 1.4-2. These are similar in concept to the categories used to specify different levels of performance for HSPA.

Table 1.4-2. Peak data rates for UE categories (derived from 36.306 [6] Tables 4.1-1 and 4.1-2)

UE category	Peak downlink data rate (Mbps)	Downlink antenna configuration (eNB transmit x UE receive)	Peak uplink data rate (Mbps)	Support for 64QAM in uplink
Category 1	10.296	1 x 2	5.16	No
Category 2	51.024	2 x 2	25.456	No
Category 3	102.048	2 x 2	51.024	No
Category 4	150.752	2 x 2	51.024	No
Category 5	302.752	4 x 2	75.376	Yes

There are other attributes associated with UE categories, but the peak data rates, downlink antenna configuration and uplink 64QAM support are the categories most commonly referenced.

The emphasis so far has been on the peak data rates but what really matters for the performance of a new system is the improvement that can be achieved in average and cell edge data rates. The reference configuration against which LTE/SAE performance targets have been set is defined in 25.913 [5] as being Release 6 UMTS. For the downlink the reference is HSDPA Type 1 (receive diversity but no equalizer or interference cancellation). For the uplink the reference configuration is single transmitter with diversity reception at the Node B. Table 1.4-3 shows the simulated downlink performance of UMTS versus the design targets for LTE. This is taken from the work of 3GPP during the LTE feasibility study [7]. Table 1.4-4 shows a similar set of results for the uplink taken from [8].

Table 1.4-3. Comparison of UMTS Release 6 and LTE downlink performance requirements

Case 1 500m inter site distance	Spectrum efficiency		Mean user throughput		Cell-edge user throughput	
	[bps/Hz/cell]	x UTRA	[bps/Hz/user]	x UTRA	[bps/Hz/user]	x UTRA
UTRA baseline 1x2	0.53	x1.0	0.05	x1.0	0.02	x1.0
E-UTRA 2x2 SU-MIMO	1.69	x3.2	0.17	x3.2	0.05	x2.7
E-UTRA 4x2 SU-MIMO	1.87	x3.5	0.19	x3.5	0.06	x3.0
E-UTRA 4x4 SU-MIMO	2.67	x5.0	0.27	x5.0	0.08	x4.4

Table 1.4-4. Comparison of UMTS Release 6 and LTE uplink performance requirements

Case 1 500m inter site distance	Spectrum efficiency		Mean user throughput		Cell-edge user throughput	
	[bps/Hz/cell]	x UTRA	[bps/Hz/user]	x UTRA	[bps/Hz/user]	x UTRA
UTRA baseline	0.332	x1.0	0.033	x1.0	0.009	x1.0
E-UTRA 1x2	0.735	x2.2	0.073	x2.2	0.024	x2.5
E-UTRA 1x2 MU-MIMO	0.675	x2.0	0.067	x2.0	0.023	x2.4
E-UTRA 1x4	1.103	x3.3	0.110	x3.3	0.052	x5.5
E-UTRA 2x2 SU-MIMO	0.776	x2.3	0.078	x2.3	0.010	x1.1

From these tables the LTE design targets of 2x to 4x improvement over UMTS Release 6 can be seen. Note, however, that UMTS is not standing still and there are Release 7 and Release 8 enhancements that significantly narrow the gap between UMTS and LTE. Although the figures in Tables 1.4-3 and 1.4-4 are meaningful and user-centric, they were derived from system level simulations and are not typical of the methods used to specify minimum performance. The simulation involved calculation of throughput by repeatedly dropping ten users randomly into the cell. From this data a distribution of performance was developed and the mean user throughput calculated. The cell edge throughput was defined as the 5th percentile of the throughput cumulative distribution. For this reason the cell edge figures are quoted per user assuming 10 users per cell, whereas the mean user throughput is independent of the number of users.

When it comes to defining minimum performance requirements for individual UEs, the simulation methods used to derive the figures in Tables 1.4-3 and 1.4-4 cannot be used. Instead, the minimum requirements for UMTS and LTE involve spot measurement of throughput at specific high and low interference conditions, and for additional simplicity, this is done without the use of closed loop adaptive modulation and coding. This is a pragmatic approach to defining performance but it means there is no direct correlation between the results from the conformance tests and the simulated system performance in Tables 1.4-3 and 1.4-4.

1.5 LTE/SAE Timeline

The timeline of LTE/SAE development is shown in Figure 1.5-1. This includes the work of 3GPP in drafting the specifications as well as the conformance test activities of the Global Certification Forum (GCF) and the trials being carried out by the LTE/SAE Trial Initiative (LSTI). The work of GCF towards the certification of UE against the 3GPP conformance specifications is covered in some detail in Section 7.4. The LSTI is an industry forum and complimentary group who are working in parallel with 3GPP and GCF with the intent of accelerating the acceptance and deployment of LTE/SAE as the logical choice of the industry for next generation networks. The work of LSTI is split into four phases. The first phase is Proof of Concept of the basic principles of LTE/SAE, using early prototypes not necessarily compliant with the specifications. The second phase is Interoperability Development Testing (IODT), which is a more detailed phase of testing using standards-compliant equipment but not necessarily commercial platforms. The third stage is Interoperability Testing (IOT), which is similar in scope to IODT but uses platforms that are intended for commercial deployment. The final phase is Friendly Customer Trials, which will run until mid 2010 when GCF is expected to certify the first UE against the 3GPP conformance tests. Dates beyond February 2009, the time of this writing, are estimates and actual dates will depend on industry conditions and progress.

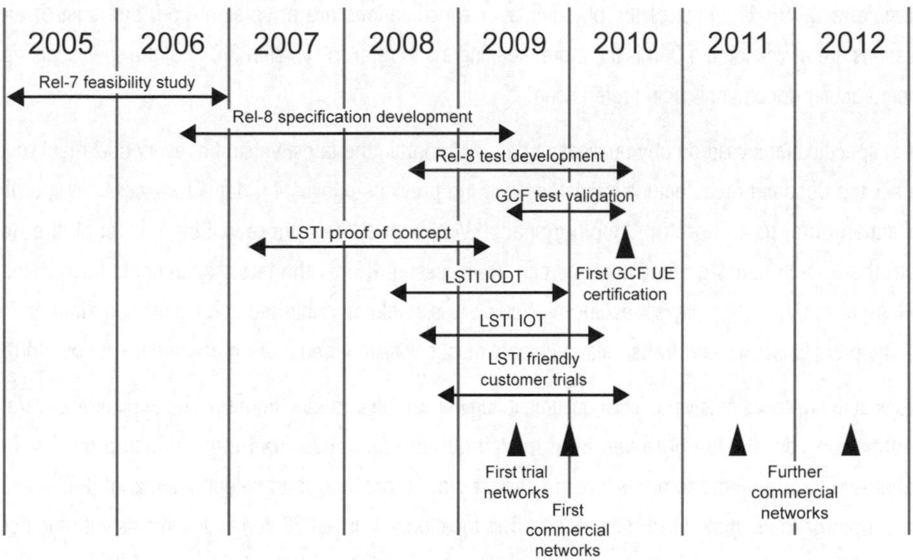

Figure 1.5-1. Projected LTE/SAE timeline

1.6 Introduction to the 3GPP LTE/SAE Specification Documents

The final section in this introductory chapter provides a summary of the LTE/SAE specification documents and where to find them.

1.6.1 Finding 3GPP Documents

A good place to start looking for documents is www.3gpp.org/specifications. From there it is possible to access the specification documents in a number of different ways, including by Release, publication date or specification number. A comprehensive list of all 3GPP specifications giving the latest versions for all releases can be found at www.3gpp.org/ftp/Specs/html-info/SpecReleaseMatrix.htm. Each document has a version number from which the status of the document can be determined. For instance with 36.101 Vx.y.z, x represents the stability of the document, y the major update and z an editorial update. If x is 1, then the document is an early draft for information only. If x is 2, then the document has been presented for approval. If x is greater than 2, then the document has been approved and is under change control. Once under change control, the value of x also indicates the Release. Therefore a 3 is Release 1999, a 4 is Release 4, a 5 is Release 5, and so on. Most documents in an active Release will get updated quarterly, which is indicated by an increment of the y digit. The document will also contain the date when it was approved by the Technical Specification Group (TSG) responsible for drafting it. This date is often one month earlier than the official quarterly publication date.

To avoid confusion, individual documents should be referenced only by the version number. Groups of documents can be usefully referenced by the publication date — e.g., 2008-12 — but note that the version numbers of the latest documents for that date will vary depending on whether they have all been updated at the same frequency. For example, at 2008-12, most of the physical layer specifications are at version 8.5.0 but most of the radio specifications are at version 8.4.0. It is therefore meaningless to refer to "version 8.x.y" of the specifications unless only one particular document is being referenced.

The set of specifications valid on any publication date will contain the latest version of every document regardless of whether the document was actually updated since the previous publication date. To access the specifications by publication date, go to ftp://ftp.3gpp.org/specs/. Within each date there will be a list of all the Releases and from there each series of specifications can be accessed. If only the latest documents for a Release are required, go to ftp://ftp.3gpp.org/specs/latest/. Newer, less stable, unpublished documents can often be found at ftp://ftp.3gpp.org/specs/Latest-drafts/, although care must be taken when making use of this type of information.

All versions of the releases of any particular document number can be accessed from ftp://ftp.3gpp.org/specs/archive/. This information can also be obtained from ftp://ftp.3gpp.org/Specs/html-info/, which provides the most comprehensive information. From this link the easiest way to proceed is to select a series of documents; e.g., ftp://ftp.3gpp.org/Specs/html-info/36-series.htm. This location will list all 36-series documents with the document numbers and titles. Selecting a document number will access a page with the full history of the document for all releases, including a named rapporteur and the Working Group (WG) responsible for drafting the document. At the bottom of the page will be a link to the Change Request (CR) history, which brings up yet another page listing all the changes made to the document and linked back to the TSG that approved the changes.

By tracing back through the CR history for a document it is possible to access the minutes and temporary documents of the TSG in which the change was finally approved. For instance, tracing back through a CR to 36.101 V8.5.0 (2008-12) would lead to a temporary document of the TSG RAN meeting that approved it stored under ftp://ftp.3gpp.org/tsg_ran/TSG_RAN/TSGR_42/. The change history of a document can also be found in the final annex of the document, but linking to the CR documents themselves has to be done via the website. The lowest level of detail is found by accessing the WG documents from a specific TSG meeting. An example for TSG RAN WG4, who develop the LTE 36.100-series radio specifications, can be found at ftp://ftp.3gpp.org/tsg_ran/WG4_Radio/TSGR4_50/. The link to this WG from the document can also be made from the html-info link given above.

The final way to gain insight into the work of the standards development process is to read the email exploders of the various committees. This capability is hosted by ETSI at http://list.etsi.org/.

1.6.2 LTE/SAE Document Structure

The feasibility study for LTE/SAE took place in Release 7, resulting in several Technical Reports of which [1] and [2] are the most significant.

The LTE RAN specifications are contained in the 36-series of Release 8 and are divided into the following categories:

- 36.100 series, covering radio specifications and eNB conformance testing
- 36.200 series, covering layer 1 (physical layer) specifications
- 36.300 series, covering layer 2 and 3 (air interface signalling) specifications
- 36.400 series, covering network signalling specifications
- 36.500 series, covering user equipment conformance testing
- 36.800 and 36.900 series, which are technical reports containing background information

The latest versions of the 36 series documents can be found at www.3gpp.org/ftp/Specs/latest/Rel-8/36_series/.

The SAE specifications for the EPC are more scattered than those for the RAN and are found in the 22-series, 23-series, 24-series, 29-series and 33-series of Release 8, with work happening in parallel in Release 9. A more comprehensive list of relevant EPC documents can be found in Chapter 5.

1.7 References

[1] 3GPP TR 21.905 V8.7.0 (2008-12) Vocabulary for 3GPP Specifications

[2] 3GPP TR 23.882 V8.0.0 (2008-09) 3GPP System Architecture Evolution: Report on Technical Options and Conclusions

[3] 3GPP TS 22.278 V9.2.0 (2008-12) Service requirements for the Evolved Packet System (EPS)

[4] 3GPP TR 25.912 V8.0.0 (2008-12) Feasibility study for evolved Universal Terrestrial Radio Access (UTRA) and evolved Universal Terrestrial Radio Access Network (UTRAN)

[5] 3GPP TR 25.913 V8.0.0 (2008-12) Requirements for Evolved Universal Terrestrial Radio Access (E-UTRA) and Evolved Universal Terrestrial Radio Access Network (E-UTRAN)

[6] 3GPP TR 36.306 V8.2.0 (2008-05) Evolved Universal terrestrial Radio Access Network (E-UTRA); User Equipment (UE) radio access capabilities

[7] 3GPP TSG RAN WG1 Tdoc R1-072578 "Summary of downlink performance evaluation," Ericsson, May 2007

[8] 3GPP TSG RAN WG1 Tdoc R1-072261 "LTE performance evaluation — uplink summary," Nokia, May 2007

Links to all reference documents can be found at www.agilent.com/find/ltebook.

Chapter 2

Air Interface Concepts

This chapter covers the radio aspects of LTE, starting in Section 2.1 with an overview of the Radio Frequency (RF) specifications. The following two sections describe the downlink and uplink modulation schemes in some detail and the last section examines the way in which LTE uses multi-antenna methods to improve performance.

2.1 Radio Frequency Aspects

The RF specifications for LTE are covered in two 3GPP technical specification documents: 36.101 [1] for the User Equipment (UE) and 36.104 [2] for the base station, which is known in LTE as the evolved Node B (eNB). One of the first things to note about LTE is the integration between the Frequency Division Duplex (FDD) and Time Division Duplex (TDD) radio access modes. In the previous Universal Mobile Telephone System (UMTS) specifications, which also supported FDD and TDD, the RF specifications for the UE FDD, UE TDD, base station FDD and base station TDD modes were covered in separate documents. However, the early decision by 3GPP to fully integrate FDD and TDD modes for LTE has resulted in only one RF specification document each for the UE and the eNB. With the higher level of integration between the two modes, the effort required to support them should be less than it was in the past.

The structure of 36.101 [1] for the UE follows the UMTS pattern of minimum requirements for the transmitter and receiver followed by performance requirements for the receiver under faded conditions. The final section covers the performance of the channel quality feedback mechanisms but at the time of this writing is not yet developed. The structure of 36.104 [2] for the eNB follows the same pattern as UMTS of transmitter, receiver and performance requirements.

The purpose of this section is to highlight those aspects of the LTE RF requirements that will be new compared to UMTS. These include issues relating to LTE's support of multiple bands and channel bandwidths as well as those RF specifications peculiar to the use of Orthogonal Frequency Division Multiple Access (OFDMA) modulation on the downlink and Single-Carrier Frequency Division Multiple Access (SC-FDMA) on the uplink. Discussion regarding RF performance aspects will be covered in Sections 6.5, 6.7 and 7.2.

2.1.1 Frequency Bands

Table 2.1-1 shows the IMT-2000 (3G) frequency bands defined by the European Telecommunications Standards Institute (ETSI) and 3GPP. Most of the frequency bands are defined in 36.101 [1] Table 5.5-1, meaning they are recognized by all three International Telecommunications Union (ITU) regions, although it should be noted that definition of a band does not imply its availability for deployment. The exceptions in Table 2.1-1 that are not defined in 36.101 [1] are bands 15 and 16. These have been defined by ETSI in TS 102 735 [3] for ITU Region 1 (Europe, Middle East and Africa) only. These bands have not been adopted at this time by ITU Region 2 (Americas) or Region 3 (Asia), which is why they do not appear in 36.101 [1].

Table 2.1-1. Defined frequency bands for IMT-2000 (MHz)

Band number	Uplink		Downlink		Uplink downlink spacing	Duplex mode
	Low	High	Low	High		
1	1920	1980	2110	2170	130	FDD
2	1850	1910	1930	1990	20	FDD
3	1710	1785	1805	1880	20	FDD
4	1710	1755	2110	2155	355	FDD
5	824	849	869	894	20	FDD
6	830	840	875	885	35	FDD
7	2500	2570	2620	2690	50	FDD
8	880	915	925	960	10	FDD
9	1749.9	1784.9	1844.9	1879.9	60	FDD
10	1710	1770	2110	2170	340	FDD
11	1427.9	1452.9	1475.9	1500.9	23	FDD
12	698	716	728	746	12	FDD
13[1]	777	787	746	756	21	FDD
14[1]	788	798	758	768	20	FDD
15[2]	1900	1920	2600	2620	680	FDD
16[2]	2010	2025	2585	2600	560	FDD
17	704	716	734	746	18	FDD
33	1900	1920	1900	1920	0	TDD
34	2010	2025	2010	2025	0	TDD
35	1850	1910	1850	1910	0	TDD
36	1930	1990	1930	1990	0	TDD
37	1910	1930	1910	1930	0	TDD
38	2570	2620	2570	2620	0	TDD
39	1880	1920	1880	1920	0	TDD
40	2300	2400	2300	2400	0	TDD

Note 1: Uplink frequency is higher than downlink frequency.
Note 2: Defined by ETSI for ITU Region 1 only.

Table 2.1-1 shows the large number of options that now exist for IMT-2000 technologies, which include LTE. When UMTS was first specified in 1999, only one frequency band was defined. This band became a point around which the industry could focus its efforts in developing specifications and products. In the years since then, bands have been gradually added, and when LTE was specified in 2008, it inherited all the existing UMTS bands plus some new ones added in Release 8. Moreover, with the integration of TDD into the LTE specifications, another eight bands were added to the list.

It is clear from Table 2.1-1 that many of the bands are overlapping or subsets of one another, so the actual RF coverage may not seem to present a problem for power amplifiers and receivers. Where the difficulty lies, however, is in handling the many combinations of filtering that are required to implement the different bands. The duplex spacing, which is the distance between the edges of the uplink and downlink bands, is not constant, which adds to the challenge of designing the specific band filters required for each implemented band. There are similar issues in designing efficient antennas to cover the wide range of possible supported bands.

In future releases of the specifications it is possible that variable duplex spacing may be introduced. For a specified FDD band, this means the currently fixed relationship between the uplink and downlink channels could become variable. This would increase deployment flexibility but also would increase the complexity of the specifications, the equipment design and network operation.

2.1.2 Channel Bandwidths

A trend in recent years has been for radio systems to be ported to new frequency bands, although typically these systems support only one channel bandwidth. The first release of UMTS, which supported both FDD and TDD modes, used a common CDMA chip rate of 3.84 Mcps and a channel spacing of 5 MHz. Release 4 of UMTS introduced a Low Chip Rate (LCR) TDD option (also known as TD-SCDMA) that used the lower 1.28 Mcps with a correspondingly narrower channel spacing of 1.6 MHz. This was followed in Release 7 by the 7.68 Mcps option with its 10 MHz channel spacing. Now in Release 8 there is work on a dual carrier version of HSDPA; however, the wider bandwidth comes from two separate 5 MHz channels.

The situation for LTE is very different. The OFDMA modulation scheme upon which UMTS is based has as one of its properties the ability to scale its channel bandwidth linearly without changing the underlying properties of the physical layer — these being the subcarrier spacing and the symbol length. The details of the LTE modulation schemes are discussed fully in Sections 2.2 and 2.3. It is sufficient to say at this point that LTE was designed from the start to support six different channel bandwidths. These are 1.4 MHz, 3 MHz, 5 MHz, 10 MHz, 15 MHz and 20 MHz. Earlier versions of the specifications also supported 1.6 MHz and 3.2 MHz for interworking with LCR TDD, but these were removed when the LTE TDD frame structure was aligned with the FDD frame structure rather than the TD-SCDMA frame structure from UMTS.

The choice of many channel bandwidths means that LTE has more deployment flexibility than previous systems. The wide channel bandwidths of 10, 15 and 20 MHz are intended for new spectrum, with the 2.6 GHz and 3.5 GHz bands being likely candidates. These wider channels offer more efficient scheduling opportunities, which can increase overall system performance. With the potential of having a much wider channel available, individual users might perceive that they have a high bandwidth connection when in fact they are sharing the bandwidth with many other users. An individual user's perception of "owning" the channel comes from the fact that the demand typically is variable and what matters is the peak rate available at the time of the demand. This perception is known as the trunking effect, wherein the wider the channel, the greater the gains. Narrowband systems such as GSM with only 200 kHz channel bandwidths are not in a position to instantaneously offer more capacity, even if other users are not making full use of their channel.

The other benefit of a wider channel is the possibility of scheduling users as a function of the channel conditions specific to them. This topic is discussed in more detail in Sections 3.4 and 6.7, but the essence is that OFDMA has the ability to schedule traffic over a subset of the channel and thus, with appropriate feedback of the instantaneous channel conditions can target transmissions at frequencies exhibiting the best propagation conditions and lowest interference.

Table 2.1-2. Combinations of channel bandwidth and frequency band for which RF requirements are defined (36.101 [1] Table 5.6.1-1)

E-UTRA band	Channel bandwidth					
	1.4 MHz	3 MHz	5 MHz	10 MHz	15 MHz	20 MHz
1			Yes	Yes	Yes	Yes
2	Yes	Yes	Yes	Yes	Yes[1]	Yes[1]
3	Yes	Yes	Yes	Yes	Yes[1]	Yes[1]
4	Yes	Yes	Yes	Yes	Yes	Yes
5	Yes	Yes	Yes	Yes[1]		
6			Yes	Yes[1]		
7			Yes	Yes	Yes	Yes[1]
8	Yes	Yes	Yes	Yes[1]		
9			Yes	Yes	Yes[1]	Yes[1]
10			Yes	Yes	Yes	Yes
11			Yes	Yes[1]	Yes[1]	Yes[1]
12						
13	Yes	Yes	Yes[1]	Yes[1]		
14	Yes	Yes	Yes[1]	Yes[1]		
17	Yes	Yes	Yes[1]	Yes[1]		
33			Yes	Yes	Yes	Yes
34			Yes	Yes	Yes	
35	Yes	Yes	Yes	Yes	Yes	Yes
36	Yes	Yes	Yes	Yes	Yes	Yes
37			Yes	Yes	Yes	Yes
38			Yes	Yes		
39			Yes	Yes	Yes	Yes
40				Yes	Yes	Yes

Note 1: Bandwidth for which a relaxation of the specified UE receiver sensitivity requirement (36.101 Clause 7.3) is allowed.

The 5 MHz option for LTE is an obvious choice for re-farming of existing UMTS spectrum. This re-farming will not benefit from trunking gains over UMTS but still has the possibility of gains through frequency-selective scheduling. The 1.4 MHz and 3 MHz options are targeted at re-farming of narrowband systems such as GSM and cdma2000. Even the 1.4 MHz option will have significant trunking gains over 200 kHz GSM as well as the ability to do some frequency-selective scheduling.

The consequence of a system that has so much flexibility in terms of frequency bands and channel bandwidths is the complexity that this creates. Several of the LTE RF requirements described in this section reflect this growth in complexity, and requirements that in UMTS were expressed as single figures are now represented by multi-dimensional tables.

Although the LTE system could be operated in any of the defined bands at any channel bandwidth, there are combinations that are not expected in real deployment. For such cases no RF performance requirements are defined. Table 2.1-2 shows the combination of channel bandwidths for which performance requirements exist (or do not exist) for the different frequency bands.

Some obvious exceptions can be seen in Table 2.1-2: for example, no requirements are defined for the 1.4 MHz and 3 MHz bandwidths for several bands including E-UTRA band 1 (the primary UMTS operating band at 2.1 GHz) as this combination of deployment is not likely. The table also shows that for some combinations there are relaxations in the requirements. For example, there are several bands for which the receiver sensitivity requirements are relaxed when operating at 15 MHz and 20 MHz channel bandwidths. At the time of this writing these relaxations are limited to reference sensitivity although the list of affected requirements may grow over time.

2.1.3 UE Transmit Power

Over time the transmit power requirements for the UE have become more complex. In earlier standards such as GSM and UMTS Release 99, the transmit power specification was a simple one to one relationship between the power class of the UE and the maximum output power. Over time this relationship has become more complicated with relaxations that take into account the crest factor of higher-order modulation formats. This trend started in Release 5 for UMTS with the introduction of a fixed back-off for 16 Quadrature Amplitude Modulation (16QAM). In Release 6 the fixed back-off was superseded by a more advanced "cubic" metric that related the allowed back-off to a formula that included the cube of the voltage waveform relative to a standard Quadrature Phase Shift Keying (QPSK) waveform.

There are four power classes defined for the LTE UE. At the time of this writing, a maximum power requirement is defined only for class 3 and is specified as 23 dBm ±2 dB for all bands. However, the flexibility of the LTE air interface requires consideration of additional dimensions including the channel bandwidth and the size of the power allocation within that bandwidth.

Table 2.1-3 shows the additional Maximum Power Reduction (MPR) that applies for power class 3 depending on the modulation being used and the number of Resource Blocks (RB) transmitted in each channel bandwidth. An RB is the minimum unit of transmission and is 180 kHz wide and 0.5 ms in duration.

Table 2.1-3. Maximum power reduction for power class 3 (36.101 [1] Table 6.2.3-1)

Modulation	Channel bandwidth/transmission bandwidth configuration [RB]						MPR (dB)
	1.4 MHz	3.0 MHz	5 MHz	10 MHz	15 MHz	20 MHz	
QPSK	> 5	> 4	> 8	> 12	> 16	> 18	≤ 1
16QAM	≤ 5	≤ 4	≤ 8	≤ 12	≤ 16	≤ 18	≤ 1
64QAM	> 5	> 4	> 8	> 12	> 16	> 18	≤ 2

The trend shown in Table 2.1-3 is that with increasing modulation depth (meaning higher signal peaks) and increasing transmitted bandwidth, the maximum power is reduced.

On top of the relaxations for reference sensitivity and maximum power, which apply at all times, there is another class of dynamic MPR restrictions known as Additional MPR (A-MPR), which apply when the network signals the UE. At the time of this writing seven different network signalling values have been defined, as shown in Table 2.1-4. The behavior of the UE depends on which band it is using, which channel bandwidth, the number of resource blocks allocated, the modulation depth, the allowed A-MPR and the specific spurious emissions requirements that have to be met under these conditions.

Table 2.1-4. A-MPR/spectrum emission requirements (36.101 [1] Table 6.2.4-1)

Network signalling value	Requirements (subclause)	E-UTRA band	Channel bandwidth (MHz)	Resources blocks	A-MPR[1] (dB)
NS_01	–	–	–		
NS_02	6.6.2.4.1 6.6.3.3.1	1, 6, 9, 11	10	> 42	≤ 1
			15	> 44	≤ 1
			20	> 48	≤ 1
NS_03	6.6.2.2.1	2, 4, 10, 35, 36	3	> 5	≤ 1
	6.6.2.2.1	2, 4, 10, 35, 36	5	> 6	≤ 1
	6.6.2.2.1	2, 4, 10, 35, 36	10	> 6	≤ 1
	6.6.2.2.1	2, 4, 10, 35, 36	15	> 8	≤ 1
	6.6.2.2.1	2, 4, 10, 35, 36	20	> 10	≤ 1
NS_04	6.6.2.2.2	TBD	TBD	TBD	
NS_05	6.6.3.3.1	1	10, 15, 20	≥ 50 for QPSK	≤ 1
NS_06	6.6.2.2.3	12, 13, 14, 17	1.4, 3, 5, 10	n/a	n/a
NS_07	6.6.2.2.3 6.6.3.3.2	13	10	TBD	TBD
..					
NS_32	–	–	–	–	–

Note 1: 0 ≤ A-MPR ≤ 3

For example, a UE receiving NS_03 from the network when operating in bands 2, 4, 10, 35 or 36 with a 15 MHz channel bandwidth and >8 RB allocated is allowed to reduce its maximum power by up to an additional 1 dB above the allowed MPR in order to meet the additional spurious emission requirements defined in 36.101[1] subclause 6.6.2.2.1.

Five types of additional requirements have been defined. For the example quoted, 36.101 [1] subclause 6.6.2.2.1 refers to additional requirements for the Spectrum Emission Mask (SEM). These requirements are shown in Table 2.1-5. Other additional requirements are for spurious emissions and Adjacent Channel Leakage Radio (ACLR).

Table 2.1-5. Additional spectrum emission requirements for NS_03 (36.101 [1] Table 6.6.2.2.1-1)

	Spectrum emission limit (dBm)/Channel bandwidth						
Δf_{OOB} (MHz)	1.4 MHz	3.0 MHz	5 MHz	10 MHz	15 MHz	20 MHz	Measurement bandwidth
±0–1	[TBD]	[TBD]	–15	–18	–20	–21	30 kHz
±1–2.5	[TBD]	[TBD]	–13	–13	–13	–13	1 MHz
±2.5–5	[TBD]	[TBD]	–13	–13	–13	–13	1 MHz
±5–6	[TBD]	[TBD]	–13	–13	–13	–13	1 MHz
±6–10	[TBD]	[TBD]	–25	–25	–25	–25	1 MHz
±10–15	[TBD]	[TBD]		–25	–25	–25	1 MHz
±15–20	[TBD]	[TBD]			–25	–25	1 MHz
±10–25	[TBD]	[TBD]				–25	1 MHz

Table 2.1-5 shows another consequence of LTE's channel bandwidth flexibility, in this case the additional SEM requirements, which are a function not just of the frequency offset as in UMTS but also of the channel bandwidth.

It should be evident at this point how complex the rules are which govern the maximum power that the UE can use under different conditions and the requirements, both static and dynamic, that have to be met. Checking for correct behavior under all possible conditions will be a substantial verification exercise.

Given the complexity of the maximum power specifications several terms have been defined to help clarify what is happening:

- P_{EMAX} is defined in 36.331 [4] and is the maximum allowed power defined by higher layers.
- P_{UMAX} is defined in 36.101 [1] and is the maximum power for the UE power class adjusted according to the rules for MPR and A-MPR.
- P_{CMAX} is defined in 36.101 [1] as the configured UE transmitted power. The relationship between these quantities is: $P_{CMAX} = \text{MIN} \{ P_{EMAX}, P_{UMAX} \}$

There are further tolerances defined for the accuracy of P_{CMAX} based on measurement of the actual output power. These accuracies are not yet fully defined but will be tight at high power (in the region of ±2 dB) and relaxed at lower powers down to the –40 dBm lower limit.

2.1.4 UE Power Control

For those familiar with UMTS, the RF specifications cover familiar territory in regard to the requirements for open loop power control accuracy (±10.5 dB), minimum power (–40 dBm) and off power (–50 dBm). Where things start to get interesting is with the power dynamics. In UMTS these were limited to slot-based power profiles and, lately, the addition of relative code-domain power accuracy. With OFDMA the power profile of the uplink becomes a function of each symbol and in a 0.5 ms timeslot there are seven symbols for the normal Cyclic Prefix (CP) case. The CP is described in detail in Section 2.2.

2.1.4.1 Power Time Mask

The on/off requirements for slot-based transmissions are similar to UMTS. Figure 2.1-1 shows the profile for the general on/off time mask.

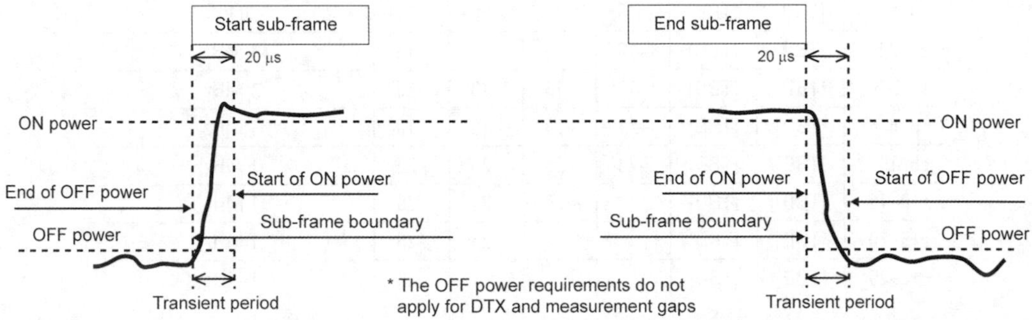

Figure 2.1-1. General ON/OFF Time Mask (36.101 [1] Figure 6.3.4.1-1)

The general requirement is used any time the signal turns on or off. The measurement duration is at least one subframe excluding any transient period. Note that the transient period is not symmetrical with the subframe boundary; the on power ramp transient period starts after the subframe boundary but the off power ramp starts after the end of the subframe. There is no ideal position for the transient period in an FDD system in which no gaps are defined, and the solution specified is a compromise. The choice made for FDD is to minimize any interference to adjacent subframes during the ramp up but allow the ramp down to be delayed until after the end of the subframe.

There is a similar mask for the Physical Random Access Channel (PRACH) and Sounding Reference Signal (SRS), but the on period is one PRACH symbol or one SRS symbol and the on ramp is shifted to before the symbol start making it symmetrical with the off ramp. This shift is particularly important for the SRS since the SRS symbol can be transmitted in isolation for approximately 70 µs and is used by the eNB to estimate the uplink channel conditions. If this symbol were not stable for its nominal duration, the eNB might get an incorrect estimate of the uplink channel. A symmetrical mask was not chosen for the general on/off case since there are times when it is important to protect the symbol just prior to a power change.

Apart from the traditional on and off transitions, other transitions from one power state to another are sometimes necessary. These include changes to the transmit power and transitions into and out of the SRS. In addition, a change to the allocated frequency can trigger a power transient due to baseband compensation for known unflatness in the transmission path.

A common example of a frequency-induced power transient occurs when the UE is transmitting the Physical Uplink Control Channel (PUCCH). The PUCCH generally transmits one timeslot at the lower end of the channel followed by another timeslot at the upper end. (See measurement example in Section 6.4.6.7) This is shown in Figure 3.2-13. The requirements for spectrum flatness in 36.101 [1] subclause 6.5.2.4 specify that at the band edge (which for wide channels in narrow bands means most of the channels are at the band edge); the UE is allowed to have a variation in power across the channel of +3 to –5 dB. This could represent a slope of some 8 dB. In extreme conditions the allowance rises to 12 dB. When the UE transmits the PUCCH or narrow allocations of the Physical Uplink Shared Channel (PUSCH), it may be necessary to compensate for known flatness issues. This then creates the possibility of a power transient at baseband and RF even though the nominal power remains constant.

The requirements for maintaining PUSCH/PUCCH power accuracy apply to the second and subsequent subframes after the start of a contiguous block of subframes. This requirement also applies to non-contiguous transmissions provided the gap is less than or equal to 20 ms (two frames). There are also requirements for the Physical Random Access Channel (PRACH) that apply to the second and subsequent PRACH preambles. Requirements for the SRS are still to be elaborated.

Table 2.1-6. Relative power tolerance for transmission (normal conditions) (36.101 [1] Table 6.3.5.2.1-1)

Power step size (up or down) ΔP [dB]	PUSCH/PUCCH [dB]	SRS [dB]	PRACH [dB]
$0 \le \Delta P \le 4$	[±MAX {2.0, ΔP/2+2}]		[±MAX {0.5, ΔP/2}]
$4 < \Delta P \le 10$	[±4.0]		[±3.0][1]
$10 < \Delta P \le 15$	[±5.0]		n/a
$15 < \Delta P \le 20$	[±6.0]		n/a
$20 < \Delta P$	[±6.0]		n/a

Note 1: For PRACH the maximum power step is 6 dB.

From Table 2.1-6 it can be seen that even for no change to the nominal power, the relative power can vary by up to 2 dB. This makes allowance for the case when transmissions are contiguous in time but not in frequency. For changes to the configured power the allowance increases up to a maximum of ±6 dB for steps between 15 dB and 20 dB. Under extreme conditions the tolerance rises to ±8 dB.

There is a growing trend within UE design to reduce cost through the use of multi-stage power amplifiers. These reduce the dynamic range that has to be covered in one section but also introduce the possibility of power and phase transients at the power level where the switching between gain stages takes place. This is a known issue being studied in the specifications and it is likely that there will be some number of exceptions to the requirements in Table 2.1-6 to allow for gain stage switching with appropriate limits on hysteresis to avoid unnecessary transients.

2.1.5 Uplink Transmit Signal Quality

Subclause 6.5 of 36.101 [1] defines the in-channel signal quality requirements. These are split into five categories: frequency error, Error Vector Magnitude (EVM), IQ component, in-channel emissions and spectrum flatness. These measurements are fully defined in 36.101 [1] Annex F. Figure 2.1-2 shows the block diagram of the measurement points.

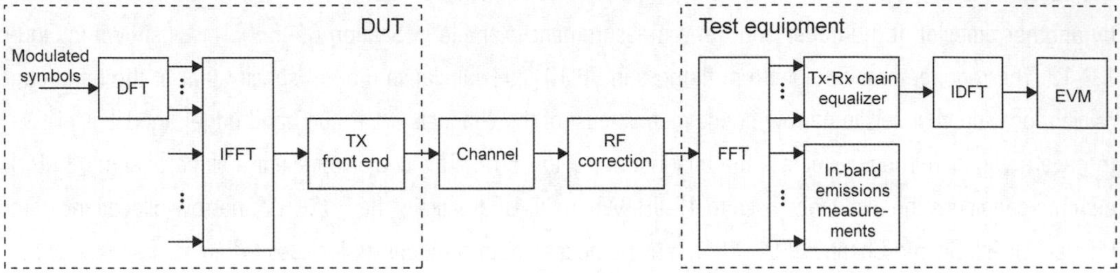

Figure 2.1-2. EVM measurement points (36.101 [1] Figure F.1-1)

The frequency error component is a residual result from measuring EVM and identical in concept to UMTS, so will not be discussed further here.

2.1.5.1 Error Vector Magnitude Definition

The EVM definition is also similar in concept to UMTS but there are two new elements specific to SC-FDMA that need to be explained. The first relates to the presence of the TX-RX chain equalizer block from Figure 2.1-2 and the second relates to the time window over which EVM is defined.

EVM Equalizer Definition

In UMTS, the EVM measurement was defined through an RRC filter matched to the filter defined for UE transmissions. This same filter was assumed in the UMTS base station and was required in order to optimize the received signal quality. In LTE no such transmit filter is defined. This opens up a significant new challenge in determining how to specify transmitter performance. In real-life operation the eNB will attempt to determine the amplitude and phase characteristics of the transmitted signal as seen through the imperfect radio channel. It is essential for accurate demodulation that this equalization process take place, but the LTE specifications for the eNB do not define the method or a reference receiver. This has partly to do with the complexity of the problem, which is a complex function of noise and dynamic channel conditions. As a result this technology is considered proprietary and therefore undefined within the standards.

The lack of a standard equalizer through which the uplink signal quality should be measured presents a problem for the EVM definition. It is known that metrology-grade test equipment working in non-real-time can perform iterative corrections on the signal that would not be possible for the eNB to mimic in a live network. For this reason it was necessary to define a reference equalizer that would constrain the amount of correction but still be somewhat representative of what might be achieved in real operation. At the very least the equalizer definition provides a stable reference against which alternative receiver designs can be compared.

One of the challenges in defining an equalizer for the uplink is that the signal contains noise. In a test environment this noise is primarily generated as a result of any crest factor reduction techniques used in the UE such as baseband clipping. In real operation the uplink will be further degraded by interference. Noise can always be averaged but short uplink signal transmissions do not make this easy. With intra-subframe hopping enabled the UE can be transmitting one RB (180 kHz for 0.5 ms) at one end of the channel and the next RB could be 20 MHz away. Although it is possible to average such signals, the errors are not correlated so the end result may not improve. For this reason the EVM definition is based on the smallest possible transmission of one RB.

The only part of this signal that is known is the RS symbol, which for the normal CP case is the fourth of seven symbols transmitted within each active timeslot allocation (see Figure 3.2-13). The RS represents a known amplitude and phase on each subcarrier. The subcarriers are spaced at 15 kHz intervals across the transmission bandwidth. For one RB this represents only 12 data points in frequency lasting around 70 μs and is considered insufficient to provide a stable reference for the equalizer. To allow for more averaging, the EVM definition makes use of the six data symbols in each timeslot to provide a more stable time-averaged reference. This makes EVM measurements vulnerable to data decode errors since unlike the RS pattern, the data is not known in advance. However, provided the noise is below a critical threshold the addition of the data symbols to the averaging improves the measurement accuracy.

EVM Window Length

The other difference between UMTS EVM and LTE EVM lies in the timing of the measurement. For successful decoding of the CDMA signals used in UMTS the decoder has to be precisely aligned to within a few ns of the signal timing, otherwise the perceived EVM rises sharply and decode errors occur. For CDMA there is only one point in time at which the signal looks at its best. In OFDMA and SC-FDMA systems the situation is very different. The symbols are much longer and have an additional extension, the CP, which adds redundancy in the time domain to mitigate multipath distortion. It is sufficient to say at this point that without multipath, the signal can be successfully decoded over a range of timing equal to the length of the CP.

When multipath is present the error-free decoding window reduces in size such that even if the receiver observes multiple delayed signals up to the length of the CP, there will always be an error-free symbol position for decode. If, however, the signal (rather than the channel) contains any time-domain distortion, this distortion eats into the effective length of the CP. When constructing the transmission system there is always a trade-off between in-channel signal quality (EVM) and out of channel signal quality (spectral re-growth, etc.). When the channel and duplex filters are designed to meet the out-of-channel performance, the quality of the in-channel signal can degrade. This degradation can include time domain effects that resemble multipath Inter Symbol Interference (ISI) distortion on the signal. Such a signal measured through a perfect channel would no longer be error-free over the full range of the CP. To limit the amount of time-domain distortion in the signal the EVM is measured at two points either side of the ideal timing. Table 2.1-7 shows the EVM window length as a function of channel bandwidth.

Table 2.1-7. EVM window length for normal CP (36.101 [1] Table F.5.3-1)

Channel bandwidth MHz	Cyclic prefix length N_{cp} for symbol 0	Cyclic prefix length N_{cp} for symbols 1 to 6	Nominal FFT size	Cyclic prefix for symbols 1 to 6 in FFT samples	EVM window length W	Ratio of W to CP for symbols 1 to 6[1]
1.4	160	144	128	9	[5]	[55.6]
3			256	18	[12]	[66.7]
5			512	36	[32]	[88.9]
10			1024	72	[66]	[91.7]
15			1536	108	[102]	[94.4]
20			2048	144	[136]	[94.4]

Note 1: These percentages are informative and apply to symbols 1 through 6. Symbol 0 has a longer CP and therefore a lower percentage.

It can be seen from Table 2.1-7 that the narrower channel bandwidths are allowed to use up much more of the useful CP length than the wider channels. This reflects the challenge of designing suitable filters for the narrower bands that meet both the in-channel and out-of-channel requirements. Example measurements of EVM versus time on distorted signals are given in Section 6.4.6.

2.1.5.2 IQ Component Definition

Signal distortions in the IQ plane such as IQ offset lead to Local Oscillator (LO) leakage, also known as carrier leakage or carrier feedthrough. This distortion shows up in the frequency domain as energy at the center of the channel although if the transmission is allocated across the center of the channel the error energy is spread by the SC-FDMA processing across the allocation and is not visible. Table 2.1-8 shows the requirements for Relative Carrier Leakage Power (RCLP).

Table 2.1-8. Minimum requirements for relative carrier leakage power (36.101 [1] Table 6.5.2.2.1-1)

Output power	Relative limit (dBc)
>0 dBm	–25
–30 dBm ≤ output power ≤ 0 dBm	–20
–40 dBm ≤ output power < –30 dBm	–10

Note how the requirement is relaxed at low signal power. This is because the mechanisms that create RCLP tend to be linked with residual errors in the IQ modulator, and these errors become more apparent at low signal powers. The RCLP is removed from the signal prior to applying the equalizer for the calculation of EVM.

2.1.5.3 In-Band Emissions

The EVM definition is a measure of the quality of the allocated part of the signal. In UMTS the allocated part by definition was the entire signal, since all transmissions occupied the entire channel bandwidth. With SC-FDMA this is no longer the case since it is normal for the UE to be allocated only a portion of the channel bandwidth. In such circumstances the unallocated part of the channel is available for use by other UE. It is therefore necessary to specify limits on the amount of power the UE may transmit into the unallocated RB. This is similar in concept to the SEM and ACLR requirements for adjacent channel protection except that now it is unallocated resources within the channel bandwidth that need to be protected.

Table 2.1-9 defines limits for three different types of in-band emissions; general, IQ image and DC. The limit that applies for any specific unallocated RB is the highest value calculated for all three types.

Table 2.1-9. Minimum requirements for in-band emissions (36.101[1] Table 6.5.2.3.1-1)

Parameter description	Unit	Limit		Applicable frequencies
General	dB	$\max\{-30,\ -25-10\cdot\log_{10}(N_{RB}/L_{CRBs}),\ 20\cdot\log_{10}EVM-3-5\cdot(\Delta_{RB}-1)/L_{CRBs},\ -57\,dBm/180kHz-P_{RB}\}$		Any non-allocated RB measured relative to average allocated RB power
IQ Image	dB	–25		Any non-allocated image RB measured relative to average allocated RB power
DC	dBc	–25	Output power > 0 dBm	Any non-allocated RB containing or adjacent to the carrier feedthrough measured relative to total allocated RB power
		–20	–30 dBm ≤ Output power ≤ 0 dBm	
		–10	–40 dBm ≤ Output power < –30 dBm	

General In-Band Emissions

The formula defining the requirement for the general in-band emission is particularly complicated and deserves further explanation. The general requirement can be considered as the overall in-band noise component for unallocated RB that is not covered by the more specific allowances for DC at the channel center and the image RB. In specifying a general noise component, it is tempting to set a fixed noise floor for each unallocated RB. This would work well for narrow allocations in which the overall noise generated in the channel would be the sum of all the noise from many UE. However, when the transmission from one UE gets wider, a fixed noise limit becomes more challenging to achieve and less important to the system performance. If the UE occupies almost the entire channel, there are fewer UE generating noise and so the general limit for unallocated RB for UE transmitting on many RB can be higher. Due to the shape of the SC-FDMA spectrum, the unallocated RB closest to the allocated RB have a higher noise limit. The requirement also takes into account the modulation depth being evaluated. The use of higher-order modulation implies better channel conditions, which in turn imply a lower path loss to the eNB. The significance of any noise generated is therefore larger and so there is a component in the requirement that lowers the allowed noise when the EVM limit is lower.

The formula takes into account all these factors starting with the size of the allocation L_{CRBs} relative to the maximum number of RB in the channel N_{RB}. When the allocation reaches the maximum ($L_{CRBs} = N_{RB}$), the second term reaches an upper limit of –25 dB, representing a relaxation for wide allocations. The third term starts with a level defined by the EVM limit for the modulation depth being analyzed, which is then reduced as a function of the separation Δ_{RB} between the last allocated RB and the non-allocated RB being measured. The final term sets an absolute noise floor of –57 dBm/180 kHz, which becomes relevant when P_{RB}, the average power per allocated RB, is less than –27 dBm.

IQ Image In-Band Emissions

One of the classic OFDM distortion mechanisms, which also applies to SC-FDMA, is the presence of an image of the allocated RB reflected around the center of the channel. Quadrature error and IQ gain imbalance are usually the cause. The mathematics of this is described in "Effects of physical layer impairments on OFDM systems" [5]. Measurement examples are discussed in Section 6.4.6.9. The limit for image power is set at –25 dB.

DC In-Band Emissions

The distortion mechanisms that create the DC component are the same as those that create RCLP. The difference between them is that RCLP is a requirement of the wanted signal whereas the in-band emissions' DC component is specified in terms of its impact on other UE. For this reason the way that the DC component is measured differs from that of RCLP. In the case of RCLP, the signal is first passed through an equalizer and then the DC component is estimated prior to its removal. The DC component is measured as it is seen by the victim UE, without equalization.

The RB over which the DC component needs to be evaluated depends on the number of RB supported by the channel bandwidth (see Table 3.2-7). The subcarriers used for the SC-FDMA uplink are offset from the channel center frequency by half a subcarrier spacing (7.5 kHz). For channel bandwidths of 3 MHz, 5 MHz and 15 MHz there are an odd number of RBs. In this case the carrier leakage is contained within the central RB, and only this RB needs to be measured for the DC component.

For the 1.4 MHz, 10 MHz and 20 MHz bandwidths there is an even number of RBs, which means that the carrier leakage falls in between the RB on either side of the center frequency. The carrier leakage impacts both RB so both need to be measured for the DC component. The situation for the downlink is different since it has one subcarrier reserved at the channel center frequency for carrier leakage and is therefore orthogonal to the RB allocated on either side.

2.1.5.4 Spectrum Flatness

The fact that EVM is measured through an equalizer makes it desirable to define an unequalized spectrum flatness limit. Without such a limit, large variations in power across the channel could be removed by the EVM measurement and thus go unnoticed. In practice, the equalizer in the eNB will be limited in performance due to noise in the channel and so an additional flatness requirement helps constrain the signal quality when the equalizer is unable to correct for large errors.

The spectrum flatness measurement is a residual result from the calculation of the EVM equalizer coefficients. Table 2.1-10 defines the requirements.

Table 2.1-10. Minimum requirements for spectrum flatness (normal conditions) (36.101 [1] Table 6.5.2.4.1-1)

Spectrum	Relative limit (dB)
If $F_{UL\_measurement} - F_{UL\_low} \geq 3$ MHz and If $F_{UL\_high} - F_{UL\_measurement} \geq 3$ MHz	+2/–2
If $F_{UL\_measurement} - F_{UL\_low} < 3$ MHz or If $F_{UL\_high} - F_{UL\_measurement} < 3$ MHz	+3/–5

Note: FUL_low and FUL_high refer to each E-UTRA frequency band specified in 36.101 [1] Table 5.5-1.
Note: FUL_measurement refers to frequency tone being evaluated.

The requirements are split into two groups. For RB more than 3 MHz from the band edge the requirement is ±2 dB but near the band edge the requirements are relaxed considerably to allow for the additional effect of the duplex filter, which has to attenuate the out-of-channel emissions falling into the adjacent band. It can be seen that at the band edge there could be up to 8 dB of unflatness across the channel. Since LTE supports up to 20 MHz channel bandwidths and since some bands are not much larger than this, it can be seen that the band edge condition can apply to a large proportion of the channels.

It is also important to limit the absolute phase correction applied by the equalizer, but currently no requirements are defined for this.

2.1.6 UE Receiver Characteristics

One of the biggest differences between UMTS and LTE is that all the receiver characteristics assume the UE has two receiver ports as part of the baseline functionality. Previous systems have had this as an option. Support for four receiver ports is for future study.

2.1.6.1 UE Reference Sensitivity

The most basic receiver requirement is reference sensitivity. This is similar in concept to UMTS although there is a new dimension added with the introduction of the Maximum Sensitivity Degradation (MSD) parameter. This is a relaxation in the reference sensitivity level that applies when the UE is transmitting at maximum power (with MPR applied) using the maximum number of RB allowed for the channel bandwidth. Under these conditions it is expected there will be a loss of sensitivity in the UE receiver.

The remaining receiver requirements — maximum input level, adjacent channel selectivity, blocking, spurious response, intermodulation and spurious emissions — are all similar to UMTS.

2.1.7 Uplink Reference Measurement Channels

Due to the flexible nature of the uplink transmissions, it is important that the signal definition be explicit when performance targets are specified. As a result, many of the UE transmitter requirements in 36.101 [1] subclause 6 and some of the receiver requirements in subclause 7 are defined relative to specific uplink configurations. These are known as Reference Measurement Channels (RMCs). A similar principle was used in UMTS and the main difference for LTE is the use of SC-FDMA rather than W-CDMA for the air interface.

Since the uplink RMCs are primarily used for testing UE transmitter performance, many of the variables that will be used in real operation are disabled. These include "no incremental redundancy" (1 HARQ transmission), "normal cyclic prefix only," "no PUSCH hopping," "no link adaptation" and "for partial allocation the RB are contiguous starting at the channel edge." Table 2.1-11 shows an example uplink RMC for a partially allocated (75%) 64QAM case.

Table 2.1-11. Reference channels for 20 MHz QPSK with partial RB allocation (36.101 [1] Table A.2.2.2.1-6)

Parameter	Unit	Value	Value	Value	Value	Value
Channel bandwidth	MHz	20	20	20	20	20
Allocated resource blocks		1	18	25	50	75
DFT-OFDM symbols per subframe		12	12	12	12	12
Modulation		QPSK	QPSK	QPSK	QPSK	QPSK
Target coding rate		1/3	1/3	1/3	1/3	1/3
Payload size	Bits	72	1864	2216	5160	6712
Transport block CRC	Bits	24	24	24	24	24
Number of code blocks – C		1	1	1	1	2
Code block CRC size	Bits	0	0	0	0	24
Total number of bits per subframe	Bits	288	5184	7200	14400	21600
Total symbols per subframe		144	2592	3600	7200	10800

2.1.8 Downlink Reference Measurement Channels

An example of a single antenna downlink RMC for use with 64QAM PUSCH and common (cell-specific rather than UE-specific) Demodulation Reference Symbols (DMRS) is given in Table 2.1-12. This RMC will be used for performance testing under faded channel conditions.

Table 2.1-12. Fixed reference channel 64QAM R=3/4 (36.101 [1] Table A.3.3.1-3)

Parameter	Unit	Value					
Reference channel			[R.5 FDD]	[R.6 FDD]	[R.7 FDD]	[R.8 FDD]	[R.9 FDD]
Channel bandwidth	MHz	1.4	3	5	10	15	20
Allocated resource blocks			15	25	50	75	100
Allocated subframes per radio frame			10	10	10	10	10
Modulation		64QAM	64QAM	64QAM	64QAM	64QAM	64QAM
Target coding rate		3/4	3/4	3/4	3/4	3/4	3/4
Information bit payload							
For subframes 1,2,3,4,6,7,8,9	Bits		8504	14112	30576	46888	61664
For subframe 5	Bits		7992	13536	30576	45352	61664
For subframe 0	Bits		6456	12576	28336	45352	61664
Number of code blocks per subframe			2	3	5	8	11
Binary channel bits per subframe							
For subframes 1,2,3,4,6,7,8,9	Bits		11340	18900	41400	62100	82800
For subframe 5	Bits		10476	18036	40536	61236	81936
For subframe 0	Bits		8820	16380	38880	59580	80280
Maximum throughput averaged over 1 frame	Mbps		8.25	13.9	30.4	46.6	61.7

Note 1: Two symbols allocated to PDCCH for 20 MHz, 15 MHz and 10 MHz channel BW; three symbols allocated to PDCCH for 5 MHz and 3 MHz; four symbols allocated to PDCCH for 1.4 MHz.
Note 2: Reference signal, synchronization signals and PBCH allocated per TS 36.211.

It can be seen from Table 2.1-12 that these RMC are for a fully allocated downlink, and the maximum throughput this represents reaches a maximum of 61.7 Mbps for the 20 MHz channel bandwidth case. Note that this figure represents the maximum transmitted data rate and is in no way intended to indicate the performance of the downlink in real radio conditions. This peak figure is the reference used for specifying the expected performance, which will be specified relative to the maximum figures.

2.1.9 UE Performance Requirements

The performance requirements set minimum levels of performance for the reception by the UE of various physical channels according to the downlink RMC configurations in 36.101 [1] A.3 and the channel propagation conditions in Annex B. Requirements cover all the essential downlink data and control channels at the supported modulation depths of QPSK, 16QAM and 64QAM. The conditions under which performance is measured take into account the various antenna configurations of receive diversity; transmit diversity, single-user spatial multiplexing (open and closed loop) and multi-user spatial multiplexing. There are further options for cell-specific and user-specific reference signals. The performance requirements will be discussed further in Sections 6.5, 6.7 and 7.2.

2.1.10 Downlink Transmit Signal Quality

The requirements for the downlink in-channel signal quality are less complex than for the uplink and are covered by EVM. Although not always fully allocated, the downlink signal bandwidth is always nearly at the full channel bandwidth due to the presence of the RS subcarriers, which are always transmitted. The consistency of the signal means that its quality can be defined over a full 10 ms frame which avoids the noise concerns when evaluating the 0.5 ms uplink bursts.

Figure 2.1-3 shows the reference point for the EVM definition.

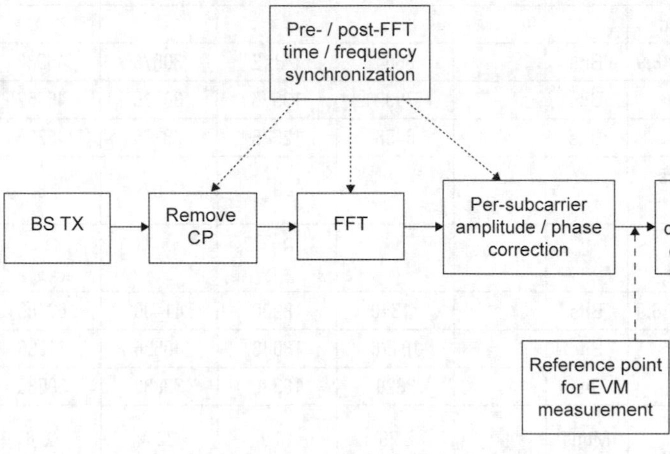

Figure 2.1-3. Reference point for EVM measurement (36.104 [2] Figure E.1-1)

The downlink definition is similar to the uplink definition in that it is necessary to specify EVM through an equalizer, described in Figure 2.1-3 as a per-subcarrier amplitude and phase correction. As with the uplink, the references for the equalizer are the RS embedded in the signal. However, due to the way the downlink RS are mapped, the downlink equalizer definition is quite different from that used for the uplink. The pattern of the RS for a two-antenna system is shown later in Figure 2.4-3. A fully unconstrained equalizer would take the amplitude and phase of every reference symbol and then interpolate amplitude and phase correction values for the intermediate subcarriers to correct the entire signal. Although it is possible to construct such an equalizer in the conformance test system, this would have provided optimistic results compared to what a realistic UE equalizer might provide. The solution was to define a simpler constrained equalizer using moving average smoothing in the frequency domain. The RS on the reference subcarriers from one 10 ms frame are averaged in time into a linear array, which results in one amplitude and phase correction value for every third subcarrier. A moving average is then calculated by sliding a window of length 19 across the array according to Figure 2.1-4.

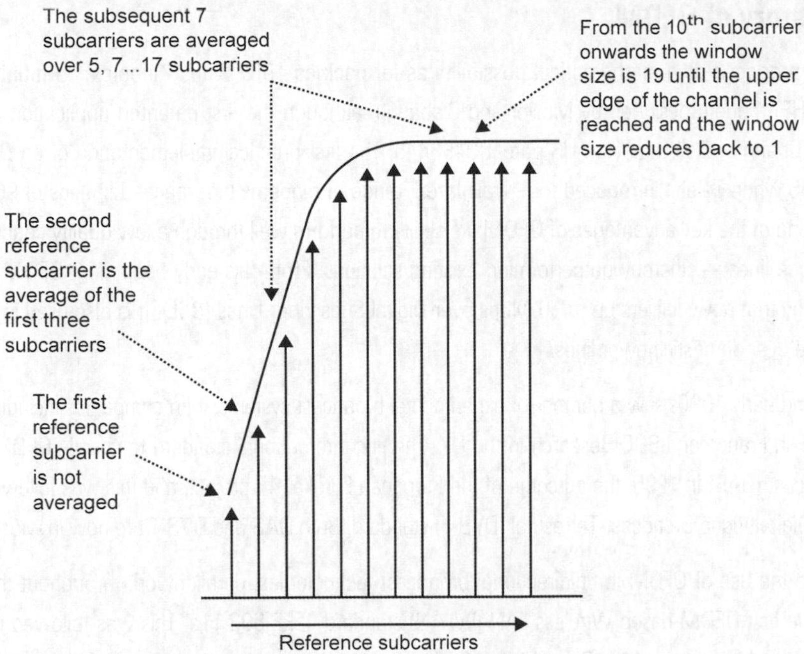
The subsequent 7 subcarriers are averaged over 5, 7...17 subcarriers
From the 10th subcarrier onwards the window size is 19 until the upper edge of the channel is reached and the window size reduces back to 1
The second reference subcarrier is the average of the first three subcarriers
The first reference subcarrier is not averaged
Reference subcarriers

Figure 2.1-4. Reference subcarrier smoothing in the frequency domain (36.104 [2] Figure E.6-1)

At the channel edges the width of the moving average gradually decreases until at the outermost reference subcarriers there is no averaging. The effect this has on the equalizer performance is that in the middle of the signal where it is expected to be flat there is the least amount of correction whereas at the channel edge where filter roll-off is expected, the equalizer can do the most correction. The only downside of shortening the moving average window is that the equalization at the outermost subcarriers is more susceptible to noise. There is an EVM window length requirement for the downlink similar to that described in Section 2.1.5.1 for the uplink.

2.2 Orthogonal Frequency Division Multiplexing

Orthogonal Frequency Division Multiplexing (OFDM) is the modulation scheme chosen for the LTE downlink. It is a digital multi-carrier scheme that uses a large number of closely-spaced subcarriers to carry data and control information. Each individual subcarrier is modulated at a low symbol rate with a conventional modulation format such as Quadrature Amplitude Modulation (QAM). The combination of the many low-rate subcarriers provides overall data rates similar to conventional single-carrier modulation schemes using the same bandwidth. Today, OFDM is widely used in applications from digital television and audio broadcasting to wireless networking and wired broadband internet access.

2.2.1 History of OFDM

OFDM was proposed as a mathematical possibility as far back as 1957 with "Kineplex," a multi-carrier High Frequency (HF) modem designed by Mosier and Clabaugh, although the first patented application was not until 1966 when Chang of Bell Labs filed US patent 3488445. The first practical implementation of an OFDM system came in 1985 when Telebit introduced the "Trailblazer" range of modems that reached speeds of 9600 bps. This highlighted one of the key advantages of OFDM: its ability to perform well through a low quality channel — in this case telephone lines — thereby outperforming existing solutions. From this early beginning, OFDM has become the technology that now delivers up to 10 Mbps over Digital Subscriber Lines (DSL). It is also used in systems that communicate over domestic power lines.

The 1980s and early 1990s saw a number of experimental broadcast systems, with companies including Thomson-CSF and TDF in France and BBC Research in the UK. The first international standard to specify OFDM was Digital Audio Broadcast (DAB) in 1995, the outcome of the European Eureka147 project, and this was followed two years later by the Digital Video Broadcast-Terrestrial (DVB-T) standard. Both DAB and DVB-T are now in widespread use.

In addition to the use of OFDM in unidirectional broadcast technologies, parallel work throughout the 1990s led in 1999 to the first OFDM-based Wireless LAN (WLAN) standard, IEEE 802.11a. This was followed in succession by 802.11g, 802.11n (adding MIMO) and 802.16d (fixed WiMAX™), although the most widely deployed WLAN standard is still 802.11b, which uses direct sequence spread spectrum.

The use of OFDM for cellular systems was first briefly considered back in the late 1980s as a candidate technology for GSM, but was quickly dropped due to lack of cost-effective computing power. A decade later, OFDM was seriously considered as one of the candidates for 3GPP's UMTS but was ruled out in favor of Wideband Code Division Multiple Access (W-CDMA). Again the decision was influenced by the cost of computing power and the associated power consumption in the terminals.

However, with today's availability of small, low-cost, low-power chipsets, OFDM has become the technology of choice for the next generation of cellular wireless. The first cellular system to adopt OFDM was 802.16e (Mobile WiMAX™). It was followed soon after by 802.20, the basis for 3GPP2's Ultra-Mobile Broadband (UMB), and most recently by 3GPP for the long-term evolution of UMTS. It now seems apparent that the evolution of these newest so-called 3.9G systems towards 4G will not result in any change to the underlying air interface, so OFDM will likely be the technology of choice for cellular wireless systems well into the future. The new OFDM cellular systems all focus on delivering high-speed data services and have similar goals in terms of improving spectral efficiency, with the widest bandwidth systems providing the highest single-user data rates.

2.2.1 OFDM Basic Signal Construction

The basic OFDM signal comprises a large number of closely spaced Continuous Wave (CW) tones in the frequency domain. The most basic form of modulation applied to the subcarriers is square wave phase modulation, which produces a frequency spectrum represented by a sinc or $\frac{sin(x)}{x}$ function that has been convolved around the subcarrier frequency. A truncated sinc function is shown in Figure 2.2-1.

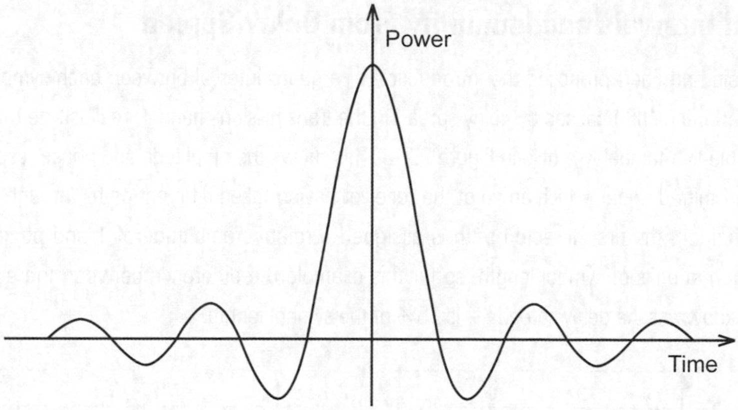

Figure 2.2-1. Spectrum of a single modulated OFDM subcarrier (truncated)

The rate of change of the phase modulation will determine the position of the zero crossings in frequency. The trick that makes OFDM a practical transmission system is to link the subcarrier modulation rate to the subcarrier spacing such that the nulls in the spectrum of one subcarrier line up with the peaks of the adjacent subcarriers. For standard LTE each modulating symbol lasts 66.7 μs. By setting the subcarrier spacing to be 15 kHz, which is the reciprocal of the symbol rate, the peaks and nulls line up perfectly such that at any subcarrier frequency, the subcarriers are orthogonal; i.e., there is no interference between them. This can be seen in Figure 2.2-2.

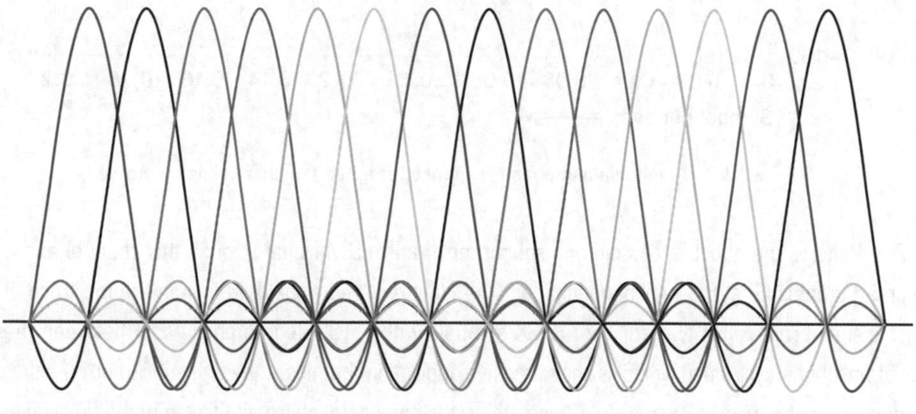

Figure 2.2-2. Spectrum of multiple OFDM subcarriers of constant amplitude

In Figure 2.2-2 each subcarrier has the same magnitude, which is the case when any of the LTE-supported constant amplitude modulation formats are used: Zadoff-Chu sequences, Binary Phase-Shift Keying (BPSK) and Quadrature Phase-Shift Keying (QPSK). It is also possible for the subcarriers to vary in amplitude since LTE also supports 16 Quadrature Amplitude Modulation (16QAM) and 64 Quadrature Amplitude Modulation (64QAM).

Compared to the 3.84 Msps of UMTS, the 15 ksps subcarrier symbol rate of LTE is very low, but in the same 5 MHz channel bandwidth, LTE can simultaneously transmit 300 subcarriers to provide an aggregate 4.5 Msps rate. Thus on first inspection, CDMA and OFDM have similar capacity for carrying data.

2.2.2 Guard Intervals and Immunity From Delay Spread

In 1971 Weinstein and Ebert proposed the introduction of a guard interval between each symbol to reduce the Inter-Symbol Interference (ISI) caused by delay spread in the transmission channel. To illustrate the principle of ISI, consider the simple five-tap delay profile in Figure 2.2-3. This shows the amplitude and phase response of delayed copies of the transmitted signal, which arrive at the receiver having taken different paths through the transmission channel. By definition, the first detected path is assigned a relative amplitude of 1 and phase of 0 degrees. The X-axis is given in units of symbol length, so for this example the difference between the earliest and latest components — known as the delay spread — is 15% of the symbol length.

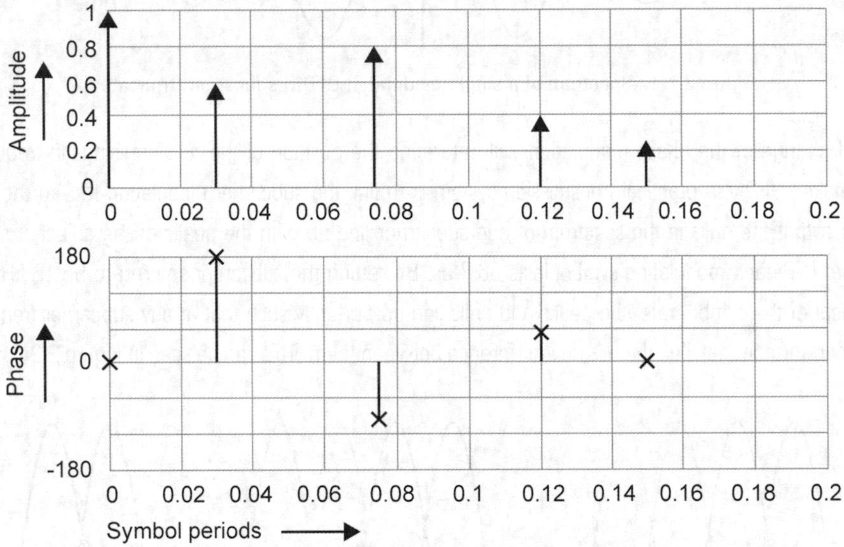

Figure 2.2-3. Amplitude and phase response for a five-tap channel delay profile

Figure 2.2-4 shows the effect of passing one subcarrier of an OFDM signal through this channel and how the delay spread creates ISI at the symbol boundaries. The ideal received signal is shown in the top trace of Figure 2.2-4. This signal represents two adjacent BPSK symbols with a 180 degree phase shift between them. The number of baseband cycles per symbol is shown as five, indicating that this is the fifth subcarrier on either side of the channel center frequency. The next four traces show the amplitude, phase and timing of the delayed copies of the ideal signal at the receiver. The bottom trace represents the composite received signal, being the sum of the five components. In order to show the extent of the delay spread, the dotted line in the bottom trace is a copy of the ideal signal. From this it is very evident that during the period from 1.05 to 1.2, the received signal is severely distorted and of negative value to the demodulation process. The received signal is undistorted only after the last component has arrived and before the first component leaves. For this delay profile the undistorted symbol is reduced to 85% of its transmitted length.

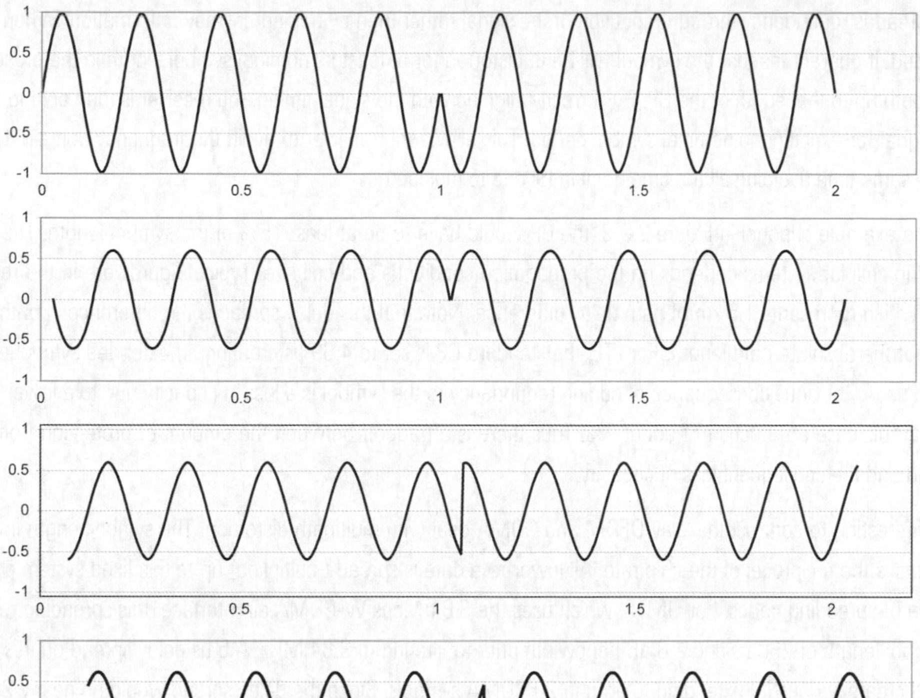

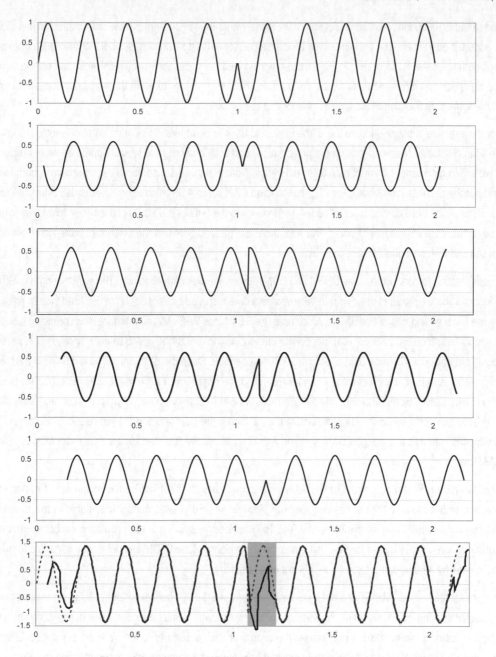

Figure 2.2-4. Inter-symbol interference caused by delay spread

In order to optimize demodulation performance and reject Inter-Carrier Interference (ICI), the symbol must be sampled for exactly its nominal length. At baseband, each successive subcarrier has one more cycle during the OFDM symbol period. When error energy from an adjacent subcarrier is added to the wanted subcarrier, the only time period for which the signals are orthogonal (multiply and integrate to zero) is at the reciprocal of the subcarrier spacing.

The CP adds redundancy through repetition of the signal rather than by adding any new information. When the CP is added, it guarantees that the symbol will be undistorted for at least its nominal symbol length in the presence of multipath up to the length of the CP. By correctly aligning with the signal timing, the receiver is then able to sample the signal for exactly one nominal symbol period. This allows the receiver to avoid the frequency domain ICI while at the same time avoiding all the time domain ISI due to multipath.

For the example channel in Figure 2.2-3, the CP would have to be at least 15% of the symbol length. The choice of CP in cellular systems depends on the propagation conditions and cell size. Typical figures are in the region of 5 µs, which represents 1.5 km of path delay difference. Note that this delay spread is the difference in path length and not the absolute path length. For LTE, the standard CP is set to 4.69 µs creating an extended symbol of some 71.35 µs. An obvious consequence of adding redundancy to the symbol is a loss in capacity due to a lower symbol rate, in this case a reduction of about 7%. Thus there is a tradeoff between the amount of protection from delay spread and the consequent loss of capacity.

It is interesting to contrast the way OFDM and CDMA deal with multipath distortion. The symbol length in CDMA systems is the reciprocal of the chip rate. All lower-rate data is spread (multiplied) up to this fixed system chip rate by use of spreading codes. For UMTS, which uses the 3.84 Mcps W-CDMA air interface, this spreading results in a symbol length of 260 ns and a 3 dB bandwidth prior to filtering of 3.84 MHz. A 5 µs delay spread on this system would create serious ISI extending to around 20 CDMA symbols. Since the delay spread would be nearly 20 times the symbol length, it is impractical to consider extending the symbol with a CP in the way described for OFDM. This is why CDMA systems have to rely on rake receivers and frequency-domain equalizers to untangle the ISI. In CDMA systems, the wider the channel bandwidth, the higher the chip rate and the worse the ISI becomes. This is why it is impractical to design CDMA systems with channel bandwidths much wider than the 5 MHz of today's UMTS.

This situation is in sharp contrast to OFDM, whose symbol length is set not by the reciprocal of the channel bandwidth but rather by the subcarrier spacing. This makes OFDM systems highly scalable in the frequency domain with no impact on the symbol length. The 15 kHz subcarrier spacing in LTE provides a symbol length that is 256 times longer than is used for W-CDMA, and the sheer length of the OFDM symbol makes it feasible to extend the symbol by 4.69 µs with a loss of only 7% in system capacity.

It is reasonable to ask why OFDM does not continue to make the symbols even longer by using ever-narrower subcarrier spacing. However, there are practical considerations which limit how close the subcarriers can become. The first factor is phase noise, which causes the energy of each subcarrier to leak into the adjacent subcarriers causing ICI. The second factor is the consequence of frequency errors between the transmitter and receiver, which can shift energy sideways in the frequency domain also causing ICI. Simple frequency errors due to Doppler shift or other single-sided errors can be corrected using normal closed loop frequency tracking methods. Even then, the closer the subcarrier spacing, the better these tracking loops have to perform.

There is, however, a double-sided frequency error that can occur if the UE simultaneously receives downlink signals from behind and in front as a result of reflections. If the UE is moving towards or away from the reflector, one signal could be reduced in frequency while the other is increased. This creates a symmetrical image in the frequency domain that cannot be removed using a simple frequency tracking loop. This kind of ICI is possible to remove using digital techniques but the process can require huge amounts of computing power if the ICI becomes significant. This and the earlier reasons are why practical subcarrier spacing in OFDM systems do not get much lower than the 7.5 kHz defined for LTE's optional Multimedia Broadcast over Single Frequency Network (MBSFN) service.

2.2.3 Example of OFDM Signal Generation

Figure 2.2-5 illustrates the principles of OFDM signal generation using a simple four subcarrier example.

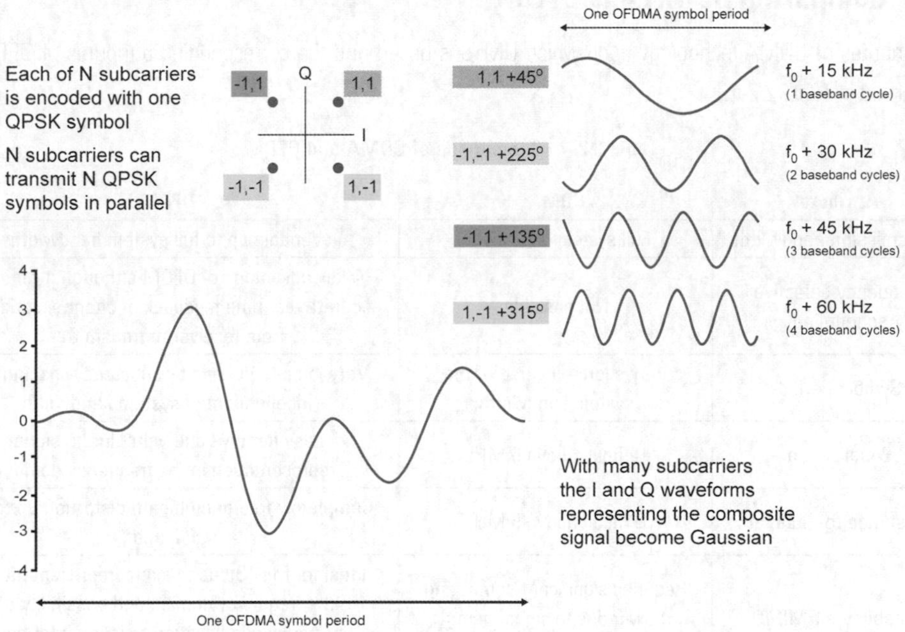

Figure 2.2-5. Example of OFDM signal generation using four subcarriers

Since four subcarriers are used in this example, it will be possible to transmit four data symbols in parallel. The four possible data symbols are represented by phases of the subcarrier, which in the IQ plane are represented as (1, 1), (–1, 1), (–1, –1) and (1, –1). One of these symbols will be mapped to each subcarrier for the duration of an OFDM symbol. The four possible subcarrier phases are shown. Each subcarrier is defined in the frequency domain by a vector, which represents the amplitude and phase of the data symbol that has been mapped to it. After symbol mapping, the subcarriers are each converted to time domain waveforms using an Inverse Fast Fourier Transform (IFFT). At this point the CP is inserted for each waveform and then the waveforms are vector summed to produce the composite waveform for transmission.

The lower trace in Figure 2.2-5 shows the composite waveform (without the CP, for simplicity) resulting from the parallel transmission of the four symbols shown. Due to the summation of the four waveforms, the peak of the signal now reaches nearly four times the voltage of one subcarrier. With increasing numbers of subcarriers the I and Q waveforms that represent the composite signal become Gaussian, which creates a chi-square power distribution.

This simple example illustrates one of the key disadvantages of OFDM, which is that the Peak to Average Power Ratio (PAPR) of the composite signal can have peaks exceeding 12 dB above the average signal power, which presents significant challenges for transmission by an eNB operating at high power. There are many steps that can be taken to reduce the signal peaks and to extend the useful operating range of the power amplifier. These are discussed further in Section 6.4.1.4.

2.2.4 Comparing CDMA and OFDM

The attributes of CDMA technology upon which UMTS is based and the corresponding attributes of OFDM are summarized in Table 2.2-1.

Table 2.2-1. Comparison of CDMA and OFDM

Attribute	CDMA	OFDM
Transmission bandwidth	Full system bandwidth	Variable up to full system bandwidth
Frequency-selective scheduling	Not possible	A key advantage of OFDM although it requires accurate real-time feedback of channel conditions from receiver to transmitter
Symbol period	Very short – inverse of the system bandwidth	Very long — defined by subcarrier spacing and independent of system bandwidth
Equalization	Difficult above 5 MHz	Easy for any bandwidth due to signal representation in the frequency domain
Resistance to multipath	Difficult above 5 MHz	Completely free of multipath distortion up to the CP length
Suitability for MIMO	Requires significant computing power due to signal being defined in the time domain	Ideal for MIMO due to signal representation in the frequency domain and possibility of narrowband allocation to follow real-time variations in the channel
Sensitivity to frequency domain distortion and interference	Averaged across the channel by the spreading process	Vulnerable to narrow-band distortion and interference
Separation of users	Scrambling and orthogonal spreading codes	Frequency and time although scrambling and spreading can be added as well

The commercial use of OFDM until now has been primarily for broadcast and wired applications in which interference has not been a major factor. OFDM is used in some of the WLAN protocols, which are typically found in hotspot deployments; however, to date there are no large-scale deployments of cellular systems based on OFDM. The first such systems are likely to be based on the 802.16e standard. Cellular systems are different from broadcast and hotspot systems in that they have to operate seamlessly across a wide area, including the area around the cell boundaries where signal levels are at their lowest and inter-cell interference is at its highest.

It is expected that OFDM will be more difficult to operate than CDMA at the cell edge. CDMA relies on scrambling codes to provide protection from inter-cell interference at the cell edge, whereas OFDM has no such intrinsic feature. In addition, the interference profile at the cell edge for CDMA is relatively stable across frequency and can be modeled and removed using interference cancelling receivers. The situation for OFDM is more complex because the presence or absence of interference is a function of narrow-band scheduling in the adjacent cell, and the resulting noise profile is likely to be far less stable and predictable. One solution to this is to use some form of frequency planning at the cell edge. Figure 2.2-6 gives one example of how this might be done. The white central area of the cell is where the entire channel bandwidth would get used and the colored areas show a frequency reuse pattern with a repetition factor of four.

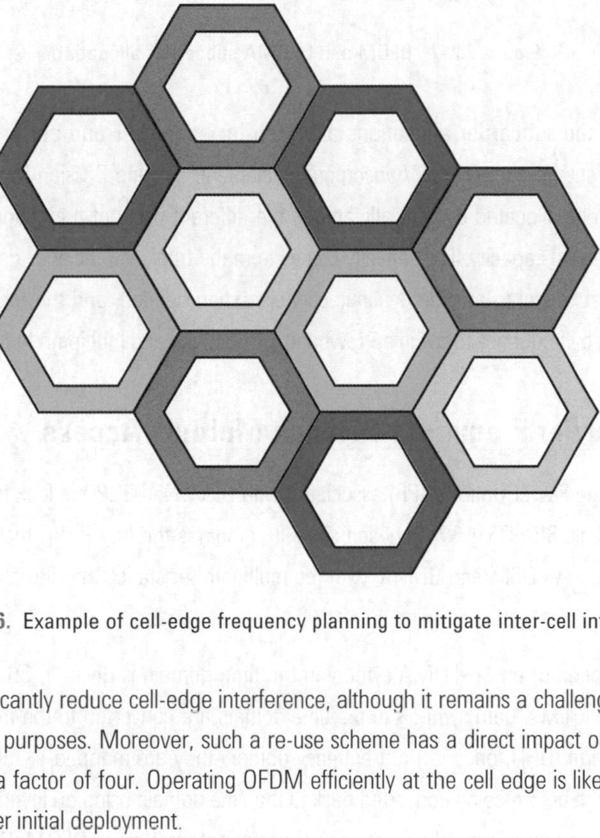

Figure 2.2-6. Example of cell-edge frequency planning to mitigate inter-cell interference

This approach can significantly reduce cell-edge interference, although it remains a challenge to know the location of the UE for scheduling purposes. Moreover, such a re-use scheme has a direct impact on cell edge capacity, in this case reducing it by a factor of four. Operating OFDM efficiently at the cell edge is likely to require significant network optimization after initial deployment.

2.2.5 Orthogonal Frequency Division Multiple Access

Until now the discussion has been about OFDM, but LTE uses a variant of OFDM for the downlink called Orthogonal Frequency Division Multiple Access (OFDMA). Figure 2.2-7 compares OFDM and OFDMA.

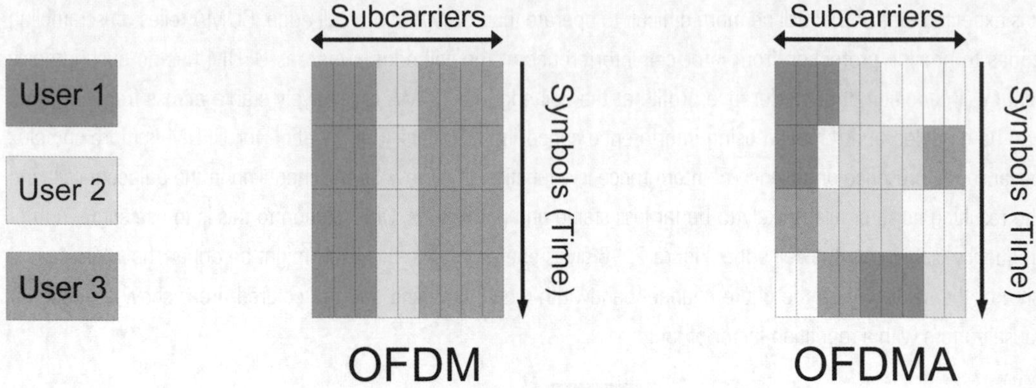

Figure 2.2-7. OFDM and OFDMA subcarrier allocation

With standard OFDM the subcarrier allocations are fixed for each user and performance can suffer from narrowband fading and interference. OFDMA incorporates elements of Time Division Multiple Access (TDMA) so that the subcarriers can be allocated dynamically among the different users of the channel. The result is a more robust system with increased capacity. The capacity comes from the trunking efficiency gained by multiplexing low rate users onto a wider channel to provide dynamic capacity when needed, and the robustness comes from the ability to schedule users by frequency to avoid narrowband interference and multipath fading.

2.3 Single-Carrier Frequency Division Multiple Access

The high Peak-to-Average Power Ratio (PAPR) associated with OFDM led 3GPP to look for a different modulation scheme for the LTE uplink. SC-FDMA was chosen since it combines the low PAPR techniques of single-carrier transmission systems, such as GSM and CDMA, with the multipath resistance and flexible frequency allocation of OFDMA.

A mathematical description of an SC-FDMA symbol in the time domain is given in 36.211 [6] sub-clause 5.6. A brief description is as follows: data symbols in the time domain are converted to the frequency domain using a Discrete Fourier Transform (DFT); once in the frequency domain they are mapped to the desired location in the overall channel bandwidth before being converted back to the time domain using an Inverse FFT (IFFT). Finally, the CP is inserted. SC-FDMA is sometimes called Discrete Fourier Transform Spread OFDM (DFT-S-OFDM) because of this process, although this terminology is becoming less common.

2.3.1 OFDMA and SC-FDMA Compared

A graphical comparison of OFDMA and SC-FDMA as shown in Figure 2.3-1 is helpful in understanding the differences between these two modulation schemes. As will be described in section 3.2, real uplink SC-FDMA signals are allocated in units of 12 adjacent subcarriers known as Resource Blocks (RB). However, for clarity, this example uses only four (M) subcarriers over two symbol periods with the payload data represented by Quadrature Phase Shift Keying (QPSK) modulation.

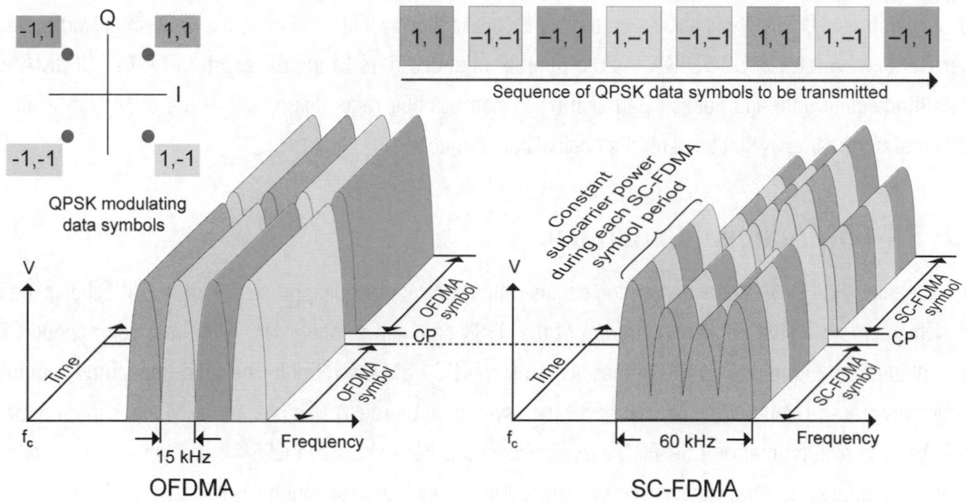

Figure 2.3-1. Comparison of OFDMA and SC-FDMA transmitting a series of QPSK symbols

On the left side of Figure 2.3-1, M adjacent 15 kHz subcarriers — already positioned at the desired place in the channel bandwidth — are each modulated for the OFDMA symbol period of 66.7 μs by one QPSK data symbol. In this four subcarrier example, four symbols are taken in parallel. These are QPSK data symbols so only the phase of each subcarrier is modulated and the subcarrier power remains constant between symbols. After one OFDMA symbol period has elapsed, the CP is inserted and the next four symbols are transmitted in parallel. For visual clarity, the CP is shown as a gap; however, it is actually filled with a copy of the end of the next symbol, which means that the transmission power is continuous but has a phase discontinuity at the symbol boundary. To create the transmitted signal, an IFFT is performed on each subcarrier to create M time-domain signals. These in turn are vector-summed to create the final time-domain waveform used for transmission.

In contrast, SC-FDMA signal generation begins with a special precoding process but then continues in a manner similar to OFDMA. However, before getting into the details of the generation process it is helpful to describe the end result as shown on the right side of Figure 2.3-1. The most obvious difference between the two schemes is that OFDMA transmits the four QPSK data symbols in parallel, one per subcarrier, while SC-FDMA transmits the four QPSK data symbols in series at four times the rate, with each data symbol occupying a wider M x 15 kHz bandwidth.

Visually, the OFDMA signal is clearly multi-carrier with one data symbol per subcarrier, but the SC-FDMA signal appears to be more like a single-carrier (hence the "SC" in the SC-FDMA name) with each data symbol being represented by one wide signal. Note that OFDMA and SC-FDMA symbol lengths are the same at 66.7 μs; however, the SC-FDMA symbol contains M "sub-symbols" that represent the modulating data. It is the parallel transmission of multiple symbols that creates the undesirable high PAPR of OFDMA. By transmitting the M data symbols in series at M times the rate, the SC-FDMA occupied bandwidth is the same as multi-carrier OFDMA but, crucially, the PAPR is the same as that used for the original data symbols. Adding together many narrowband QPSK waveforms in OFDMA will always create higher peaks than would be seen in the wider-bandwidth, single-carrier QPSK waveform of SC-FDMA. As the number of subcarriers M increases, the PAPR of OFDMA with random modulating data approaches Gaussian noise statistics but, regardless of the value of M, the SC-FDMA PAPR remains the same as that used for the original data symbols.

2.3.2 SC-FDMA Signal Generation

As noted earlier, SC-FDMA signal generation begins with a special precoding process. Figure 2.3-2 shows the first steps, which create a time-domain waveform of the QPSK data sub-symbols. Using the four color-coded QPSK data symbols from Figure 2.3-1, the process creates one SC-FDMA symbol in the time domain by computing the trajectory traced by moving from one QPSK data symbol to the next. This is done at M times the rate of the SC-FDMA symbol such that one SC-FDMA symbol contains M consecutive QPSK data symbols. Time-domain filtering of the data symbol transitions occurs in any real implementation, although it is not discussed here.

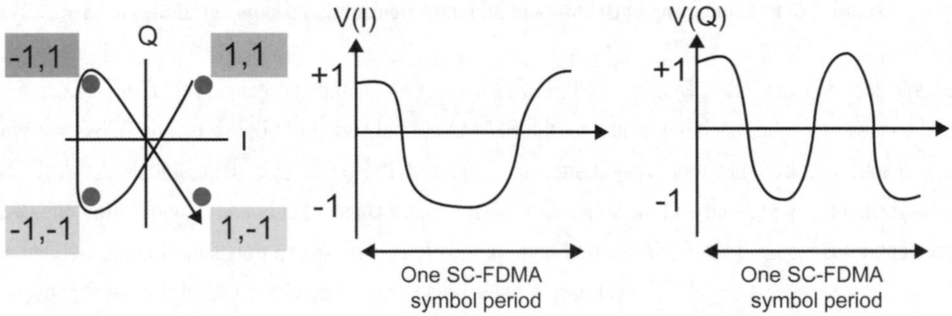

Figure 2.3-2. Creating the time-domain waveform of an SC-FDMA symbol

Once an IQ representation of one SC-FDMA symbol has been created in the time domain, the next step is to represent that symbol in the frequency domain using a DFT. This is shown in Figure 2.3-3. The DFT sampling frequency is chosen such that the time-domain waveform of one SC-FDMA symbol is fully represented by M DFT bins spaced 15 kHz apart, with each bin representing one subcarrier in which amplitude and phase are held constant for 66.7 μs.

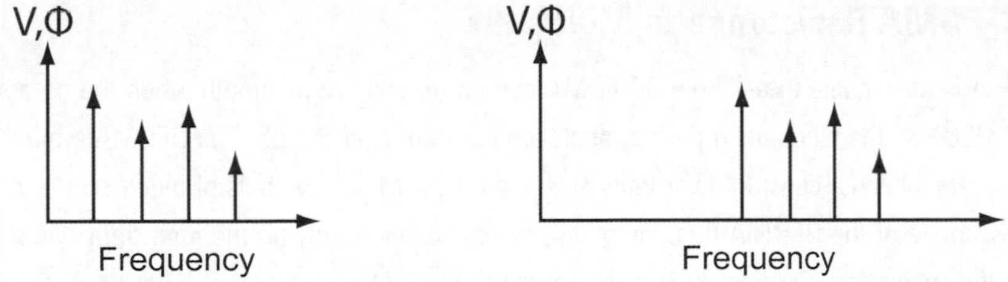

Figure 2.3-3. Baseband and frequency-shifted DFT representations of an SC-FDMA symbol

A one-to-one correlation always exists between the number of data symbols to be transmitted during one SC-FDMA symbol period and the number of DFT bins created. This in turn becomes the number of occupied subcarriers. When an increasing number of data symbols are transmitted during one SC-FDMA period, the time-domain waveform changes faster, generating a higher bandwidth and hence requiring more DFT bins to fully represent the signal in the frequency domain. Note in Figure 2.3-3 that there is no longer a direct relationship between the amplitude and phase of the individual DFT bins and the original QPSK data symbols. This differs from the OFDMA example in which data symbols directly modulate the subcarriers.

The next step of the signal generation process is to shift the baseband DFT representation of the time-domain SC-FDMA symbol to the desired part of the overall channel bandwidth. Because the signal is now represented as a DFT, frequency-shifting is a simple process achieved by copying the M bins into a larger DFT space of N bins. This larger space equals the size of the system channel bandwidth, of which there are six to choose from in LTE, spanning 1.4 to 20 MHz. The SC-FDMA signal, which is almost always narrower than the channel bandwidth, can be positioned anywhere in the channel bandwidth, thus executing the Frequency Division Multiple Access (FDMA) essential for efficiently sharing the uplink between multiple users.

To complete SC-FDMA signal generation, the process follows the same steps as for OFDMA. Performing an IDFT converts the frequency-shifted signal to the time domain and inserting the CP provides the fundamental robustness of OFDMA against multipath. The relationship between SC-FDMA and OFDMA is illustrated in Figure 2.3-4.

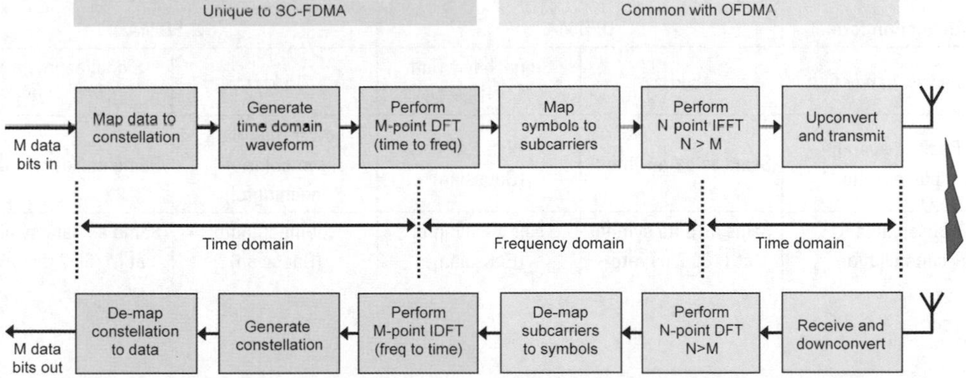

Figure 2.3-4. Simplified model of SC-FDMA and OFDMA signal generation

2.3.3 SC-FDMA Resistance to Multipath

At this point, it is reasonable to ask how SC-FDMA can be resistant to multipath when the data symbols are still short. In OFDMA, the modulating data symbols are constant over the 66.7 μs OFDMA symbol period, but an SC-FDMA symbol is not constant over time since it contains M sub-symbols of much shorter duration. The multipath resistance of the OFDMA demodulation process seems to rely on the long data symbols that map directly onto the subcarriers. Fortunately, it is the constant nature of each subcarrier, not the data symbols, that provides the resistance to delay spread. As shown in Figure 2.3-1 and Figure 2.3-3, the DFT of the time-varying SC-FDMA symbol generated a set of DFT bins constant in time during the SC-FDMA symbol period, even though the modulating data symbols varied over the same period. It is inherent to the DFT process that the time-varying SC-FDMA symbol — made of M serial data symbols — is represented in the frequency domain by M time-invariant subcarriers. Thus, even SC-FDMA with its short data symbols benefits from multipath protection.

It may seem counterintuitive that M time-invariant DFT bins can fully represent a time-varying signal. However, the DFT principle is simply illustrated by considering the sum of two fixed sine waves at different frequencies. The result is a non-sinusoidal time-varying signal, fully represented by two fixed sine waves.

2.3.4 Analysis of SC-FDMA Signals

Table 2.3-1 summarizes the differences between the OFDMA and SC-FDMA modulation schemes. When OFDMA is analyzed one subcarrier at a time, it resembles the original data symbols. At full bandwidth, however, the signal looks like Gaussian noise in terms of its PAPR statistics and the constellation. The opposite is true for SC-FDMA. In this case, the relationship to the original data symbols is evident when the entire signal bandwidth is analyzed. The constellation (and hence low PAPR) of the original data symbols can be observed rotating at M times the SC-FDMA symbol rate (ignoring the seven percent rate reduction that is due to adding the CP). When analyzed at the 15 kHz subcarrier spacing, the SC-FDMA PAPR and constellation are meaningless because they are M times narrower than the information bandwidth of the data symbols.

Table 2.3-1 Analysis of OFDMA and SC-FDMA at different bandwidths

Modulation format	OFDMA		SC-FDMA	
Analysis bandwidth	15 kHz	Signal bandwidth (M * 15 kHz)	15 kHz	Signal bandwidth (M * 15 kHz)
Peak-to-average power ratio	Same as data symbol	High PAPR (Gaussian)	Lower than data symbol (not meaningful)	Same as data symbol
Observable IQ constellation	Same as data symbol at 1/66.7 μs rate	Not meaningful (Gaussian)	Not meaningful (Gaussian)	Same as data symbol at M/66.7 μs rate

2.4 Multi-Antenna Operation and MIMO

This section describes the multi-antenna mechanisms adopted by LTE to increase coverage and physical layer capacity. It focuses largely on the air interface as many of the operational details of the system are left to the designers of the eNB.

Adding additional antennas to a radio system gives the possibility of fundamental performance improvements because the radiated signals will take different physical paths. There are three main application categories. First is to make direct use of path diversity in which one radiated path may be subject to fading loss and another may not. Second is to do beamsteering by controlling the phase relationship of the electrical signals radiated at the antennas to physically steer transmitted energy. Third is to put to use the path differences introduced by separating the antennas — i.e., spatial separation — through the use of spatial multiplexing or beamforming, also known as Multiple-Input Multiple-Output (MIMO) techniques.

The section begins with an overview of multi-antenna techniques and terms and an explanation of how spatial multiplexing works. The distinction between diversity and MIMO is also explained. Next comes a description of the signals and the hardware configurations for multi-antenna downlink operation, including the diversity techniques used at the eNB and UE and in Single User MIMO (SU-MIMO). The section continues with the uplink and explains how Multi-User MIMO (MU-MIMO) operates. These sections include basic information about the expected physical layer performance of the links. New terms such as layer, precoding and codeword are introduced. Having described the system operation and how MIMO in particular works, the section concludes with a description of the main features of open and closed loop operation and how diversity, beamsteering and MIMO can be combined.

2.4.1 Overview of Multi-Antenna Techniques

As shown in Figure 2.4-1, there are four ways to make use of the radio channel. For simplicity only those using one or two antennas are shown. The mode of operation changes once there is more than one antenna, and in theory, any number could be used.

The terms that describe the access modes, such as Multiple-Input Single-Output (MISO) and MIMO, use the labels input and output to refer to the channel, not the transmitters or receivers. The channel includes the transmission medium (the air); the antennas, and the cabling and analog circuits connected to the antennas. Thus antennas are vital components in the link. With multi-antenna operation, the physical relationship between the antennas becomes a new variable to deal with, affecting the relationship between the paths the signals take. The relationship between the paths is referred to as correlation.

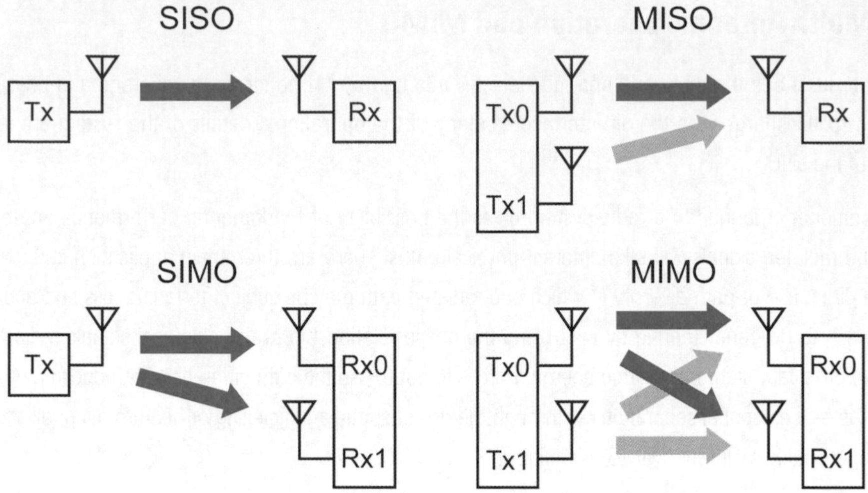

Figure 2.4-1. Radio channel access modes

The significance of the inclusion of analog circuits will become apparent when some of the LTE design challenges and measurements are covered in Chapter 6.

Employing a single antenna at the transmitter and a single antenna at the receiver, Single-Input Single-Output (SISO) is the most basic radio channel access mode. It is the default configuration referred to elsewhere in this book, and it gives the baseline for assessing the performance improvements possible when more antennas are used.

Single-Input Multiple-Output (SIMO) describes receive diversity, a method which isn't generally dependant on the technology being used. SIMO is suited to low Signal to Noise Ratio (SNR) conditions; for example, due to cell edge operation or fading. There is no improvement in data rates, beyond what comes from improved signal robustness in low SNR conditions.

The colored arrows in the MISO and MIMO cases indicate the use of different user data for each transmitter. Multiple-Input Single-Output (MISO) is a transmit diversity technique and only requires a single receive antenna. It has been used for some time in cellular systems with Alamouti Space Time Block Coding (STBC), where it can offer significant gains in signal robustness under fading channel conditions but, like SIMO, does not improve data rates.

The use of STBC involves the duplication of data onto multiple antennas. The signals for additional antennas are distinguished by a combination of reversing the time allocation and applying a complex conjugation to part of the signal. Space Frequency Block Coding (SFBC) uses the Alamouti principle but copies data onto different frequencies instead of using blocks of time. In LTE, only SFBC is used.

More than one receive antenna can be used with MISO, but it is important to note that the simultaneous use of transmit and receive diversity, MISO plus SIMO, does not equal MIMO. There may be two transmitters and two receivers involved but still only one stream of data.

To increase spectral capacity, MIMO operation relies on spatial multiplexing in which multiple input data streams are transmitted simultaneously. The terms MIMO and spatial multiplexing are generally synonymous, but some texts also use MIMO to describe MISO with more than one receiver.

2.4.2 MIMO Operation

The basics of MIMO operation can be understood by using a static, four port network to represent the channel, as shown in Figure 2.4-2. In this figure, two different signals are transmitted and received. At this point, there is no need to specify the intended destination of the data. It could be intended for one user or several users.

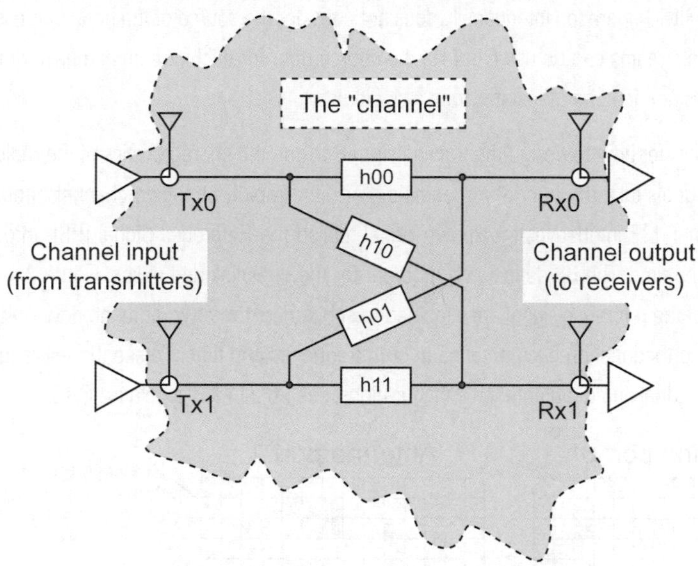

Figure 2.4-2. Basic 2 x 2 MIMO channel configuration

In the ideal case, to use the same frequency and time simultaneously, isolated connections would be established from transmitter 0 to receiver 0 and transmitter 1 to receiver 1. In practice, this is not possible, and there will inevitably be coupling between the signals as soon as they are transmitted. The challenge, therefore, is to reverse the coupling after the signals have been received. As with other radio systems such as IEEE 802.11 and 802.16, LTE uses a "non-blind" technique. Pre-defined orthogonal training signals are transmitted from each antenna. The receiver knows which training signal was used for each antenna and therefore can calculate the channel amplitude and phase responses, h00, h10 and h11, h01. Note that a convention of the channel matrix definition is to specify the receiver first; i.e., hR,T. In this way the receiver can be informed of the transformation that the signals from each antenna have undergone. Since the unknown data is sent at or around the same time as the known training signals, the receiver can assume that the unknown part of the signal from each antenna has undergone the same transformation as the known part of the signal. In essence, MIMO is using a "trick": known training signals are mixed with the randomly varying data in such a way that the unknown data can be recovered.

Conceptually, the simplest way to recover the unknown data is to multiply the received signals by the inverse of the channel matrix. In practice this zero forcing technique is vulnerable to noise, and more sophisticated techniques can be used that involve the minimizing of errors during the recovery process.

A key point to note about MIMO is that there must be at least as many receiving antennas as there are transmitted data streams. However, this number of streams should not be confused with the number of transmitting antennas, which may be higher than the number of streams if transmit diversity is mixed with MIMO. The minimum number of receivers is determined by what is mathematically required for the calculation of the channel matrix H. With fewer receivers, the composite received signal from more than one transmitter looks like interference.

This description of MIMO operation intentionally does not consider the source of the data. There is a lot of flexibility in how the two data streams can be used. In LTE, the source data for each stream can have different modulation and coding and does not need be associated with a single user.

It is necessary to consider how to design the training signals to suit the characteristics of the radio channel. In IEEE 802.11n, training signals take the form of a preamble. For more rapidly changing channels, and to suit the frame structure of the signal, LTE interleaves the known signal, called the Reference Signal (RS), throughout the frame in both frequency and time. The RS definition is different for the downlink and uplink. Figure 2.4-3 shows how the individual symbols of the reference signal are allocated to subcarriers for a two-antenna downlink signal. Note how the RS symbols are orthogonal on each antenna in both frequency and time. To see the full range of downlink RS allocations for single, dual and quad antenna configurations, see 36.211 [6] subclause 6.10.

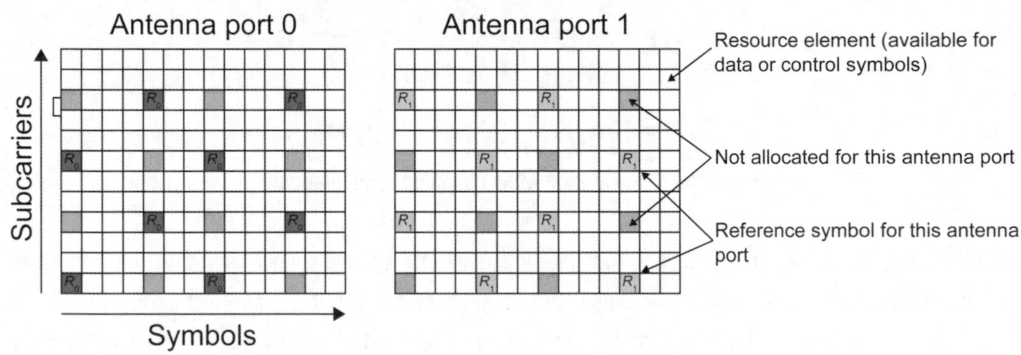

Figure 2.4-3. Orthogonal structure of downlink reference symbols for dual antenna (adapted from 36.101 [1] Figure 6.10.1.2-1)

The RS allocation for the LTE uplink is very different from the downlink allocation. For data transmission the RS occupies all subcarriers for one symbol of each timeslot. This is explained in more detail in Section 3.2.8. At the time of this writing, uplink SU-MIMO has not been fully specified, although it is known that rather than using orthogonal time and frequency allocations for the RS to identify each antenna, the uplink will use different Zadoff-Chu phase sequences. This use of different codes in the same frequency and time is similar to the approach used for 802.11n.

As with any radio signal, signal recovery depends on the Signal to Noise Ratio (SNR). The Shannon-Hartley capacity theorem predicts the error-free capacity C of a radio channel as:

$$C = B\,[\log_2 (1 + SNR)]$$

where

C = Channel capacity in bits per second

B = Occupied bandwidth in Hz

SNR = The linear signal-to-noise ratio

The performance of a MIMO system introduces additional simultaneous paths plus a further dependency, which is the cross-coupling of interfering signals between the different paths from each transmitting antenna to each receiving antenna through the radio channel. The long-form version of the channel capacity theorem can be written as:

$$C = B\,[\,\log_2 (1+(\sigma/N)\,\rho_1^2) + \log_2 (1+(\sigma/N)\,\rho_2^2)\,]$$

where

σ/N = signal to noise ratio and ρ = a singular value of the channel matrix, H.

It is useful to highlight the potential asymmetry in performance between the streams in a MIMO link. In the ideal, but impractical, case of no cross-coupling, the values of ρ_i will be 1, 1 indicating a doubling of channel capacity. However, in the case of total in-phase coupling, the values of ρ_i will be 2, 0 indicating that the capacity has dropped back to that of a SISO channel. Note that in either case, for a fair comparison, the equivalent SISO transmitter power is shared between each MIMO stream.

The potential increase in instantaneous system capacity can be derived from the ratio of singular values of H, also known as the condition number. The condition number can also be used to indicate the increase in SNR needed to recover the MIMO signal, relative to the SISO case.

From the above the following can be concluded:

- For the 2 x 2 case the increase in channel capacity will not exceed twice the SISO case, and achieving this may require a substantial improvement in SNR at the receivers if the values of ρ_i are < 1.
- If the matrix coefficients are known by the transmitters, the asymmetry in stream performance can allow a higher order modulation format on the stronger stream, or the outgoing signals can be modified (precoded) to equalize the performance between the streams. Precoding requires real time feedback from receiver to transmitter, so this is also known as closed loop MIMO. The relative signal phase between transmitters must be stable over the time interval of the feedback process.

The long form capacity equation shows the situation for a snapshot in time of the channel. In practice, the highly variable nature of the channel and the impact of the antenna configurations need to be included. More details on this and the use of channel correlation factors are provided in Section 6.6.

The use of MIMO in non-OFDM systems such as CDMA is possible, as evidenced by its use in UMTS Release 7 for HSDPA, although the processing to recover the same quality of channel information is more difficult. OFDM is particularly well-suited to MIMO operation because the channel is defined by a single vector coefficient for each subcarrier, which makes the required digital processing in the frequency domain much more straightforward than in systems such as CDMA that are defined in the time domain.

2.4.3 LTE Terminology for Multiple Antennas

The terms codeword, layer and precoding have been adopted specifically for LTE to refer to signals and their processing. Figure 2.4-4 shows the processing steps to which they refer. The terms are used in the following ways:

- Codeword: A codeword represents user data before it is formatted for transmission. One or two codewords, CW0 and CW1, can be used depending on the prevailing channel conditions and use case. In the most common case of SU-MIMO, two codewords are sent to a single UE, but in the case of the less common downlink MU-MIMO, each codeword is sent to only one UE.
- Layer: The term layer is synonymous with stream. For spatial multiplexing, at least two layers must be used. Up to four are allowed. The number of layers is denoted by the symbol ν (pronounced nu). The number of layers is always less than or equal to the number of antennas.
- Precoding: Precoding modifies the layer signals before transmission. This may be done for diversity, beamsteering or spatial multiplexing. As noted earlier, the MIMO channel conditions may favor one layer (data stream) over another. If the eNB is given information about the channel — e.g., information sent back from the UE — it can add complex cross-coupling to counteract the imbalance in the channel.

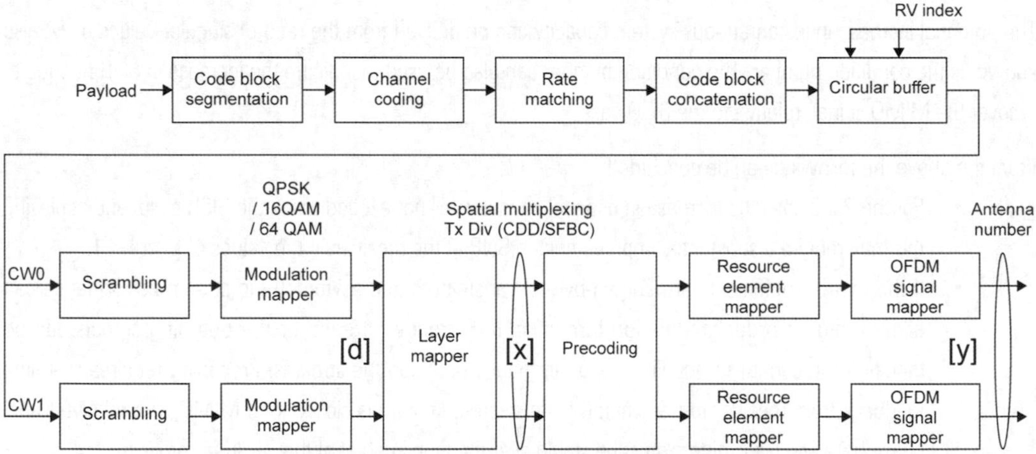

Figure 2.4-4. Signal processing for transmit diversity and spatial multiplexing (MIMO) (Adapted from 36.211 [6] Figure 6.3-1)

The symbols d, x and y are used in the specifications to denote signals before and after layer mapping and after precoding, respectively.

2.4.4 Multi-Antenna Operation in the Downlink

Five multi-antenna techniques have been defined for LTE to improve the downlink performance.

- Receive diversity at the mobile
- Transmit diversity using SFBC at the eNB
- MIMO spatial multiplexing at the eNB, for one or two users
- Cyclic Delay Diversity (CDD) at the eNB, used in conjunction with spatial multiplexing
- Beamsteering (user specific)

The first two are relatively conventional diversity methods. The third and fourth methods make use of space frequency coding mechanisms to spread data across multiple antennas. Cyclic delay diversity introduces deliberate delays between the antennas to create artificial multipath. It is applied more dynamically in LTE than in other radio systems

The techniques are applied differently, depending on the type of physical signal or physical channel, according to Table 2.4-1. The signal and channel definitions are discussed fully in Section 3.2. Some details, such as the reference signal not being subject to any addition processes, give important benefits for measurements and will be discussed further in Section 6.6.

Table 2.4-1. Summary of diversity and spatial multiplexing techniques applied to LTE downlink signals

Physical signal or physical channel	Transmit diversity	Spatial multiplexing	CDD
Reference signal	No	No	No
Primary synchronization signal	No	No	No
Secondary synchronization signal	No	No	No
Physical broadcast channel	Yes	No	No
Physical downlink control channel	Yes	No	No
Physical hybrid ARQ indicator channel	Yes*	No	No
Physical control format indicator channel	Yes	No	No
Physical multicast channel	Yes	Yes	No
Physical downlink shared channel	Yes	Yes	Yes

*Precoding type depends on PHICH group number.

2.4.4.1 UE Diversity Reception

UE diversity reception refers to the Single Input Multiple Output (SIMO) mode and is mandatory for the UE. It is typically implemented using maximum ratio combining.

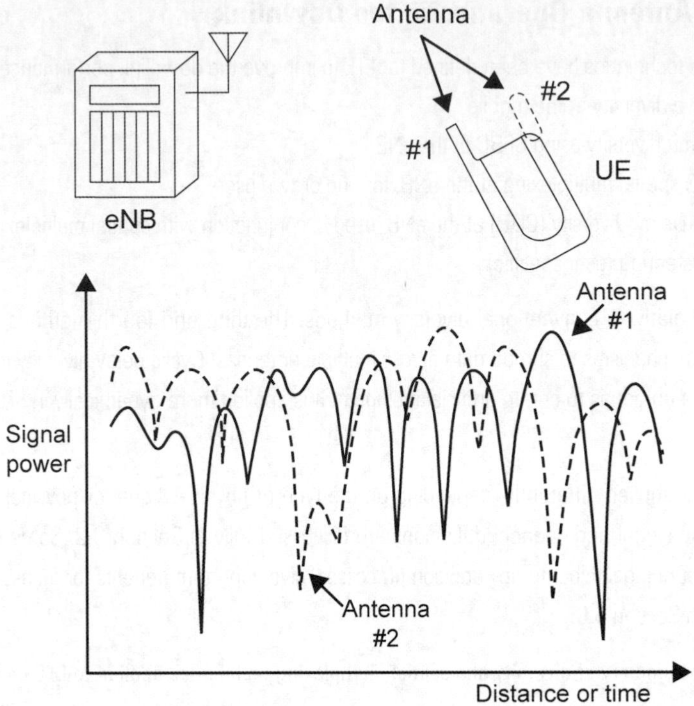

Figure 2.4-5 Example of diversity reception through loosely correlated paths

In a cellular environment, the signal from a single receive antenna will suffer level fluctuations due to various types of fading. A two antenna example is shown in Figure 2.4-5. With the broadband nature of the wider LTE channel bandwidths; there may also be a noticeable frequency dependency on the signal level. By combining the signal received from both antennas, the UE can recover a more robust signal. Receive diversity provides up to 3 dB of gain in low SNR conditions. Note the use of a lower performance, secondary, channel may be of value for diversity reception but is likely to cause problems in a MIMO receiver, as MIMO requires matched receivers for best performance.

2.4.4.2 SFBC Diversity Transmission

The transmit diversity technique uses Space Frequency Block Coding (SFBC) at the eNB. This contrasts with the space time block coding method used in 802.16, which takes pairs of OFDM symbols and transmits them in reverse time order on the antennas. In LTE, a single codeword is mapped onto two or four layers, which directly relates to the number of transmitters available. Data is interleaved onto different subcarriers on each antenna, according to the expressions in Table 2.4-2.

The letter d denotes the input modulation symbol (codeword) and x denotes the modulation symbol mapped onto the subcarrier of a layer. Thus even numbered modulation symbols are mapped to even layers, and odd symbols to odd layers.

Table 2.4-2. Codeword to layer mapping for transmit diversity (Ref 36.211 [6] Table 6.3.3.3-1)

Number of layers	Number of code words	Codeword-to-layer mapping $i = 0,1\ldots, M_{\text{symb}}^{\text{layer}} - 1$	
2	1	$x^{(0)}(i) = d^{(0)}(2i)$ $x^{(1)}(i) = d^{(0)}(2i+1)$	$M_{\text{symb}}^{\text{layer}} = M_{\text{symb}}^{(0)}/2$
4	1	$x^{(0)}(i) = d^{(0)}(4i)$ $x^{(1)}(i) = d^{(0)}(4i+1)$ $x^{(2)}(i) = d^{(0)}(4i+2)$ $x^{(3)}(i) = d^{(0)}(4i+3)$	$M_{\text{symb}}^{\text{layer}} = M_{\text{symb}}^{(0)}/4$

This open loop diversity technique is identical in concept to that used for UMTS. However, for reasons of simplicity the more complex closed loop transmit diversity techniques from UMTS have not been defined for LTE, partly because LTE has closed loop methods defined for MIMO which is considered more important. Two or four transmitter diversity is supported. Figure 2.4-6 shows the processing steps for the four transmitter case.

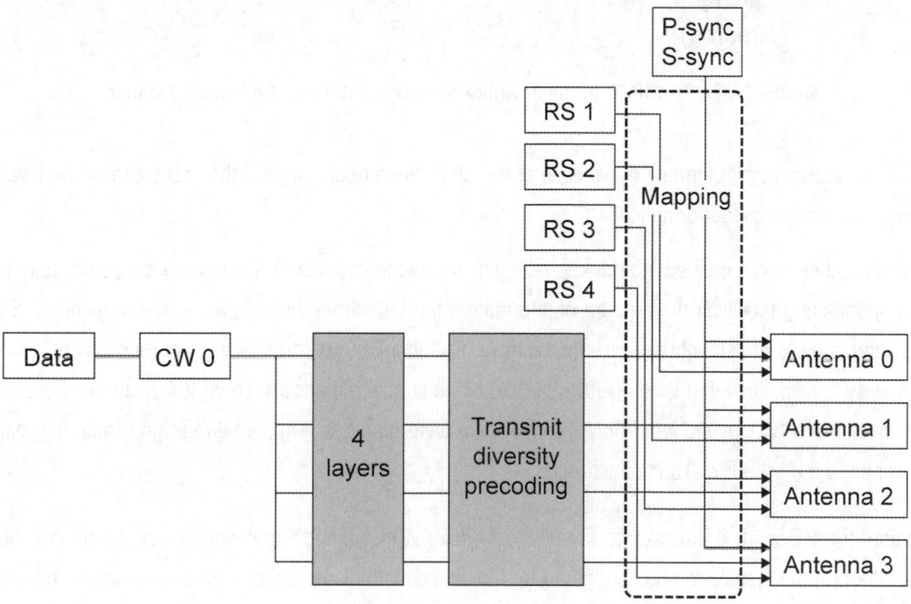

Figure 2.4-6. Configuration used for four transmitter diversity

Transmit diversity precoding is automatically applied for all control channels regardless of the physical downlink shared channel precoding mode that is used. A modified MISO scheme is used for the Multimedia Broadcast over Single Frequency Network (MBSFN) scheme in which a network of many eNBs transmit a common signal to improve cell edge performance for broadcast services.

2.4.4.3 Single User and Multi User MIMO

Figure 2.4-7 shows how both codewords are used for a single user to provide downlink SU-MIMO. It is also possible for the codewords to be allocated to different users to create downlink MU-MIMO.

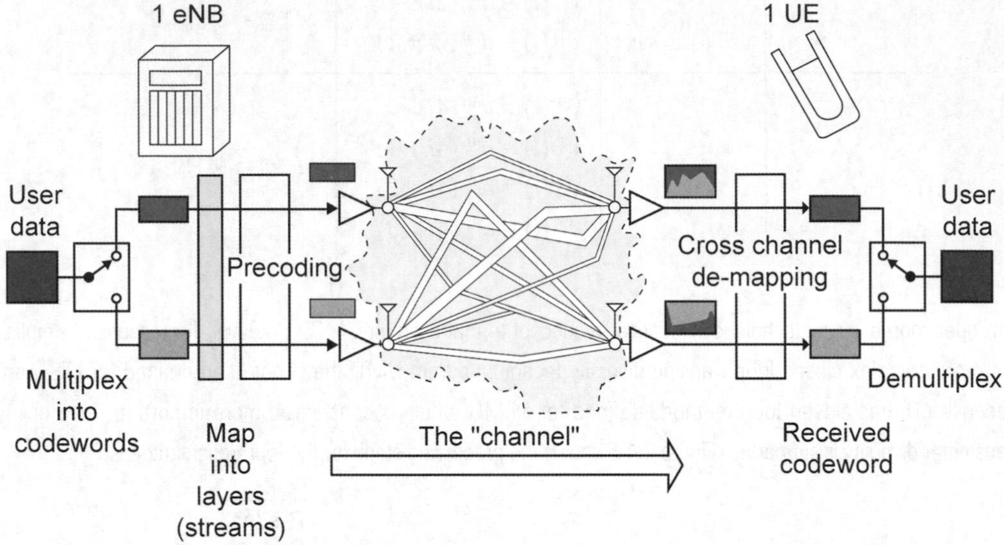

Figure 2.4-7. SU-MIMO in the downlink with two antennas; Codebook 0 shown

Depending on the channel information available at the eNB, the modulation and the precoding of the layers may be different to equalize the performance.

The precoding choices are defined in a lookup table known as the codebook. A codebook is used to quantize the available options and thus limit the amount of information fed back from the receiver to the transmitter. Some of the precoding choices are straightforward; for example, Codebook Index (CI) 0 is a direct mapping of codewords to layers and CI 1 applies what is referred to in 802.11 as spatial expansion. Table 2.4-3 shows the codebook choices for one and two layers. Note only the two-layer case employs spatial multiplexing. Precoding with one layer is limited to a 0°, ±90° or 180° phase shift.

In operation, the UE sends a message to the eNB scheduler with the codebook index most closely matching the channel, although the system can be configured for multiple codebook values, one for each resource block group. To use this information while it is still valid, the scheduler has to respond rapidly, within milliseconds, depending on the rate of change of the channel. If the UE is instructed to provide channel information more regularly, the information will be more accurate but the proportion of resources used for signalling will increase and place higher demands on the eNB.

Table 2.4-3. Codebook for transmission on antenna ports 0,1 (36.211 [6] Table 6.3.4.2.3-1)

Codebook index	Number of layers υ	
	1	2
0	$\frac{1}{\sqrt{2}}\begin{bmatrix}1\\1\end{bmatrix}$	$\frac{1}{\sqrt{2}}\begin{bmatrix}1 & 0\\0 & 1\end{bmatrix}$
1	$\frac{1}{\sqrt{2}}\begin{bmatrix}1\\-1\end{bmatrix}$	$\frac{1}{2}\begin{bmatrix}1 & 1\\1 & -1\end{bmatrix}$
2	$\frac{1}{\sqrt{2}}\begin{bmatrix}1\\j\end{bmatrix}$	$\frac{1}{2}\begin{bmatrix}1 & 1\\j & -j\end{bmatrix}$
3	$\frac{1}{\sqrt{2}}\begin{bmatrix}1\\-j\end{bmatrix}$	-

2.4.4.3 Cyclic Delay Diversity

Cyclic delay is a delay introduced between multi-antenna signals. In several other radio systems, including 802.11n and 802.16, cyclic delay is used to reduce the impact of possible unwanted signal cancellation that can occur if the same signal is transmitted from multiple antennas and the channel is relatively flat. The addition of a delay — typically on the order of a few microseconds — to one of the transmit paths introduces a frequency dependant phase shift as shown in Figure 2.4-8. When the signals from two transmitters combine at the receiver, peaks and nulls are the result, depending on the exact phase of the paths for a given frequency (subcarrier). Operationally, there are tradeoffs in choosing the length of delay, with no single value suiting all situations and channel bandwidths.

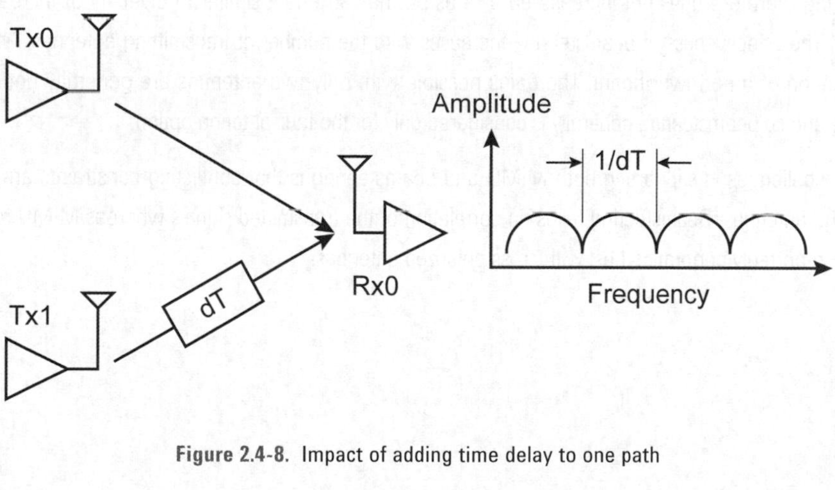

Figure 2.4-8. Impact of adding time delay to one path

LTE uses a type of cyclic delay known as large delay CDD. It is larger than the cyclic delay used by 802.11n or 802.16, and it is used in a different way. (The concept of small delay CDD was removed from the LTE specifications in March 2008.) The intent of large delay CDD is to position signals on the peak of the frequency response that results from the addition of a delay. The reference signal subcarriers do not have CDD applied, which allows the UE to report the actual channel response to the scheduler in the eNB, which then uses that information to determine the use of cyclic delay and frequency allocations for that specific UE. As shown in Table 2.4-4, the delay is expressed as a phase shift for adjacent subcarriers.

Table 2.4-4. Cyclic phase shifts for two, three and four eNB antennas

Number of transmitters	Phase shift per subcarrier (overall delay)
2	180° ($t_{symbol}/2$)
3	120° ($t_{symbol}/3$)
4	90° ($t_{symbol}/4$)

Expressed in terms of time, the two antenna case CDD is half the symbol length, which is 33.33 μs.

2.4.4.5 Beamsteering

Conventional phased array beamsteering introduces phase and amplitude offsets to the whole of the signal feeding each transmitting antenna. The intention is to focus the signal power in a particular direction. The same technique of applying phase and amplitude offsets can be used on the receiving antennas to make the receiver more sensitive to signals coming from a particular direction. In LTE, the amplitude and phase of individual RBs can be adjusted, making beamsteering far more flexible. Beamsteering is implemented using precoding methods similar to those used for MIMO. Only one codeword is used for beamsteering, however, and in this case the purpose of the precoding function is to correlate the signals from each transmitter towards the receiver of an individual user. Beamsteering therefore does not increase data rates but has an effect similar to diversity of increasing signal robustness. The effectiveness of beamsteering increases with the number of transmitting antennas, which allows for the creation of a narrower beam. The gains possible with only two antennas are generally not considered worthwhile and so beamsteering generally is considered only for the four-antenna option.

One of the challenges in supporting both MIMO and beamsteering is that conflicting constraints are put on the design of the antennas. Beamsteering relies on correlation of the transmitted signals whereas MIMO relies on de-correlation, reportedly performing best with cross polarized antennas.

2.4.6 Multiple Antenna Operation in the Uplink

There are three types of multiple antenna operation defined for the uplink:

- Receive diversity at the eNB
- Single-User MIMO (SU-MIMO) for single UE
- Multi-User MIMO (MU-MIMO) for multiple UE

Receive diversity at the eNB is nothing new and will not be discussed further.

2.4.6.1 Single-User MIMO in the Uplink

SU-MIMO is within the scope of LTE but at the time of writing it is not fully defined. To implement SU-MIMO the UE would require two transmitters. This is a significant challenge in terms of cost, size and battery consumption, and for these reasons SU-MIMO is not currently a priority for development. Also, the increased data rates in the uplink that might be possible from SU-MIMO are not as important as they are in the downlink due to asymmetrical traffic distribution. Furthermore, if the system is deployed to be uplink-performance-limited, it may be impractical to increase the transmit power from the UE sufficiently to achieve the SNR needed at the eNB receivers.

2.4.6.2 Multi-User MIMO in the Uplink

Although a UE typically has a single transmitter in its baseline configuration, it nevertheless is still capable of supporting a novel form of MIMO. As suggested by Figure 2.4-2 and the description of MIMO, spatial multiplexing, unlike the receive function, does not require the transmitters to be in the same physical device or location. Thus uplink MIMO can be implemented using two transmitters belonging to two different UEs. This creates the potential for an increase in uplink capacity, although an individual user will see no increase in data rates. See Figure 2.4-9.

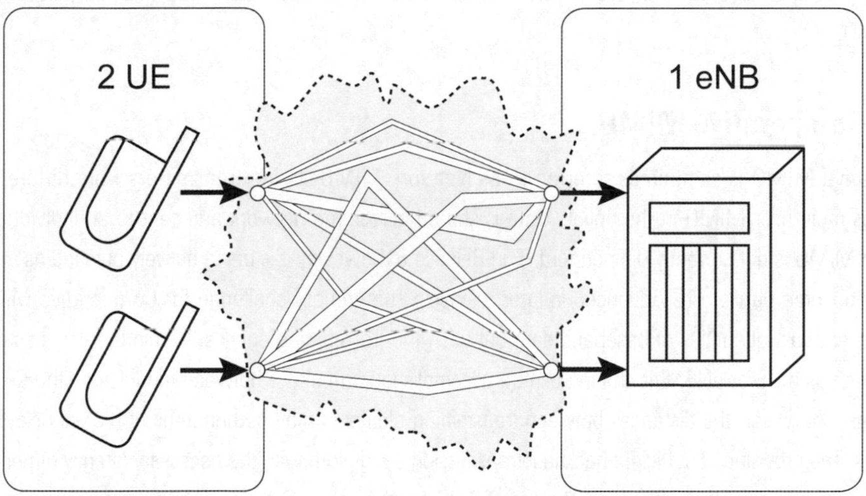

Figure 2.4-9. Multi-user MIMO in the uplink

The fact that the transmitters are physically separate has two consequences. First, there is no possibility of precoding since the source data cannot be shared between the two UEs to create the necessary cross-coupling of the data streams. This reduces the potential gains that co-located transmitters may have had. Second, the separation of the transmitters increases the probability that the radio channels seen by the eNB will be uncorrelated. Indeed, when the eNB has to select two UEs for pairing with MU-MIMO, the primary criterion will be the presence of de-correlated channels. Any potential gains lost through lack of precoding will be more than compensated for by the gains likely from better channel de-correlation. MU-MIMO therefore could be a valuable technique for improving uplink capacity.

OFDM signal recovery is tolerant of small timing and frequency errors. Normal uplink operation will result in each UE adjusting its frequency quite precisely to that of the eNB. The eNB will also instruct the UE to adjust its timing and power so that all signals arrive at the eNB receiver at approximately the same level and time. With the antennas located in different devices, the transmit paths are assumed to be uncorrelated. These conditions give the eNB scheduler the opportunity to control two UEs to transmit data simultaneously using the same subcarriers.

Multi-user MIMO involves the simultaneous transmission of codewords via layers from different UEs at the same time and frequency. The use of normal radio management techniques will ensure adequate frequency, timing and power alignment of the signals received at the eNB. Aligning the received power from the UEs at the eNB will be the most difficult thing to control if the potential capacity gains are to be realized.

As stated earlier, precoding cannot be used for MU-MIMO because the transmitters do not have access to each other's signals. Even if they did, precoding still would not work because it involves matching the phase of the transmitted signals to that of the channel, and the phase between the two UEs is uncontrolled. However, the eNB will support receive diversity with two or four antennas, and the latter case will help improve performance with MU-MIMO.

2.4.7 Co-operative MIMO

Co-operative MIMO is sometimes referred to as Network MIMO. Using transmitters from different cells, it resembles multi-user MIMO in the uplink. Data is shared across the network and sent to an individual UE. Co-operative MIMO is not currently defined for LTE in Release 8; however, it is being actively pursued as a technique that may become part of LTE-Advanced in later releases. The primary challenge for Co-operative MIMO is the need to share vast quantities of baseband data between the transmitting entities. Within the confines of a single device, such as a UE or eNB, this sharing can be accomplished on-chip or between modules. In the Co-operative MIMO case, however, the distances between transmitting elements may be hundreds of meters or even several kilometers. The provision of sufficient backhaul transmission bandwidth with the necessary latency of perhaps 1 ms is a challenge that remains to be solved. The use of Distributed Antenna Systems (DAS) is one potential solution.

2.4.8 Combining Multi-Antenna Techniques

With a matched channel and good SNR, spatial multiplexing offers incremental benefits while making use of the additional hardware already required for diversity techniques. The performance loss from path correlation can be mitigated by adding diversity to spatial multiplexing. Figure 2.4-10 describes the mapping of two codewords using Serial-to-Parallel (S/P) converters to three or four layers, with 16 indices being available in the codebook. This configuration enables the limited use of beamsteering.

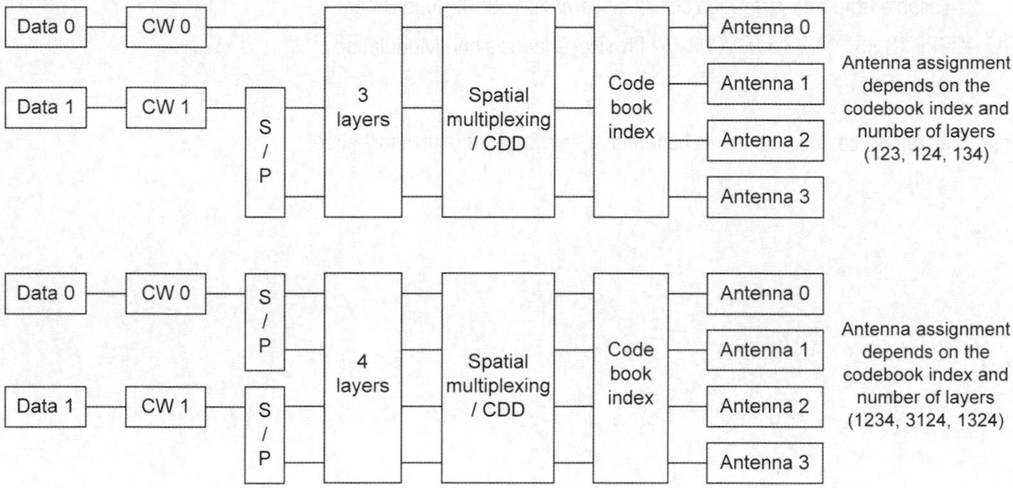

Figure 2.4-10. Processing steps to map two codewords to three or four antennas

2.4.9 Conclusion

The multiple antenna techniques used in LTE include transmit and receive diversity and spatial multiplexing. Diversity techniques increase the robustness of the signal path but do not increase the data rates. Spatial multiplexing leverages the addition of transmit and receive antennas to increase the fundamental channel capacity. Suitable channel conditions are needed to make this practicable, and LTE supports the combination of transmit diversity with spatial multiplexing to improve the likely performance.

LTE uses multi antenna techniques dynamically, placing considerable demands on the eNB and UE to report the correct channel state information and react to it appropriately. These topics are considered in further detail in Sections 6.6 and 6.7.

2.5 References

[1] 3GPP TS 36.101 V8.4.0 (2008-12) UE Radio Transmission and Reception

[2] 3GPP TS 36.104 V8.4.0 (2008-12) Base Station Radio Transmission and Reception

[3] ETSI TR 102 735 V7.0.1 (2007-08) Band-specific Requirements for UMTS

[4] 3GPP TS 36.331 V8.4.0 (2008-12) Radio Resource Control (RRC) Protocol Specification

[5] Cutler, Bob, "Effects of physical layer impairments on OFDM systems," RF Design, pp. 36-44, May 2002. Available from http://rfdesign.com/images/archive/0502Cutler36.pdf.

[6] 3GPP TS 36.211 V8.5.0 (2008-12) Physical Channels and Modulation

Links to all reference documents can be found at www.agilent.com/find/ltebook.

Chapter 3

Physical Layer

3.1 Introduction to the Physical Layer

This chapter describes the LTE (E-UTRA) physical layer design. A general description of the LTE physical layer can be found in 36.201 [1] with the detailed design found in the 36.2XX technical specifications as follows:

36.211 Physical channels and modulation [2]
36.212 Multiplexing and channel coding [3]
36.213 Physical layer procedures [4]
36.214 Physical layer — Measurements [5]

Due to the complexity and scope of the physical layer no book of this length can begin to serve as a comprehensive reference. The goal here is to provide an introduction to the subject that will facilitate further study of the specifications themselves.

The physical layer covers the downlink transmission from the evolved Node B (eNB) base transceiver station to the User Equipment (UE), and the uplink transmission from the UE to eNB. As discussed in the previous chapter, 3GPP has selected a new OFDMA modulation scheme for the physical layer. This is one of the key differences between LTE and existing 3G systems such as UMTS and cdma2000 that are based on CDMA.

3.2 Physical Channels and Modulation

3.2.1 General Description of the Radio Interface

The physical layer supports two multiple access schemes: OFDMA on the downlink and SC-FDMA on the uplink. In addition, both paired and unpaired spectrum are supported by using Frequency Division Duplexing (FDD) and Time Division Duplexing (TDD), respectively.

The LTE air interface needs to be described in both the time and frequency domains. The frame structure defines the frame, slot and symbol in the time domain. Two types of frame structures are defined: type 1 for FDD and type 2 for TDD. Although the downlink and uplink utilize different multiple access schemes, they share a common frame structure.

In order to simplify the system, LTE supports only packet-switched communication carried by shared channels, so LTE does not have any dedicated channels.

Two types of physical layer channels are defined: physical channels, which carry information originating from higher layers, and physical signals, which are generated in the physical layer and are used for system synchronization, cell identification, and radio channel estimation.

3.2.2 Frame Structure

The frame structure defines frame, subframe, slot and symbol in the time domain. The time length is expressed in time units of $T_s = 1/(15000 \times 2048) = 32.55$ ns unless otherwise stated.

3.2.2.1 FDD Frame Structure

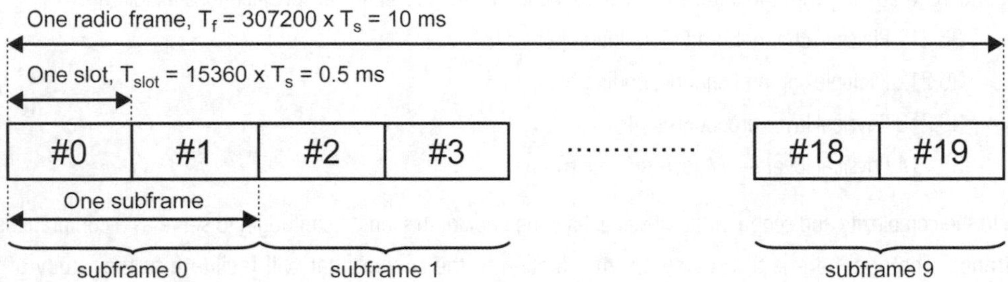

Figure 3.2-1. Frame structure type 1 (FDD mode) (36.211 [2] Figure 4.1-1)

Frame structure type 1 is defined for FDD mode. Each radio frame is 10 ms long and consists of 10 subframes. Each subframe contains two slots. In FDD, both uplink and downlink have the same frame structure but use different spectra.

3.2.2.2 TDD Frame Structure

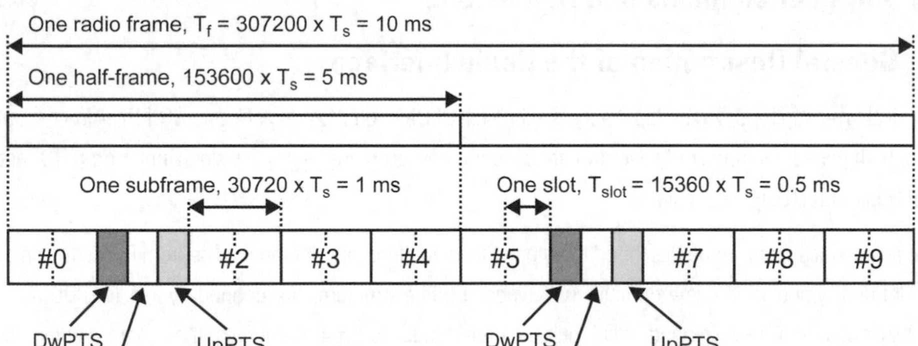

Figure 3.2-2. Example of frame structure type 2 (TDD mode) (Based on 36.211 [2] Figure 4.1-1)

Frame structure type 2 is defined for TDD mode. There are seven configurations defined for frame structure type 2 as shown in Table 3.2-1. Each radio frame is 10 ms long and consists of two half frames. Each half frame contains 5 subframes. Subframe #1 and sometimes subframe #6 consist of three special fields: Downlink Pilot Timeslot (DwPTS), Guard Period (GP) and Uplink Pilot Timeslot (UpPTS). The length of DwPTS, GP and UpPTS is given by Table 3.2-2. The total length of DwPTS, GP and UpPTS is equal to $30720*T_s = 1ms$. The other eight subframes in the radio frame hold two slots each. "D" denotes a subframe reserved for downlink transmissions, "U" denotes a subframe reserved for uplink transmissions and "S" denotes a special subframe with the three fields DwPTS, GP and UpPTS.

Table 3.2-1. Uplink-downlink configurations (36.211 Table 4.2-2)

Uplink-downlink configuration	Downlink-to-uplink switch-point periodicity	Subframe number									
		0	1	2	3	4	5	6	7	8	9
0	5 ms	D	S	U	U	U	D	S	U	U	U
1	5 ms	D	S	U	U	D	D	S	U	U	D
2	5 ms	D	S	U	D	D	D	S	U	D	D
3	10 ms	D	S	U	U	U	D	D	D	D	D
4	10 ms	D	S	U	U	D	D	D	D	D	D
5	10 ms	D	S	U	D	D	D	D	D	D	D
6	5 ms	D	S	U	U	U	D	S	U	U	D

The flexible assignment for downlink or uplink slot direction in a frame enables asymmetric data rates. Depending on the switch-point periodicity of 5 ms or 10 ms, there can be one or two changes of direction within the frame, providing considerable deployment flexibility. It is necessary, however, to coordinate the frame structure configuration between adjacent cells to avoid simultaneous transmit and receive on the same frequency and time.

Table 3.2-2. Configuration of special subframe (lengths of DwPTS/GP/UpPTS) (Based on 36.211 [2] Table 4.2-1)

Special subframe configuration	Normal cyclic prefix			Extended cyclic prefix		
	DwPTS	GP	UpPTS	DwPTS	GP	UpPTS
0	$6592*T_s$	$21936*T_s$	$2192*T_s$	$7680*T_s$	$20480*T_s$	$2560*T_s$
1	$19760*T_s$	$8768*T_s$		$20480*T_s$	$7680*T_s$	
2	$21952*T_s$	$6576*T_s$		$23040*T_s$	$5120*T_s$	
3	$24144*T_s$	$4384*T_s$		$25600*T_s$	$2560*T_s$	
4	$26336*T_s$	$2192*T_s$		$7680*T_s$	$17920*T_s$	$5120*T_s$
5	$6592*T_s$	$19744*T_s$	$4384*T_s$	$20480*T_s$	$5120*T_s$	
6	$19760*T_s$	$6576*T_s$		$23040*T_s$	$2560*T_s$	
7	$21952*T_s$	$4384*T_s$		-	-	-
8	$24144*T_s$	$2192*T_s$		-	-	-

3.2.3 Slot Structure

3.2.3.1 OFDM Symbol and Cyclic Prefix

One of the key advantages in OFDM systems (including SC-FDMA in this context) is the ability to protect against multipath delay spread. As discussed in Section 2.2.2, the long OFDM symbols allow the introduction of a guard period between each symbol to eliminate inter-symbol interference due to multipath delay spread. If the guard period is longer than the delay spread in the radio channel, and if each OFDM symbol is cyclically extended into the guard period (by copying the end of the symbol to the start to create the cyclic prefix), then the inter-symbol interference can be completely eliminated.

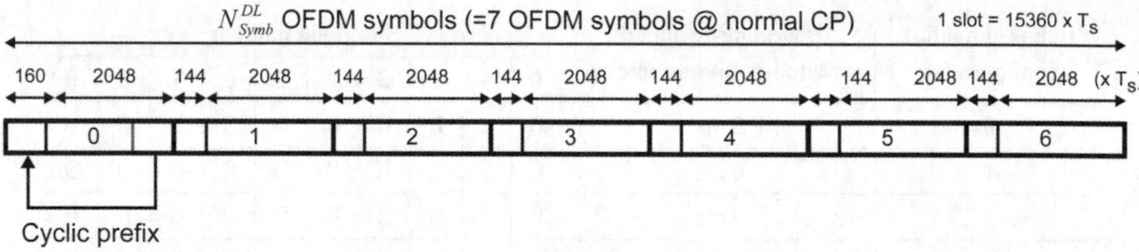

Figure 3.2-3. OFDM symbol structure for normal cyclic prefix case (downlink)

Figure 3.2-3 shows the seven symbols in a slot for the normal cyclic prefix case. The length of the cyclic prefix is shown for the uplink in Table 3.2-3 and the downlink in Table 3.2-4. In the latter table, Δf represents the 15 kHz or 7.5 kHz subcarrier spacing.

Table 3.2-3. SC-FDMA cyclic prefix length (uplink) (36.211 [2] Table 5.6-1)

Configuration	Cyclic prefix length $N_{CP,l}$
Normal cyclic prefix	160 for $l = 0$ 144 for $l = 1,2,...,6$
Extended cyclic prefix	512 for $l = 0,1,...,5$

Table 3.2-4. OFDM cyclic prefix length (downlink) (36.211 [2] Table 6.12-1)

Configuration		Cyclic prefix length $N_{CP,l}$
Normal cyclic prefix	$\Delta f = 15$ kHz	160 for $l = 0$ 144 for 1,2,...,6
Extended cyclic prefix	$\Delta f = 15$ kHz	512 for 0,1,...,5
	$\Delta f = 7.5$ kHz	1024 for 0,1,2

The normal cyclic prefix of 144 x T_s (4.69 μs) protects against multi-path delay spread of up to 1.4 km. Note that the delay spread represents the variation in path delay in the cell and not the cell size, which is likely to be larger. The longest cyclic prefix provides protection for delay spreads up to 10 km.

3.2.3.2 Resource Element and Resource Block

A resource element is the smallest unit in the physical layer and occupies one OFDM or SC-FDMA symbol in the time domain and one subcarrier in the frequency domain. This is shown in Figure 3.2-4.

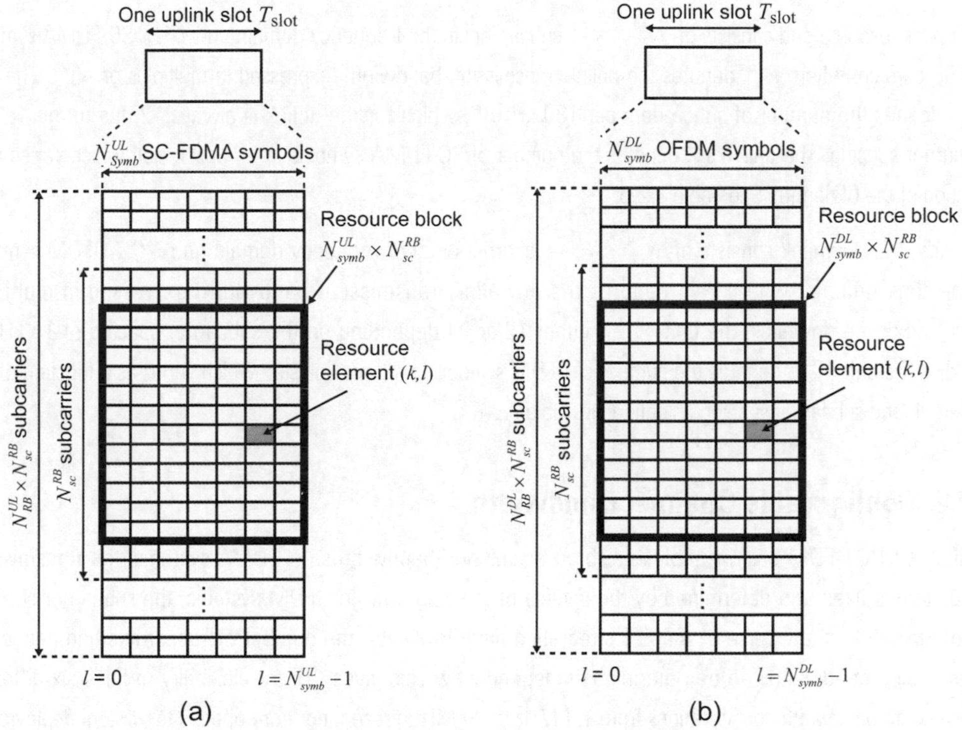

Figure 3.2-4. Resource grid for uplink (a) and downlink (b) (36.211 [2] Figures 5.2.1-1 and 6.2.2-1)

A resource block (RB) is the smallest unit that can be scheduled for transmission. An RB physically occupies 0.5 ms (= 1 slot) in the time domain and 180 kHz in the frequency domain. The number of subcarriers per resource block N_{sc}^{RB} and the number of symbols per resource block N_{Symb}^{UL} and N_{Symb}^{DL} vary as a function of the cyclic prefix length and subcarrier spacing, as shown in Tables 3.2-5 and 3.2-6.

Table 3.2-5. Resource block parameters for the uplink

Configuration	N_{sc}^{RB}	N_{Symb}^{UL}
Normal cyclic prefix	12	7
Extended cyclic prefix	12	6

Table 3.2-6. Resource block parameters for the downlink

Configuration		N_{sc}^{RB}	N_{Symb}^{DL}
Normal cyclic prefix	$\Delta f = 15$ kHz	12	7
Extended cyclic prefix	$\Delta f = 15$ kHz		6
	$\Delta f = 7.5$ kHz	24	3

The obvious difference between the uplink and downlink is that the downlink transmission supports 7.5 kHz subcarrier spacing, which is used for Multimedia Broadcast over Single Frequency Network (MBSFN). The 7.5 kHz subcarrier spacing means that the symbols are twice as long, which allows the use of a longer CP to combat the higher delay spread seen in the larger MBSFN cells.

The uplink resource grid consists of $N_{RB}^{UL} \times N_{sc}^{RB}$ subcarriers in the frequency domain and N_{Symb}^{UL} SC-FDMA symbols in time domain, where N_{RB}^{UL} denotes the uplink transmission bandwidth, expressed in multiples of N_{sc}^{RB}. The unit N_{sc}^{RB} defines the number of subcarriers per 180 kHz RB, which for the uplink is always 12 due to the 15 kHz subcarrier spacing. The unit N_{Symb}^{UL} denotes the number of SC-FDMA symbols in an uplink slot, which varies as a function of the CP length. See Table 3.2-5.

Similarly, the downlink consists of $N_{RB}^{DL} \times N_{sc}^{RB}$ subcarriers in the frequency domain and N_{Symb}^{DL} OFDM symbols in the time domain, where N_{RB}^{DL} denotes the downlink transmission bandwidth, expressed in multiples of N_{sc}^{RB}. For the downlink, the unit N_{sc}^{RB} is either 12 or 24 depending on the subcarrier spacing of 15 kHz or 7.5 kHz. The unit N_{Symb}^{DL} denotes the number of OFDM symbols in a downlink slot, which varies as a function of the CP length and subcarrier spacing as defined in Table 3.2-6.

3.2.4 Configurable Channel Bandwidth

Unlike CDMA, OFDM easily enables flexible transmission bandwidths. In CDMA systems, the transmission bandwidth is fixed and determined by the inverse of the chip rate. In OFDM systems, the subcarrier spacing is determined by the inverse of the FFT integration time. However, the number of subcarriers and hence the transmission bandwidth can be determined independently. This gives LTE the flexibility to have six different transmission bandwidth configurations from 1.4 MHz to 20 MHz, presenting more options for system deployment. The terminology to describe the flexibility of the LTE air interface is given in Figure 3.2-5.

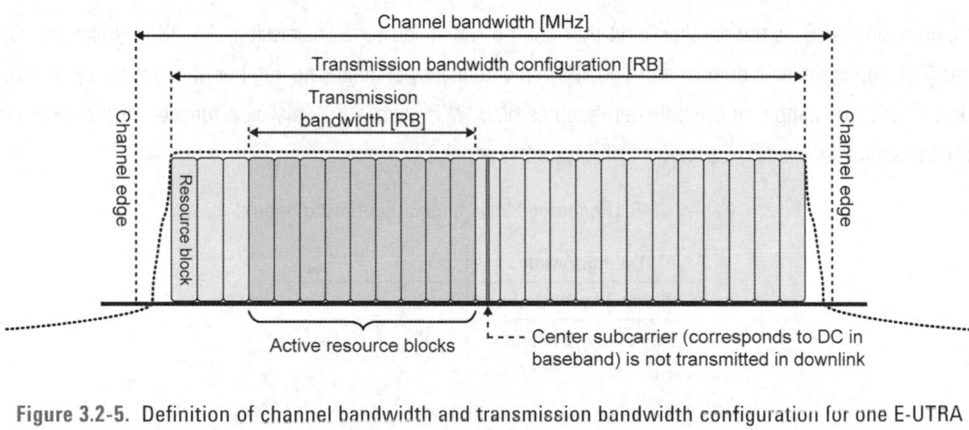

Figure 3.2-5. Definition of channel bandwidth and transmission bandwidth configuration for one E-UTRA carrier (36.101 [6] Figure 5.6-1)

The channel bandwidth defined in MHz represents the nominal occupied channel, which in effect becomes the channel spacing. The transmission bandwidth configuration defined in units of RB represents the maximum number of RB that can be transmitted for any channel bandwidth. The transmission bandwidth also defined in RB represents the number of RB allocated to any specific transmission and can vary from one up to the maximum RB allowed for that channel bandwidth.

The different channel bandwidths and associated transmission bandwidth configurations are given in Table 3.2-7.

Table 3.2-7. Transmission bandwidth configuration (based on 36.101 [6] Table 5.6-1)

Channel bandwidth (MHz)	**1.4**	**3**	**5**	**10**	**15**	**20**
Transmission bandwidth configuration (MHz)	1.08	2.7	4.5	9	13.5	18
Transmission bandwidth configuration (N_{RB}^{UL} or N_{RB}^{DL}) (RB)	6	15	25	50	75	100

3.2.5 Downlink Physical Signals and Channels

Table 3.2-8 defines the physical signals and physical channels for downlink transmission. These will be explained in the following sections.

Table 3.2-8. List of downlink physical signals and physical channels

Physical signals	**Physical channels**
Primary synchronization signal	Physical Downlink Shared Channel (PDSCH)
Secondary synchronization signal	Physical Broadcast Channel (PBCH)
Reference signals	Physical Downlink Control Channel (PDCCH)
	Physical Multicast Channel (PMCH)
	Physical Control Format Indicator Channel (PCFICH)
	Physical Hybrid Automatic Repeat Request (ARQ) Indicator Channel (PHICH)

3.2.5.1 Primary Synchronization Signal

Both primary and secondary synchronization signals are designed to be detected by all types of UE. They are transmitted twice per 10 ms radio frame. The synchronization signals always occupy the central 62 subcarriers of the channel, which makes the cell search procedure the same regardless of the channel bandwidth. Although 72 subcarriers (6 RB) are available, only 62 subcarriers are used so that the UE can perform the cell search procedure using an efficient length 64 FFT.

The primary synchronization signal subcarriers are modulated using a frequency-domain Zadoff-Chu sequence. Each subcarrier has the same power level with its phase determined by the root index number in a sequence generator as defined in 36.211 [2] subclause 6.11.1. Three different cell identities are used for the primary synchronization signal. The root index number corresponds to the cell identity $N_{ID}^{(2)}$. Figure 3.2-6 shows an example of a constellation plot of the primary synchronization signal.

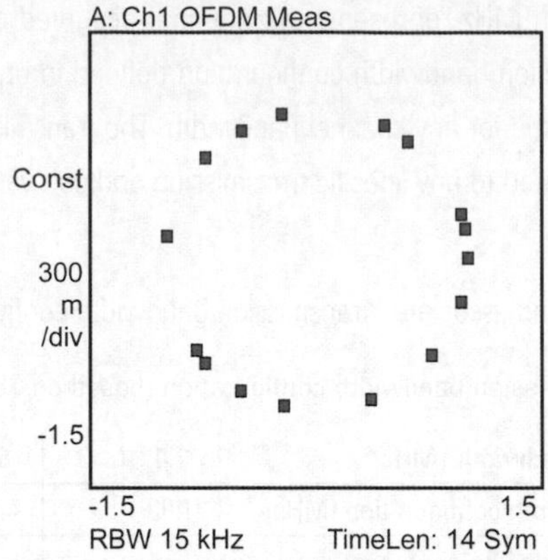

Figure 3.2-6. I/Q constellation sample of a primary synchronization signal

3.2.5.2 Secondary Synchronization Signal

The secondary synchronization signal is used to identify cell-identity groups. The number and position of subcarriers are the same as for the primary synchronization signal: that is, the central 62 subcarriers. The sequence generation function utilizes an interleaved concatenation of two length-31 binary sequences as defined in 36.211 [2] subclause 6.11.2. The secondary synchronization signal gives a cell-identity group number from 168 possible cell identities $N_{ID}^{(1)}$.

In the cell search procedure, the primary synchronization signal is used first. The UE determines the timing and center frequency by detecting the primary synchronization signal. There are 504 unique cell identities, N_{ID}^{cell}, grouped into 168 unique cell-identity groups, $N_{ID}^{(1)}$, with each group containing three unique identities $N_{ID}^{(2)}$. The primary synchronization signal gives the identity information, which is one of the three unique identities $N_{ID}^{(2)}$. The procedure is further described later in this chapter. Figure 3.2-7 shows an example of a constellation plot of the secondary synchronization signal.

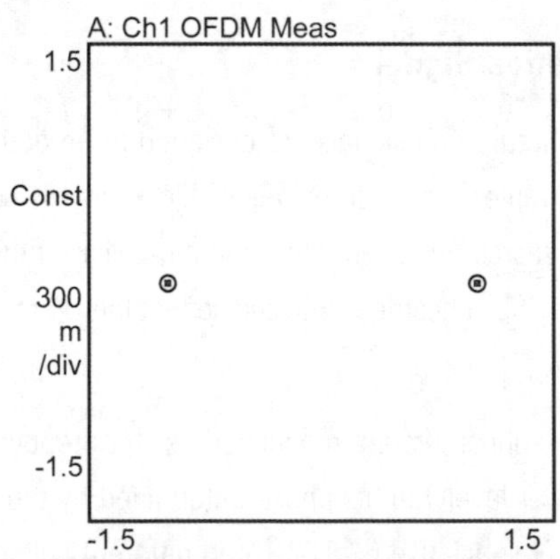

Figure 3.2-7. I/Q constellation of a secondary synchronization signal

This concept is similar to the Scrambling Code Group and cell search procedure in UMTS (FDD). In UMTS, the secondary synchronization code gives the Scrambling Code Group, and then the primary scrambling code (one of 512 scrambling codes) can be determined.

3.2.5.3 Reference Signals

There are three types of downlink reference signals, cell-specific reference signals (for non-MBSFN transmission), MBSFN reference signals, and UE-specific reference signals. This section covers cell-specific reference signals.

For the normal cyclic prefix, the sequence generation is a product of a two-dimensional orthogonal sequence and a two-dimensional pseudo-random sequence. The orthogonal sequence holds three different sequences that correspond to the cell identity given by the primary synchronization signal. At the same time, the pseudo-random sequence holds 168 different sequences that correspond to the cell-identity group given by the secondary synchronization signal. In the cell search procedure, after detecting the primary and secondary synchronization signals, a UE can calculate which reference signal is being used in the cell.

The reference signals play a very important role, as they enable the UE to mitigate amplitude, phase and timing errors in the received signal that can be attributed to in-band flatness error introduced by the radio channel and impairments from the eNB transmitter. The reference signals hold known amplitude and phase, and they are uniformly allocated every six subcarriers in the frequency domain and every two symbols per slot in the time domain. From these references the UE can calculate corrections and thus minimize the probability of demodulation errors.

3.2.5.4 Physical Broadcast Channel

The Physical Broadcast Channel (PBCH) is the physical channel that carries the Broadcast Channel (BCH) transport channel. The BCH carries various cell-specific content and is used for all types of UE. As with the synchronization signals, the PBCH is transmitted in the center of the channel but it occupies 6 RB (72 subcarriers), which is the whole of the narrowest channel bandwidth. The PBCH supports only the QPSK modulation scheme. The PBCH is located in slot #1 at OFDM symbols #0, #1, #2 and #3.

3.2.5.5 Physical Downlink Shared Channel

The Physical Downlink Shared Channel (PDSCH) is the physical channel that carries the traffic data. As its name suggests, this channel is shared in the time domain between multiple users. The PDSCH supports QPSK, 16QAM, and 64QAM modulation schemes and carries the Downlink Shared Channel (DL-SCH) or Paging Channel (PCH) transport channels.

3.2.5.6 Physical Downlink Control Channel

The Physical Downlink Control Channel (PDCCH) is the physical channel that carries the channel allocation and control information. It consists of one or more consecutive Control Channel Elements (CCEs), where a control channel element corresponds to nine resource element groups. The number of OFDM symbols allocated for the PDCCH is given by the Control Format Indicator (CFI) carried on the PCFICH. The CFI can take the values 1, 2 and 3. For transmission bandwidth configurations greater than 10 RB (1.8 MHz), the number of PDCCH symbols per subframe is the CFI value. For transmission bandwidth configurations less than or equal to 10 RB, the number of PDCCH symbols per subframe is the CFI value +1. The PDCCH supports only the QPSK modulation scheme. Multiple PDCCHs can be transmitted in a subframe.

3.2.5.7 Physical Multicast Channel

The Physical Multicast Channel (PMCH) is the physical channel that carries the Multicast Channel (MCH) transport channel. The PMCH is similar to the PDSCH except that it carries information to multiple users for point-to-multipoint broadcast services. It uses QPSK, 16QAM or 64QAM modulation.

3.2.5.8 Physical Control Format Indicator Channel

The Physical Control Format Indicator Channel (PCFICH) is the physical channel that carries the number of OFDM symbols used for transmission of PDCCHs in a subframe. PCFICH is located at OFDM symbol #0 of every subframe, and the assignment to the subcarriers is determined by Cell ID information.

3.2.5.9 Physical Hybrid ARQ Indicator Channel

The Physical Hybrid Automatic Repeat Request (ARQ) Indicator Channel (PHICH) is the physical channel that carries the Hybrid ARQ Indicator (HI). The HI contains the Acknowledgement/Negative Acknowledgement (ACK/NACK) feedback to the UE for the uplink blocks received by the eNB.

3.2.6 Example FDD Downlink Mapping to Resource Elements

The primary and secondary synchronization signals, reference signals, PDSCH, PBCH and PDCCH are almost always present in a downlink radio frame. There is a priority rule for allocation (physical mapping) as follows. Signals (reference signal, primary/secondary synchronization signal) take precedence over the PBCH. The PDCCH takes precedence over the PDSCH. The PBCH and PDCCH are never allocated to the same resource elements, thus they are not in conflict.

Figures 3.2-8 and 3.2-9 show an LTE FDD mapping example. The primary synchronization signal is mapped to the last symbol of slot #0 and slot #10 in the central 62 subcarriers. The secondary synchronization signal is allocated in the symbol just before the primary synchronization signal. The reference signals are located at symbol #0 and symbol #4 of every slot. The reference signal takes precedence over any other allocation.

The PBCH is mapped to the first four symbols in slot #1 in the central 6 RB. The PDCCH can be allocated to the first three symbols (four symbols when the number of RB is equal or less than 10) of every subframe as shown in Figure 3.2-8. The remaining unallocated areas can be used for the PDSCH.

Note how the five subcarriers on either side of the primary and secondary synchronization signals remain unallocated.

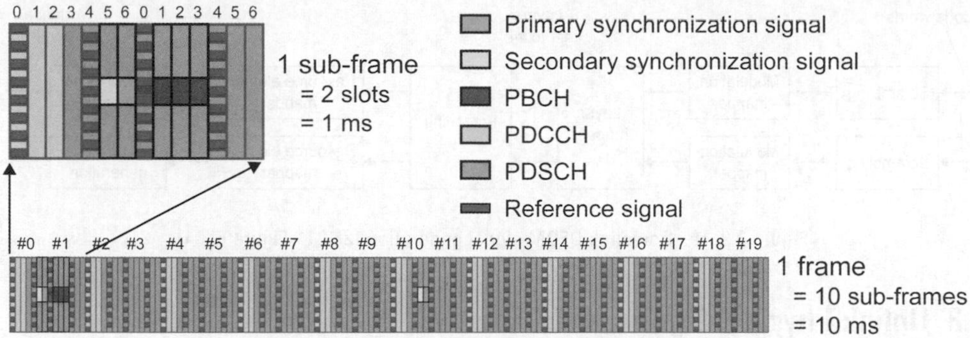

Figure 3.2-8. Example of downlink mapping (normal cyclic prefix)

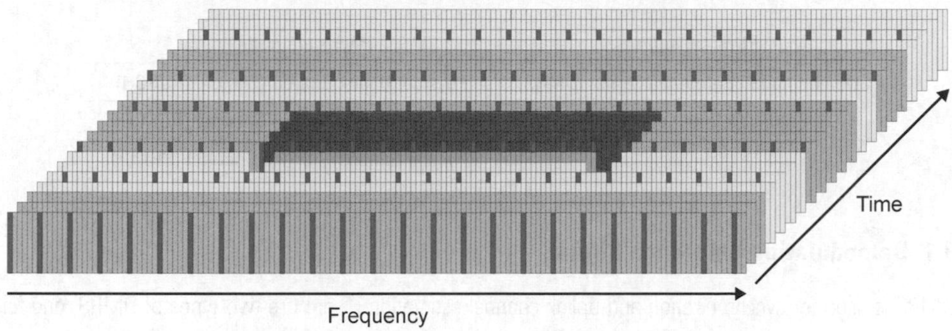

Figure 3.2-9. Example of downlink mapping showing frequency (subcarriers) vs. time

3.2.7 OFDM (Downlink) Baseband Signal Generation

Figure 3.2-10 shows the major stages in OFDM signal generation. The first stage is to scramble the incoming bit stream before modulation mapping. In scrambling, pseudo-random sequence generation is used; in this case a length-31 Gold sequence. At the second stage, mapping of these bits to symbols is applied. For example, the PDSCH can use QPSK, 16QAM or 64QAM, which require 2 bits, 4 bits or 6 bits per symbol, respectively. At the third stage, layer mapping is applied to support various antenna configurations. At the next stage, precoding is applied to adjust the phase and amplitude for each antenna and adjust the total power of multiple antennas. The phase rotation schemes differ by application; that is, by cyclic delay diversity, transmit diversity, and so on. At the last two stages, resource mapping is applied and the OFDM signal is generated for each antenna.

In receiving, the signal demodulation follows the inverse process.

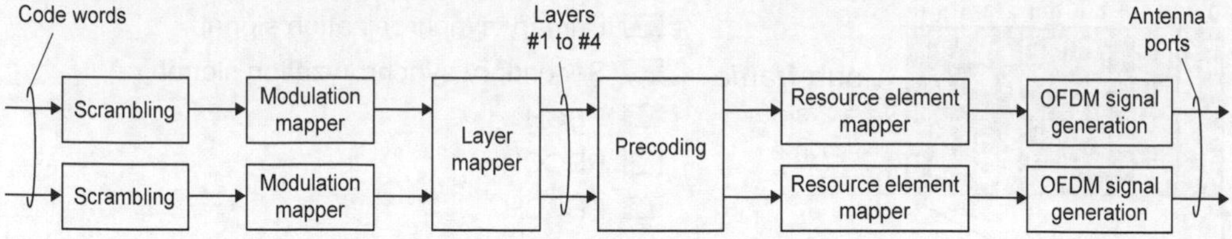

Figure 3.2-10. Downlink OFDM signal generation (36.211 Figure 6.3-1)

3.2.8 Uplink Physical Signals and Channels

Table 3.2-9 shows the signals and channels defined for the uplink.

Table 3.2-9. List of uplink physical signals and physical channels

Physical signals	Physical channels
Demodulation Reference Signal (DMRS)	Physical Uplink Shared Channel (PUSCH)
Sounding Reference Signal (SRS)	Physical Uplink Control Channel (PUCCH)
	Physical Random Access Channel (PRACH)

3.2.8.1 Demodulation Reference Signal

The DMRS is used for synchronization and uplink channel estimation. There are two types of DMRS; one for the PUSCH and one for the PUCCH.

The DMRS for the PUSCH are assigned to SC-FDMA symbol #3 (normal CP case) and SC-FDMA symbol #2 (extended CP case) in a PUSCH slot. The DMRS for the PUCCH is assigned according to the PUCCH format and cyclic prefix mode. For example, when the PUCCH format is set to 1/1a/1b and normal cyclic prefix is selected, the DMRS for the PUCCH is assigned to the SC-FDMA symbols #2, #3 and #4 in a PUCCH slot.

3.2.8.2 Sounding Reference Signal

When no PUCCH or PUSCH is scheduled, the eNB can request transmission of the SRS, which allows the eNB to estimate the uplink channel characteristics. The allocation to subcarriers is determined by the SRS bandwidth configuration. The SRS is transmitted in the last SC-FDMA symbol of the subframe. The cycle period and subframe offset can be configured.

3.2.8.3 Physical Uplink Shared Channel (PUSCH)

The Physical Uplink Shared Channel (PUSCH) is the physical channel that carries the traffic data. The PUSCH supports QPSK, 16QAM, and 64QAM modulation. The PUSCH carries the Uplink Shared Channel (UL-SCH) transport channel and the Uplink Control Information (UCI).

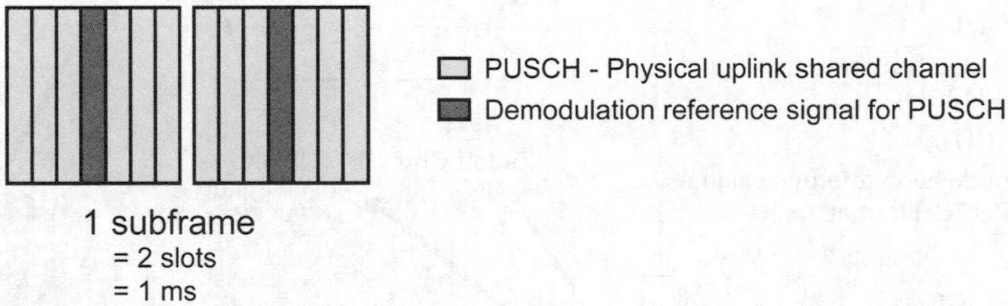

Figure: 3.2-11. Mapping of PUSCH and demodulation reference signal for the PUSCH

3.2.8.4 Physical Uplink Control Channel (PUCCH)

The Physical Uplink Control Channel (PUCCH) is the physical channel that carries the uplink control information, such as scheduling requests, Hybrid ARQ Acknowledgement/Negative Acknowledgement (HARQ ACK/NACK) and Channel Quality Indicator (CQI). The PUCCH is transmitted exclusively with the PUSCH from the same UE. The PUCCH supports BPSK and QPSK modulation schemes. A mapping for PUCCH format 1a/1b is shown in Figure 3.2-12. Other PUCCH formats exist that use the inner Resource Block (RB).

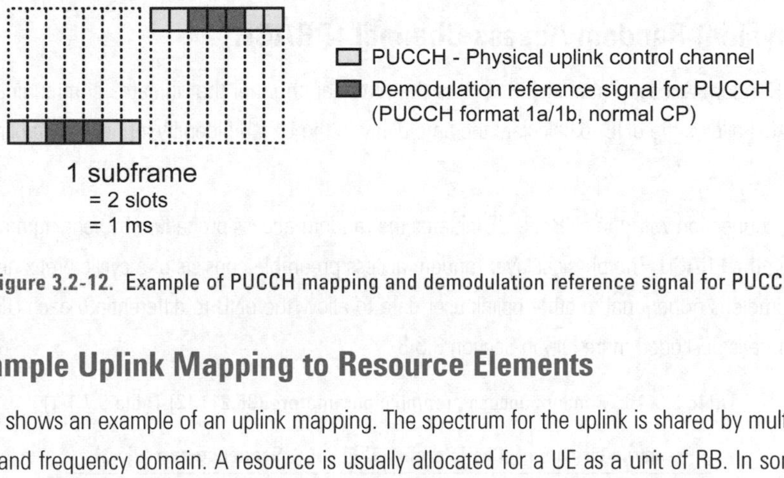

Figure 3.2-12. Example of PUCCH mapping and demodulation reference signal for PUCCH

3.2.9 Example Uplink Mapping to Resource Elements

Figure 3.2-13 shows an example of an uplink mapping. The spectrum for the uplink is shared by multiple UE in the time domain and frequency domain. A resource is usually allocated for a UE as a unit of RB. In some cases, the same RB in time is allocated to multiple UE, which are identified using orthogonal spreading codes as in CDMA.

The constellations for PUCCH and the DMRS for PUCCH and PUSCH may be rotated based on parameters given by higher layers; for example, cyclic shift and sequence index. The constellations shown in Figure 3.2-13 are without rotation. The PUCCH modulation is more fully described in Section 6.4.6.7.

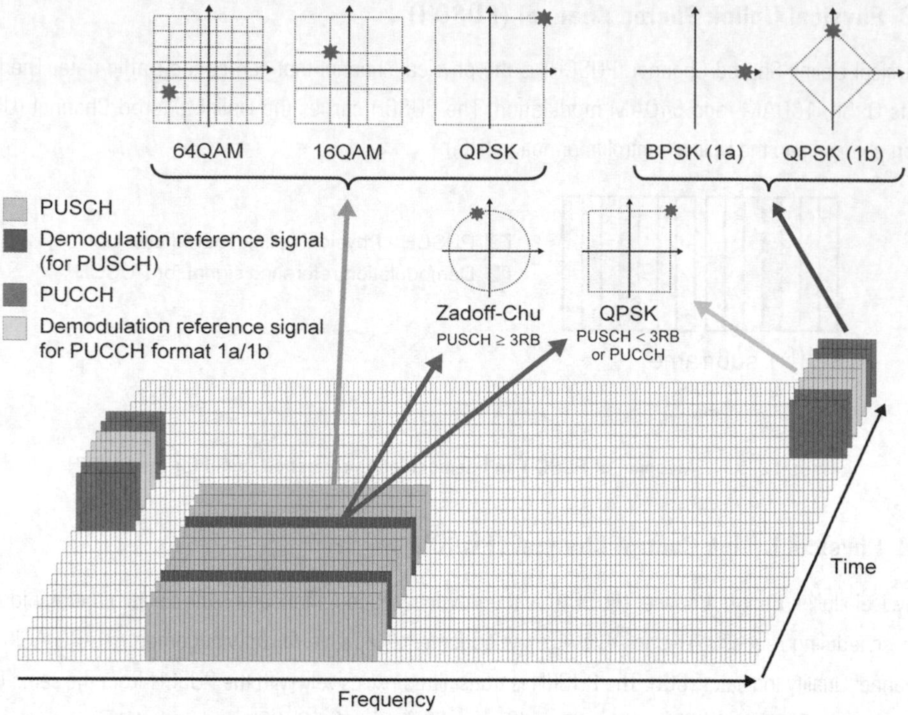

Figure 3.2-13. Example of uplink mapping showing frequency (subcarriers) vs. time

3.2.10 Physical Random Access Channel (PRACH)

The Physical Random Access Channel (PRACH) is the physical channel that initiates communication with the eNB. The PRACH allows the eNB to calculate the time delay to the UE and identify it prior to establishing a packet connection.

To establish a connection with the eNB the UE initiates the random access procedure by sending a random access preamble using the PRACH. The physical layer random access preamble consists of a cyclic prefix and a sequence part. This preamble is orthogonal to other uplink user data to allow the eNB to differentiate each UE. The random access procedure is described more fully in Section 3.5.3.

Table 3.2-10. Random access preamble parameters (36.211 [2] Table 5.7.1-1)

Preamble format	Cyclic prefix (T_{CP})	Sequence part (T_{SEQ})
0	$3168*T_s$	$24576*T_s$
1	$21024*T_s$	$24576*T_s$
2	$6240*T_s$	$2*24576*T_s$
3	$21024*T_s$	$2*24576*T_s$
4 (frame structure type 2 only)	$448*T_s$	$4096*T_s$

3.2.11 Example TDD Mapping to Resource Elements

Figures 3.2-14 and 3.2-15 show examples of 5 ms and 10 ms TDD switch point periodicity. The primary synchronization signal is mapped to the third symbol of slot #2 and slot #12 in the central 62 subcarriers. The secondary synchronization signal is allocated in the last symbol of slot #1 and slot #11. The reference signals are located at symbol #0 and symbol #4 of every slot. The reference signal takes precedence over any other allocation. The PBCH is mapped to the first four symbols in slot #1 in the central 6 RB. The PDCCH can be allocated to the first three symbols of every subframe as shown here. The remaining unallocated areas can be used for the PDSCH.

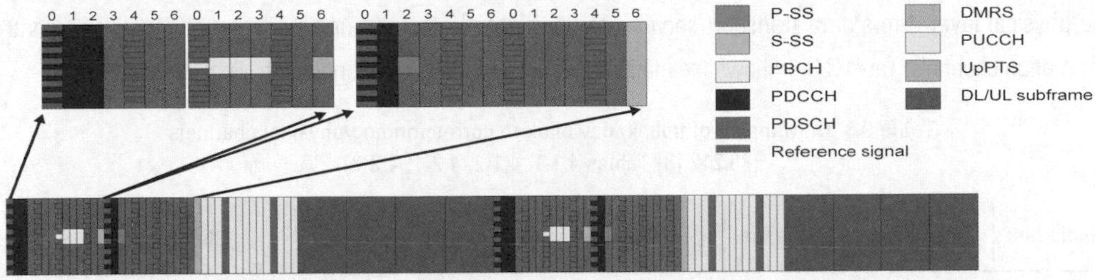

Figure 3.2-14. Example of LTE TDD 5 ms switch periodicity mapping

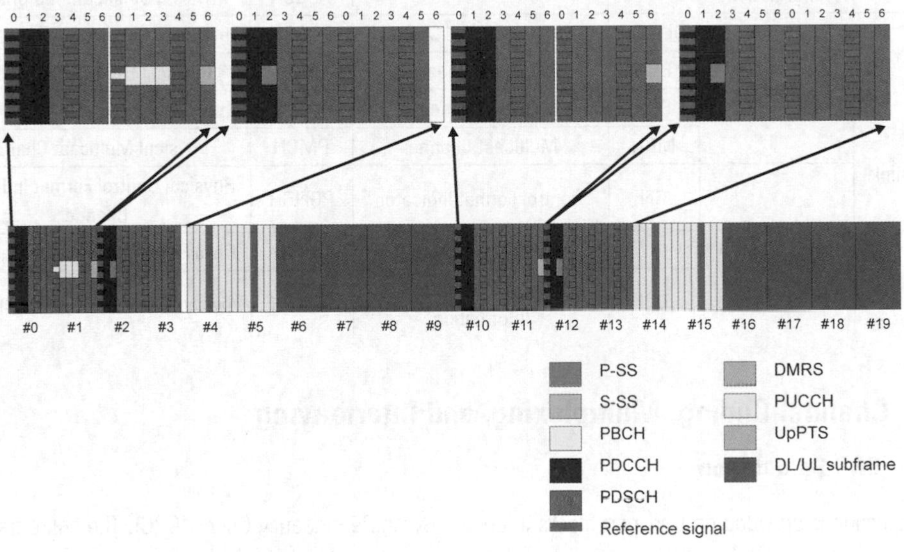

Figure 3.2-15. Example of LTE TDD 10 ms switch periodicity mapping

Note: The acronyms P-SS for Primary Synchronization Signal and S-SS for Secondary Synchronization Signal are not formally defined in the 3GPP specifications but are used for convenience.

3.3 Multiplexing and Channel Coding

This section describes the air interface multiplexing and channel coding according to 36.212 [3]. It covers Transport Channel (TrCH) and control channel information. Channel coding is a combination of error detection, segmentation, error correcting, rate matching, concatenation, and interleaving. The main focus here is on FDD mode; note that the FDD and TDD modes of LTE differ less than do the FDD and TDD modes of UMTS.

3.3.1 Mapping to Physical Channels

The physical layer offers data transport services to the higher layers through transport channels and control information channels. Table 3.3-1 shows the mapping of these to the corresponding physical channels.

Table 3.3-1. Mapping of uplink/downlink to corresponding physical channels (36.212 [3] Tables 4.1-1, 4.1-2, 4.2-1, 4.2-2)

Radio link	Channel type	Channel	Channel name	Physical channel	Channel name
Uplink	TrCH	UL-SCH	Uplink Shared Channel	PUSCH	Physical Uplink Shared Channel
Uplink	TrCH	RACH	Random Access Channel	PRACH	Physical Random Access Channel
Uplink	Control information	UCI	Uplink Control Information	PUCCH, PUSCH	Physical Uplink Control Channel, Physical Uplink Shared Channel
Downlink	TrCH	DL-SCH	Downlink Shared Channel	PDSCH	Physical Downlink Shared Channel
Downlink	TrCH	BCH	Broadcast Channel	PBCH	Physical Broadcast Channel
Downlink	TrCH	PCH	Paging Channel	PDSCH	Physical Downlink Shared Channel
Downlink	TrCH	MCH	Multicast Channel	PMCH	Physical Multicast Channel
Downlink	Control information	CFI	Control Format Indicator	PCFICH	Physical Control Format Indicator Channel
Downlink	Control information	HI	HARQ Indicator	PHICH	Physical HARQ Indicator Channel
Downlink	Control information	DCI	Downlink Control Information	PDCCH	Physical Downlink Control Channel

3.3.2 Channel Coding, Multiplexing, and Interleaving

3.3.2.1 CRC Calculation

Error detection is provided on transport blocks through a Cyclic Redundancy Check (CRC). The entire transport block is used to calculate the CRC parity bits which are appended to the transport block. The parity bits are generated by one of the following cyclic generator polynomials. The CRC24A generator is shown in Figure 3.3-1.

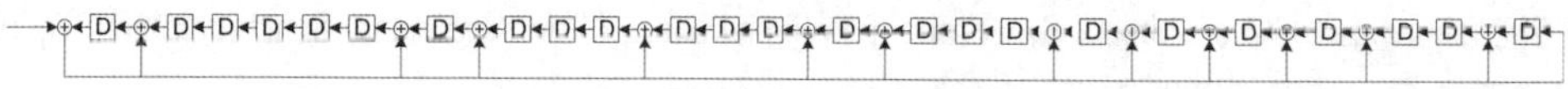

Figure 3.3-1. CRC24A generator

The mathematical equations for CRC24A and some of the other CRC codes are as follows:

CRC24A: $g_{CRC24A}(D) = [D^{24} + D^{23} + D^{18} + D^{17} + D^{14} + D^{11} + D^{10} + D^{7} + D^{6} + D^{5} + D^{4} + D^{3} + D + 1]$ for a CRC length = 24

CRC24B: $g_{CRC24B}(D) = [D^{24} + D^{23} + D^{6} + D^{5} + D + 1]$ for a CRC length = 24

CRC16: $g_{CRC16}(D) = [D^{16} + D^{12} + D^{5} + 1]$ for a CRC length = 16

CRC8: $g_{CRC8}(D) = [D^{8} + D^{7} + D^{4} + D^{3} + D + 1]$ for a CRC length = 8

Errors detected on the transport channels and control information are reported to higher layers. Table 3.3-2 shows the usage of CRC calculation and CRC scrambling for transport channels and control information.

Table 3.3-2. Usage of CRC calculation and CRC scrambling

Radio link	Channel	CRC calculation scheme	CRC scrambling
Uplink	UL-SCH	Transport Block CRC: CRC24A Code Block CRC: CRC24B	Not applicable
	UCI	CRC8	Not applicable
Downlink	DL-SCH	Transport Block CRC: CRC24A Code Block CRC: CRC24B	Not applicable
	BCH	CRC16	The CRC bits are scrambled by the PBCH CRC mask, which is according to the eNB transmit antenna configuration.
	PCH	Transport Block CRC: CRC24A Code Block CRC: CRC24B	Not applicable
	MCH	Transport Block CRC: CRC24A Code Block CRC: CRC24B	Not applicable
	DCI	CRC16	The CRC bits are scrambled by the antenna selection mask and Radio Network Temporary Identity (RNTI).

3.3.2.2 Code Block Segmentation and Code Block CRC Attachment

If the input bit sequence of code block segmentation is larger than the maximum code block size of 6144 bits, segmentation of the input bit sequence is performed and an additional CRC sequence equal to 24 bits (CRC24B) is attached to each of the code blocks. If the input bit sequence of code block segmentation is less than 40 bits, filling bits are added. The code block segmentation and transport block/code block CRC attachment process is shown in Figure 3.3-2.

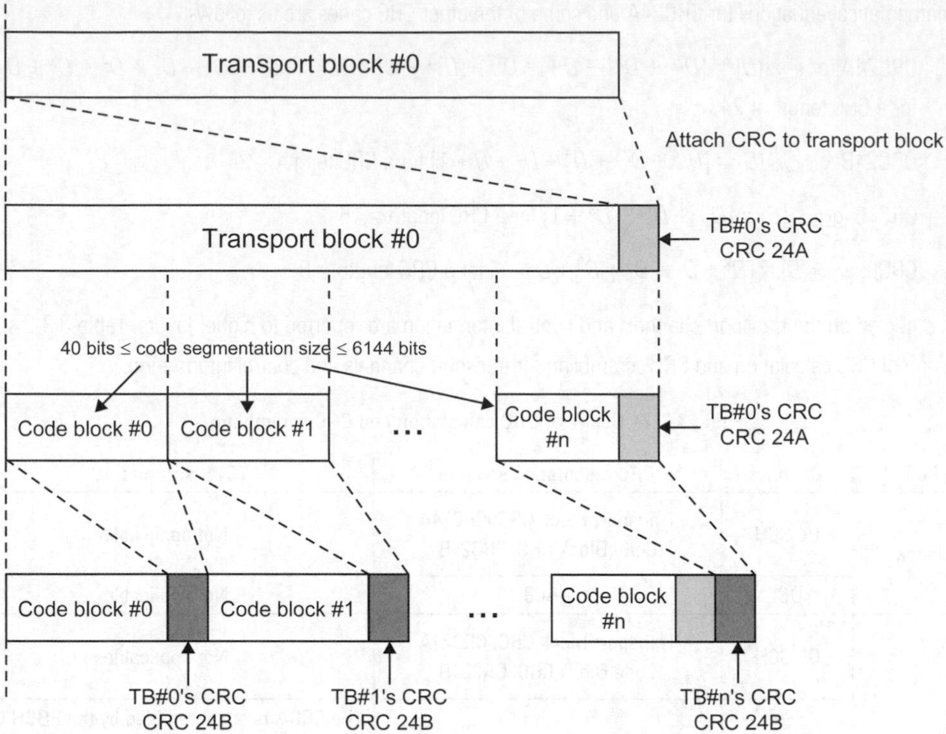

Figure 3.3-2. Code block segmentation and Transport Block (TB)/Code Block (CB) CRC

3.3.2.3 Channel Coding

Table 3.3-3. Usage of channel coding scheme and coding rate for transport channel and control information (36.212 [3] Tables 5.1.3-1 and 5.1.3-2)

Channel type	Channel	Coding scheme	Coding rate
TrCH	UL-SCH	Turbo coding	1/3
	DL-SCH		
	PCH		
	MCH		
	BCH	Tail biting convolutional coding	1/3
Control information	DCI	Tail biting convolutional coding	1/3
	CFI	Block code	1/16
	HI	Repetition code	1/3
	UCI	Block code	variable
		Tail biting convolutional coding	1/3

Channel coding gives Forward Error Correction (FEC) to the transport channel and control information. There are two types of channel coding: tail biting convolutional coding and turbo coding. Table 3.3-3 shows which channel coding schemes and coding rates are used for the transport channel and control information. Coding rate is defined as the ratio of the input bits to the output bits, and it represents the loss in capacity caused by adding redundancy and hence robustness to the signal.

A tail biting convolutional code with constraint length 7 and coding rate 1/3 is used for control information coding as shown Figure 3.3-3.

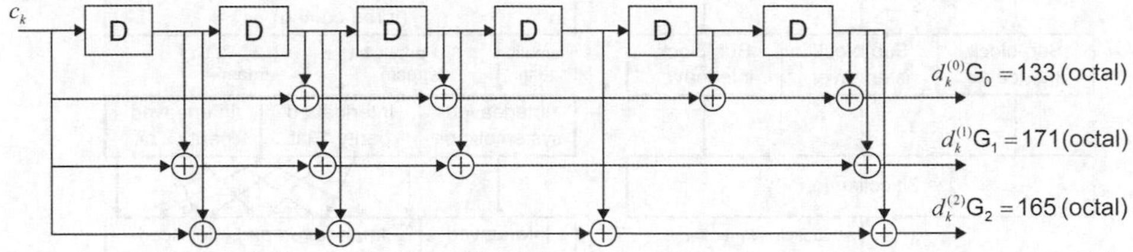

Figure 3.3-3. Rate 1/3 tail biting convolutional encoder (36.212 [3] Figure 5.1.3-1)

Turbo coding is used mainly for transport channel coding. The scheme of the turbo encoder is a Parallel Concatenated Convolutional Code (PCCC) with two 8-state constituent encoders and one turbo code internal interleaver as shown in Figure 3.3-4.

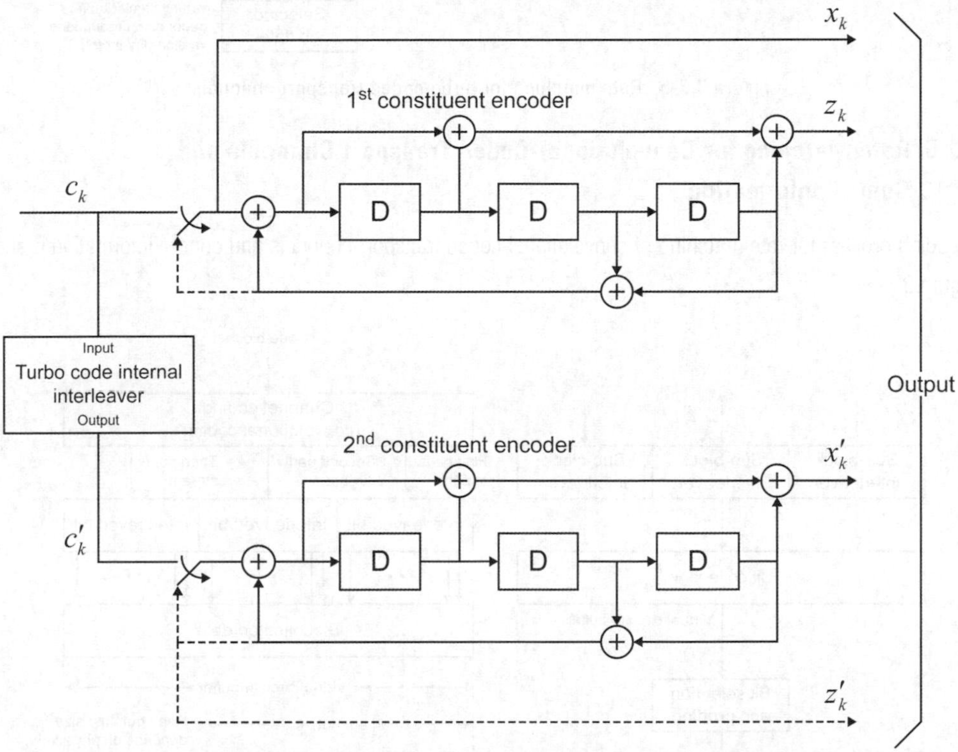

Figure 3.3-4. Structure of rate 1/3 turbo encoder (dotted lines apply for trellis termination only) (36.212 [3] Figure 5.1.3-2)

3.3.2.4 Rate Matching for Turbo-Coded Transport Channels

Rate matching provides data length control between the transport channel and the physical channel and Hybrid ARQ (HARQ) using a virtual circular buffer as shown in Figure 3.3-5.

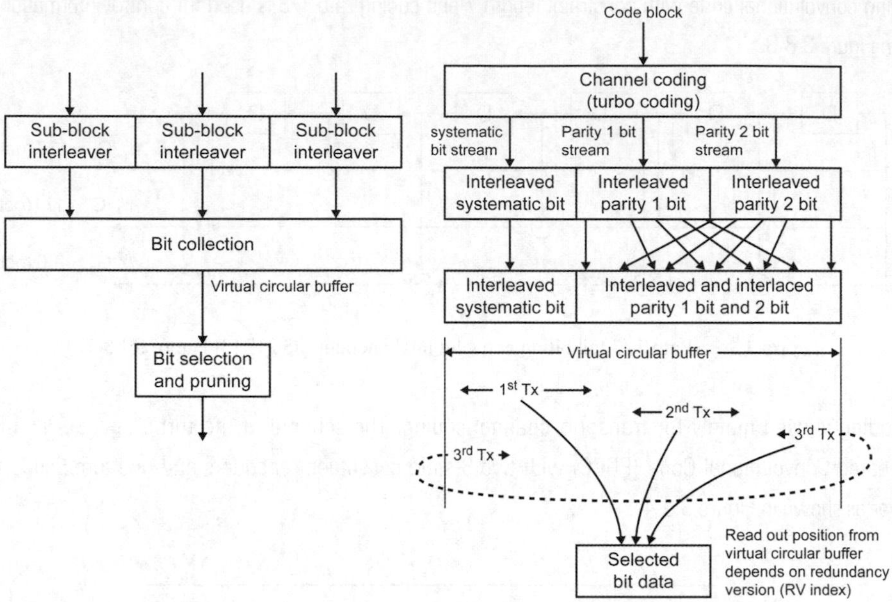

Figure 3.3-5. Rate matching for turbo-coded transport channels

3.3.2.5 Rate Matching for Convolutional-Coded Transport Channels and Control Information

The coding process for rate matching of convolutional-coded transport channels and control information is shown in Figure 3.3-6.

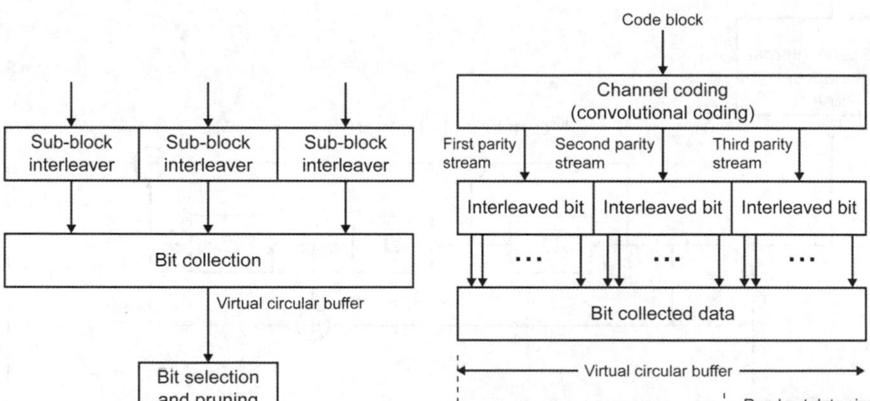

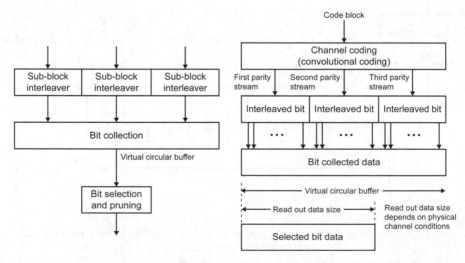

Figure 3.3-6. Rate matching for convolutional-coded transport channels and control channels

3.3.2.6 Code Block Concatenation

The code blocks from the rate matching outputs are the inputs to the code block concatenation process. The code block concatenation sequentially concatenates these different code blocks as shown in Figure 3.3-7.

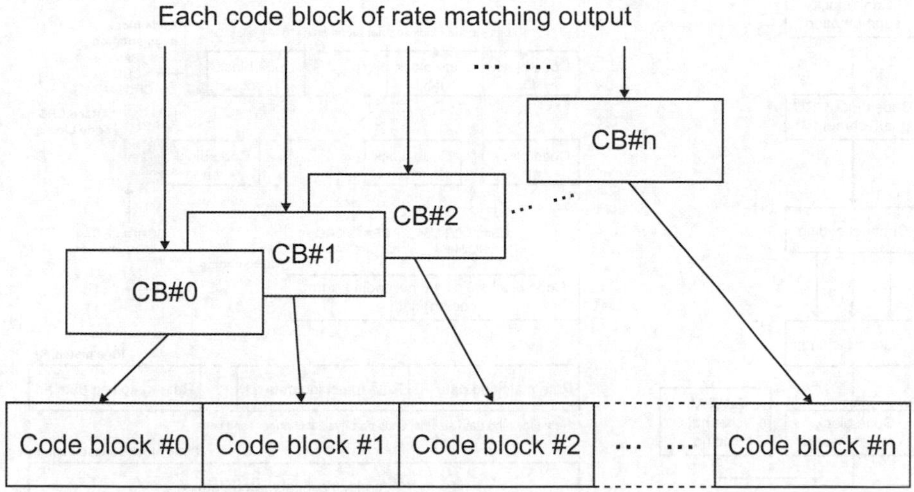

Figure 3.3-7. Code block concatenation

3.3.3 Uplink Shared Channel

The UL-SCH is a transport block with dynamic transport format size. The coded UL-SCH transport block is mapped to the physical uplink shared channel every 1 ms Transmission Time Interval (TTI). The UL-SCH transport channel coding, shown in Figure 3.3-8, comprises the transport block CRC attachment, code block segmentation, code block CRC attachment, turbo coding, rate matching and code block concatenation. Parameters carried on the UL-SCH include the Channel Quality Indicator (CQI), Precoding Matrix Indicator (PMI), Rank Indication (RI) and Redundancy Version (RV). These parameters are discussed in Section 3.4. The HARQ process controls which RV index is to be used for the transmission. The channel feedback parameters CQI and PMI have two channel coding cases, one for a payload size less than or equal to 11 bits and the other for a payload size greater than 11 bits. In the first case the channel coder uses simple block coding. The second case involves CRC attachment, convolutional coding, and rate matching. The RI is also coded and multiplexed onto the UL-SCH.

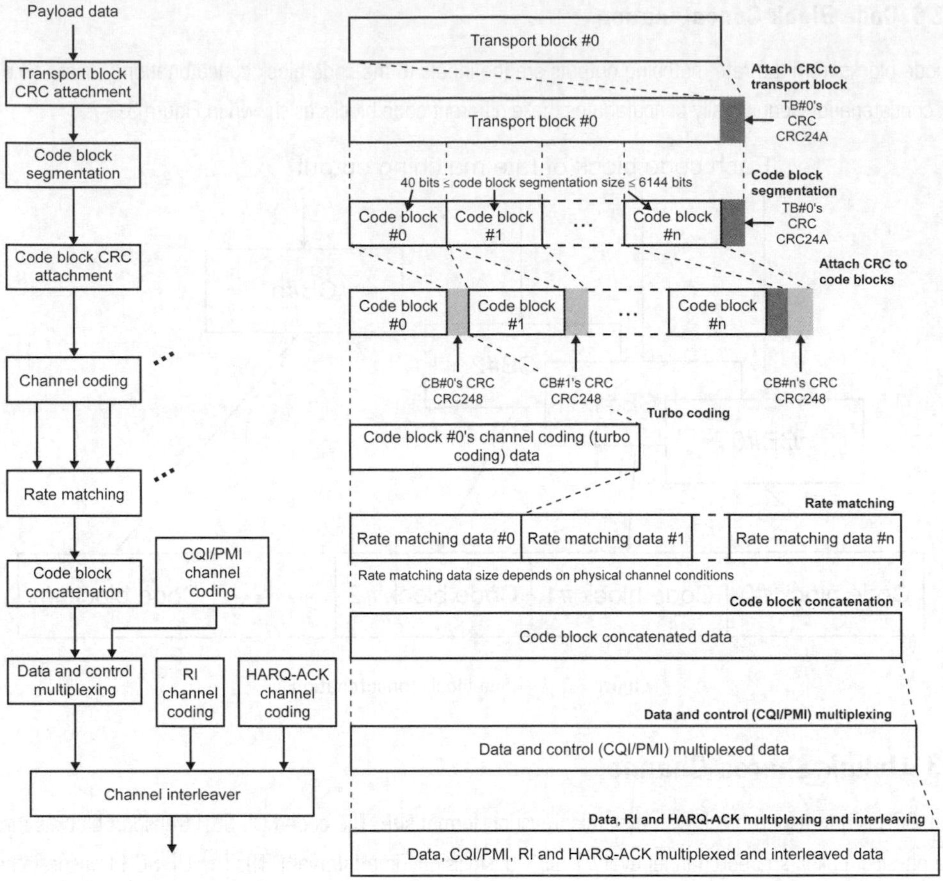

Figure 3.3-8. Transport channel processing for UL-SCH

3.3.3.1 Uplink Control Information Mapping

Uplink Control Information (UCI) can be mapped to the PUCCH and PUSCH on the physical layer. For PUCCH the UCI coding process depends on the type of control information being scheduled as shown in Table 3.3-4. In the case of spatial multiplexing, CQI includes the necessary feedback information of PMI and RI. The HARQ response from the UE for the downlink data transmission integrity contains one ACK/NACK bit per HARQ process. The number of UCI bits "A" to encode varies and they are processed using a (20, A) code, which is a linear combination of the 13 basis sequences defined in 36.212 [3] Table 5.2.3.3-1.

Uplink control information can be carried on any scheduled PUSCH, even if no transport data is available to be carried.

Table 3.3-4. Relation between UCI and PUCCH formats (based on 36.211 [2] Table 5.4-1)

Control information	PUCCH format	Modulation scheme	Number of bits per subframe, M_{bit}
Scheduling Request	1	N/A	N/A
HARQ-ACK (1bit)	1a	BPSK	1
HARQ-ACK (2bits)	1b	QPSK	2
CQI	2	QPSK	20
CQI + HARQ-ACK (1bit)	2a	QPSK + BPSK	21
CQI + HARQ-ACK (2bits)	2b	QPSK + QPSK	22

3.3.4 Downlink Transport Channel and Control Information Overview

Figure 3.3-9 shows an overview of the downlink transport channel and control information physical channel processing for all of the downlink. In the case of spatial multiplexing, two code words can be used whereupon scrambling and modulation can be independent for each code word.

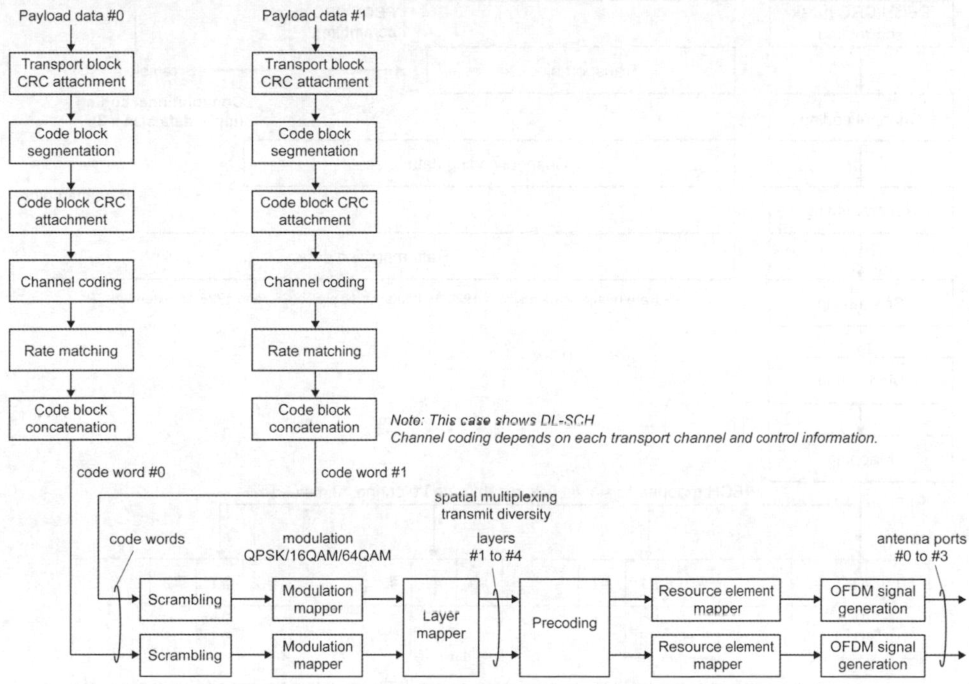

Figure 3.3-9. Overview of downlink transport channel and control information to physical channel processing (Based on 36.211 [2] Figure 6.3-1)

3.3.5 Downlink Transport Channel Coding

3.3.5.1 Broadcast Channel

The Broadcast Channel (BCH) is a pre-defined transport format of fixed size and carries information broadcast to the entire coverage area of the cell. The BCH is mapped to the Physical Broadcast Channel (PBCH) in the physical layer. The coded BCH transport block is mapped to four subframes (four OFDM symbols of slot #1 within subframe #0) within a 40 ms BCH TTI. Each subframe is self-decodable and can be blind-detected. The BCH transport channel coding comprises the CRC attachment, convolutional coding, and rate matching. No HARQ or channel interleaving is applied. The BCH-specific coding is PBCH CRC mask scrambling (CRC + PBCH CRC mask) Mod 2 as shown in Figure 3.3-10 and Table 3.3-5.

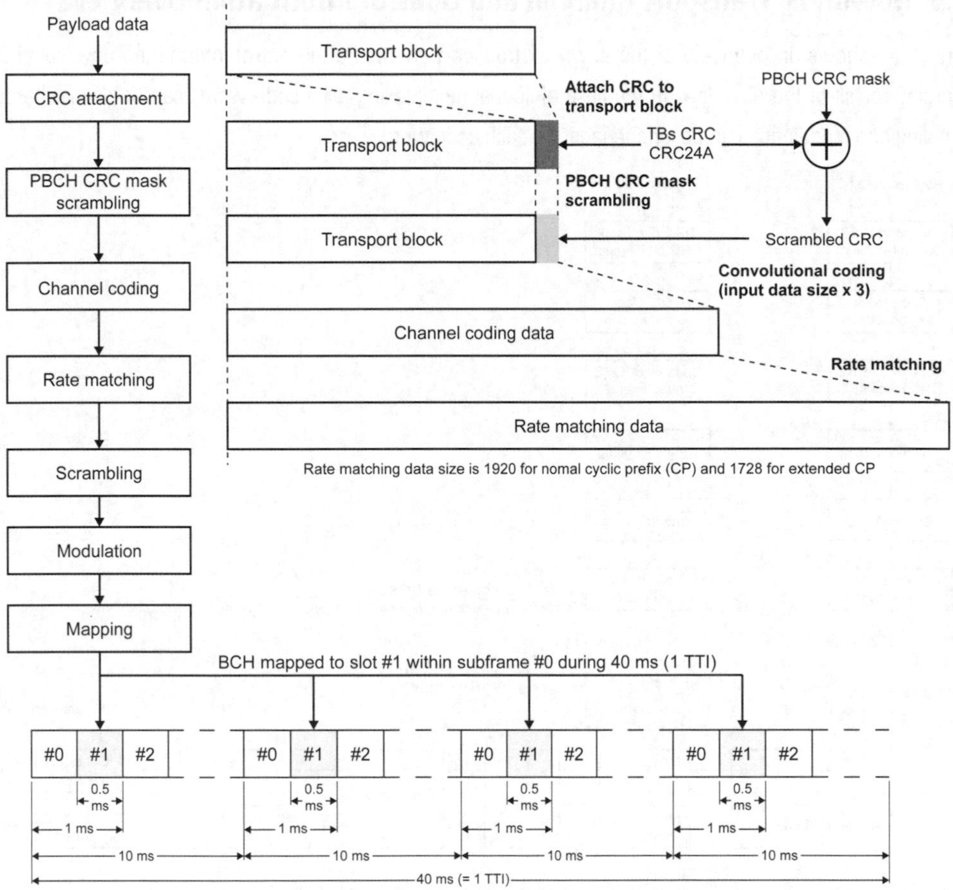

Figure 3.3-10. Transport channel processing and mapping for BCH

Table 3.3-5. CRC mask for PBCH (36.212 [3] Table 5.3.1.1-1)

Number of transmit antenna ports at eNB	PBCH CRC mask $< x_{ant,0}, x_{ant,1}, \ldots, x_{ant,15} >$
1	<0, 0, 0, 0, 0, 0, 0, 0, 0, 0, 0, 0, 0, 0, 0, 0>
2	<1, 1, 1, 1, 1, 1, 1, 1, 1, 1, 1, 1, 1, 1, 1, 1>
4	<0, 1, 0, 1, 0, 1, 0, 1, 0, 1, 0, 1, 0, 1, 0, 1>

3.3.5.2 Downlink Shared Channel

The Downlink Shared Channel (DL-SCH) has up to two transport blocks of dynamic transport format size. The coded DL-SCH transport block is mapped to the PDSCH every 1 ms TTI. The DL-SCH transport channel coding, shown in Figure 3.3-11, comprises the transport block CRC attachment, code block segmentation, code block CRC attachment, turbo coding, rate matching, and code block concatenation.

3.3.5.3 Paging Channel

The Paging Channel (PCH) carries information for broadcast in the entire coverage area of the cell. The coded PCH transport block is mapped to the PDSCH every 1 ms TTI. The PCH transport channel coding, shown in Figure 3.3-11, comprises the transport block CRC attachment, code block segmentation, code block CRC attachment, turbo coding, rate matching and code block concatenation.

3.3.5.4 Multicast Channel

The Multicast Channel (MCH) carries information for broadcast in the entire coverage area of the cell. The MCH transport block is mapped to the PMCH every 1 ms TTI. The MCH transport channel coding, shown in Figure 3.3-11, comprises the transport block CRC attachment, code block segmentation, code block CRC attachment, turbo coding, rate matching and code block concatenation.

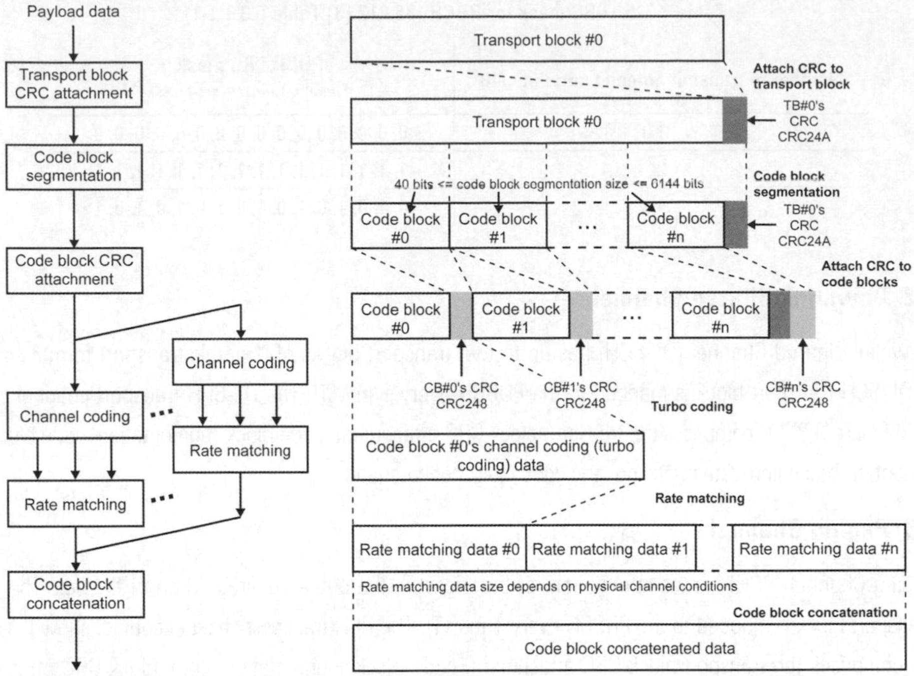

Figure 3.3-11. Transport channel processing for DL-SCH, PCH and MCH

3.3.6 Downlink Control Information Coding

The Downlink Control Information (DCI) is mapped to the PDCCH in the physical layer. The DCI carries information regarding the following:

- Transport format information: modulation scheme, coding scheme, redundancy version, new data indicator, cyclic shift for demodulation RS, UL index, CQI request downlink assignment index, HARQ process number, code word information
- Resource allocation information: RB assignment, hopping resource allocation, localized/distributed Virtual Resource Block (VRB) assignment flag, HARQ information)
- Transmit Power Control (TPC) command

Each DCI carries its own Radio Network Temporary Identity (RNTI) to identify the target user. The DCI can have several formats depending on the transmission mode as shown in Table 3.3-6. DCI coding, shown in Figure 3.3-12, comprises the CRC attachment, convolutional encoding and rate matching. The coded data is multiplexed with other data onto the PDCCH. DCI-specific coding includes CRC scrambling (CRC + RNTI + antenna selection mask) Modulo 2 shown in Figure 3.3-12.

Table 3.3-6. DCI transmission mode and format (based on 36.213 [4] Table 7.1-1)

Transmission mode	Condition of transmission mode	Reference DCI format
1	Single-antenna port; port 0	1, 1A
2	Transmit diversity	1, 1A
3	Open loop spatial multiplexing	2A
4	Closed loop spatial multiplexing	2
5	Multi-user MIMO	1D
6	Closed loop rank=1 precoding	1B
7	Single-antenna port; port 5	1, 1A

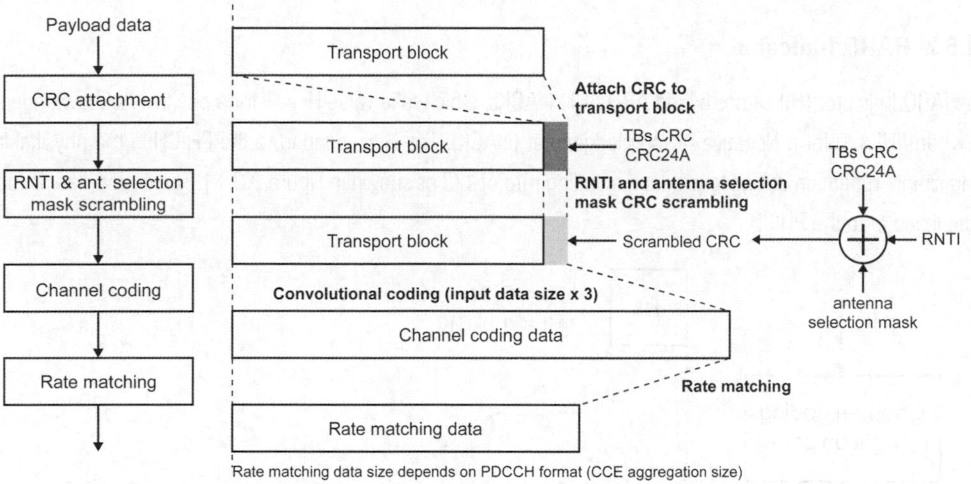

Figure 3.3-12. Control information processing for DCI

3.3.6.1 Control Format Indicator

The Control Format Indicator (CFI) is mapped to the Physical Control Format Indicator Channel (PCFICH) in the physical layer. The CFI defines how many OFDM symbols are used for the PDCCHs in a subframe. The CFI channel coding, shown in Figure 3.3-13, is a block code with coding rate 1/16. The strong coding indicates the importance of this channel since any decode errors will result in failure to read the PDCCH correctly. The CFI can take the values 1, 2 and 3. For transmission bandwidth configurations greater than 10 RB (1.8 MHz), the number of PDCCH symbols per subframe is the CFI value. For transmission bandwidth configurations less than or equal to 10 RB, the number of PDCCH symbols per subframe is the CFI value plus 1.

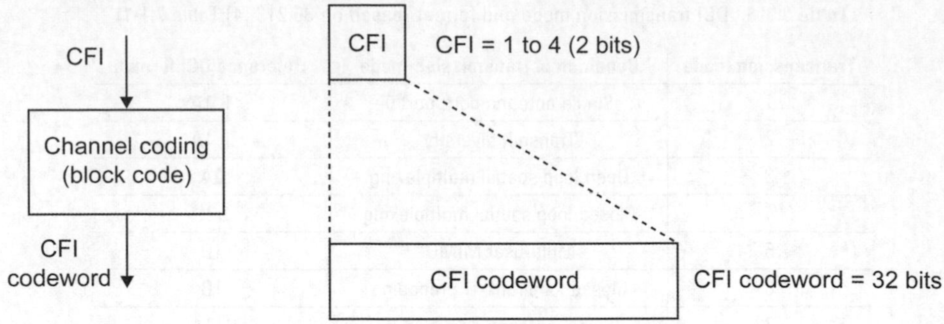

Figure 3.3-13. CFI coding

3.3.6.2 HARQ Indicator

The HARQ Indicator (HI) carries hybrid ARQ ACK/NACKs, which take value HI = 1 for a positive Acknowledgement (ACK) and HI = 0 for a Negative Acknowledgement (NACK). The HI is mapped to the PHICH in the physical layer using simple repetition coding to produce a coding rate of 1/3 as shown in Figure 3.3.14. The coded data is further multiplexed onto the PHICH.

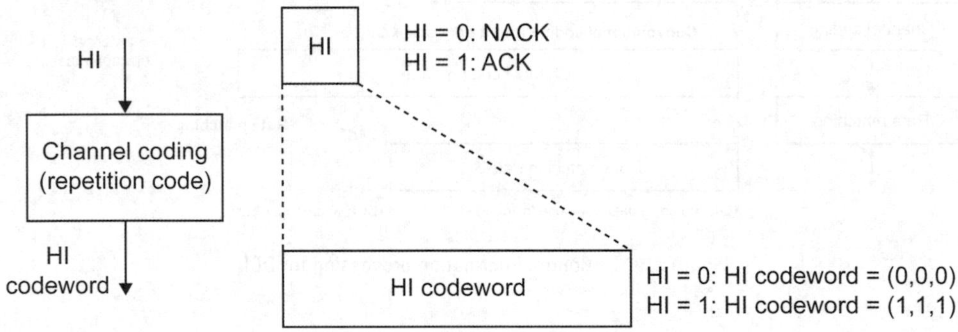

Figure 3.3-14. HI coding and codeword

3.4 Introduction to Physical Layer Signalling

Throughput and latency are two important measures of performance for digital communication systems. High throughput is needed if someone wants to download large files, but superb throughput is possible by shipping a box of DVDs overnight. The delay (latency) in this case, however, may not be acceptable. Low latency is needed because some applications, such as web browsing and peer-to-peer games, require a quick response to a user's requests.

Many of the underlying network protocols, such as Transmission Control Protocol (TCP), work by passing short messages back and forth for every request at the application level. A simple request by the user may result in hundreds of TCP messages being sent and received. Any reduction in the time needed to send each of these messages is multiplied over and over.

LTE employs a number of mechanisms in the physical layer to improve both the latency and the overall throughput of the system. This section describes the Hybrid Automatic Repeat Requests (HARQ) and Adaptive Modulation and Coding (AMC) procedures as well as the parameters used by the system to report channel state information.

3.4.1 ARQ and HARQ

Automatic Repeat Request (ARQ) is a Layer 2 protocol that has been used for years in the telecommunications industry to ensure that data is sent reliably from one node to another. It uses Error Detecting (ED) codes such as CRC and a sliding window to identify when an error has occurred in a transmission. If an error occurs, the destination requests a retransmission from the source. The ARQ protocol suffers under poor channel conditions due to excessive retransmissions.

3.4.1.1 Type-I HARQ

Prior to HSDPA and HSUPA, UMTS Rel-99 used Type-I HARQ to overcome ARQ's high retransmission rates by adding Forward Error Correction (FEC) in the form of convolutional or turbo codes. Although the FEC significantly improved the probability of successful transmission in poor signal conditions, the increased redundancy of the FEC code unnecessarily and significantly decreased the amount of user data that was transmitted under strong signal conditions for a given bandwidth.

3.4.1.2 Type-II HARQ

Type-II HARQ is used in HSDPA, HSUPA, HSPA+ and LTE to get around this performance limitation. Like Type-I HARQ, Type-II HARQ uses FEC and ED, but it does so in an iterative manner. On the first transmission of a packet, a subset of the coded bits is transmitted with sufficient information for the receiver to decode the original information bits of the packet and the CRC, but probably with only a small amount of redundancy. This results in high efficiency under good channel conditions in which minimal protection is needed. If the packet is not decoded correctly, a retransmission is triggered. However, rather than re-send the same data, the HARQ process selects a different set of coded bits representing the original information bits and the destination node adds this new information to what it received during the first transmission. This process is known as incremental redundancy. With each retransmission the effective code rate decreases until the destination has enough information to decode the packet correctly.

Type-II HARQ uses a mother code that can be punctured to achieve the desired code rate. For LTE this mother code is a rate 1/3 turbo code. This code contains systematic bits, which means that the data and CRC input bits are also present in the output. The first transmission of the packet sends most of these systematic bits plus some redundancy bits. Subsequent retransmissions send fewer of the systematic bits and more of the redundancy bits. The different transmitted versions of the packet that contain different mixes of redundancy and systematic bits are called Redundancy Versions (RVs). LTE uses four RVs. These are repeatedly sequenced through until the packet is either received correctly or a maximum number of retransmissions have been sent, at which time HARQ declares a failure and leaves it up to ARQ running in the Radio Link Control (RLC) layer to try again with a new packet. More details are included later in Section 3.4.2, Adaptive Modulation and Coding.

3.4.1.3 HARQ Processes

HARQ uses a stop and wait protocol. It transmits a packet, waits till it receives an acknowledgement (ACK) or negative acknowledgement (NACK) from the destination and then sends the next packet. As a result of processing and transmission delays, this cycle takes several subframes. Since it takes only one subframe to transmit the data, quite a bit of bandwidth is underutilized. To fully utilize this bandwidth, HARQ makes use of multiple processes offset in time from each other. Each process transmits a packet to the destination receiver, and before the time the next transmission allocation for that process arrives, the HARQ process will have received the ACK or NACK from the destination transmitter and created the next packet for (re)transmission.

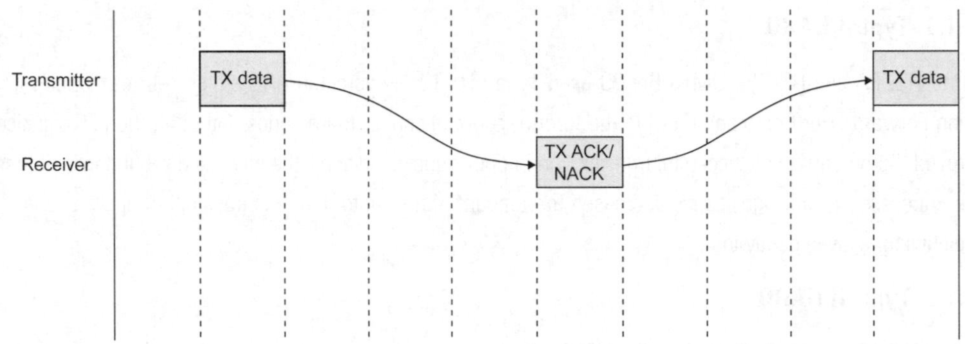

Figure 3.4-1. A single HARQ process

It should be noted that LTE TDD supports a configurable number of HARQ processes with varying timing requirements.

For the FDD uplink the number of HARQ processes is fixed at eight per UE. Thus there are always eight subframes between transmission opportunities for a specific uplink HARQ process. The FDD downlink also supports up to eight HARQ processes per UE, but each process can transmit on any subframe. This technique is more flexible but requires that the HARQ process number be transmitted with the downlink resource assignment. This extra step is not necessary in the uplink since the process number is automatically defined by the position in the frame.

One HARQ entity exists in the eNB for each UE, managing all uplink HARQ processes associated with that UE. Another entity, or the same entity, manages all downlink HARQ processes. The specifications are somewhat ambiguous in this regard, allowing a single HARQ entity to handle both uplink and downlink HARQ processes. However, the specifications clearly do not allow multiple HARQ entities for one UE in one direction.

3.4.1.4 Synchronous vs. Asynchronous HARQ

The downlink uses asynchronous Type-II HARQ transmission. The receiver does not know ahead of time what's being transmitted, so the HARQ process identifier and the RV must be sent along with the data. The RV specifies which combination of systematic and redundancy bits are being sent to the UE. This is done through the PDSCH resource allocation messages sent on a PDCCH simultaneous to the corresponding PDSCH transmission. The advantage of such a scheme is that the scheduling algorithm has considerable freedom in deciding which UEs and HARQ processes are scheduled during any one subframe.

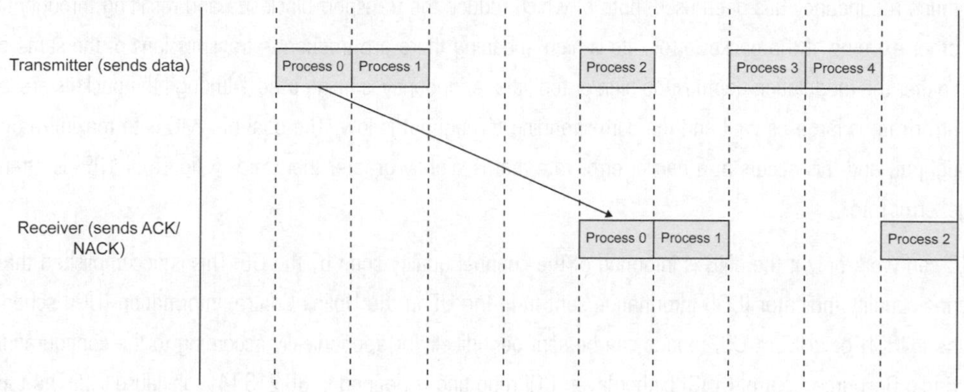

Figure 3.4-2. Downlink HARQ processes associated with a particular UE transmit when data is available and scheduled

In contrast the uplink uses synchronous HARQ transmission. Transmission is synchronous in the sense that once a HARQ process starts, any required retransmissions occur every eighth subframe. By using a fixed interval, the uplink does not have to specify a HARQ identifier in the PDCCH allocation message. However, the scheduling algorithm in the uplink is not quite as flexible as that in the downlink as a consequence of this fixed interval.

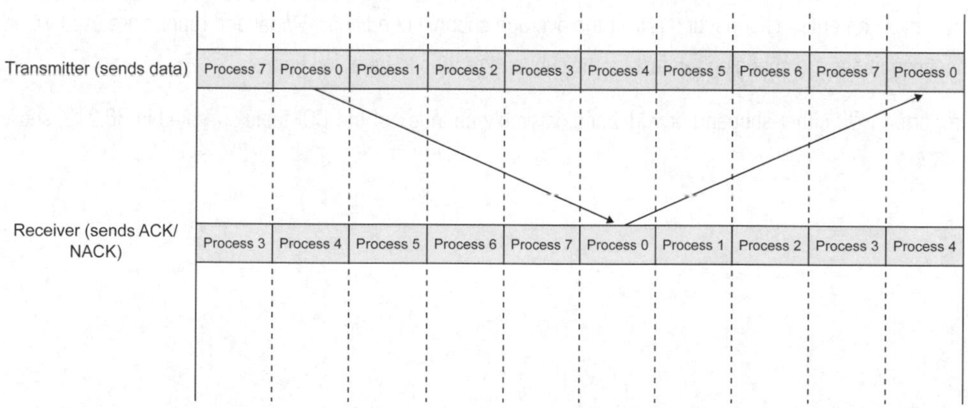

Figure 3.4-3. Retransmissions of an uplink HARQ process occur every eighth subframe

3.4.2 Adaptive Modulation and Coding

Adaptive Modulation and Coding (AMC) attempts to match the transmissions from a HARQ process to the channel conditions. Under good channel conditions a higher order modulation format such as 64QAM is used with less redundancy in the initial transmission, allowing a larger transport block to be carried in the allocated channel resources. Under poorer channel conditions a lower order modulation format such as QPSK and possibly more redundancy bits are sent initially to improve the probability of reception. This means, however, that a smaller transport block must be sent. A very low packet error rate implies that the modulation format is too low or that too much redundancy has been used, both of which reduce the transport block size and resulting throughput. At the other extreme, if the packet error rate is high, meaning there are frequent retransmissions of the same data, then either the modulation depth is too high or too little redundancy is being used. Although the packets are large, the error rate is large as well and the corresponding throughput is low. The goal of AMC is to maximize overall throughput, and this occurs at a packet error rate that is slightly greater than zero. A figure of 10% is often the target error rate.

AMC can work only if the eNB is informed of the channel quality seen by the UE. This is accomplished through Channel Quality Indicator (CQI) information sent from the UE in the Uplink Control Information (UCI) scheduled on the PUCCH or PUSCH. CQI reports can be sent periodically or aperiodically according to the configuration by the Radio Resource Control (RRC) higher layer. CQI reporting is defined in 36.213 [4] subclause 7.2. The topic is discussed more fully in Section 3.4.6.

Given the wide bandwidths supported by LTE and the fact that a particular UE is usually allocated to only a portion of the subcarriers, it is advantageous to allocate the UE to those subcarriers that the UE can best receive. Such frequency-dependent scheduling can only be accomplished if the eNB scheduling algorithm is informed of the channel quality corresponding to different portions of the downlink as seen by the UE. LTE accomplishes this through subband CQI reports in which the UE sends CQI information for independent subbands within the downlink channel. An LTE UE can be configured by the eNB to send either subband or wideband CQI reports. Wideband reports cover the entire channel and reflect the average channel conditions. Wideband reports are used when the channel conditions are changing too fast for the subband reports to be acted upon.

The reported CQI, either subband or wideband, is simply an index of the CQI table specified in 36.213, shown in Table 3.4-1.

Table 3.4-1. 4-bit CQI Table (36.213 [4] Table 7.2.3-1)

CQI index	Modulation	Coding rate x 1024	Efficiency
0	out of range		
1	QPSK	78	0.1523
2	QPSK	120	0.2344
3	QPSK	193	0.3770
4	QPSK	308	0.6016
5	QPSK	449	0.8770
6	QPSK	602	1.1758
7	16QAM	378	1.4766
8	16QAM	490	1.9141
9	16QAM	616	2.4063
10	64QAM	466	2.7305
11	64QAM	567	3.3223
12	64QAM	666	3.9023
13	64QAM	772	4.5234
14	64QAM	873	5.1152
15	64QAM	948	5.5547

Each row of the table consists of a specific modulation and code rate. For each CQI reporting period the UE is required to return the highest CQI index that would have resulted in an error probability of less than 10% for a single PDSCH transport block transmitted using the reported modulation and code rate.

The eNB is not mandated to use the modulation and code rate associated with the received CQI for the target 10% error probability. The eNB's scheduling algorithm uses the CQI as a guide in selecting from the transport block size table (defined in 36.213 [4] Table 7.1.7.2.1-1), which specifies the permissible combinations of transport block size, resource allocation and modulation scheme that are available for transmission. For example, when the rate of change of the CQI reports exceeds the ability of the HARQ process to keep up, the eNB might use some form of statistical averaging or peak detection of the CQI reports to determine the optimal parameters for transmission. Thus to maintain the high Quality of Service (QoS) required by a service such as Voice over Internet Protocol (VoIP), the eNB might sacrifice some capacity by selecting a lower error rate target to minimize retransmissions.

Retransmissions of a particular HARQ process use the same modulation and coding scheme as the initial transmission. Each subsequent retransmission simply reduces the effective code rate through incremental redundancy.

In the event that the channel characteristics change considerably after the initial transmission, the Medium Access Control (MAC) higher layer is free to abort that transmission and start a new one using a more appropriate modulation and coding scheme. This is done by toggling the New Data Indication (NDI) bit in the PDSCH or PUSCH allocation message sent by the PDCCH.

LTE uses a clever algorithm to implement incremental redundancy and adaptive coding.

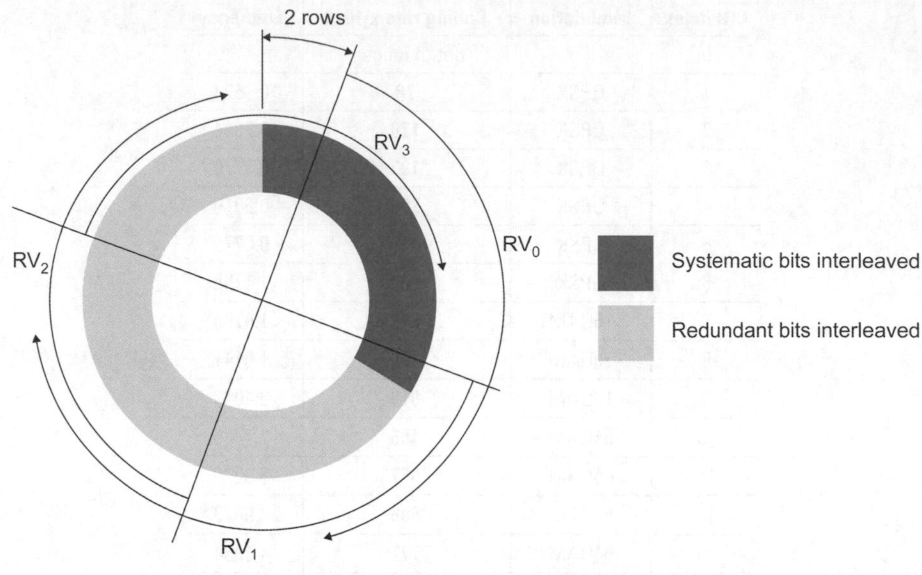

Figure 3.4-4. LTE incremental redundancy algorithm

All the redundant bits from the turbo encoder are included in the circular buffer for the uplink. The number of redundant bits included in the circular buffer for the downlink is configured by the eNB.

The systematic bits from the turbo encoder are interleaved and placed into a circular buffer called the soft buffer. The redundancy bits are then interleaved and placed after the systematic bits. All the redundancy bits are included in the soft buffer used for uplink transmissions, but the number of redundancy bits included for downlink transmissions is defined by upper layers. Bits are copied from the buffer starting at a position that is dependent on the RV. The starting position for RV_n is approximately n/4 of the way around the circular buffer, plus a fixed offset of two interleaved rows. The number of bits pulled from the circular buffer for each RV is dependent on the target code rate. For poor channel conditions the code rate approaches 0.1, in which case the entire soft buffer is transmitted multiple times for each RV. In excellent channel conditions the code rate approaches 0.92, which means that the number of bits transmitted in each RV is slightly more than the number of bits in the transport block.

3.4.3 ARQ Assist

An ARQ receiver has to rely on a skipped sequence number to identify when a packet has been corrupted in transit. This technique assumes that a subsequent packet will be received that identifies the gap in the sequence numbers. Once this gap has been identified, a retransmission can be requested immediately by the receiver.

In practice, ARQ on its own cannot fully rely on skipped sequence numbers. Suppose that the last packet transmitted was corrupted. In that case a subsequent packet will not be received to identify the gap in sequence numbers. The receiver will simply wait idly for the next packet and the system will stall. To avoid this problem ARQ is assisted by a timer that starts when a packet is transmitted. If the sender does not receive either an ACK or a

NACK response from the receiver before the timer expires, a retransmission is attempted. In most cellular standards the ARQ timer is configurable but typically is set for around 100 ms, which is a long time by LTE standards.

Recall that a HARQ process will repeatedly send a packet approximately every 8 ms until it is acknowledged by the receiver. After a configurable number of attempts HARQ will give up and inform ARQ that the transmission attempt has failed. ARQ can immediately attempt a retransmission, possibly with different modulation and coding. No timer is needed and the delay is minimized.

3.4.4 Technical Challenges

The LTE specifications impose constraints on the UE and eNB regarding the amount of time they have to complete the HARQ process.

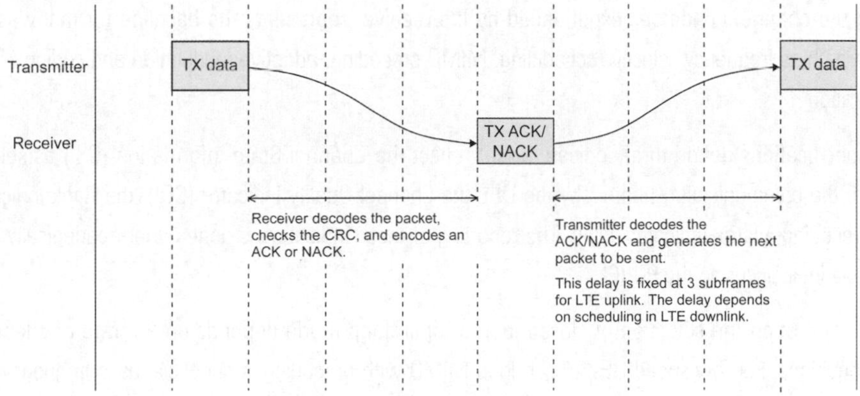

Figure 3.4-5. A single HARQ process

The receiver has three subframes to decode the packet, check the CRC and encode the ACK/NACK. Assuming that the transmitter sent the data in subframe n, the ACK/NACK must be sent back to the transmitter in subframe n+4.

The transmitter now also has three subframes in which to decode the ACK/NACK returned from the receiver, construct the next transport block based on the ACK/NACK (this is a job for RLC and MAC) and finally encode the transport block if it hopes to transmit this HARQ process in subframe n+8. This short turnaround time is required in the uplink, but can be delayed in the downlink through scheduling. A lower cost eNB such as a Home eNB (femtocell) might use this technique to reduce the processing demands it imposes on itself.

Although the specifications allow the eNB to retransmit a particular HARQ process earlier than subframe n+8, such an early retransmission would impose significantly more technical challenges on the eNB processing elements.

Given that each subframe is utilized by a different HARQ process, some assumptions can be made regarding the execution times allowed for each of the processing steps listed above. If only one processing unit for each step is multiplexed in time between all HARQ processes, the computations associated with each step cannot exceed 1 ms. Should any one of the steps exceed 1 ms, the processing unit won't keep up with the continuous flow of HARQ information in consecutive subframes.

3.4.5 Summary of HARQ and AMC

Type-II HARQ and AMC work together to provide a very adaptive transport mechanism in LTE. Adaptive modulation and coding tunes the initial HARQ transmission to use a coding rate that results in approximately the ideal packet error ratio from a throughput perspective. Type-II HARQ then uses incremental redundancy to add redundancy bits for each successive retransmission, thereby reducing the effective code rate until the packet can be decoded correctly. The result, although not perfect, is a means of optimizing the overall throughput over wide ranges of dynamically changing channel conditions while minimizing latency.

3.4.6 Uplink Control signalling

3.4.6.1 Introduction to Uplink Control Signalling

Reporting the channel conditions experienced by the receiver represents the baseline for many adaptation algorithms such as frequency selective scheduling, MIMO precoding, adaptive modulation and coding (AMC) and rank adaptation.

The LTE specifications define three indicators that reflect the Channel State Information (CSI) as seen by the recipient of the communication (that is, by the UE): the Channel Quality Indicator (CQI), the Rank Indication (RI) and the Precoding Matrix Indicator (PMI). The reporting of these indicators is done either aperiodically using the PUSCH or periodically using the PUCCH.

For MIMO operation the selection of closed loop or open loop mode depends on the rate of change in the channel conditions. For low speed UEs, closed loop MIMO with precoding is beneficial as is frequency selective RB scheduling. Indeed, the likelihood of variable MIMO conditions across the channel means closed loop MIMO works best in conjunction with frequency selective scheduling. For moderate to high speed UEs, the preferred mode of operation is Space Frequency Block Coded (SFBC) transmit diversity or spatial multiplexing with a fixed precoding matrix (open loop MIMO).

3.4.6.2 Channel Quality Indicator

The CQI plays a central role in LTE scheduling and link adaptation. The CQI is computed at the UE receiver for each codeword on either the full transmission bandwidth configuration (wideband CQI) or on groups of resource blocks known as subbands. The CQI reflects the level of noise and interference experienced by the receiver on a particular portion of the channel. It can be thought of as a measure of Signal to Interference plus Noise Ratio (SINR) but in fact is coded in terms of the Modulation and Coding Scheme (MCS) required for a particular error rate probability. Moreover, some compression is used when reporting subband CQI using differential encoding.

Depending on the reporting mode (all subbands, wideband or preferred subbands) the CQI is used by the eNB as an input to the process for scheduling traffic. When the eNB receives the indices of those subbands in which the receiver experiences the highest CQI, it can allocate those subbands to efficiently schedule user transmissions. This technique is called frequency selective scheduling.

3.4.6.3 Rank Indication

The RI is a value computed by the UE representing the preferred number of layers to be used in the next downlink transmissions to the UE. The value reflects the actual usable rank of the channel; in other words, the maximum number of spatially parallel transmissions supported by the channel but limited to the UE capabilities. The maximum number of layers is four, but some UE categories support only one or two layers. See 36.306 [7] Table 4.1-1.

Typically, the RI is computed as follows: for each possible rank, the subbands are ordered by decreasing level of throughput. The M best subbands are selected and the sum throughput is derived. The rank maximizing the sum throughput is chosen and fed back to the transmitter. Computing the rank on the best subbands is justified by the fact that the UE is likely to be scheduled on these subbands.

3.4.6.4 Precoding Matrix Indicator

One of the techniques used in LTE to improve Single User Spatial Multiplexing (SU-MIMO) performance is precoding. Precoding involves adapting the transmitted signal to the current CSI. In the FDD mode, CSI in the downlink can be very different from CSI in the uplink due to the duplex frequency spacing. Thus a method for reporting the CSI to the transmitter is needed. The PUSCH and PUCCH are used to carry this information.

In theory, a full CSI report for each resource block at the maximum update rate achieves the best performance, but the accompanying overhead in the uplink channel is unacceptable. Compression mechanisms have therefore been designed to decrease the amount of feedback. These introduce important loop parameters such as granularity, feedback rate and codebook size. There are many methods that can be used for compression but the one chosen for LTE is linear codebook based precoding. In codebook-based techniques, the preferred precoding matrix is chosen from a finite set of pre-defined matrices (the codebook) that are based on some selection criteria.

The size of the codebook defined for LTE varies with the number of antenna ports and rank. For transmissions using two antenna ports, a codebook of four unitary matrices is defined, while in the four antenna port case the codebook size is equal to 16. When the number of layers is smaller than number of antenna ports (i.e., when transmit diversity is being used) subsets of the full rank codebook are defined.

The codebook for four antenna transmission is based on Householder reflection matrices. The codebook matrices W_n are derived from unit vectors u_n by the following equation:

$$W_n = I - \frac{2}{\|u_n\|^2} u_n u_n^H$$

The codebooks and unit vectors definitions can be found in 36.211 [2] subclause 6.3.4.2.3.

The PMI is defined as the index to the preferred precoding matrix within the codebook matrices. The PMI is four bits wide for four antenna ports or two bits wide for two antenna ports. The PMI selection process is not specified and left as an implementation choice. It will usually be based on metrics such as SINR maximization and sum throughput maximization.

To further reduce the amount of feedback, the PMI is compressed in both the time and frequency domains. Since adjacent resource blocks are likely to share the same PMI, they are grouped in subbands and one PMI is computed per subband. A subband is defined as a localized frequency resource unit for which a separate CQI is reported. In practice, a subband is a group of k adjacent resource blocks. The early LTE specifications considered distributed RB allocation as a means of achieving frequency diversity but dropped this in favor of localized allocation in conjunction with frequency selective scheduling.

Defining the optimal size k of a subband in terms of performance and overhead is called the granularity trade-off. The optimal granularity is highly dependent on the coherence bandwidth of the channel. For frequency selective channels in which conditions vary significantly across the channel, subband size is preferably small while for flat fading (or correlated fading) channels, a wideband value (one value for all subbands) is enough. To reflect this, various reporting modes have been defined.

The fastest PMI reporting rate is once every 1 ms subframe. Longer periodicity values are possible up to a 160 ms interval. The reporting rate is semi-statically configured by higher layers.

3.4.6.5 Methods of Reporting

The CQI, PMI and RI are reported in control indication fields on either the PUCCH (periodically) or the PUSCH (aperiodically). The time and frequency resources for reporting the indicators are managed and semi-statically configured by the eNB. Whether to use PUCCH or PUSCH depends on the existence of an UL-SCH; that is, whether the user is already scheduled on the PUSCH for that particular subframe. The periodic reporting on PUCCH is used only on those subframes in which the UE has no PUSCH allocation. If the user has been allocated a PUSCH, the CQI, PMI and RI are sent over it even if there is no additional user data to transmit.

The reporting can be roughly categorized in three modes:

- Wideband
- UE selected
- eNB selected (PUSCH only)

In wideband mode, the CQI report is valid for the entire transmission bandwidth configuration (the entire channel). This is referred to as reporting over the entire set of Subbands (S). One value of CQI and one or multiple values of PMI are reported.

In UE selected mode, the reports are derived on the so-called best-M subbands. The UE selects the M subbands (usually covering 25% of the bandwidth) with the highest CQI. A single CQI plus PMI is computed reflecting the channel conditions as if using these preferred bands only. Moreover, wideband values are also reported.

In eNB selected mode, CQI and PMI are reported per subband. To help reduce the uplink overhead, differential encoding with respect to the wideband value is used.

The subband size as well as the M number of preferred bands are signalled by higher layers and vary with the channel bandwidth.

Aperiodic Reporting

Aperiodic reporting is done exclusively on the PUSCH and is triggered by an indication sent in the scheduling grant. The following modes are available when reporting on the PUSCH:

Table 3.4-2. CQI and PMI feedback types for PUSCH reporting modes (36.213 [4] Table 7.2.1-1)

		PMI feedback type		
		No PMI	**Single PMI**	**Multiple PMI**
PUSCH CQI feedback type	**Wideband (wideband CQI)**			Mode 1-2
	UE-selected (subband CQI)	Mode 2-0		Mode 2-2
	Higher layer-configured (subband CQI)	Mode 3-0	Mode 3-1	

PUSCH Modes 2-0 and 3-0

These modes are used in single stream and open loop systems (SISO, transmit diversity and open loop spatial multiplexing). The PMI is not reported and a wideband CQI plus a subband CQI (mode 2-0, differential encoding) or a best-M subband CQI (mode 3-0) are reported for the first codeword.

PUSCH Modes 1-2, 2-2 and 3-1

These modes are exclusively used in combination with closed loop spatial multiplexing. One wideband CQI value is computed (mode 1-2) plus a best-M subband CQI (mode 2-2) or a per-subband CQI (mode 3-1). Each CQI value is reported per codeword and differentially encoded. The PMI is reported once for the full system bandwidth (mode 3-1), once for each subband (mode 1-2, mode 2-2) and once assuming transmission on the best-M subbands (mode 2-2).

The RI is reported in all modes and is computed over the full system bandwidth. In UE-selected modes, the preferred M subband locations are also reported by the UE using a uniquely defined combinatorial index (label).

Periodic Reporting

Periodic reporting is done exclusively on the PUCCH. Since the PUCCH supports only very low data rates, some of the aperiodic reporting modes are unavailable or modified accordingly. In the case of multiple subband reports, CQI values are given for particular parts of the bandwidth (called Bandwidth Parts or BP). Each BP spans one or several consecutive subbands in the frequency domain. An example of the concept is given in Figure 3.4-6 for a 10 MHz bandwidth (50 RB). There are 6 RB per subband, nine subbands and three BPs.

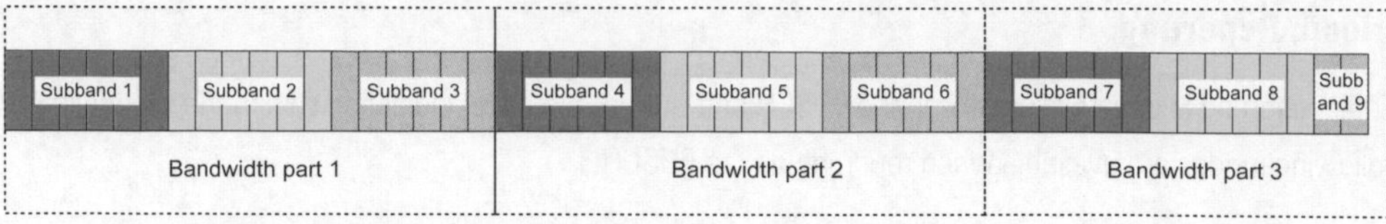

Figure 3.4-6. Illustration of the concept of subbands and bandwidth parts

The periodicity, the reporting offsets and the reporting modes are parameters configured by higher layers. The RI reports are configured so that their periodicity is a multiple of the CQI and PMI reporting periods. Strict priority rules are applied to avoid collision between the reports.

The modes available when reporting on the PUCCH are shown in Table 3.4-3.

Table 3.4-3. CQI and PMI feedback types for PUCCH reporting modes (36.213 [4] Table 7.2.2-1)

		PMI feedback type	
		No PMI	**Single PMI**
PUCCH CQI feedback type	**Wideband (wideband CQI)**	Mode 1-0	Mode 1-1
	UE-selected (subband CQI)	Mode 2-0	Mode 2-1

PUCCH Modes 1-0 and 2-0

These modes are used in single stream and open loop systems. The following indicators are reported:

- RI (open loop spatial multiplexing only) calculated on the full system bandwidth
- Wideband CQI (conditioned by RI, computed on the full system bandwidth)
- Additional UE-selected subband CQI wideband report (mode 2-0 only). Selection of preferred subbands is done within a bandwidth part. One CQI value is computed assuming transmission in the preferred subbands only. Reports for each BP are given consecutively on successive reporting instances. To indicate the location of the preferred subbands, a bit label is also reported.

Modes 1-1 and 2-1

These modes are used in combination with closed loop spatial multiplexing, closed loop rank one precoding and Multiuser MIMO (MU-MIMO). The following indicators are reported:

- RI calculated on the full system bandwidth
- PMI calculated on the full system bandwidth, conditioned by RI
- Wideband CQI (conditioned by RI, computed on the full system bandwidth assuming that single matrix precoding was applied)
- 3-bit wideband spatial differential CQI (if RI>1)

- Additional UE selected subband CQI wideband report (mode 2-1 only) as in mode 2-0 above
- Additional 3 bit spatial differential CQI (mode 2-1 only) calculated by taking the difference between the CQI value for codeword 1 and codeword 2 (assuming usage of latest matrix precoding and full system bandwidth)

Scheduling

Each mode defines a number of reports, combining several report types in a report instance. The parameters for the scheduling of the different reports are semi-statically configured by higher layers as follows:

J = number of bandwidth parts

K = number of reports of subband CQI needed per BP

N_P = reporting period between two CQI reports

$H = J*K + 1$ = reporting instances required for a complete CQI/PMI report ($J*K$ reports of subband CQIs + 1 report of wideband CQI/PMI)

N_P*H = reporting period of complete CQI/PMI (wideband + subbands)

M_{RI} (multiple of P) = reporting period of RI

$N_{OFFSET,RI}$ = offset between RI report and wideband CQI/PMI report

The following example depicts a Mode 2-1 report with the following parameters:

$N_P = 2, J = 3, K = 1, H = 4, M_{RI} = 8, N_{OFFSET,RI} = 1.$

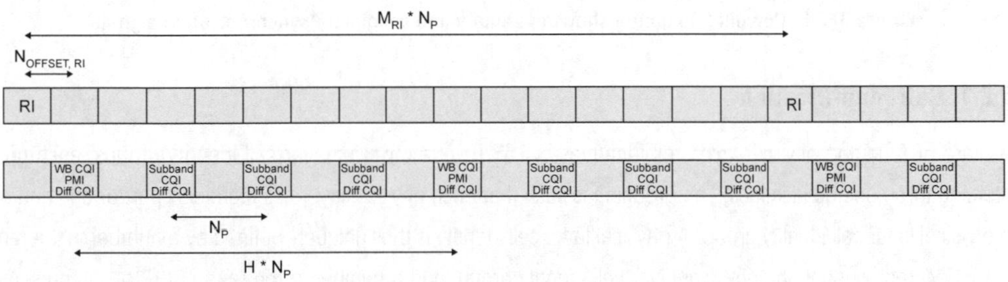

Figure 3.4-7. Reporting scheduling example for Mode 2-1 and 10 MHz BW (RI>1)

3.5 Physical Layer Procedures

This section describes two important physical layer procedures:

- cell search and synchronization using the primary and secondary synchronization signals in conjunction with the BCH
- the random access procedure using the PRACH

3.5.1 Synchronization and Cell Search

Cell search is the procedure by which a UE acquires time and frequency synchronization with a cell and detects that cell's physical layer Cell ID. LTE cell search supports a scalable overall transmission bandwidth corresponding to six or more resource blocks. LTE cell search is based on the downlink physical signals: the primary and secondary synchronization signals, the reference signals and the physical broadcast channel (PBCH). As described more fully in Section 3.2.6, the primary synchronization signal and secondary synchronization signal are transmitted over the center 62 subcarriers (930 kHz) in the first and sixth subframe of each 10 ms frame. The reference signals are transmitted on every sixth subcarrier across the entire channel. Neighbour-cell search is also based on the same downlink signals as the initial cell search. The presence of these signals at the center of the channel means that one set of procedures will work for all six supported LTE channel bandwidths of 1.4 MHz, 3 MHz, 5 MHz, 10 MHz, 15 MHz and 20 MHz.

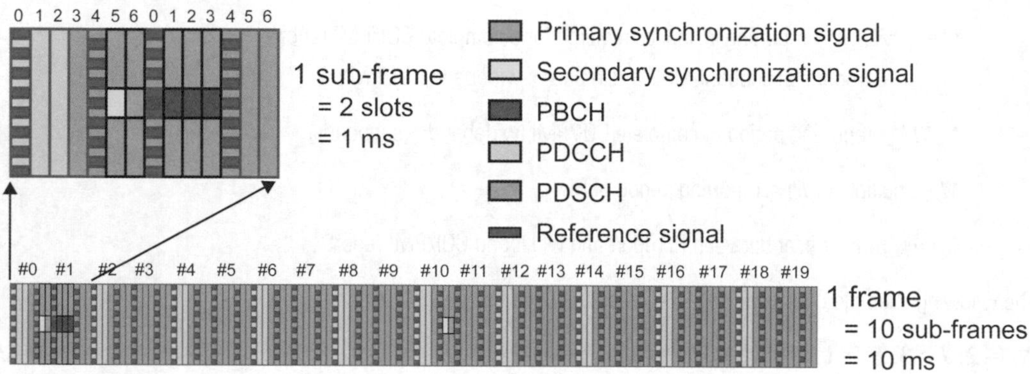

Figure 3.5-1. Downlink mapping showing primary and secondary synchronization signals

3.5.2.1 Cell Identification

There are 504 unique physical layer cell identities in 168 unique physical layer cell identity groups, each group containing three unique identities. The grouping is such that each physical layer cell identity is part of one and only one physical layer cell identity group. A physical layer cell identity is thus uniquely defined by a number in the range of 0 to 167, representing the physical layer cell identity group, and a number in the range of 0 to 2, representing the physical layer identity within the physical layer cell identity group. Refer to 36.211 [2] subclause 6.11.

3.5.2.2 Cell Search Procedure

The initial cell search begins when the UE is switched on causing the Universal Subscriber Identity Module (U-SIM) to issue a cell search request procedure. At first the UE does not have information of nearby cells, so it starts to look for the strongest cells in the band of interest. When the UE finds the strongest subcarriers carrying the synchronization signals and the PBCH, the frequency synchronization procedure begins. Figure 3.5-2 outlines the process.

The UE first looks for the primary synchronization signal from which it will be able to find the exact carrier frequency and the timing of slot 0 or 10. At this point the UE cannot tell which half of the frame structure it has found since

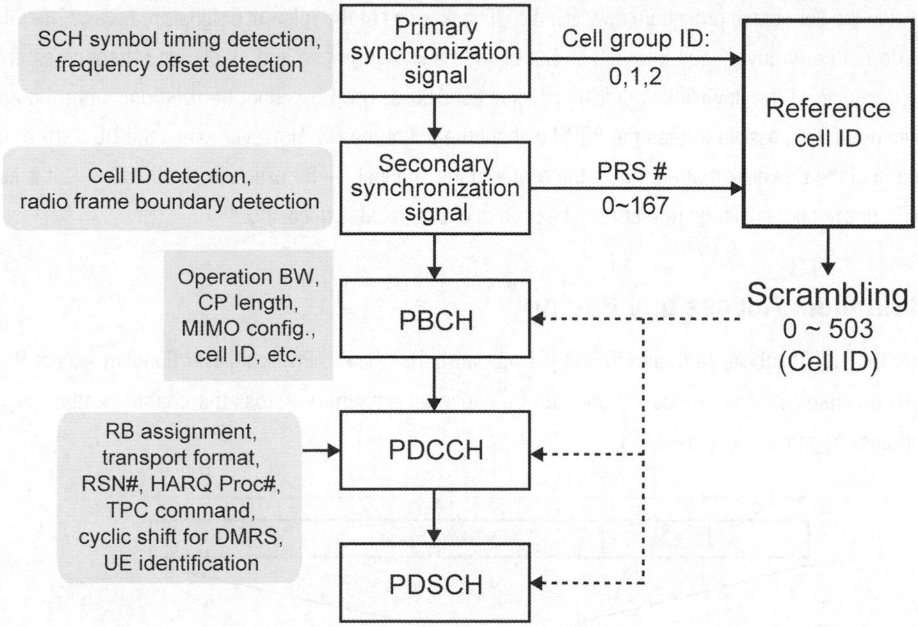

Figure 3.5-2. Cell search procedure

the primary synchronization signal is repeated twice per frame. By trial and error the UE will determine the Cyclic Prefix (CP) configuration. The next step is to decode the primary synchronization signal to determine which of three identities the cell belongs to. The primary synchronization signal is encoded as a Zadoff-Chu sequence of phase shifts. Each of the 62 subcarriers has the same power level with its phase determined by the root index number in a Zadoff-Chu sequence generator as defined in 36.211 [2] subclause 6.11.1. This produces the characteristic circular constellation pattern seen earlier in Figure 3.2-6. The Zadoff-Chu sequence is chosen because of its excellent autocorrelation properties and the low cross correlation with the other sequences. This makes it easy for the UE to decode to which of the three identities the cell belongs.

Next the UE decodes the secondary synchronization signal, which is transmitted one OFDM symbol before the primary synchronization signal. The secondary synchronization signal is encoded as an interleaved concatenation of two length-31 binary sequences as defined in 36.211 [2] subclause 6.11.2. This creates a BPSK pattern as seen earlier in Figure 3.2-7. The first 31 subcarriers use one sequence and the second 31 carriers use the other sequence. By cyclic shifting each sequence it is easy to create the necessary 168 unique identity groups. Once the secondary synchronization signal is decoded, the UE will have removed the uncertainty in the frame timing and be able to calculate the cell ID from the 504 possibilities.

With the cell ID and frame timing known the UE can read the PBCH. The PBCH carries the system information messages on the BCH transport channel, and from these the Public Land Mobile Network (PLMN) identity can be decoded. Once a valid PLMN identity is known, the UE can start to register with the cell.

The point in the cell search procedure at which the UE makes use of the reference signals may vary. The reference signals do not carry any unique information but provide a known phase and amplitude reference essential for reliable decoding of the downlink in difficult channel conditions. The RS cannot be used until after the cell ID is determined but it is possible to read the PBCH without the aid of the RS. However, when the UE starts to decode other parts of the downlink that are not in the center of the channel — for example, the PDCCH — it is essential for the RS phase and amplitude reference to be used to ensure reliable decoding.

3.5.3 Random Access and Paging

Refer to 36.213 [3] subclause 6 and 36.300 [9] subclause 10.1.5. The Physical Layer Random Access Preamble (PRACH) occupies six contiguous RB and can be allocated anywhere across the channel and in any of the 10 subframes as shown in Figure 3.5-3.

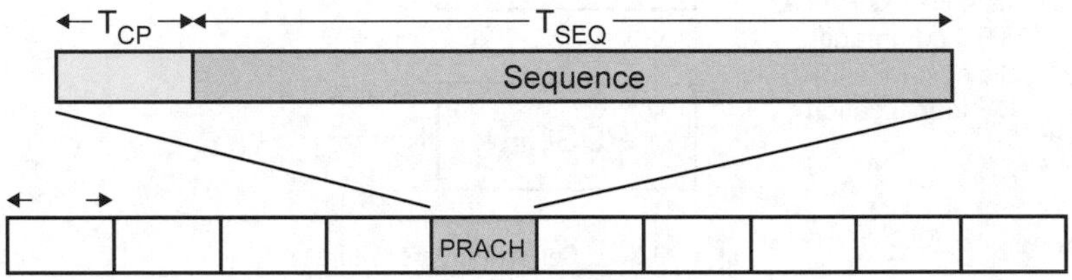

Figure 3.5-3. PRACH structure

The PRACH subframe consists of a cyclic prefix of length T_{CP} and a sequence part of length T_{SEQ}. The parameter values, listed in Table 3.5-1, depend on the preamble format, which is controlled by the higher layers.

Table 3.5-1. Random access preamble parameters

Preamble format	Cyclic prefix (T_{CP})	Sequence part (T_{SEQ})
0	$3168*T_s$	$24576*T_s$
1	$21024*T_s$	$24576*T_s$
2	$6240*T_s$	$2*24576*T_s$
3	$21024*T_s$	$2*24576*T_s$
4 (frame structure type 2 only)	$448*T_s$	$4096*T_s$

For PRACH preamble format 0, T_{SEQ} represents a long Zadoff-Chu sequence of 24756*T_S or 800 μs. The PRACH is created in the frequency domain. When converted to the time domain, a cyclic shift can be applied and a CP is added. The UE transmits the PRACH at zero Timing Advance (TA) but it is received at the eNB sometime later. To prevent interference between PRACH from two UE scheduled in adjacent subframes but possibly at very different positions within the cell, it is necessary to insert a guard period in the form of the CP such that the eNB can decode the PRACH regardless of how late it arrives, up to the length of the CP. For PRACH format 0, T_{CP} is 3168 T_S or 103 μs. This represents a round-trip distance of 30 km, which indicates a maximum cell radius of 15 km.

The transmission of a random access preamble, if triggered by the MAC layer, is restricted to certain time and frequency resources. These resources are enumerated in increasing order of the subframe number within the radio frame and the physical resource blocks in the frequency domain such that index 0 corresponds to the lowest numbered physical resource block and subframe within the radio frame.

For preamble formats 0 to 3, there is at most one random access resource per subframe for FDD. Table 3.5-2 lists the subframes in which random access preamble transmission is allowed for a given PRACH configuration. The start of the random access preamble is aligned with the start of the corresponding uplink subframe at the UE assuming a timing advance of zero. For configurations 0, 1, 2 and 15, the UE may for handover purposes assume an absolute value of the relative time difference between the radio frame in the current cell and the target cell of less than 153600*T_S.

Table 3.5-2. PRACH timing for different PRACH configuration

PRACH configuration	System frame number	Subframe number
0	Even	1
1	Even	4
2	Even	7
3	Any	1
4	Any	4
5	Any	7
6	Any	1, 6
7	Any	2 ,7
8	Any	3, 8
9	Any	1, 4, 7
10	Any	2, 5, 8
11	Any	3, 6, 9
12	Any	0, 2, 4, 6, 8
13	Any	1, 3, 5, 7, 9
14	Any	0, 1, 2, 3, 4, 5, 6, 7, 8, 9
15	Even	9

3.5.3.1 Application of PRACH in LTE

The Zadoff-Chu sequences of the PRACH preamble are excellent for auto-correlation. In the eNB, the cross-correlation of the received signal with respect to the ideal preamble is performed in order to determine the transmission delay. This allows the UE TA to be set such that future transmissions from different UEs arrive aligned to the uplink frame structure at the eNB.

A preamble root sequence is a non-repeating waveform with a basic length of 800 μs, which fits into one subframe. It can be used to identify the timing of a UE for distances up to 120 km (240 km round trip) from the base station. If the eNB receives two peaks within the time range of one cell, it will consider the condition to be a collision and not reply to either UE.

In case of large cells, the eNB allocates many root sequences for the PRACH to differentiate between the UEs. Each additional root sequence makes the PRACH detection process for the eNB harder. The situation becomes easier when the cells are smaller since then a fewer number of PRACH root sequences can be cyclically shifted in time relative to each other to differentiate between the UEs. When a UE is transmitting a cyclically shifted sequence, the eNB will have a late peak but will know that this peak was actually generated by a UE close by.

3.5.3.2 Detection Effort of the PRACH Preambles

There is a tradeoff between the cell size and the detection effort of the 64 PRACH preambles. Table 3.5-3 shows the relation between effort, cell radius, the number of root sequences and the number of cyclic shifts per root sequence.

Table 3.5-3. PRACH detection effort vs. cell radius

Cell radius (Km)	Number of PRACH preambles and detection effort in %	No. of cyclic shifts per root preamble
0 – 1.875 km	1 – 100%	64
1.875 – 3.75 km	2 – 200%	32
3.75 – 7.5 km	4 – 400%	16
7.5 – 15 km	8 – 800%	8
15 – 30 km	16 – 1600%	4
30 – 60 km	32 – 3200 %	2
> 60 km	64 – 6400%	1

When the cell radius is smaller than 1.875 km, only one single root sequence is needed within 64 possible cyclic shifts to achieve the lowest PRACH detection effort.

3.5.3.3 Random Access Procedure

At the beginning of the random access procedure, the UE is informed about the parameters and the allowed location in frequency and time of the PRACH. The procedure is similar to UMTS whereby the UE randomly chooses between the root sequences and their cyclically shifted versions, and transmits periodically according to a power ramping procedure until it receives a response from the eNB. This is shown in Figure 3.5-4.

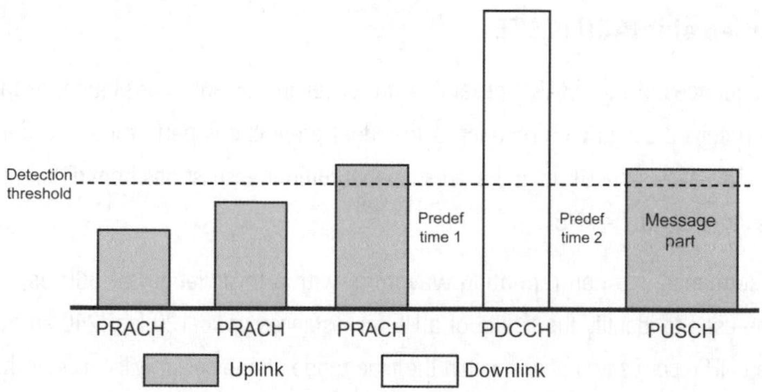

Figure 3.5-4 Random access procedure

The procedure in LTE is slightly different than in UMTS, because there is no Acquisition Indictor Channel (AICH) and so the eNB responds on the PDCCH to provide the Sequence Number (SN), the TA and the allocated resources on the PUSCH. The UE responds on the PUSCH with the random access message. Consequently, the Random Access Channel (RACH) messages are scheduled similar to the normal uplink packets.

3.6 Physical Layer Measurements and Radio Resource Management

The UE and the eNB are required to make physical layer measurements of the downlink and uplink radio characteristics, respectively. The measurement definitions are specified in 36.214 [5]. The measurements are reported to the higher layers and are used for a variety of purposes including intra- and inter-frequency handover, inter-Radio Access Technology (inter-RAT) handover, timing measurements and other purposes in support of Radio Resource Management (RRM).

Although the physical layer measurements are defined in 36.214 [5], the measurement conditions and accuracy requirements are provided in subclauses 9 and 10 of the RRM specification 36.133 [10]. The broader subject of RRM will be discussed in Section 3.6.3.

3.6.1 UE Physical Layer Measurements

The UE physical layer measurements are all either measures of absolute power or power ratios. They are defined for operation within LTE-only systems. In addition, to enable interworking of LTE with other radio access technologies, LTE UE must have the ability to measure equivalent parameters from the other systems LTE is defined to work with. These are UMTS FDD, UMTS TDD, GSM and cdma2000 based systems.

3.6.1.1 Reference Signal Receive Power

Reference Signal Receive Power (RSRP) is the most basic of the UE physical layer measurements and is the linear average (in watts) of the downlink Reference Signals (RS) across the channel bandwidth. Since the RS exist only for one symbol at a time, the measurement is made only on those Resource Elements (RE) that contain cell-specific RS. It is not mandated for the UE to measure every RS symbol on the relevant subcarriers. Instead, accuracy requirements have to be met. There are requirements for both absolute and relative RSRP. The absolute requirements range from ±6 dB to ±11 dB depending on the noise level and environmental conditions. Measuring the difference in RSRP between two cells on the same frequency (intra-frequency measurement) is a more accurate operation for which the requirements vary from ±2 dB to ±3 dB. The requirements widen again to ±6 dB when the cells are on different frequencies (inter-frequency measurement).

Knowledge of absolute RSRP provides the UE with essential information about the strength of cells from which path loss can be calculated and used in the algorithms for determining the optimum power settings for operating the network. Reference signal receive power is used both in idle and connected states. The relative RSRP is used as a parameter in multi-cell scenarios.

3.6.1.2 Reference Signal Receive Quality

Although RSRP is an important measure, on its own it gives no indication of signal quality. Reference Signal Receive Quality (RSRQ) provides this measure and is defined as the ratio of RSRP to the E-UTRA carrier Received Signal Strength Indicator (RSSI). The RSSI parameter represents the entire received power including the wanted power from the serving cell as well as all co-channel power and other sources of noise. Measuring RSRQ becomes particularly important near the cell edge when decisions need to be made, regardless of absolute RSRP, to perform a handover to the next cell. Reference signal receive quality is used only during connected states.

Intra- and inter-frequency absolute RSRQ accuracy varies from ±2.5 to ±4 dB, which is similar to the inter-frequency relative RSRQ accuracy of ±3 dB to ±4 dB.

3.6.1.3 UTRA FDD CPICH Received Signal Code Power

Received Signal Code Power (RSCP) is inherited from UMTS and is a measure of the absolute power of one code channel within the overall UTRA CDMA signal. UTRA FDD CPICH RSCP is therefore a measure of the code power of the Common Pilot Indicator Channel (CPICH) and is used for interworking between LTE and UMTS. It has the same basic function as RSRP in LTE and is used in LTE inter-RAT idle and inter-RAT connected states.

3.6.1.4 UTRA FDD Carrier Received Signal Strength Indicator

UTRA FDD Received Signal Strength Indicator (RSSI) is also inherited from UMTS. It is a measure of the total received power, including thermal noise and noise generated in the receiver, within the bandwidth defined by the receiver pulse shaping filter. It is the UTRA equivalent of the E-UTRA carrier RSSI defined as part of RSRQ.

3.6.1.5 UTRA FDD CPICH E_C/N_O

This final measurement from UMTS is the ratio of the CPICH to the power density in the channel. If receive diversity is not being used by the UE, CPICH E_C/N_O is the same as CPICH RSCP divided by RSSI. A typical value in a UMTS cell without significant noise would be around –10 dB; indicating the CPICH had been set 10 dB below the total power of the cell. UTRA FDD CPICH E_C/N_O is used in LTE inter-RAT idle and connected states.

3.6.1.5 GSM Carrier RSSI

When LTE has to interwork with GSM-based systems including GPRS and E-GPRS (EDGE), the GSM version of RSSI must be measured. GSM RSSI is measured on the Broadcast Control Channel (BCCH). It is used in LTE inter-RAT idle and connected states.

3.6.1.6 UTRA TDD Carrier RSSI

This measurement is used for interworking with UTRA TDD systems and performs the same basic function as the other RSSI measurements. It is used in LTE inter-RAT idle and connected states.

3.6.1.7 UTRA TDD P-CCPCH RSCP

This measurement is the UTRA TDD equivalent of RSRP. It is a measure of the code power of the Primary Common Control Physical Channel (P-CCPCH) and is used in LTE inter-RAT idle and connected states.

3.6.1.8 cdma2000 1xRTT Pilot Strength

This measurement is the RSRP equivalent for cdma2000-based technologies. These technologies all share the same Radio Transmission Technology (RTT) bandwidth based on the 1.2288 Mcps chip rate that is referred to as 1x. Multi-carrier versions of cdma2000 such as 3xRTT have been standardized but no multicarrier measurement is yet defined. The cdma2000 pilot is carried on Walsh code 0, typically at around –7 dB from the total downlink power.

3.6.1.9 cdma2000 High Rate Packet Data Pilot Strength

High Rate Packet Data (HRPD) systems including 1xEV-DO Releases 0, A and B do not use the code domain pilot signal defined for the speech-capable cdma2000. The cdma2000 HRPD pilot is defined in the time domain, existing for 9.375% of the frame. Its measurement is therefore necessary for LTE interworking with HRPD systems and is another version of LTE RSRP.

3.6.2 Evolved Node B Physical Layer Measurements

There are fewer physical layer measurements for the eNB than for the UE, primarily because the base station is not mobile and does not need to measure non-LTE systems.

3.6.2.1 Downlink RS Tx Power

The first eNB measurement is different in two respects from the UE measurements described so far: first, it describes the eNB transmission itself rather than a transmission from another entity, and second, it is not so much a measurement as a report generated by the eNB reflecting the transmitted power. Even so, the report has to be accurate and take into account losses between the baseband (where power is defined) through the transmit chain to the antenna connector.

3.6.2.2 Received Interference Power

The uplink received interference power is a measure of the interference power and thermal noise within an RB that is not scheduled for transmission within the cell. The absolute accuracy has to be ±4 dB for interference measured between –117 dBm and –96 dBm. This measure will be used to identify narrowband co-channel interference from neighbour cells on the same frequency.

3.6.2.3 Thermal Noise Power

The uplink thermal noise power measurement is a broadband version of received interference power and is measured optionally at the same time under the same conditions. The definition is (N_0*W) where N_0 is the white noise power spectral density and W is the transmission bandwidth configuration (see Figure 3.2-5).

3.6.3 Radio Resource Management

Having introduced the underlying physical layer measurements that support RRM, it is possible to describe how they are used in the operation of the system. The subject of RRM, specified in 36.133 [10], covers a broad range of procedures that can seem rather impenetrable upon first study. A good analogy for RRM in cellular systems is to consider air transportation. Suppose the base station could be equated with an airport and the UE with an airplane. Provided we have two airports and one plane, we have the beginnings of a transportation system. Such a simple system could be operated with almost no procedures since the one plane could take off and land knowing that there would be no "interference" from other air traffic.

However, to turn such a simple example into something resembling a high-capacity transportation system requires that there be many airports and even more planes. In such a crowded environment it becomes evident that to avoid collisions, an Air Traffic Control (ATC) system is necessary. To the extent to which the analogy is useful, RRM provides for the cellular industry the same essential traffic management functions that ATC provides for the air transportation industry.

The RRM requirements in 36.133 [10] are divided into two major parts. First are the individual performance requirements for the core functions supporting RRM. These are defined in subclauses 4 through 10. Second, Annex A provides normative test case descriptions that will be used as the basis for the RRM conformance tests described in Section 7.2.8. These test cases combine many of the underlying core requirements into typical operating scenarios, which is preferable to testing each function individually. Subclauses 9 and 10 specify requirements for physical layer measurements described in Section 3.6.1. The remainder of this chapter will describe the core requirements in subclauses 4 through 8.

3.6.3.1 E-UTRAN RRC_IDLE State Mobility

Refer to 36.133 [10] subclause 4. This section covers the two most basic of procedures carried out when the UE is in idle state (not on a call). These procedures are cell selection, which is performed after the UE is switched on, and cell re-selection, which is the procedure performed when the UE moves from one cell to another.

Cell Selection

The complexity of the processes for cell selection can be seen in the idle state transition diagram in Figure 3.6-1. The most obvious parameter to specify for cell selection performance is the time taken to camp onto an appropriate cell for a given radio scenario. One of the most complex scenarios commonly occurs when the UE is switched on in a rich radio environment; for example, in a foreign airport where competition for roaming customers can be fierce. There are many ways of configuring parameters in the network that can influence the behavior of the UE when it initially chooses a cell on which to camp. It is perhaps due to the complexity of the cell selection process that in UMTS, no requirements were specified. It is likely that LTE will take the same approach. This might seem surprising but as things stand, this aspect of UE performance is left as a competitive rather than a regulated issue.

Cell Re-selection

For cell re-selection, the situation is quite different as LTE specifies numerous performance requirements for this process. When the UE is camped on the serving cell, it will be commanded to detect, synchronize and monitor intra-frequency, inter-frequency and inter-RAT cells to determine whether a more suitable cell on which to camp can be found. Sometimes the serving cell will provide a neighbour list for the intra-frequency and inter-frequency

LTE cells, but at other times only the carrier frequency and bandwidth will be provided. The rules for neighbour cell reporting allow the UE to limit its measurement activity in complex situations.

The goal of the cell re-selection process is the evaluation of the cell selection criterion S for each detected cell. This measure, which is defined in 36.304 [8] subclause 5.2.3.2, is based on relative and absolute power measurements

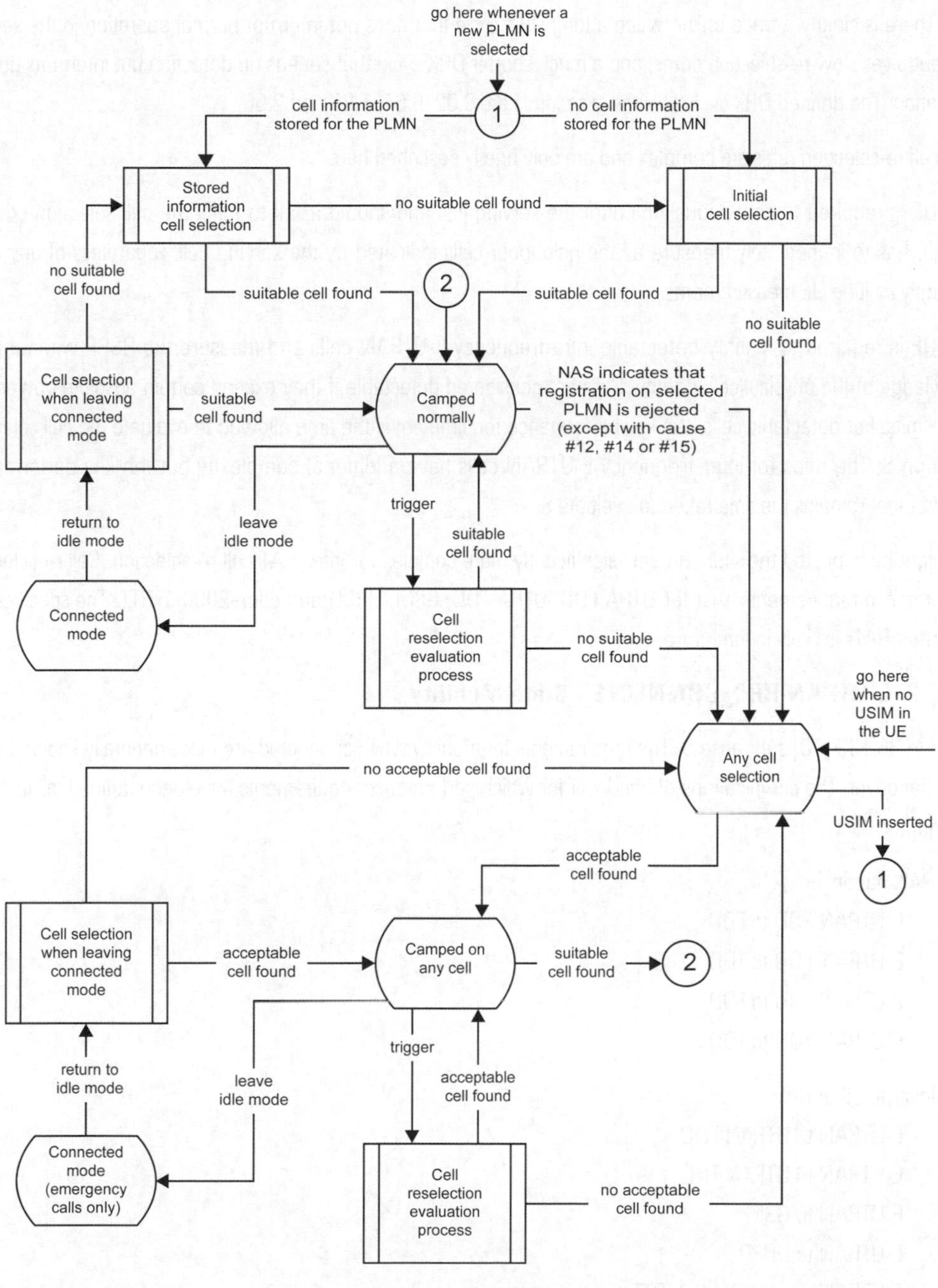

Figure 3.6-1: RRC_IDLE Cell Selection and Reselection (36.304 [8] Figure 5.2.2-1)

and is used to determine the most favorable cell for the UE to camp on. The cell re-selection performance requirements are defined in terms of three time allowances: the time allowed to detect and evaluate S for a new cell, the time allowed to re-evaluate S for an existing cell and the maximum time allowed between measurements of the cell. One of the important parameters impacting cell re-selection performance is the Discontinuous Reception (DRX) cycle length. This is the time between attempts by the UE to measure cells other than the serving cell. There is clearly a trade-off between a long DRX cycle that does not interrupt normal operation in the serving cell but gives slow re-selection times, and a much shorter DRX cycle that speeds up detection but interrupts normal operation. The defined DRX cycle lengths in seconds are 0.32, 0.64, 1.28 and 2.56.

The cell re-selection rules are complex and are only briefly described here.

The UE is required to continuously monitor the serving cell and should it fail to fulfill the cell selection criteria, the UE has to immediately measure all the neighbour cells indicated by the serving cell, regardless of any rules currently limiting UE measurements.

The UE is required to identify detectable intra-frequency E-UTRAN cells and measure the RSRP without prior knowledge of the physical cell identity. Cells are considered detectable if they exceed certain absolute power and SNR limits. For detectable cells, the key performance requirement is the time allowed to evaluate the cell selection criterion S. The rules for inter-frequency E-UTRAN cells have additional complexity but the key performance requirement remains the time taken to evaluate S.

As might be expected the situation gets significantly more complex for inter-RAT cell re-selection. Cell re-selection performance requirements exist for UTRA FDD, UTRA TDD, GSM, HRPD and cdma2000 1xRTT. The specification of further RATs is likely in the future.

3.6.3.2 E-UTRAN RRC_CONNECTED State Mobility

Refer to 36.133 [10] subclause 5. The requirements for mobility while connected are more generally known by the term handover. The combinations of handover for which performance requirements have been defined fall into two categories:

E-UTRAN handover

- E-UTRAN FDD to FDD
- E-UTRAN FDD to TDD
- E-UTRAN TDD to FDD
- E-UTRAN TDD to TDD

Handover to other RAT

- E-UTRAN to UTRAN FDD
- E-UTRAN to UTRAN TDD
- E-UTRAN to GSM
- E-UTRAN to HRPD
- E-UTRAN to cdma2000 1xRTT

For each scenario two performance parameters are defined. These are the handover delay and the interruption time. Both parameters are necessary as the first is a measure of the delay from the start of the process to its completion and needs to be kept low, while the second parameter is the shorter period of time during which communication is interrupted.

3.6.3.3 RRC Connection Mobility Control

Refer to 36.133 [10] subclause 6. At time of writing the requirements for RRC connection mobility control are for RRC re-establishment following a failure in the RRC connection and for random access. The most likely causes of a failure are if the radio link drops below an acceptable quality or if a handover fails. The requirements are written based on the time allowed to re-establish the RRC connection. The procedure is specified in 36.331 [11] subclause 5.3.7.

The re-establishment delay is determined by four parameters: the number of frequencies being monitored, the time to search each frequency, the time to read the system information from each cell and the delay in the PRACH procedure. For simple cases in which the target cell is known by the UE and has been recently measured, the delay may be as short as 160 ms. More difficult situations that require searching for a suitable cell on which to re-establish the link could be in the order of one second per frequency searched.

The requirements for random access relate to correct behavior when a random access response and other messages are received from the eNB.

3.6.3.4 Timing and Signalling Characteristics

Refer to 36.133 [10] subclause 7.

UE Transmit Timing

A critical performance requirement in any wireless system is the ability of the UE to maintain timing synchronization with the base station. The unit for measuring timing is T_s , where T_s = 1/(15000*2048) seconds. The timing reference point for the UE is the first detected path from the eNB. The nominal transmit timing of the UE is specified in advance of this reference time as $N_{TA}*T_s$, where N_{TA} is the timing advance parameter.

Requirements exist for the initial timing accuracy, the maximum step in any one timing adjustment and finally the maximum and minimum timing adjustment rates. These requirements are necessary in order that the worst case timing error between the eNB and UE is bounded. Timing errors can be caused by large changes in multipath delay (such as with shadow fading) or by a handover to a cell with different timing.

The initial timing accuracy requirement is $\pm 12*T_s$ and should this be exceeded, the UE is required to adjust its timing to get to within the allowed range. During the adjustment process the maximum allowed step size is $\pm 2*T_s$ and the rate of change has to be between $2*T_s$ and $7*T_s$ seconds per second.

UE Timer Accuracy

Many of the RRM processes require that the UE start and stop various timers. For timers of less than four seconds the accuracy is fixed at 0.1 seconds and for longer timers the UE is given a greater allowance of 0.25%. These are not critical figures but are specified in order to give guidance to the UE designer about the precision required for timer implementation.

Timing Advance

The timing advance process is specified in 36.321 [12] subclause 5.2. When the UE receives a new timing advance command in frame number n it is required to implement the new timing in frame $n + 6$ to an accuracy of $\pm 4{*}T_S$.

Cell Phase Synchronization Accuracy (TDD)

This requirement controls the frame start timing for any two cells that share the same frequency and overlap coverage areas. It is necessary to control the timing between such cells to avoid the transmission from one cell occurring at the same time as reception by the other. At the time of this writing the requirement for small cells is less than 3 μs. The definition for large cells remains open as does the definition for the break point between small and large cells.

Synchronization Requirements for E-UTRAN to cdma2000 1xRTT and HRPD Handover

In order for successful handover to cdma2000 1xRTT and HRPD it is necessary for the UE to know the CDMA system timing reference. This is achieved by the eNB providing the timing via a system information message. Once the UE knows the system timing, it can report the timing of the target system's pilot signals. The basic requirement is for the eNB to be within ±10 μs of the CDMA system time. The eNB is expected to be synchronized to GPS time and to maintain ±10 μs accuracy for a period of up to 8 hours should GPS synchronization be lost. The eNB also has to ensure that the message transmitting the CDMA system time is transmitted within 10 μs of the expected time.

Radio Link Monitoring

The UE is required to monitor the quality of the downlink for the purposes of determining if the radio link is good enough to continue transmission. This is done through the parameters Q_{out} and Q_{in}. The threshold for Q_{out} is defined as the level at which the downlink radio link cannot be reliably received. There is no direct measure, but the assumption is that Q_{out} corresponds to an approximate 10% block error ratio of a hypothetical PDCCH transmission taking into account a number of network settings and radio conditions. Q_{in} is defined as having a much higher probability of reception than Q_{out}. The Q_{in} threshold is nominally a 2% block error ratio of the hypothetical PDCCH for a defined set of network settings and radio conditions. The requirements for the UE to monitor the radio link quality are specified in terms of how long the UE takes to switch off when the quality drops below Q_{out} and how long it takes for the UE to switch back on when the quality rises above Q_{in}.

3.6.3.5 UE Measurements Procedures in RRC_CONNECTED State

Refer to 36.133 [10] subclause 8. The requirements for connected state mobility have been introduced in Section 3.6.3.2 of this book but the discussion was limited to the physical process of performing the handover. However, in cellular systems it is not the handover itself that is difficult; it is knowing when and where to make the handover. An analogy is changing lanes while driving on a multi-lane road. The action of turning the steering wheel is easy. The difficult bit, especially in heavy traffic, is knowing when and where to make the change. To make good handover decisions requires knowledge of the environment and this applies equally to cellular radio and motoring.

By measuring and reporting the radio environment when in a connected state, the UE provides the system with the raw material needed to make the correct handover decisions. Many parameters can be measured, and the rules for how and when to gather and report these parameters are complex. The requirements, which are split according to RAT, are the following: E-UTRA intra-frequency, E-UTRA inter-frequency, inter-RAT UTRA FDD, UTRA TDD and GSM. The parameters to measure are defined in 36.214 [5] and are introduced here in Section 3.6.1. The required measurement accuracy is defined in 36.133 [10] subclause 9.

With the exception of intra-frequency measurements, it is not possible for the UE to gather information on different frequencies or RATs without implementing a transmission gap. During this period the UE is able to retune its receiver (DRX) to monitor other frequencies. The options for configuring the UE can become quite complex, especially when the radio environment includes multiple bands and RATs. Trade-offs have to be made between the desire for full knowledge of the radio environment, which requires frequent gaps, and the desire for less interruption and fewer measurements, which leads to slower and less optimized handover decisions.

3.7 Summary

It should be evident from this chapter that LTE employs some very advanced tools in the physical layer to optimize throughput and latency. The challenge with these tools will be to optimize their use in the dynamic channel conditions that are the norm in cellular wireless. Many of the projected gains for LTE over existing systems rely on the potential advantages of having a wider channel available and taking advantage of transitory variations in channel conditions including spatial multiplexing. These opportunities will become advantages only when the closed loop algorithms to control these mechanisms are optimized. It is worth pointing out that there is no intention within the scope of the 3GPP specifications to provide such algorithms. They are intentionally left to the implementation and so will remain a competitive differentiator in the market.

3.8 References

[1] 3GPP TS 36.201 V8.2.0 (2008 12) LTE Physical Layer–General description
[2] 3GPP TS 36.211 V8.5.0 (2008-12) Physical Channels and Modulation
[3] 3GPP TS 36.212 V8.5.0 (2008-12) Multiplexing and Channel Coding
[4] 3GPP TS 36.213 V8.5.0 (2008-12) Physical Layer Procedures
[5] 3GPP TS 36.214 V8.5.0 (2008-12) Physical Layer Measurements
[6] 3GPP TS 36.101 V8.4.0 (2008-12) UE Radio Transmission and Reception
[7] 3GPP TS 36.306 V8.2.0 (2008-05) UE Radio Access Capabilities
[8] 3GPP TS 36.304 V8.4.0 (2008-12) UE Procedures in Idle Mode
[9] 3GPP TS 36.300 V8.7.0 (2008-12) E-UTRA, E-UTRAN, Overall Description; Stage 2
[10] 3GPP TS 36.133 V8.4.0 (2008-12) Requirements for support of Radio Resource Management
[11] 3GPP TS 36.331 V8.4.0 (2008-12) Radio Resource Control (RRC) Protocol Specification
[12] 3GPP TS 36.321 V8.4.0 (2008-12) Medium Access Control (MAC) Protocol Specification

Links to all reference documents can be found at www.agilent.com/find/ltebook.

Chapter 4

Upper Layer Signalling

4.1 Access Stratum

The Access Stratum (AS) contains the functionality associated with access to the radio network and the control of active connections between a UE and the radio network. The AS consists of a user plane and a control plane. The user plane is mainly concerned with carrying user data — e.g., Internet Protocol (IP) packets — through the access stratum. The control plane is concerned with controlling the connection between the UE and the network.

An overall description of the Evolved UMTS Terrestrial Radio Access (E-UTRA) and the Evolved UMTS Terrestrial Radio Access Network (E-UTRAN) can be found in 36.300 [1]. In contrast to earlier 3GPP protocols, LTE has located the entire access stratum inside one network entity: the base transceiver station or evolved Node B (eNB). The aim of this is to simplify the architecture and speed up the control signalling, leading to improved overall performance of LTE. The majority of the physical layer (L1) is explained in Chapter 3; however, there is an important L1/L2 control protocol called Downlink Control Information (DCI) that resides in the physical layer and is covered in detail here in Section 4.1.3. The remainder of the AS covers four protocols: the Medium Access Control (MAC), 36.321 [2]; the Radio Link Control (RLC), 36.322 [3]; the Packet Data Convergence Protocol (PDCP), 36.323 [4]; and the Radio Resource Control (RRC), 36.331 [5].

4.1.1 User Plane

Figure 4.1-1 shows the protocol stack for the user plane, which is divided into three sublayers: the Packet Data Convergence Protocol (PDCP), the Radio Link Control (RLC) and the MAC. These protocols carry data from one side of the radio network to the other. The PDCP and RLC protocols are similar in the eNB and the UE, performing such functionality as header compression, ciphering, and running acknowledged-mode protocols. The MAC protocols, however, behave differently in the eNB and in the UE. This is mainly because the scheduler runs in the eNB, determining from subframe to subframe which UEs in the cell should be allowed access to the network.

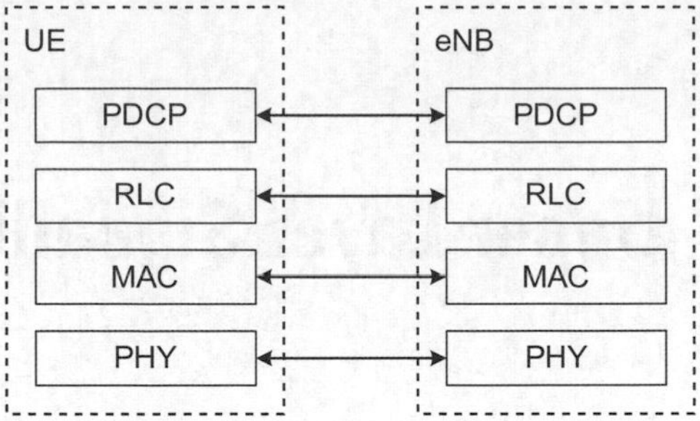

Figure 4.1-1. User plane protocol stack

4.1.2 Control Plane

Figure 4.1-2 shows the protocol stack for the control plane. The PDCP, RLC and MAC protocols behave exactly as they do in the user plane, although in the control plane their function is to carry control messaging from the RRC, which may contain Non Access Stratum (NAS) messaging rather than user data. In the control plane, however, the RRC is unique, performing such functions as broadcast messaging and connection control. The NAS is described in Section 4.2.

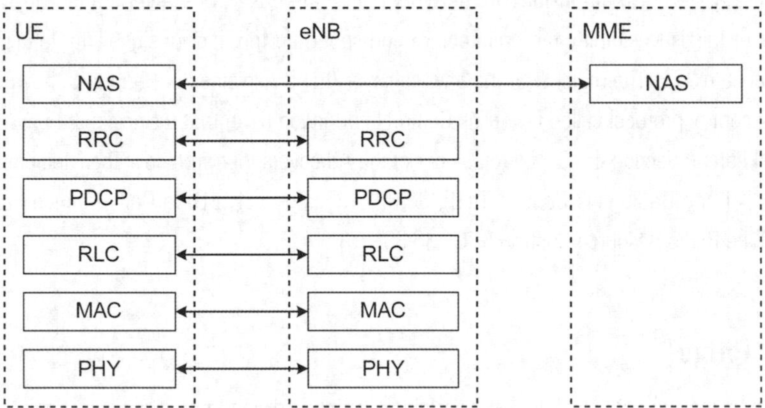

Figure 4.1-2. Control plane protocol stack

4.1.3 Physical Layer Downlink Control Information

The physical layer was described in Chapter 3. There are protocol messages sent from the eNB to the UE that are carried directly on the Physical Downlink Control Channel (PDCCH) without passing through the MAC. These messages are key to the establishment of LTE connections and are known as Downlink Control Information (DCI) messages. The presence of DCI was introduced in Chapter 3 but is now more fully described.

4.1.3.1 Downlink Control Information Functions

A DCI message performs one of three functions:

- Providing downlink scheduling information
- Providing uplink scheduling information
- Providing uplink power control information

The eNB normally transmits many DCI messages per subframe, each using a different PDCCH. Each message is intended to be received by one or many UEs. A UE does not know which PDCCH channels have been used on a particular subframe by the eNB and, of those used, whether the PDCCH contains a DCI message intended for that UE. To receive DCI messages a UE must perform a large number of blind decodes every subframe. The DCI messages intended for that UE will be decoded successfully, whereas those not intended for that UE will fail the Cyclic Redundancy Code (CRC) check.

4.1.3.2 Identification of a DCI Message

The intended recipient or recipients of a DCI message are distinguished by use of a different Radio Network Temporary Identity (RNTI), which is an identifier used by the UE MAC. This identifier is encoded into the CRC of the message. A UE will be able to successfully decode only those DCI messages that contain an RNTI the UE is expecting to receive.

A UE may expect several RNTI values at any given time, and some RNTI values will be expected by all the UEs in a cell. The DCI messages containing downlink scheduling for System Information (SI) and Paging (P) messages are transmitted using special RNTI values known as the SI-RNTI and P-RNTI. Uplink scheduling messages transmitted in response to a Physical Random Access Channel (PRACH) preamble sent by a UE are identified using an RNTI known as the Random Access RNTI (RA-RNTI), which is derived from the time and frequency resource used to transmit the PRACH. An established Downlink Shared Channel (DL-SCH) or Uplink Shared Channel (UL-SCH) is identified with an RNTI unique to a particular UE (the Cell RNTI, or C-RNTI). No other UE in the cell looks for DCI messages coded with that unique RNTI value.

4.1.3.3 Downlink Scheduling Information

One reason for sending DCI messages is to transmit downlink scheduling information to the UE. The UE needs this information to successfully decode the data that is being transmitted to it on the Physical Downlink Shared Channel (PDSCH) of the same subframe. Before the UE can find and decode the PDSCH data, it must know the following:

- Which resource blocks are carrying data allocated for this UE. These resource blocks may or may not be contiguous in frequency.
- Which modulation and transport block size to use on these resource blocks.
- Which redundancy version to use during the rate-matching process.
- Whether or not to use spatial multiplexing.
- If spatial multiplexing is used, what pre-coding matrix to apply to the data.

After successfully decoding the PDSCH data, the UE then needs to know:

- The downlink Hybrid Automatic Repeat Request (HARQ) process for which this data is intended.
- Whether this data is new or a retransmission of previously transmitted data.

4.1.3.4 Uplink Scheduling Information

The DCI messages providing uplink scheduling information are addressed to only one UE at a time. These messages tell the UE how it should transmit information on the Physical Uplink Shared Channel (PUSCH). In contrast to the DCI messages that provide downlink scheduling information and which refer to a PDSCH in the same subframe, the uplink scheduling information messages refer to the PUSCH subframe that comes four subframes after the subframe containing the scheduling message.

Prior to transmitting data on the PUSCH, the UE must know the following:

- Which resource blocks to use. In contrast to the downlink, these are always contiguous in frequency due to the limitations imposed by SC-FDMA.
- Which modulation and transport block size to use.
- Which redundancy version to use.
- Whether or not to use PUSCH hopping.
- Whether to send new data or retransmit old data.
- Whether or not to alter the power that is used to transmit the PUSCH.

4.1.3.5 Power Control Information

The downlink and uplink scheduling information messages described above include power control parameters such that the UE will know what power level to use on the PUSCH or PUCCH. There are cases, however — such as semi-persistent scheduling or non-adaptive retransmissions — in which the UE may be sending data for a number of Transmission Time Intervals (TTIs) without receiving downlink or uplink scheduling information messages. In these cases, the eNB may still want to alter the power levels used by the UE. Therefore, a simple type of DCI message is available which has the sole purpose of adjusting the power level. Two such DCI messages are defined, allowing the power level to be adjusted with different levels of granularity.

4.1.4 Medium Access Control (MAC)

The Medium Access Control (MAC) layer is a protocol layer that runs in both the UE and the eNB. It has different behaviors when running in each, generally giving commands in the eNB and responding to them in the UE. As the name suggests, MAC arbitrates and controls access to the shared transmission medium.

The main functions of the MAC are:

- Providing data transfer services to the RLC via logical channels.
- Multiplexing data from one or more logical channels into transport blocks. These are delivered to the physical layer on transport channels.
- Error correction through HARQ.
- Deciding which UEs will be allowed to send or receive data on the shared physical resource (eNB MAC only).
- Transport format selection — that is, choosing the modulation and coding rate that will be used to send data to the UE (eNB MAC only).

4.1.4.1 Logical Channels and Transport Channels

Logical channels are the Service Access Points (SAPs) provided by the MAC to the RLC. Logical channels are distinguished by the type of information transferred. Transport channels are SAPs used by the MAC and provided by the physical layer to achieve data transfer. Transport channels are distinguished by how the data is transferred. The MAC provides a Transport Format (TF) that specifies how the transport channel is mapped to the physical layer. Table 4.1-1 and Figure 4.1-3 show the mapping between the logical channels and the transport channels for the uplink.

Table 4.1-1. Uplink logical channel to transport channel mapping

Logical channel	Transport channel	Purpose of logical channel
Common Control Channel (CCCH)	UL-SCH	Carries RRC signalling before the UE has been identified; e.g., for connection setup
Dedicated Control Channel (DCCH)	UL-SCH	Carries signalling from the RRC
Dedicated Traffic Channel (DTCH)	UL-SCH	Carries user data

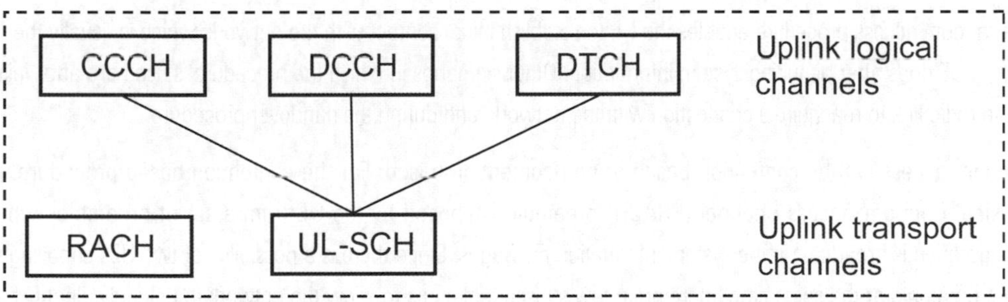

Figure 4.1-3. Uplink logical channel mapping onto transport channels

Table 4.1-2 and Figure 4.1-4 show the mapping between the logical channels and the transport channels for the downlink.

Table 4.1-2. Downlink logical channel to transport channel mapping

Logical channel	Transport channel	Purpose of logical channel
Broadcast Control Channel (BCCH)	Broadcast Channel (BCH)	Carries master information block
BCCH	Downlink Shared Channel (DL-SCH)	Broadcast of system information messages
Paging Control Channel (PCCH)	Paging Channel (PCH)	Carries paging messages
CCCH	DL-SCH	Carries RRC signalling before the UE has been identified; e.g., for connection setup
DCCH	DL-SCH	Carries signalling from the RRC
DTCH	DL-SCH	Carries user data

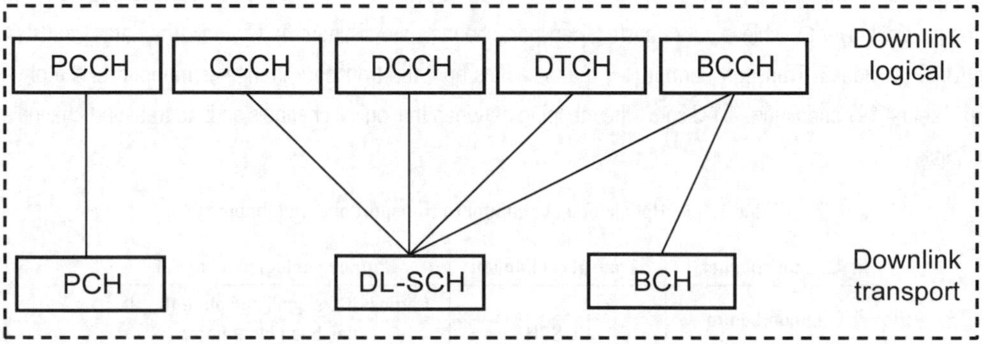

Figure 4.1-4 Downlink logical channel mapping onto transport channels

4.1.4.2 Random Access, Scheduling Request, Timing Alignment and Contention Resolution Support

The random access procedure enables the UE to establish initial contact with the network, which is usually the first thing a UE does after acquiring system information. Other scenarios in which the procedure is used are after failure of the radio link to reacquire a connection with the network, and during the handover procedure.

Random access can be contention based or non-contention based. For the contention based procedure, the Physical Random Access Channel (PRACH) preamble is chosen by the UE from a set of preambles whose configuration is broadcast in the system information messages. Since there is a possibility of two UEs choosing the same preamble at the same time, there are a few subsequent steps to allow the network to uniquely identify each UE. In contrast, for non-contention based random access, the eNB MAC assigns a dedicated preamble to each UE, which allows the UE to be uniquely identified from the start of the procedure.

The UE decodes the Random Access Channel (RACH) transport channel configuration options from the system information messages. This informs the UE of the allowed random access configurations in the cell. The random access procedure is initiated by the UE's MAC transmitting a PRACH preamble on the RACH. The eNB MAC can choose to respond to the UE's MAC PRACH preamble with an uplink grant including an estimate of the UE's timing alignment, or with a back-off value to the UE not to perform another random access for the signalled back-off duration. The uplink grant transmission is done on the DL-SCH transport channel addressed with a Random Access Radio Network Temporary Identity (RA-RNTI).

If the eNB MAC provides an uplink grant, the UE schedules a UL-SCH transmission and starts a timing alignment timer. The eNB MAC periodically sends the timing advance MAC control element to the UE, whereupon the UE applies the timing advance and restarts its timing alignment timer. The UE MAC can also signal a Scheduling Request (SR) to signal to the eNB MAC that the UE needs more uplink resources. The SR can be used only if the UE's timing alignment timer is running. After the UE's timing alignment timer expires, the UE has to use the random access procedure before scheduling further uplink transmissions.

The MAC also participates in the contention resolution procedure. The UE MAC starts the contention resolution timer after performing a scheduled transmission in response to a random access uplink grant. If, during the period that the contention resolution timer is running, the UE MAC detects its Cell Radio Network Temporary Identity (C-RNTI) on the PDCCH or detects a match of the UE's contention resolution identity in a DL-SCH transmission addressed to the UE's temporary C-RNTI, then the UE's contention has been successfully resolved.

4.1.4.3 Paging and Discontinuous Reception Support

Paging is used by the network to locate a UE in RRC_IDLE state within a tracking area. The MAC provides support for transmitting Paging Information (PI) over the PCCH logical channel. The PCCH transmission is done over the PCH transport channel in transparent mode (that is, the MAC does not insert or remove any headers) and is signalled using P-RNTI on the PDCCH.

The MAC also supports Discontinuous Reception (DRX) in order to conserve the UE's battery power. With DRX the UE does not have to monitor PDCCH transmissions on every subframe. The eNB MAC takes account of the UE's DRX configuration before scheduling any transmissions or receptions for the UE.

4.1.4.4 DL and UL Data Transfer, Multiplexing and De-multiplexing Support

Perhaps the most important function of the MAC is to enable downlink and uplink data transfer. Data transmissions in the downlink support the CCCH, DCCH and DTCH logical channels that are carried on the DL-SCH transport channel. Downlink assignments for these transmissions are signalled over the PDCCH using one of several methods: C-RNTI; Semi Persistent Scheduling (SPS) C-RNTI; Temporary C-RNTI or RA-RNTI. Data transmissions in the uplink support the CCCH, DCCH and DTCH logical channels and are made over the UL-SCH transport channel. Uplink grants for these network-scheduled transmissions are signalled over the PDCCH using the C-RNTI, SPS C-RNTI or the Temporary C-RNTI.

The MAC Protocol Data Units (PDUs) are variable-size, byte-aligned data units consisting of a MAC header, zero or more MAC Service Data Units (SDUs), zero or more MAC Control Elements (MCE) and, optionally, padding. The MAC header in turn is a combination of MAC PDU sub-headers in which each sub-header identifies a MAC SDU, an MCE or padding. One or two MAC PDUs (or transport blocks) can be transmitted in a subframe depending on the physical layer transport format.

The transmitting MAC multiplexes SDUs from multiple logical channels plus any MCEs and padding (if required) to form a PDU. The PDU is then de-multiplexed at the receiving MAC. The SDUs are delivered to the corresponding logical channels and the MCEs are acted upon by the receiving MAC.

MAC control elements are control messages sent to the peer MAC. Information such as timing alignment, contention resolution, power headroom reporting and DRX commands are sent using these messages.

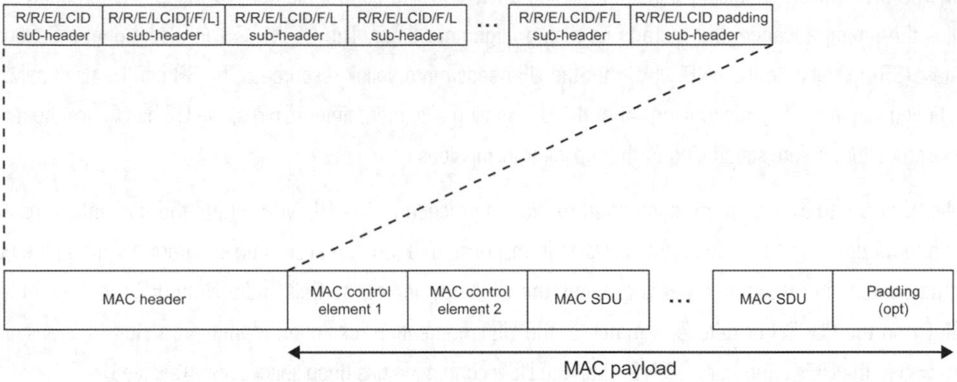

Figure 4.1-5 Example of MAC PDU consisting of a MAC header, MAC control elements, MAC SDUs and padding (36.321 [2] Figure 6.1.2-3)

4.1.4.5 Logical Channel Prioritization and Quality of Service Support

The MAC supports Quality of Service (QoS) by prioritizing data transmissions of logical channels based on their configured priority and Prioritized Bit Rate (PBR). Logical channel prioritization is specified for the UE MAC. In practice, the eNB MAC also performs logical channel prioritization. Logical channels are served in order of their priority such that on average their PBR targets are met. Any remaining resources are distributed in order of priority. In other words, a logical channel will get any remaining resources if all logical channels with higher priority have no data to send. These guidelines are enforced over several subframes on average, in order to avoid unnecessary RLC segmentation and padding.

4.1.4.6 Scheduling and Radio Resource Allocation

The scheduling function rests in the network scheduler, and scheduling decisions are signalled to the UE MAC. The eNB scheduler performs Resource Block (RB) allocation to individual transport blocks in a subframe and modulation and coding rate selection for transport blocks. The TF defines the physical layer coding for a transport block. The number of resource blocks and an Index Modulation and Coding Scheme (IMCS) parameter that identifies the modulation and transport block size are signalled to the UE MAC.

Various means are defined to signal scheduling decisions (uplink grants and downlink assignments) to the UE MAC. The most flexible method is dynamic scheduling in which a downlink assignment is sent for each DL-SCH transmission and an uplink grant is sent by the eNB MAC for each UL-SCH transmission. Although this scheme provides full flexibility on each subframe, it can generate excessive control information.

A more efficient method is semi-persistent scheduling in which a downlink assignment and uplink grant apply to N transmissions or receptions instead of applying to just one transmission or reception. The value N is configured and signalled by the RRC. The result reduces control information but also reduces flexibility. Another option is TTI bundling in the uplink in which a number of subframes are combined and only one HARQ feedback is sent for the entire bundle. This is especially useful for limiting the required power for transmission; for example, at the cell border.

Factors affecting network scheduling decisions include the number of UEs in a cell, the bandwidth of the cell, the amount of buffered data available to the transmitting MAC, the capability of the UE to support advanced modulation schemes, the capability of the UE in terms of number of supported layers for spatial multiplexing and, finally, the prevailing radio channel conditions as reported by the UE or as measured by the network.

4.1.4.7 Measurements to Support Scheduling and Radio Resource Allocation

To assist the network scheduler, the UE MAC performs and reports channel measurements. The channel measurements are described in detail in Section 3.4. Buffer status reports inform the network of the state of transmission buffers in the UE; i.e., the amount of data buffered. Power headroom reports inform the network of the difference between the UE's current transmit power and its maximum transmit power.

The Channel Quality Indicator (CQI) report uses measurements of the downlink radio conditions to report to the scheduler a combination of modulation and coding rate that would have resulted in a 10% block error ratio had this modulation and coding been used during the period covered by the CQI report. The CQI can be provided for the entire channel bandwidth (wideband CQI) or for a specified part of the bandwidth (subband CQI). The subbands for which CQI is reported can be network selected or UE selected. Subband CQI helps the network scheduler in performing frequency selective scheduling.

4.1.5 Radio Link Controller (RLC)

The radio link controller acts as an interface and buffer between the higher layers of the protocol stack (usually PDCP in the user plane) and the MAC layer, which has almost no buffering capability and acts more as a router than anything else. The RLC's main functions are:

- Passing SDUs received from the higher layers to its peer via the MAC. Data units are passed as PDUs.
- Receiving PDUs from the MAC and extracting SDU data from them to be passed to higher layers.
- Re-ordering of received PDUs.
- Acknowledged mode operation (depending on configuration).

SDUs are simple blocks of binary data arranged in octet (or character) arrays. They are the basic units managed by the RLC.

The RLC maintains a count of the amount of data it has stored for transmission. This is called its Buffer Occupancy (BO). The BO is incremented when SDUs are received from the higher layers and decremented when PDUs are sent to the MAC for transmission. The MAC can read the BO values of all RLCs. When there is an opportunity to schedule data, the MAC can decide which RLC to request data from and how large a PDU it should request.

There are optimal sizes for PDUs that give the best data transfer performance. These sizes depend on the configuration of the physical layer and the prevailing radio conditions at transmission time, so they can vary in size considerably. SDUs can be almost any size, so one particular task of the RLC is to either concatenate or break up SDUs into PDUs. The peer must be able to reassemble the original SDUs, so information on how the SDUs are stored in a PDU is included in the PDU as part of its header.

4.1.5.1 Operating Modes

The RLC has three modes of operation: Transparent Mode (TM), Unacknowledged Mode (UM) and Acknowledged Mode (AM). Each offers different levels of reliability with an obvious impact on latency.

Transparent Mode

In transparent mode the RLC neither concatenates nor breaks up SDUs. The PDUs must be the same size as the SDUs and may contain only a single SDU.

Unacknowledged Mode for PDU transmission

Depending on the relative sizes of the SDUs and PDUs, the SDUs can be concatenated so that several fit into one PDU or their contents can be split over several PDUs. Each PDU has a fixed header that contains either a 5 or 10 bit Sequence Number (SN), an Extension (E) indicator bit and a 2 bit Framing Indicator (FI) field. Optionally, a series of Length Indicators (LIs) and E bits can be included. The first octet following the header octets is the first data octet in the PDU.

The SN is incremented by one for every PDU. The SN allows the peer to re-order PDUs should they be received out of sequence. The FI field indicates whether the first or last octets of the SDU data in the PDU are also the start or end of an SDU. The LI indicates the end of an SDU within the PDU. The E bit indicates whether an LI/E bit pair follows the E bit. Using the LI/E bit pairs allows data from multiple SDUs to be carried by a single PDU.

Unacknowledged Mode for PDU Reception

Under normal circumstances the RLC receives PDUs in SN order. The SDU data is extracted and used to reconstruct the original SDUs. Complete SDUs are forwarded to the upper layers.

However, as the name suggests, in unacknowledged mode there is no feedback from the peer RLC, meaning lost PDUs will not be retransmitted by the RLC. If a PDU in unacknowledged mode is lost, then so is the SDU data it carried. Further, if the previous PDU contained the start of an incomplete SDU, then part of that SDU is also lost, so the rest of the SDU must also be discarded. Similarly, if the next received PDU does not start with data from a new SDU, then part of that SDU has also been lost and the remainder must also be discarded.

Fortunately, the MAC has HARQ capability, which can retransmit lost PDUs very quickly (though only a limited number of times). The RLC must cope with receiving valid but out-of-sequence PDUs. For this reason, the RLC must be able to distinguish between a lost PDU and a delayed PDU. This is done using the reordering timer.

When an out-of-sequence PDU is received, the reordering timer is started. If the lost PDUs are received before the timer expires, then the timer is stopped and the SDU data can be processed. If the timer expires, the PDUs are considered lost and discarded as above.

Acknowledged Mode

In acknowledged mode the re-ordering timer is used to cope with HARQ retransmissions but, in addition, the RLC peers acknowledge the data PDUs they receive using another type of PDU called a control PDU. Control PDUs allow the loss of a PDU to be indicated to the transmitter so that the lost PDUs can be retransmitted. Further, because the radio conditions may deteriorate, forcing the MAC to use smaller PDUs, the lost PDUs may have to be broken up into smaller segments (re-segmented) before retransmission. This can happen a number of times if radio conditions continue to deteriorate. These re-segmented PDUs can also be acknowledged using control PDUs.

4.1.5.2 PDU Formats

Acknowledged Mode PDU

The header of an AM PDU is more complex than that of a UM PDU. It includes a Data or Control (D/C) indicator bit, a Re-segmentation Flag (RF) bit and a Polling (P) indicator bit. The SN field is 12 octets. SDU boundaries are again indicated by FI, LI and E bit fields. The D/C flag indicates whether the PDU is a data PDU or a control PDU. The RF flag indicates whether the data PDU format is simple or segmented. The P flag indicates that the transmitter wants to receive a status message from its peer when it receives the AM PDU.

AM PDU Segment

When the RF flag is set, the header has two extra fields, a Segment Offset (SO) field and a Last Segment Field (LSF). The SO is the octet number in the original PDU at which the AM PDU segment's first octet begins. The LSF indicates that the data octets in this segment run from the SO to the end of the original PDU.

AM Control PDU

The header of a control PDU is completely different than that of a data PDU. The AM control PDU includes the following mandatory fields: a 3 bit Control PDU Type (CPT) field, a 12 bit Acknowledged SN (ACK_SN) field, an Extension1 (E1) bit and an Extension2 (E2) bit. It also includes three optional fields: a 12 bit Negative Acknowledgment SN (NACK_SN) field, a 15 bit Segment Offset Start (SOstart) field and a 15 bit Segment Offset stop (SOstop) field.

The CPT indicates the type of control PDU, the ACK_SN indicates the earliest correctly received (in sequence) PDU and the E1 indicates that a NACK_SN follows. E2 indicates the presence of an SOstart/SOstop pair associated with the NACK_SN. NACK_SN indicates the SN of a lost PDU or PDU segment. SOstart indicates the offset of the first octet of data in the lost segmented data PDU. SOstop indicates the offset of the last octet of data in the lost segmented data PDU.

PDU Transmission

When the MAC requests a PDU for transmission, a priority order is used to decide what type of PDU to send. If a control PDU is available, it is constructed and sent. Otherwise a PDU or PDU segment previously reported as lost is retransmitted. A retransmitted PDU may be segmented or re-segmented before being retransmitted. If no control PDUs are transmitted and no retransmissions are required, then a new PDU is constructed from the available SDU data. The BO is incremented when a control PDU is ready to send or when retransmissions of data PDUs or PDU segments are required; in this way the MAC knows that this RLC has more data to send. The size of transmitted but unacknowledged data PDUs or PDU segments are decremented from the BO.

Every data PDU or data PDU segment is stored by the transmitting entity until it has been acknowledged by the peer RLC.

PDU Reception

When a data PDU is received from the MAC, it is stored until all preceding PDUs (those out of sequence) have also been received. Then the SDU data is extracted from them and forwarded, in sequence, to the higher layers. When a data PDU segment is received, the octets of data within it are used to construct a complete PDU. Once this is achieved, the PDU is treated as above.

When a control PDU is received, all of the unacknowledged PDUs up to ACK_SN are discarded. Any PDUs identified by NACK_SNs or any PDU segments identified by NACK_SNs and SOstart/SOstop pairs are marked for retransmission and their sizes are added to the BO information supplied to the MAC.

4.1.6 Packet Data Convergence Protocol (PDCP)

The Packet Data Convergence Protocol (PDCP) layer acts as a portal between the various higher layers of the protocol stack (RRC, RTP, UDP, TCP, etc.) and the RLC layer.

The main functions of the PDCP are:

- Passing SDUs received from its higher layers to its peer via the RLC. The data units are transmitted as PDUs.
- Receiving PDUs from the RLC and extracting SDU data from them to be passed to higher layers.
- Header compression/decompression
- Ciphering/deciphering

The use of integrity and ciphering in the PDCP layer is a significant departure from the PDCP in UMTS. The use of Robust Header Compression Version 2 (RoHCv2) is an enhancement to the use of RoHCv1 when user data is compressed.

4.1.6.1 Operating Planes

PDCP can operate on either of two planes, the control plane or the user plane. The control plane is used for RRC messages. The user plane is used for all other data.

Control Plane

A PDCP connected to the control plane carries RRC messages and is connected to an AM RLC. The SDUs are converted into PDCP data PDUs by adding a header and a tail. The header is a single octet with a 7-bit SN. The SN is incremented for every new PDU and wraps from 127 back to zero. Although the RRC messages are very important, the PDCP can afford to use a small SN because the AM RLC will recover lost PDUs and present them to the receiving PDCP in their original transmitted sequence.

RRC messages have integrity protection. A 4 octet Message Authentication Code (MAC-I) is generated by an algorithm using the data in the SDU and the SN as input. Another input to the integrity algorithm is a set of key values that is generated from the secret key in the USIM. This MAC-I is appended to the SDU data in the PDU.

The entire message (SDU data plus MAC-I but not the header) is then ciphered. A cipher stream the same length as the SDU data plus MAC-I is produced using a process similar to that used to create the MAC-I. The message bits are multiplexed with the cipher stream using an Exclusive OR (XOR) function.

In the receiver, another cipher stream is generated that is XOR'd with the message to decipher it. Then the MAC-I value is calculated from the SDU data and compared with the one in the message. If they match, the SDU data is forwarded to the higher layers.

User Plane

The user plane carries data packets and can be connected to either a Unacknowledged Mode (UM) or AM RLC. If connected to a UM RLC, it can use either a 7 or 12 bit SN. If connected to an AM RLC, it always uses a 12 bit SN.

User plane SDUs are compressed using RoHCv2. The original RoHCv1 is a subset of RoHCv2. After compression, user plane data PDUs are also ciphered in the same way as control plane PDUs. User plane data PDUs are not integrity-protected. In the receiver, the PDUs are deciphered and decompressed and the SDU data is forwarded to the higher layers.

4.1.6.2 PDCP Protocol Data Units

Every PDCP PDU has a D/C indicator bit to determine whether it is a data PDU or a control PDU.

Data PDUs

Every PDCP data PDU has a header prepended that is either one or two octets in length. If the PDCP is connected to the control plane, then the header will be one octet in length and will contain a 7 bit SN. If the PDCP is connected to the user plane, then the header may be either one or two octets. In the latter case, the SN will be 12 bits long.

Control PDUs

Control PDUs should not be confused with the data PDUs generated by a PDCP connected to the control plane. They do not have an SN, are neither ciphered nor integrity-protected and are not RoHC-compressed.

There are two kinds of control PDUs: RoHC feedback PDUs and PDCP status PDUs.

RoHCv2 feedback PDUs are also called interspersed RoHC feedback packets. They are used when a bidirectional RoHC connection is available and configured. The feedback modifies the behavior of the RoHC compressor, allowing better compression techniques to be used. The PDCP status PDUs are generated when a handover occurs. They carry received PDU status information between PDCP peers.

4.1.7 Radio Resource Control (RRC)

The radio resource control layer is a Layer 3 (L3) protocol in the radio interface and is located at the top of the access stratum of the air interface. The RRC provides access through which higher layer signalling entities can gain services in the form of signalling transfer from the AS.

RRC performs many functions that are required for the reliable and efficient operation of the radio resource. The RRC performs a management role coordinating the functions of the other AS layers.

Some of RRC's main areas of functionality include:

- Broadcasting system information.
- Coordinating the functions of the other AS layers.
- Establishing, reestablishing, maintaining and releasing the RRC connection between the UE and E-UTRAN.
- Setting, altering or releasing the radio bearer in the user plane.
- Handling issues relating to link quality.

4.1.7.1 System Information Broadcast

One of the main functions of the RRC on the network side is to broadcast System Information (SI) about the cell or the network to all UEs attached to the cell.

This system information includes the collation of information elements and the scheduling of transmitted System Information Blocks (SIBs). In addition to the SIBs there is a Master Information Block (MIB).The MIB includes a limited number of the most essential and frequently transmitted parameters, and it is the first piece of information read by the UE when connecting to the cell.

System information blocks other than System Information Block Type 1 are carried in SI messages. Mapping of SIBs to SI messages is flexibly configurable by scheduling information included in System Information Block Type 1, with the following restrictions: each SIB is contained in only a single SI message; only SIBs with the same scheduling requirement (periodicity) can be mapped to the same SI message; and System Information Block Type 2 is always mapped to the SI message that corresponds to the first entry in the list of SI messages in scheduling information. There may be multiple SI messages transmitted with the same periodicity.

Unlike previous releases of UMTS in which MIB and SIBs can be transmitted on the BCH, in LTE only the MIB is transmitted on the BCH and the rest of the SIBs are transmitted on the DL-SCH.

4.1.7.2 Broadcast Procedure

The MIB uses a fixed schedule with a periodicity of 40 ms and repetitions made within 40 ms. The first transmission of the MIB is scheduled in subframe #0 of the radio frames for which the SFN mod 4 = 0, and repetitions are scheduled in subframe #0 of all other radio frames.

The System Information Block Type 1 uses a fixed schedule with a periodicity of 80 ms and repetitions made within 80 ms. The first transmission of System Information Block Type 1 is scheduled in subframe #5 of the radio frames for which the SFN mod 8 = 0, and repetitions are scheduled in subframe #5 of all other radio frames for which SFN mod 2 = 0.

The SI messages are transmitted within periodically occurring time domain windows (referred to as SI-windows) using dynamic scheduling. Each SI message is associated with an SI-window and the SI-windows of different SI messages do not overlap; that is, within one SI-window only, the corresponding SI is transmitted. The length of the SI-window is common for all SI messages and is configurable. Within the SI-window, the corresponding SI message can be transmitted a number of times in any subframe other than Multimedia Broadcast over Single Frequency Network (MBSFN) subframes, uplink subframes in TDD and subframe #5 of radio frames for which SFN mod 2 = 0. The UE acquires the detailed time domain scheduling (and other information such as frequency domain scheduling and the used transport format) from decoding the SI-RNTI on the PDCCH.

A single SI-RNTI is used to address System Information Block Type 1 as well as all SI messages. System Information Block Type 1 configures the SI-window length and the transmission periodicity for the SI messages.

4.1.7.3 RRC States

In Release 8, there are two service states defined for the UE with respect to the operation of RRC: RRC_IDLE state and RRC_CONNECTED state.

In RRC_IDLE state, the UE has no connection in place. The UE has found and registered on the system. It is monitoring the downlink system information and paging information and is making neighbour cell measurements for cell reselection.

In RRC_CONNECTED state, the UE has established an RRC connection. The UE monitors control channels associated with the shared data channel to determine if data is scheduled for the UE, provides channel quality and feedback information and performs neighbour cell measurements and measurement reporting.

Unlike a UMTS UE, the LTE UE does not have sub-states in RRC_CONNECTED state.

4.1.7.4 RRC Connection Control

RRC offers three Signalling Radio Bearers (SRB) for the control plane signalling message transfer: SRB0, SRB1 and SRB2. SRB0 is used for CCCH messages whereas SRB1 and SRB2 are used for DCCH messages. SRB1 has a higher priority than SRB2, which is set up only after security has been activated. SRB1 carries RRC messages and also NAS messages if SRB2 is not yet established, whereas SRB2 carries NAS messages only. In any case NAS messages are always encapsulated into an RRC message, with or without RRC protocol control information.

LTE RRC allows NAS messages to be piggybacked on RRC control messages for certain procedures. Examples are initial uplink NAS messages transmitted during RRC connection setup and during downlink bearer establishment, modification or release. These procedures will have joint success or failure criteria.

RRC connection establishment is the establishment of SRB1 between the UE and the E-UTRAN so that further NAS and user plane procedures can take place. Using the information provided in system information blocks, a UE sends an RRC connection request message to the E-UTRAN. The UE indicates its higher layer identity and the connection establishment cause. Lower layers perform the RACH procedure to ensure the successful transmission of the RRC connection request. The E-UTRAN can respond either with an RRC connection setup command, which configures SRB1 and the default Evolved Packet System (EPS) RAB, or an RRC connection reject command asking the UE either to retry the connection after some wait time or to try the connection on a different frequency or radio access technology.

The UE performs contention resolution before acting on the contents of the response from the E-UTRAN. Following the successful configuration of the resources, the UE transmits the message "RRC connection setup complete" to the E-UTRAN. Since each eNB can be shared by multiple Public Land Mobile Networks (PLMNs) and Mobility Management entities (MMEs), the UE indicates the selected PLMN and MME so that the E-UTRAN can establish the S1 connection with the desired PLMN/MME. To speed up this process, the UE can piggyback initial NAS messages onto the "RRC connection setup complete" response. Once security has been activated, all messages on SRB1 and SRB2 are integrity-protected and ciphered.

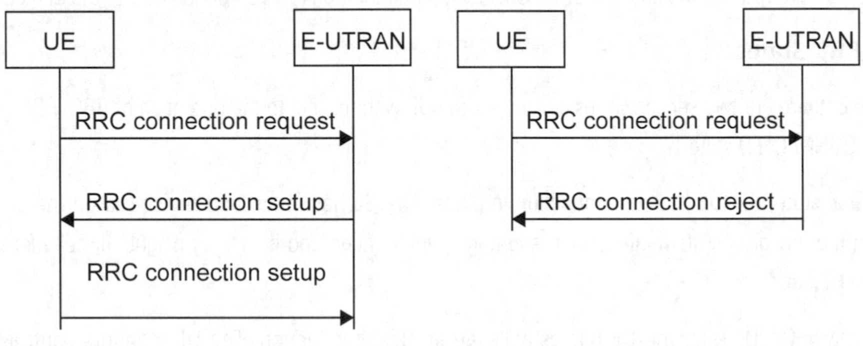

Figure 4.1-6. RRC connection setup and reject signalling (36.331 [5] Figures 5.3.3.1-1 and 5.3.3.1-2)

The RRC connection reconfiguration procedure is used to establish, modify or release signalling and user radio bearers. In LTE, RRC connection reconfiguration also involves setting up a default EPS bearer between the UE and the core network. This EPS bearer is set up on the basis of a non-guaranteed bit rate allowing the application-level signalling to take place as soon as a secure RRC connection is established.

The same RRC connection reconfiguration procedure is employed to perform handovers, NAS message transfer and configuration of measurements. However, certain types of reconfiguration cannot be performed until the AS security has been activated. As a part of this procedure, the E-UTRAN sends the "RRC connection reconfiguration" message with the appropriate information elements. Upon a successful handover, the UE responds with the message "RRC connection reconfiguration complete."

To handle temporary loss of coverage during mobility or to handle failures during reconfiguration procedures, an RRC connection re-establishment procedure is introduced. This procedure is used to resume SRB1 operation and to reactivate security. However, it is not used to resume any other radio bearers. The procedure can be initiated only if the AS security is active, otherwise the UE will drop all of its radio bearers and move to the RRC_IDLE state. The UE initiates the RRC connection reconfiguration procedure by transmitting an RRC connection reestablishment request message to the selected cell.

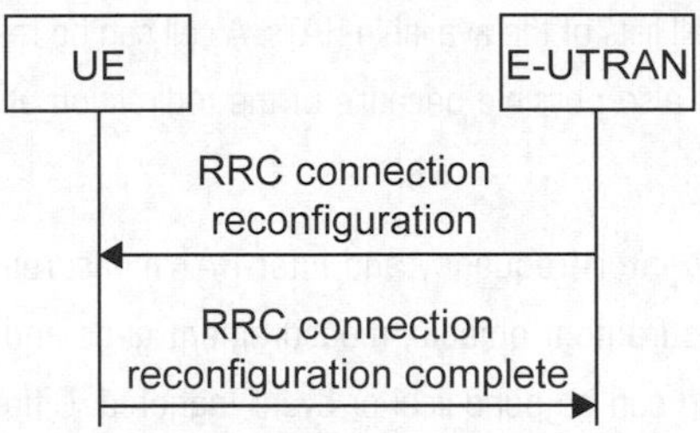

Figure 4.1-7. RRC connection reconfiguration signalling (36.331 [5] Figure 5.3.5.1-1)

If the cell can acquire a UE context based on the message sent by the UE, the E-UTRAN can reconfigure the SRB1 by sending an RRC connection reestablishment message. Alternatively the E-UTRAN can reject the reestablishment request. A MAC contention resolution similar to the one at RRC connection establishment takes place at this stage. The UE resumes SRB1 and AS security accordingly while the rest of the bearers and measurements remain suspended until an RRC connection reconfiguration takes place. Upon successful reestablishment, the UE responds with the message "RRC connection reestablishment complete."

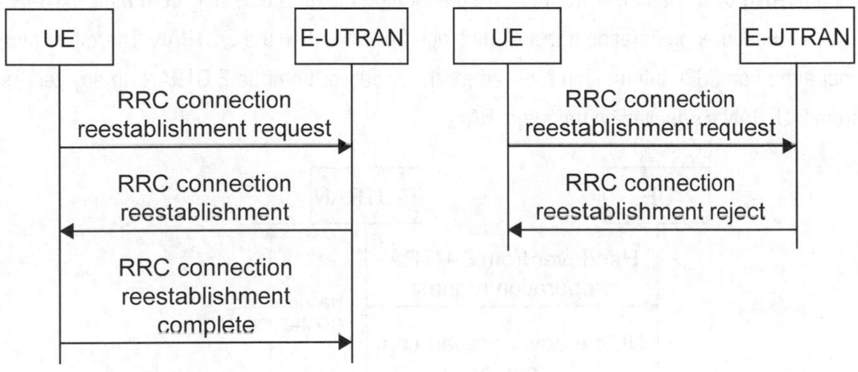

Figure 4.1-8. RRC connection reestablishment signalling (36.331 [5] Figures 5.3.7.1-1 and 5.3.7.1-2)

To tear down the RRC connection and release all radio resources associated with a UE, the E-UTRAN transmits an RRC connection release message to the UE. This message can also be used to redirect the UE to a particular RAT or cell and to update idle mode mobility information.

4.1.7.5 Inter-RAT and Intra-RAT Mobility

Idle mode mobility is controlled by the UE and is based on the system information transmitted in a cell. SIB3 carries all the information for all types of reselections: intra-frequency, inter-frequency and inter-RAT. SIB3 parameters allow the UE to determine when to start different reselection measurements. SIB4 carries all the intra-frequency neighbour cell details eligible for reselection as well as blacklisted cells that should not be considered for reselection. In a similar manner, SIB5 carries inter-frequency neighbours and blacklisted cells, whereas one SIB per RAT is used to convey neighbour cell lists of the available RATs. A cell can be reselected only if the required criteria are satisfied. Idle mode mobility is also possible because of the redirection at RRC connection establishment or release.

Connected mode intra-frequency, inter-frequency and inter-RAT measurements are configured during RRC connection reconfiguration. Measurement objects, measurement gaps and reporting requirements are also configured. Measurement reporting can be periodical or event-triggered. Different event criteria are specified to signal if the serving cell, an LTE neighbour cell or an inter-RAT neighbour cell becomes better or worse than certain thresholds. Intra-LTE handover is achieved using the RRC connection reconfiguration procedure, which is initiated by the network based on measurements or in a blind way without measurements.

Inter-RAT mobility to the E-UTRAN is achieved by sending the RRC connection reconfiguration message on the source RAT. A successful handover to the E-UTRAN results in establishment of SRBs, user radio bearers and activation of security in the E-UTRAN marked by the transmission of an RRC "connection reconfiguration complete" message by the UE. Mobility from the E-UTRAN to another RAT, whether by handover or by cell change order, is achieved by transmitting a "mobility from EUTRA" command to the UE. If the handover is to a cdma2000 RAT, this command is preceded by a "handover from EUTRA preparation request" message from the E-UTRAN to the UE followed by a "UL handover preparation transfer" message from the UE to the E-UTRAN. These two messages are used to acquire the non-3GPP information required for the handover from the E-UTRAN. In any case, success of handover from E-UTRAN is signalled on the target RAT.

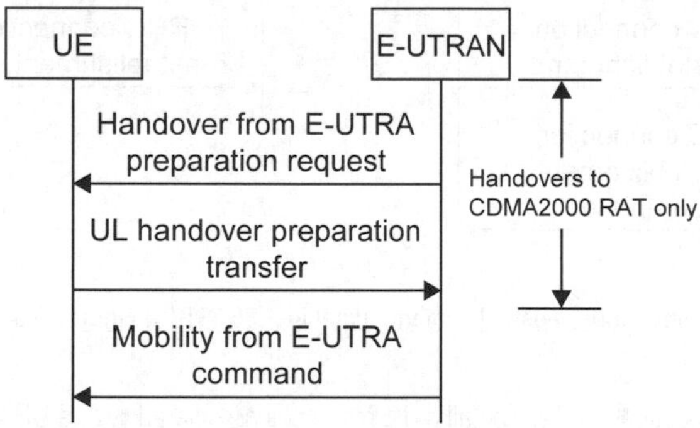

Figure 4.1-9. Handover from E-UTRAN signalling (36.331 [5] Figures 5.4.3.1-1, 5.4.4.1-1 and 5.4.5.1-1)

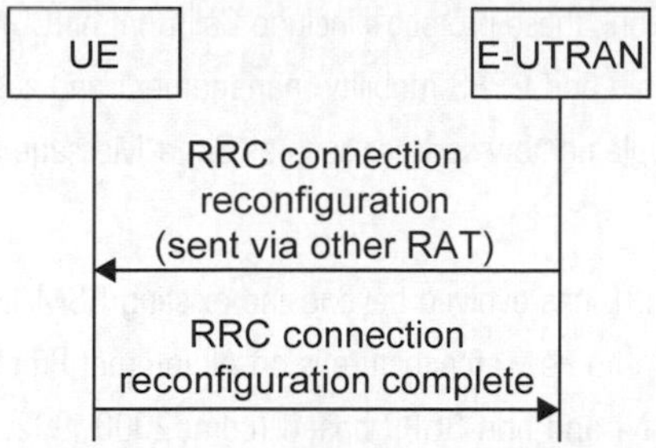

Figure 4.1-10. Handover to E-UTRAN signalling (36.331 [5] Figure 5.3.2.1-1)

4.1.7.6 Other RRC Procedures

Although it is the PDCP that actually performs ciphering and integrity check operations, it is the RRC that configures integrity protection and ciphering of the signalling plane and user plane data. The E-UTRAN RRC initiates initial security activation at RRC connection establishment by sending a security mode command to the UE. The UE responds with a security mode complete message in the case of successful activation or a security mode failure message otherwise. The security mode command and complete messages are integrity-protected, and ciphering is applied immediately after security mode activation is complete. Only after successful security activation can SRB2 and user radio bearers be established. All further security reconfigurations such as algorithm change at handovers are handled by the RRC connection reconfiguration procedure.

In addition to messages such as "RRC connection setup complete" and "RRC connection reconfiguration," which can carry piggybacked NAS messages, the RRC provides special containers called downlink information transfer and uplink information transfer. These containers are used exclusively to transfer downlink and uplink NAS messages.

If the EPC and the E-UTRAN do not have all the information related to UE capabilities (for example, during an inter-RAT handover), the E-UTRAN RRC can request this information from the UE by transmitting a message called a UE capability enquiry. The UE sends the requested capabilities back to the network in a UE capability information message.

The paging procedure is used to notify UEs in RRC_IDLE and RRC_CONNECTED states about system information changes and initiation of mobile terminating calls. The paging procedure involves the transmission of the paging message by the E-UTRAN RRC in certain designated paging occasions. Once the UE identifies a page for itself, it reacquires system information or initiates RRC connection establishment depending on the paging cause.

4.2 Non-Access Stratum

The Non-Access Stratum (NAS) contains all the functions and protocols used directly between the UE and the core network. The main NAS specification is 24.301 [6]. The NAS protocols are transparent to the access network. In the existing GSM/UMTS core network, these protocols include Call Control (CC) and Mobility Management (MM) for the Circuit Switched (CS) domain and GPRS mobility management and session management for the Packet Switched (PS) domain. Various supplementary services such as Short Message Service (SMS) are supported from either or both domains.

The core network architecture for LTE has evolved beyond the existing GSM/UMTS core network with a goal of simplifying the overall architecture. The new architecture is an All Internet Protocol Network (AIPN) that supports both 3GPP-based (UTRAN, GERAN) and non-3GPP based (cdma2000, 802.16, etc.) Radio Access Networks (RANs). The architecture also supports mobility between the various RANs. This evolved architecture is called the Evolved Packet Core (EPC) network or the System Architecture Evolution (SAE), which is the 3GPP project name.

Since the new architecture is an AIPN, the evolved core network is a PS-only network, differing significantly from all previous core networks that were built around the CS domain. The protocols defined for this new network are the Evolved Packet System (EPS) mobility management and EPS session management. These protocols manage the mobility of the UE and the activation, modification and deactivation of user-plane channels for transferring user data between the UE and the IP network. The new architecture introduces a new control plane Mobility Management Entity (MME), which implements the new protocols, and an access gateway, which consists of two logical user plane entities, the serving gateway and the PDN gateway. A detailed explanation of the new MME and an overview of the new user plane entities are given in this section. Figure 4.2-1 shows the different network elements and the interfaces connecting these elements in the new architecture.

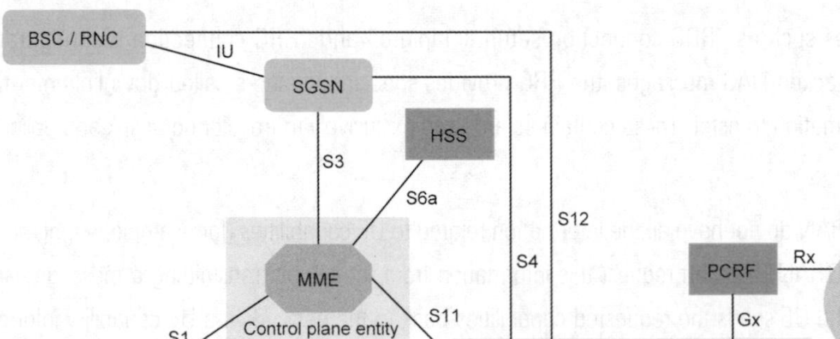

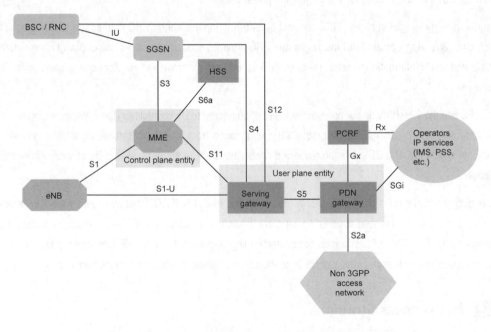

Figure 4.2-1. System architecture (based on 23.882 [7] Figure 4.2-1)

4.2.1 Network Elements

There are three main network elements in the evolved packet core: the mobility management entity, the serving gateway and the PDN gateway.

4.2.1.1 Mobility Management Entity

As stated above, the MME is the control plane entity that implements the procedures used for EPS Mobility Management (EMM) and EPS Session Management (ESM) in the EPS. The MME communicates with the Home Subscriber Server (HSS) for retrieving subscription information and with the serving gateway for establishment and release of EPS bearers. The authentication information received from the HSS is used to generate the integrity and ciphering keys, which are then used for integrity protection and ciphering of NAS control plane messages. The MME communicates with the eNB over the S1 interface using the S1 application protocol. The S3 interface between the MME and the Serving GPRS Support Node (SGSN) is used for signalling to support mobility between 3GPP access networks. Further explanation of this entity is provided in Section 4.2.3.

4.2.1.2 Serving Gateway

The serving gateway terminates the interface towards the radio network. It handles the user plane traffic routing and the forwarding of uplink and downlink packets between the PDN gateway and the radio network. Each UE communicates with only one serving gateway and the serving gateway can communicate with different PDN gateways for different UE-specific PDN connections over the S5 interface. The serving gateway acts as the anchor for inter-eNB and inter-3GPP mobility. It communicates with the Policy and Charging Rules Function (PCRF) entity for lawful interception and charging control functions.

4.2.1.3 PDN Gateway

The PDN Gateway provides PDN connectivity to the UE for different IP services provided by operators. The PDN gateway configured in the UE subscription information allocates an IP address to the UE during UE attachment to the E-UTRAN. A UE in a connected state can request connection to another PDN gateway for different IP services. The PDN gateway is responsible for uplink and downlink rate enforcement depending on the allocated maximum bit rate to the UE. It also performs the uplink and downlink service level charging and rate enforcement. The PDN gateway never changes during a session regardless of the mobility of the user. Hence it is the anchor point that manages the mobility between a 3GPP and a non-3GPP system.

4.2.2 Network Interfaces

The following interfaces have been defined for the EPC:

S1-MME: Interface for the control application protocol between the E-UTRAN and MME

S1-U: Interface for S1 user plane data for each bearer between the E-UTRAN and the serving gateway. This interface enables the serving gateway to anchor the inter-eNB handover.

S3: Interface that provides the connection between the SGSN and MME, enabling information exchange for mobility between inter-3GPP access networks

S4: Interface between the SGSN and serving gateway. It provides the user plane support for mobility support between the GPRS core and the serving gateway. It also enables the serving gateway to anchor the inter-3GPP handover.

S5: Interface that provides the user plane tunneling and tunnel management function between the serving gateway and the PDN gateway. It enables the serving gateway to connect to multiple PDN gateways for providing different IP services to the UE. It also is used for serving gateway relocation associated with UE mobility.

S6a: Interface between the MME and HSS. It is used for transfer of subscription and authentication data for authenticating and authorizing user access to the evolved packet system.

Gx: Interface that provides transfer of QoS policy and charging rules from the PCRF to the Policy and Charging Enforcement Function (PCEF) in the PDN gateway

S11: Control plane interface between the MME and serving gateway needed for EPS bearer management

SGi: Interface between the PDN gateway and the internet/intranet (equivalent to the Gi interface in GPRS)

4.2.3 Mobility Management Entity

The MME is the control plane entity that implements the EMM and ESM procedures in the EPS. The EMM procedures provide support for the mobility of the UE in the E-UTRAN, connection management services to the session management sublayer and control of security for the NAS protocols. These procedures enable an EPS-capable UE to move from an EMM-deregistered state to an EMM-registered state and vice versa. In EMM-deregistered state the MME has no knowledge of the location of the UE. The UE performs an attach procedure and registers its location with the MME. The UE is then in an EMM-registered state until it detaches from the network. In EMM-registered state the UE can communicate with the network for performing other procedures. For this communication to take place a signalling connection needs to be established with the registered MME. Depending on whether a signalling connection exists between the UE and MME, the UE is considered to be either in ECM-idle state (no signalling connection) or ECM-connected state (with signalling connection).

The ESM procedures are used for the handling of EPS bearer contexts. Together with the bearer control provided by the access stratum, these procedures are used for the activation, modification and deactivation of the user plane bearers.

4.2.4 EMM Procedures

The various EMM procedures are classified as EMM common procedures, EMM specific procedures or EMM connection management procedures.

4.2.4.1 EMM Common Procedures

EMM common procedures can be executed only when there is a signalling connection between the UE and the MME. The EMM common procedures are as follows: identification, authentication, security mode control, Globally Unique Temporary Identity (GUTI) reallocation and EMM information.

Identification Procedure

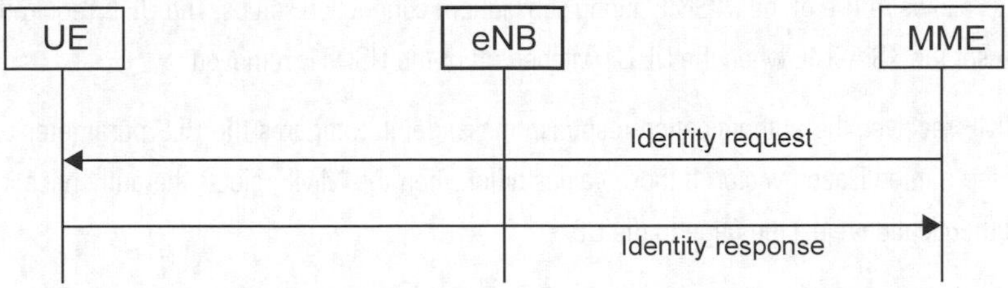

Figure 4.2-2. Identification procedure message flow (Based on 24.301 [6] Figure 5.4.4.2.1)

The identification procedure is used by the network to request that a particular UE provide specific identification parameters such as the International Mobile Subscriber Identity (IMSI) or the International Mobile Equipment Identity (IMEI). The MME initiates this procedure by sending an identity request message to which the UE responds by sending an identity response message. These messages can be transmitted without ciphering and integrity protection.

Authentication Procedure

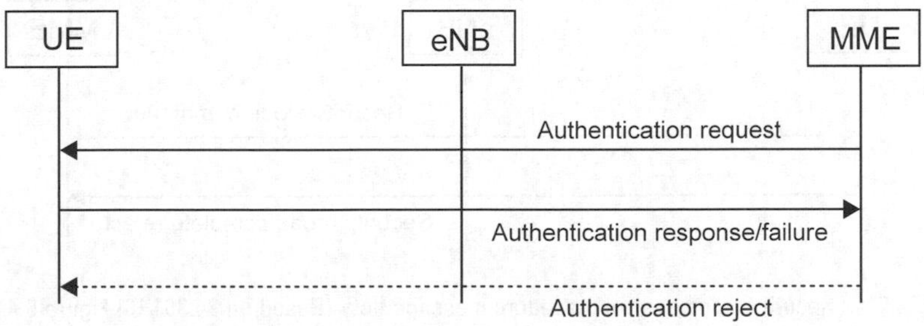

Figure 4.2-3. Authentication procedure message flow (Based on 24.301 [6] Figure 5.4.2.2.1)

The EPS Authentication and Key Agreement (AKA) procedure is used in the E-UTRAN for mutual authentication between the UE and MME. A security context is established in both entities at the end of a successful procedure.

The MME performs the AKA procedure using the authentication vectors received from the HSS. Each authentication vector consist of four parameters: a random number (RAND), the authentication token (AUTN), the expected user response (XRES) and the intermediate access security management entity key (KASME). The MME allocates a key set identifier (KSIASME) to identify KASME. The MME prepares an authentication request message including the KSIASME and the RAND and AUTN from the selected authentication vector and transmits the message to the UE.

Upon receipt of the authentication request message, the UE verifies whether AUTN can be accepted and, if so, produces a Response (RES) that is sent back to the MME in an authentication response message. From the parameter RAND, the UE generates the Ciphering Key (CK) and Integrity key (IK). Using these keys and the Serving Network Identity (SN Id) information, which comprises Mobile Country Code (MCC) and Mobile Network Code (MNC), the UE generates the KASME. The KASME and the identifier KSIASME are then stored in the UE. The network can later use the KSIASME to identify the KASME stored in the UE without invoking the authentication procedure. This allows re-use of the KASME during subsequent connection setups. The UE is required to delete the KASME and reset the KSIASME when the UE is switched off or the USIM is removed.

When the MME receives the authentication response message, it compares the RES parameter with the XRES parameter of the authentication vector. If these values differ, then the MME rejects the authentication attempt by sending an authentication reject message to the UE.

If the UE is not able to verify the authentication request message, then the UE transmits an authentication failure message to the MME.

After a successful authentication procedure, the intermediate key KASME is used to generate three other keys: the eNB key KeNB, the NAS integrity protection key KNASint and the NAS encryption key KNASenc. On the network side the KeNB is sent to the eNB during the initial context setup. The eNB uses KeNB to generate three further keys: the uplink user data encryption key KUPenc, the RRC integrity protection key KRRCint and the RRC encryption key KRRCenc. Similar key derivation also takes place in the UE.

Security Mode Control Procedure

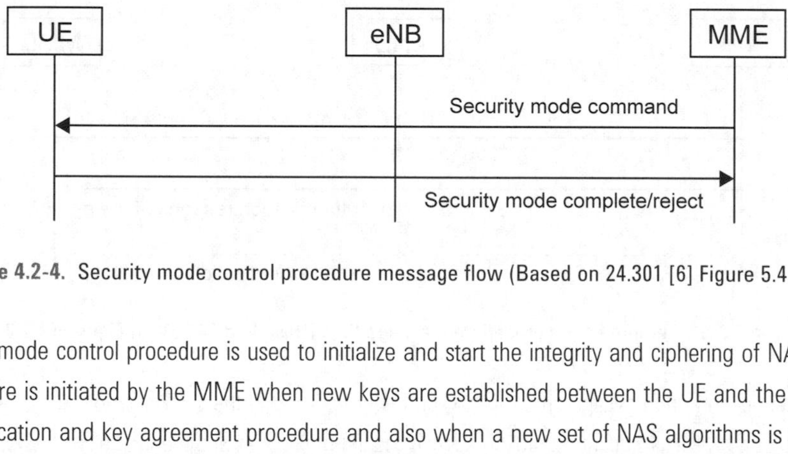

Figure 4.2-4. Security mode control procedure message flow (Based on 24.301 [6] Figure 5.4.3.2.1)

The security mode control procedure is used to initialize and start the integrity and ciphering of NAS messages. This procedure is initiated by the MME when new keys are established between the UE and the MME by the EPS authentication and key agreement procedure and also when a new set of NAS algorithms is selected. The MME starts the security mode control procedure by sending the security mode command message to the UE. This message contains the replayed security capabilities of the UE, the selected NAS algorithms and the KSIASME for identifying the KASME. The message is integrity-protected with the NAS integrity key KNASint, which is based on the KASME indicated by the KSIASME in the message.

If the UE accepts the security mode command message, it responds with the security mode complete message, which is integrity-protected using the selected NAS integrity algorithm indicated in the security mode command message and KNASint. If a "non null" ciphering algorithm was indicated in the security mode command, this message will also be ciphered with the indicated ciphering algorithm and KNASenc.

If the UE does not accept the security mode command message, it responds with a security mode reject message. The UE includes an appropriate reject cause in the rejection message.

Ciphering of the NAS messages at the MME starts after receiving the NAS security mode complete message. At the UE, NAS ciphering starts before sending the NAS security mode complete message.

GUTI Reallocation Procedure

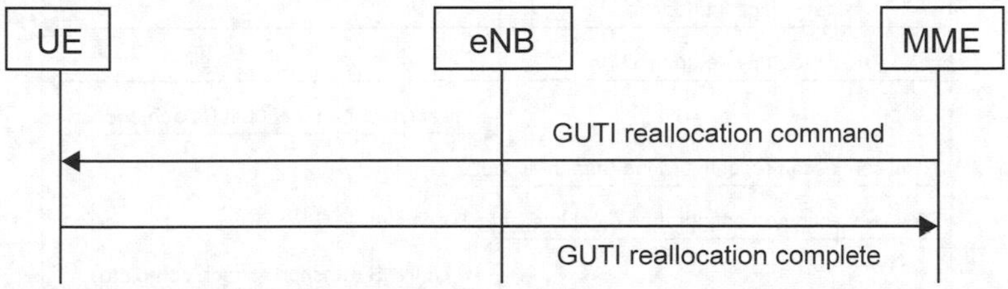

Figure 4.2-5. GUTI reallocation procedure message flow (Based on 24.301 [6] Figure 5.4.1.2.1)

The GUTI reallocation procedure is used to allocate a new GUTI and optionally to provide a new Tracking Area Identity (TAI) list to a particular UE. This procedure can be performed implicitly along with the attach or tracking area update procedure, or independently using the GUTI reallocation command message. The MME can prepare a GUTI reallocation command message and send it to the UE only in the EMM-registered state. The UE updates the new GUTI and TAI list and responds with a GUTI reallocation complete message to the MME. The GUTI reallocation procedure is usually integrity-protected and is performed in ciphered mode.

EMM Information Procedure

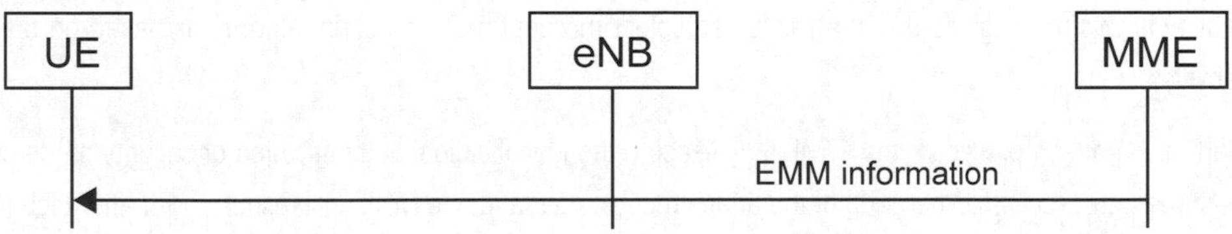

Figure 4.2-6. EMM information procedure message flow (Based on 24.301 [6] Figure 5.4.5.2.1)

The EMM information procedure enables the network to provide additional information to the UE such as network name and time zone information. This is an optional procedure and may be invoked by the network at any time during an established EMM context.

4.2.4.2 EMM-Specific Procedures

The EMM-specific procedures are complete EPC procedures used for handling UE mobility in the MME. They are the attach procedure, the tracking area update procedure and the detach procedure.

Attach Procedure

The attach procedure enables a UE to register itself to an MME for receiving packet services.

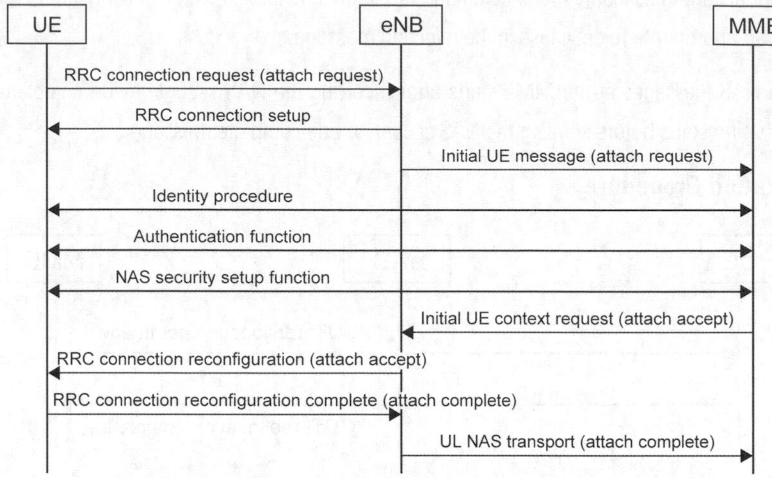

Figure 4.2-7. Attach procedure (Based on 23.401 [8] Figure 5.3.2.1-1)

After a successful attach procedure, an EMM context is established in the UE and the MME, and a default bearer is established between the UE and PDN gateway, thus enabling always-on IP connectivity to the UE. An IP address may be allocated to the UE when the default bearer is activated, or the UE can acquire an IP address after the default bearer is established using the Dynamic Host Configuration Protocol version 4 (DHCPv4) or DHCPv6.

The UE starts the attach procedure by sending an attach request message. This message may be integrity-protected if a valid NAS security context for the UE exists. The UE will include the GUTI or IMSI in this message as its identifier, which the MME uses to retrieve the UE subscription information. The UE also includes its network capability in this message so that the MME can select the appropriate security algorithms based on the UE's capabilities.

As part of the attach procedure the MME may execute the identification, authentication or security mode control procedures. After successful handling of the attach request message, the MME will respond with an attach accept message to the UE. The MME will include a list of tracking area identities in this message, which indicates the registered area of the UE. The UE may be allocated a new GUTI as its identifier in this message.

To complete the successful attach procedure the UE will send an attach complete message to the MME. If the MME does not accept the attach request message the MME responds with an attach failure message. The MME will include an appropriate reject cause in the rejection message.

The UE includes the PDN connectivity request message within the attach request message to indicate establishment of the default bearer with the default PDN. The MME includes the activate default EPS bearer context request message to activate the default bearer in the attach accept message. The UE sends the attach complete message combined with an activated default EPS bearer context accept message.

Tracking Area Update Procedure

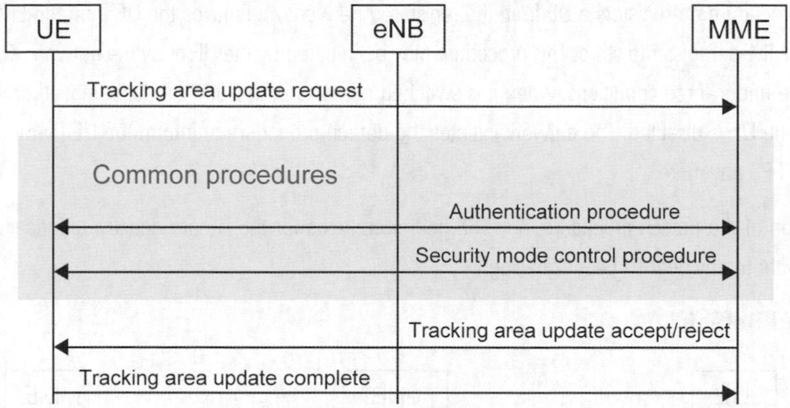

Figure 4.2-8. Tracking area update procedure message flow (Based on 24.301 [6] Figure 5.5.3.2.2.1)

The tracking area update procedure is initiated by a UE in the EMM-registered state to update the UE location to the network either periodically or when the UE moves out of the registered tracking area list. This procedure may also be initiated because of an intersystem change into the E-UTRAN.

The UE starts this procedure by sending the tracking area update request message. In this message the UE includes a GUTI as the UE identifier and the last visited registered TAI. If a UE in ECM-idle mode has uplink user data pending, then the UE may request the network to re-establish the radio and S1 bearers for all active EPS bearer contexts.

If the MME accepts the tracking area update request, the MME sends a "tracking area update accept" message to the UE. The MME may include a new GUTI or new TAI list if either has changed. In response, the UE returns a tracking area update complete message to the MME to acknowledge the received GUTI. If the network cannot accept the tracking area update request message, the MME sends a tracking area update reject message to the UE including an appropriate rejection cause.

After the tracking area update procedure has completed, the MME normally releases the signalling connection with the UE. However, the UE can request the MME to maintain the signalling connection for following procedures.

The tracking area update procedure enables the UE and MME to synchronize the EPS bearer context status. Should there be any difference in context status due to local bearer deactivation, this difference can be corrected by sending the bearer context status information indicating the active and inactive bearers in the request and accept messages. The UE and MME can then locally deactivate the bearers marked inactive.

When the UE is in an EMM-registered state, the tracking area update procedure is always integrity-protected. If the integrity check of the tracking area update request message fails, then authentication and NAS security mode procedures are performed.

Detach Procedure

The detach procedure de-registers a UE from the registered network and moves the UE from the EMM-registered state to the EMM-deregistered state. This procedure may be initiated by the UE or by the network. The UE initiates this procedure under three conditions: when it is switched off, when the USIM card is removed or when the EPS capability of the UE is disabled. The network initiates the detach procedure to inform the UE that it does not have access to the EPS any more.

After execution of the detach procedure, any EPS bearer contexts for the UE are deactivated locally in the MME and the UE without any peer-to-peer signalling.

UE-Initiated Detach

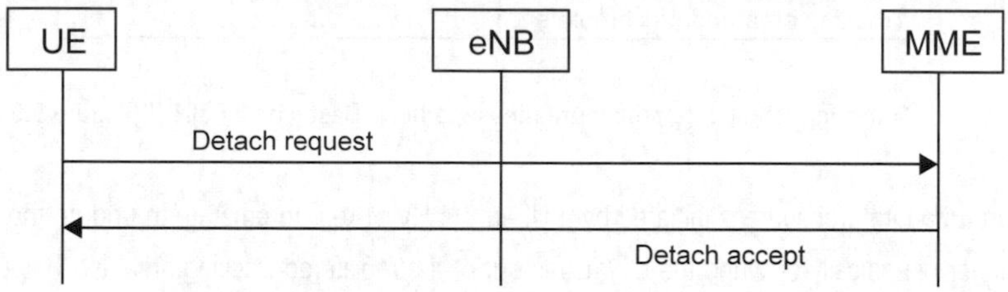

Figure 4.2-9. UE-initiated detach procedure message flow (Based on 24.301 [6] Figure 5.5.2.2.1.1)

The UE initiates the detach procedure by sending a detach request message to the MME. The UE can indicate in the detach request message if the detach is due to a switch-off situation. If the detach is not due to switch-off, the MME sends a detach accept message to the UE, otherwise the procedure is completed when the network receives the detach request message. The intermediate security key KASME and its identifier KSIASME are deleted in the MME and UE following the detach procedure.

MME-Initiated Detach

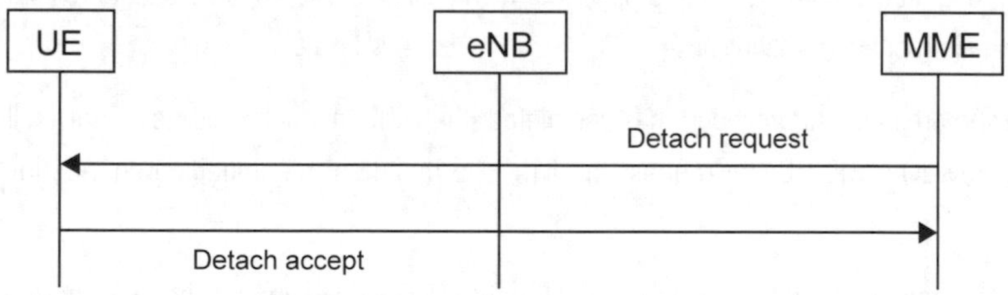

Figure 4.2-10. MME-initiated detach procedure message flow (Based on 24.301 [6] Figure 5.5.2.3.1)

The MME initiates the detach procedure by sending a detach request message to the UE. The UE responds with a detach accept message to the MME. The MME can request the UE to reattach after the detach procedure, in which case the UE starts the attach procedure immediately after the detach procedure.

4.2.4.3 EMM Connection Management Procedures

The EMM connection management procedures are used to enable the UE to move from the ECM-idle state to the ECM-connected state whenever there is a need for some data or signalling transfer. The EMM connection management procedures are the paging procedure and the service request procedure.

Paging Procedure

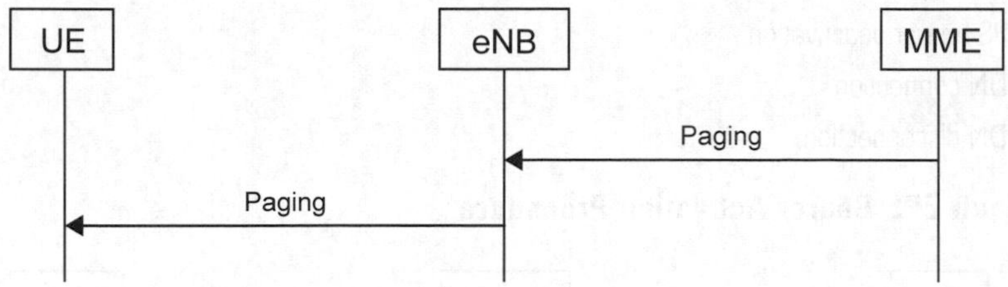

Figure 4.2-11. Paging procedure message flow

When signalling or user data needs to be sent but there is no NAS signalling connection, the paging procedure is initiated by the network to request the establishment of a NAS signalling connection to the UE. The MME sends the S1-AP paging message to the eNB. This message includes the UE identifier and the list of TAIs to which the UE is registered. The eNB uses this information to generate a Radio Resource (RR) paging message in the registered tracking areas. Upon reception of a paging indication, the UE starts a service request procedure for establishment of the signalling connection and other user plane resources.

Service Request Procedure

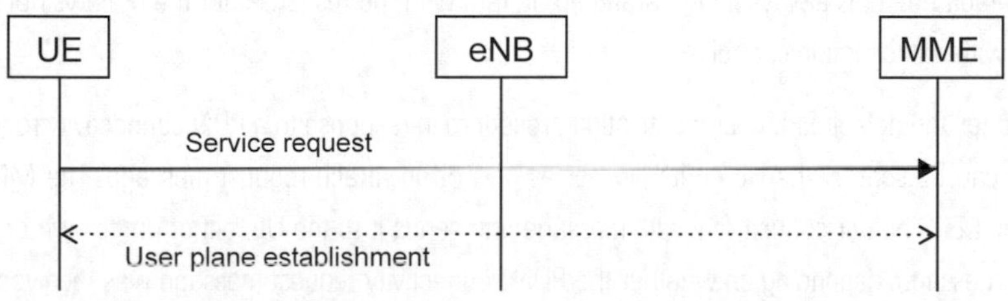

Figure 4.2-12. Service request procedure message flow

The service request procedure is triggered by a UE when there is some uplink user data or signalling that needs to be transmitted, or when the UE is paged by the network. The UE initiates the service request procedure by sending a service request message to the MME. If the MME accepts the service request message, the MME activates all the active EPS bearers. This initiates the establishment of user plane radio resources for the active EPS bearers in the eNB and the S1 user plane connection between the eNB and serving gateway. When the user plane radio bearers are fully established, the service request procedure is considered to be successful. The UE and network can then start transmitting data. If the MME does not accept the service request message, it sends a service reject message to the UE. This message includes an appropriate cause for rejecting the service request procedure.

4.2.5 ESM Procedures

The ESM procedures are used for activation, modification and deactivation of the user plane EPS bearers, which are used for data transfer between the UE and the IP network. The ESM procedures are as follows:

- Default EPS bearer activation
- Dedicated EPS bearer activation
- EPS bearer modification
- EPS bearer deactivation
- PDN connection
- PDN disconnection

4.2.5.1 Default EPS Bearer Activation Procedure

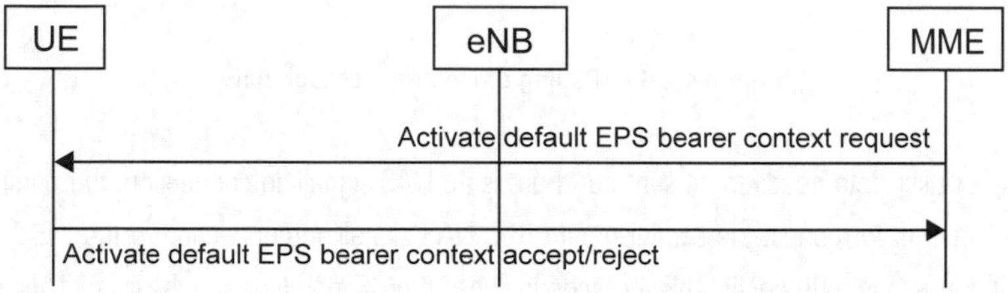

Figure 4.2-13. Default EPS bearer activation procedure message flow (Based on 24.301 [6] Figure 6.4.1.2.1)

The default EPS bearer activation procedure is triggered by the MME to establish a default EPS bearer between a UE and the PDN gateway. The default bearer is used to carry all traffic which is not associated with a dedicated bearer. The default bearer is always non-guaranteed bit rate with the resources for the IP flows not guaranteed at the eNB, and with no admission control.

The MME initiates the default EPS bearer activation procedure in response to a PDN connectivity request message. This message can be sent by the UE on its own or as part of an attach request message. The MME creates an "activate default EPS bearer context request" message and sends it to the UE, either on its own or along with an attach accept message, depending on whether the PDN connectivity request message was received on its own or as part of an attach request message.

If the UE accepts the request to activate the default EPS bearer context, it responds with an "activate default EPS bearer context accept" message. If the procedure is initiated as part of the attach procedure, this message is sent as part of the attach complete message. Otherwise it is sent on its own. Failure of the attach procedure implicitly causes the default bearer activation procedure to fail. If the UE is unable to accept the bearer request, it responds with an "activate default EPS bearer context reject" message along with an appropriate rejection cause.

4.2.5.2 Dedicated EPS Bearer Activation Procedure

The dedicated EPS bearer activation procedure is used to establish a dedicated EPS bearer with specific QoS and Traffic Flow Template (TFT) between the UE and the PDN.

Dedicated bearers are used to carry traffic for IP flows that have been identified as requiring a specific packet forwarding treatment. The dedicated bearer can be either guaranteed bit rate (GBR) or non-GBR. A GBR bearer has a guaranteed bit rate and a Maximum Bit Rate (MBR), while more than one non-GBR bearer belonging to the same UE shares an Aggregate Maximum Bit Rate (AMBR). Non-GBR bearers can suffer packet loss under congestion, while GBR bearers are immune to such losses. The dedicated EPS bearer activation procedure is initiated by the network, but may be requested by the UE by means of the UE requested bearer resource modification procedure.

Network-Initiated Dedicated EPS Bearer Activation

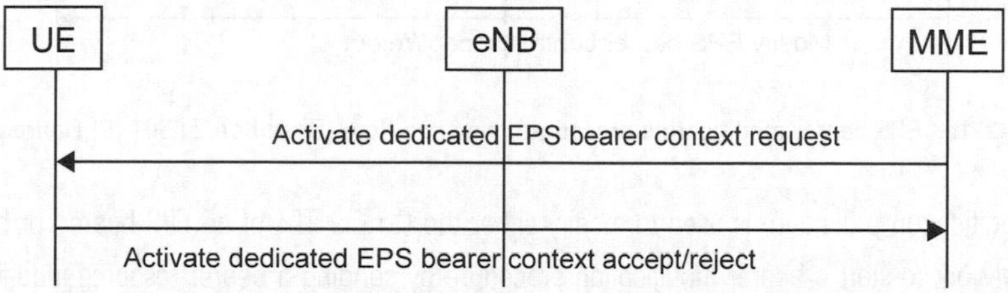

Figure 4.2-14. Network initiated EPS bearer activation procedure message flow (Based on 24.301 [6] Figure 6.4.2.2.1)

The MME creates an "activate dedicated EPS bearer context request" message and sends it to the UE. The message includes a bearer identity, a TFT, the QoS to be allocated to the bearer and a linked EPS bearer identity for the default EPS bearer connected to the PDN. If the UE accepts the dedicated bearer request, it responds with an "activate dedicated EPS bearer context accept" message.

On failure the UE responds with an "activate dedicated EPS bearer context reject" message. This message includes the EPS bearer identity and a cause value indicating the reason for rejecting the dedicated EPS bearer context activation request.

UE-Initiated Dedicated EPS Bearer Activation

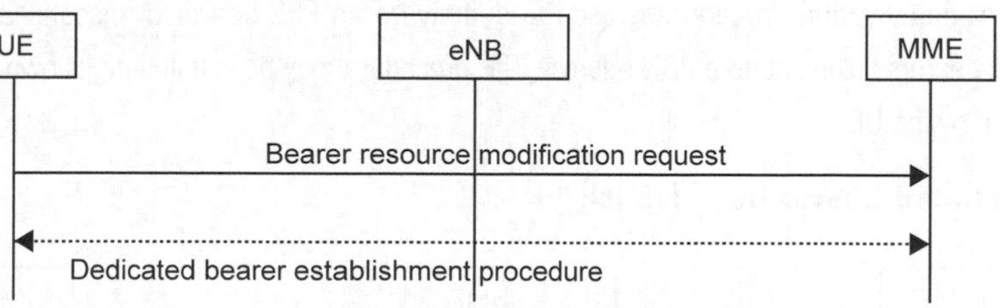

Figure 4.2-15. UE-initiated EPS bearer activation procedure message flow (Based on 24.301 [6] Figure 6.5.3.2.1)

The UE can request the establishment of a new traffic flow aggregate with a specific QoS demand and optional GBR requirement. The UE sends a "bearer resource modification request" message to the MME. This message contains the linked bearer identity of the default bearer, which indicates the PDN to which the dedicated bearer should be established. The required QoS is also included, indicating the class of service and amount of resource that needs to be allocated.

If the MME accepts the request, it triggers the dedicated bearer activation procedure to establish the requested bearer resources. If the MME does not accept the request, the MME creates a "bearer resource modification reject" message and sends it to the UE along with a cause value indicating the reason for rejecting the request.

4.2.5.3 EPS Bearer Modification Procedure

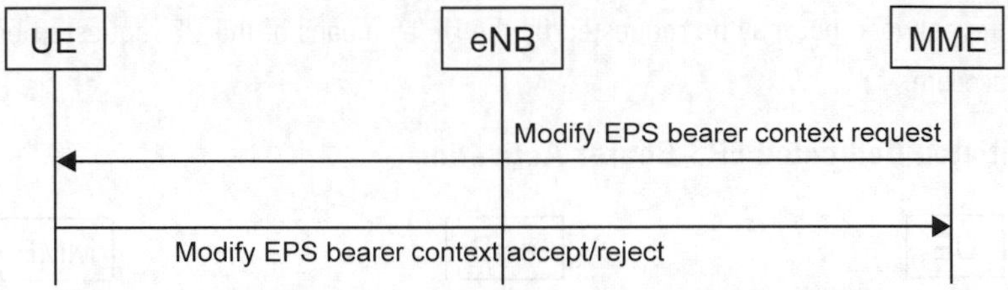

Figure 4.2-16. EPS bearer modification procedure message flow (Based on 24.301 [6] Figure 6.4.3.2.1)

The bearer modification procedure is used to modify either the QoS or TFT of an EPS bearer, or both. A UE can request the network to start a bearer modification procedure by sending a bearer resource modification request and including the bearer identity of an already established bearer.

The MME creates a "modify EPS bearer context request" message and sends it to the UE. The message contains the EPS bearer identification. Depending on whether the QoS, the TFT or both need to be modified, the new QoS and TFT information is also included. If the modification procedure involves QoS parameters, then radio resource modification is also done between the eNB and UE. Otherwise the PDN gateway and the UE update the modified TFT information locally.

If the UE accepts the modify request, it responds with a "modify EPS bearer context accept" message. If the UE does not accept the modify request, it sends a "modify EPS bearer context reject" message, including a cause value indicating the reason for rejecting the bearer context modification request.

4.2.5.4 EPS Bearer Deactivation Procedure

The EPS bearer deactivation procedure is used to deactivate an EPS bearer or disconnect from a PDN by deactivating all bearers belonging to a PDN address. This procedure may be initiated on its own by the network or when requested by the UE.

Network-Initiated Bearer Deactivation

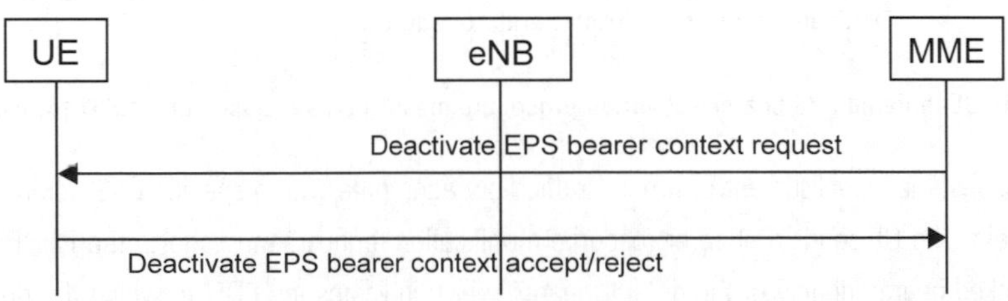

Figure 4.2-17. Network initiated bearer deactivation procedure message flow (Based on 24.301 [6] Figure 6.4.4.2.1)

When the UE is in an ECM-connected state, the MME creates a "deactivate EPS bearer context request" message and sends it to the UE. This message contains the identity of the dedicated bearer to be deactivated. If all the bearers connected to a PDN need to be released, the bearer identity is the identifier of the default bearer.

After the UE receives a deactivation request, the UE deactivates the resources for the bearer or all the bearers connected to the PDN and sends a "deactivate EPS bearer context accept" message to the MME.

When the UE is in the ECM-idle state, the MME can release all the bearer contexts locally. The bearer state is synchronized between the UE and the network at the next ECM-idle to ECM-connected transition; e.g., a service request or Tracking Area Update (TAU) procedure. When all the bearers belonging to the UE are released, the MME changes the MM state of the UE to EMM-deregistered.

UE-Initiated Bearer Deactivation

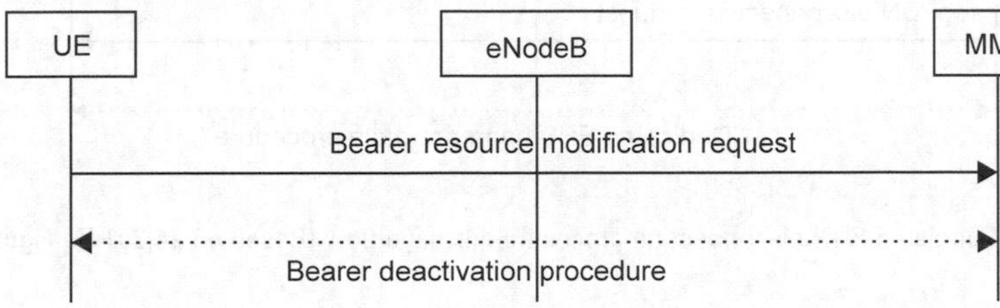

Figure 4.2-18. UE-initiated bearer deactivation procedure message flow (Based on 24.301 [6] Figure 6.5.3.2.1)

The UE can request a bearer deactivation by sending a "bearer resource modification request" message to the MME. This message contains the identity of the bearer to be released and the linked bearer identity of the default bearer connected to a PDN. On receiving this message the MME checks whether the requested bearer resource can be released, and if this is possible the MME starts the bearer deactivation procedure. If the MME is unable to accept the request, it sends a "bearer resource modification reject" message to the UE with a cause indicating the reason for failure.

4.2.5.5 UE-Initiated PDN Connectivity Procedure

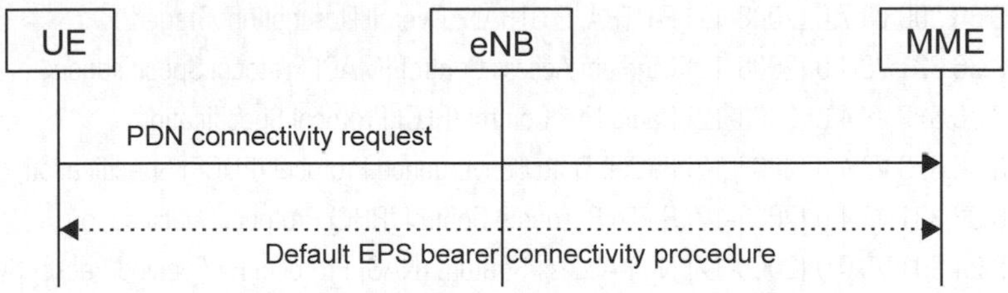

Figure 4.2-19. UE-initiated PDN connectivity procedure message flow (Based on 24.301 [6] Figure 6.5.1.2.1)

The PDN connectivity procedure allows the UE to request connectivity to a PDN including allocation of a default bearer. For the first default bearer this message may be sent as part of the attach request procedure.

The UE initiates the PDN connectivity procedure by creating a PDN connectivity request message and sending it to the MME. In this message the UE includes information about the IP version capability of the IP stack in the UE. The

UE may indicate whether it wants an IPv4 or IPv6 address to be allocated as part of the default bearer activation procedure, or whether to assign an address after the default bearer activation procedure by executing DHCPv4 or DHCPv6. The PDN connectivity request message may also include the Access Point Name (APN) information indicating the PDN to connect with. If the APN information is not provided, then the connection is made to the default PDN. If the MME accepts the PDN connectivity request message, it starts the default EPS bearer context activation procedure. If the MME cannot accept the PDN connectivity request message, it sends a "PDN connectivity reject" message with a cause value indicating the reason for rejecting the UE-requested PDN connection.

4.2.5.6 UE-Initiated PDN Disconnection Procedure

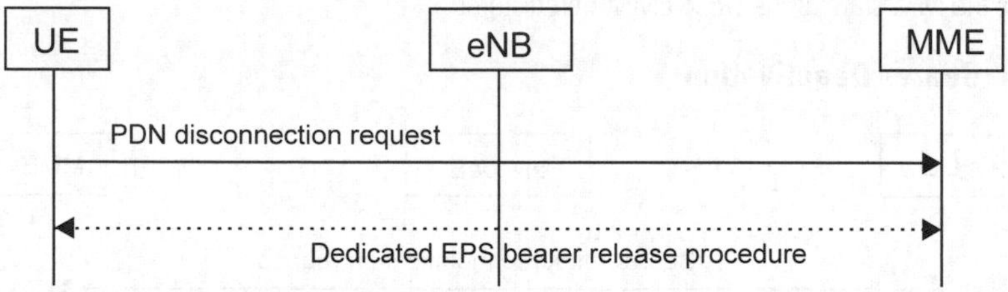

Figure 4.2-20. UE-initiated PDN disconnection procedure message flow (Based on 24.301 [6] Figure 6.5.2.2.1)

The PDN disconnection procedure allows the UE to request disconnection from one PDN. All the default and dedicated bearers connected to the PDN are deleted during this procedure. The UE initiates the procedure by creating a PDN disconnection request message and sending it to the MME. This message includes a linked bearer identity, which identifies the default bearer connected to the PDN. If the MME accepts the PDN disconnection request, it initiates the bearer deactivation procedure. If the MME does not accept the PDN disconnection request message, it sends a PDN disconnection reject message to the UE with a cause indicating the reason for rejecting the request.

4.3 References

[1] 3GPP TS 36.300 V8.7.0 (2008-12) E-UTRA, E-UTRAN, Overall Description; Stage 2
[2] 3GPP TS 36.321 V8.4.0 (2008-12) Medium Access Control (MAC) Protocol Specification
[3] 3GPP TS 36.322 V8.4.0 (2008-12) Radio Link Control (RLC) Protocol Specification
[4] 3GPP TS 36.323 V8.4.0 (2008-12) Packet Date Convergence Protocol (PDCP) Specification
[5] 3GPP TS 36.331 V8.4.0 (2008-12) Radio Resource Control (RRC) Protocol Specification
[6] 3GPP TS 24.301 V8.0.0 (2008-12) Non-Access-Stratum (NAS) Protocol for Evolved Packet System
[7] 3GPP TR 23.882 V8.0.0 (2008-09) 3GPP System Architecture Evolution: Report on Technical Options and Conclusions
[8] 3GPP TS 23.401 V8.4.0 (2008-12) General Packet Radio Service (GPRS) enhancements for Evolved Universal Terrestrial Radio Access Network (E-UTRAN) access

Links to all reference documents can be found at www.agilent.com/find/ltebook

Chapter 5

System Architecture Evolution

Development of the LTE air interface is closely linked within 3GPP to the concurrent System Architecture Evolution (SAE) project, which is defining the new overall system architecture. This architecture is called the Evolved Packet System (EPS), and it encompasses the LTE Evolved UMTS Radio Access (E-UTRA) and Evolved UMTS Radio Access Network (E-UTRAN) as well as a new Evolved Packet Core (EPC) network. The EPS is sometimes referred to as LTE/SAE; these terms are used interchangeably in this book. 3GPP has given the specifications related to the LTE/SAE architecture the name System Architecture Evolution Specification (SAES).

This chapter introduces the EPS, offering an overview of the architecture's requirements, functions and services. However, this chapter is not an exhaustive discussion of the specifications, which are still under development as this book goes to press. In this chapter all possible care has been taken to ensure that the technical details are current with the relevant standards as of February 2009. For the most up-to-date information, please refer to the latest versions of the standards documents listed below and at the end of this chapter.

Reference Documents for EPS

The EPS architecture supports heterogeneous access-system mobility within 3GPP and non-3GPP access systems, including fixed access systems. Architectural enhancements relating to 3GPP access systems including the E-UTRAN, legacy UTRAN and GERAN are detailed in 23.401 [1]. Similarly, architectural enhancements relating to non-3GPP access systems including 3GPP2 cdma2000 1xRTT and High Rate Packet Data (HRPD), WiMAX, Wireless LAN (WLAN), etc., are detailed in 23.402 [2]. This section focuses mainly on the overall EPS architecture supporting 3GPP E-UTRAN access including E-UTRAN mobility. The remaining access systems including interworking features are referenced only as necessary for the purpose of describing the EPS architecture in a more complete manner.

5.1 Requirements for an Evolved Architecture

As the worlds of fixed and mobile, wired and wireless communications converge, network architecture is evolving to support the advanced technology and services that make convergence possible. Figure 5.1-1, from "Next Generation Mobile Networks Beyond HSPA and EVDO" [3] from the Next Generation Mobile Networks (NGMN) Alliance, shows a set of criteria that are weighted in terms of priority in a new system architecture. These are intended by the NGMN Alliance to guide the development efforts of the industry. An understanding of these priorities is deemed to be essential for all parties — equipment vendors, operators, system integrators and test and measurement vendors — involved in the development of the new network architecture.

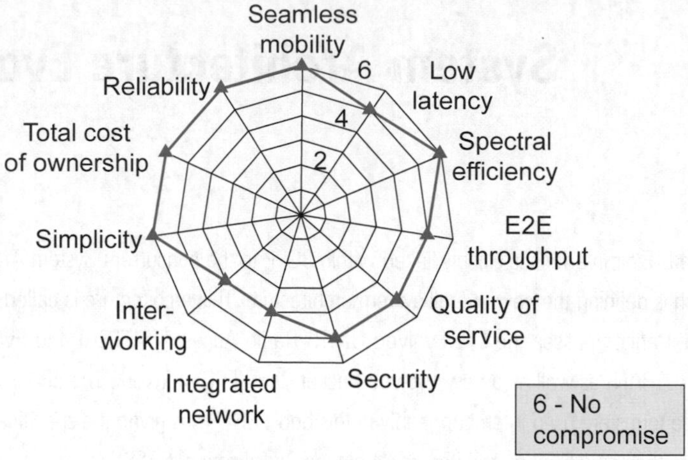

Figure 5.1-1. Wireless network operator priorities (from "Next Generation Mobile Networks Beyond HSPA and EVDO," NGMN Alliance [3])

LTE/SAE is one possible response. 3GPP's overall requirements for an evolved packet system are summarized in 22.278 [4]. This work has been ongoing for quite some time. Different parties in the industry have provided insight into the operational and developmental challenges of current networks, and this insight has been the foundation of the evolving work. The nomenclature associated with these concepts is covered in 21.905 [5].

The overall objectives for LTE and specifically the E-UTRA and E-UTRAN are summarized in Chapter 1 and detailed in Chapters 2 through 4. The overall objectives for the EPC are defined in 22.278 [4] and include the following:

- Provide higher data rates, lower latency, a higher level of security and enhanced QoS.
- Support a variety of different access systems (existing and future), ensuring mobility and service continuity between these access systems.
- Support access system selection based on a combination of operator policies, user preference and access network conditions.
- Realize improvements in basic system performance while maintaining the negotiated QoS across the whole system.
- Provide capabilities for co-existence with legacy systems and the migration of legacy systems to the EPS.

From these objectives 3GPP has established a set of requirements for the EPS, which are covered in 22.278 [4] subclause 5-10. Some of the most important items are described next.

5.1.1 User and Operational Aspects

The EPS is required to provide the means for users to access the network with fully supported mobility across a range of access technologies. The overall system must enable full interworking not only with 3GPP systems but with non-3GPP systems as well. The EPS also has to enable efficient use of system resources, especially radio resources, through signalling and transport optimization (such as overhead, terminal power, radio resources, mobility state and signalling load optimization).

5.1.2 IP Support

The EPS is required to support both Internet Protocol version 6 (IPv6) and Internet Protocol version 4 (IPv4), as well as both single and dual mode UEs. Note that an operator may enforce a policy to prohibit IPv4-only UEs from accessing the network. The operator can use both dynamic and fixed IP addresses if required from an operational perspective. The IP address allocation policy for each user is stored in the Home Location Register (HLR) or Home Subscriber Server (HSS). Service continuity between different access networks should not be dependent on the support of one version of IP or another.

IP communication in the EPS should be supported for traffic from user to a server, from user to user and from user to a group. The traffic supported can be classified as Real Time (RT) traffic such as Voice over IP (VoIP); Non-Real Time (NRT) traffic such as web browsing or Instant Messaging (IM); or mission-critical traffic such as Mobile-commerce (M-commerce).

5.1.3 Quality of Service

The EPS has to provide Quality of Service (QoS) while at the same time using system resources efficiently. Quality of service has to be maintained throughout the entire EPS including the EPC, and this QoS must meet or exceed the QoS requirements specified for GSM and UMTS. Quality of service from the customer's perspective is to be considered in phases as specified in ETSI 102 250-1 [6].

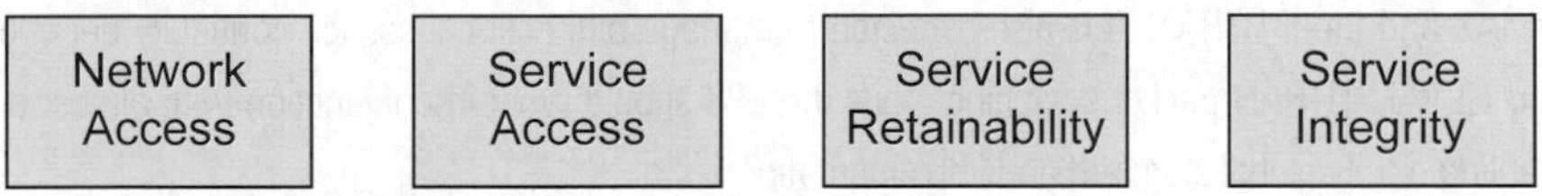

Figure 5.1-2. Phases of service use from customer's point of view (from 22.278 [4] Figure 2)

Figure 5.1-2 shows the different phases of service use from the customer's point of view. These phases are defined as follows:

- Network access: The UE display (or some other means) will inform customers that they can use the services of a particular network operator.
- Service access: If a customer wants to use a service, the network operator should provide access to the service as quickly as possible.
- Service retainability: This term describes the termination of services, which may be initiated by the customer or not.
- Service integrity: This term describes the quality of service provided to the customer during service use.

Note that the different QoS levels provided for real-time and non-real-time services will be differentiated with regard to such parameters as maximum end-to-end delay, packet size, packet drop percentage, etc. Bandwidth is not used to define a QoS level, according to 22.278 [4].

5.1.4 Multiple Access and Seamless Mobility

A major requirement of the EPS is the inclusion of multiple access technologies, with mobility between heterogeneous access systems. The EPS is expected to manage handovers between all relevant technologies: 3GPP, non-3GPP mobile and even fixed access systems.

To facilitate seamless mobility in existing networks, a function has been available in some proprietary implementations to perform "local breakout" in legacy networks. This function is now part of the requirements for the EPS. The technique can provide significant operational cost efficiencies in managing certain types of user traffic. Briefly, local breakout is a means of efficiently routing user traffic when the end points for the traffic are located within an operator-defined network region. This technique can be applied, for example, to a voice call between two users in the same cell, or to Internet access that is local to the eNB. Local breakout is fully controlled and authorized by the Home Public Land Mobile Network (HPLMN).

5.1.5 Service Continuity

A key aspect of mobility is service continuity, which is the system's ability to continue providing multicast and broadcast services during a session when the access system changes, if those services are supported in the target access system.

The EPS is required to support bidirectional service continuity between cdma2000 1xRTT, cdma2000 1xEV-DO, Mobile WiMAX and the E-UTRAN. It is also expected to manage bidirectional service continuity between Mobile WiMAX and GERAN/UTRAN packet switching. Thus the EPS should work in conjunction with almost any legacy system, enabling a truly global standard and implementation.

5.1.6 Access Network Discovery and Steering of Access

In existing W-CDMA networks, Inter-Radio Access Technology (I-RAT) handovers are often made after the UE performs certain measurements in compressed mode. However, this mechanism reduces the performance of the ongoing transmission and consumes unnecessary resources from both the network and the handset. The EPS has a requirement to facilitate service continuation by supplying relevant access-network information to the UE.

When the UE accesses the EPC via a non-3GPP Radio Access Technology (RAT), the registered Public Land Mobile Network (PLMN) may request the UE to use the E-UTRA instead, for reasons of load balancing, operator policy or service mobility. If the home PLMN and the registered PLMN have different "views" of which access technology should be selected, the registered PLMN takes precedence. Note that the UE can re-select the PLMN.

5.1.7 Performance Requirements for the EPC

The same performance is required of the EPC as of the EPS. Some of the most important requirements are repeated below:

- Ability to support instantaneous peak packet data rates of 100 Mbps on the radio access bearer downlink to the UE and 50 Mbps on the uplink.
- Ability to provide lower user and control plane latency than existing 3GPP access networks. The maximum delay should be comparable to that of fixed broadband Internet access technologies — less than 5 ms in ideal conditions.
- Ability to support large volumes of mixed voice, data and multimedia traffic. Enhanced load balancing and steering of roaming methods will be used to minimize cell congestion.

System complexity and mobility management signalling levels will be optimized to reduce infrastructure and operating costs. UE power consumption also will be minimized accordingly. Interrupt time during the handover of RT and NRT services will be kept to a minimum, not to exceed the values defined in 25.913 [7].

5.1.8 Security and Privacy Requirements

Network security and privacy must be at least as good as in previous standards and must address security threats from the Internet as well as "traditional" threats to the telecom network. Security requirements include the ability to perform lawful interception.

5.1.9 Charging Requirements

The EPS will support various charging models including all those specified in 22.115 [8].

5.2 Overview of the Evolved Packet System

The previous section covered the major requirements for the EPS. The network elements and interfaces defined by 3GPP for the new system, along with legacy Packet Switched (PS) and Circuit Switched (CS) elements, are shown in Figure 5.2-1. The new elements and interfaces are defined in Chapter 4, and their functions will be discussed in this chapter. The high level functions of the overall system will be considered next.

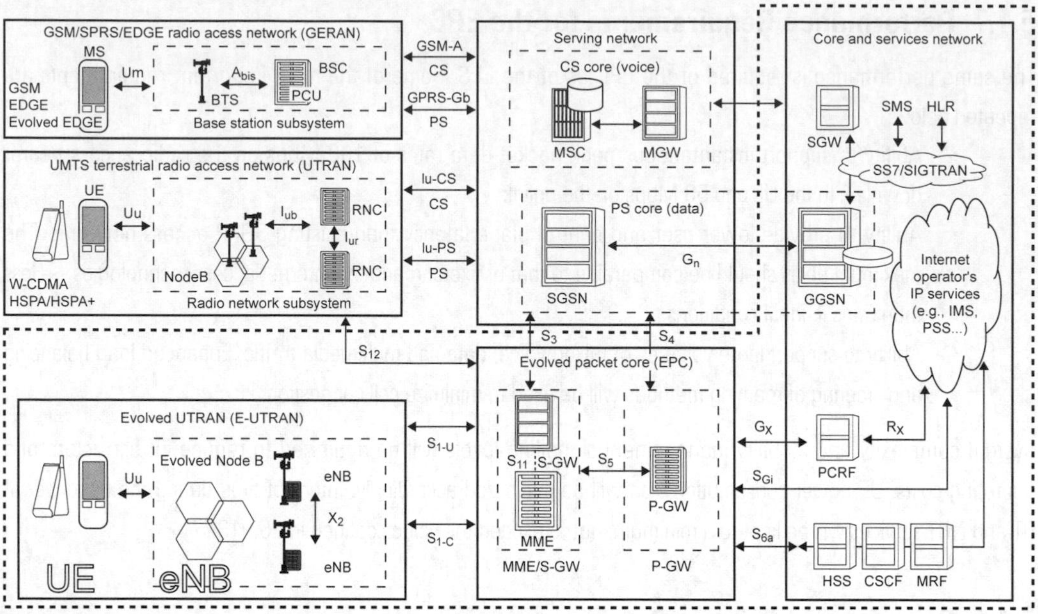

Figure 5.2-1. Overview of the EPS and legacy 3GPP RANs

5.2.1 High Level Functions of the EPS

The logical functions performed within the EPS are listed here. Each one will be described briefly.

- Network access control
- Packet routing and transfer
- Security
- Mobility management
- Radio resource management
- Network management
- Selection
- IP network
- S1-flex
- E-UTRAN sharing

5.2.1.1 Network Access Control

Network/access network selection functionality provides a means by which a UE selects a PLMN access network from which to gain IP connectivity. The network/access network selection procedure varies for different access technologies. For 3GPP access networks, the network selection principles are described in 23.122 [9]. The access network selection procedures are described in 36.300 [10], 43.022 [11] and 25.304 [12]. Architectural impacts stemming from support for network/access network selection procedures for non-3GPP access, and between 3GPP and non-3GPP accesses, are described in 23.402 [2].

Authentication and authorization functionality performs the identification and authentication of the service requester and the validation of the service request type to ensure that the user is authorized to use the particular network services. The authentication function is performed by the Mobile Management Entity (MME) and HSS/HLR in association with the EPS mobility management functions.

Admission control functionality determines whether requested radio and network resources are available and, if so, reserves those resources. Radio admission control is performed, for example, at the target eNB during intra-LTE handovers. Criteria for consideration include QoS requirements and priority levels for sessions in progress and sessions to be admitted.

Policy and charging enforcement functionality includes service data flow detection, policy enforcement and flow-based charging as defined in 23.203 [13]. This function is located at the Packet Data Network Gateway (PDN-GW) for EPS, supporting both online and offline charging functions as outlined in 32.240 [14].

Lawful interception functionality allows the network operator or service provider to make certain information available for law enforcement purposes. Lawful interception general requirements within the 3G mobile system are outlined in 33.106 [15]. Stage 2 architecture and functional requirements for EPS and 3G mobile systems in general are described in 33.107 [16]. Stage 3 handover interfaces for lawful interception for UMTS and EPS networks are covered in 33.108 [17].

5.2.1.2 Packet Routing and Transfer

For packet routing and transfer, IP header compression functionality optimizes the use of radio capacity. IP header compression techniques such as Robust Header Compression (RoHC) are used for user plane data in the eNB.

5.2.1.3 Security

Security functionality in the EPS provides the following:

- Protection from unauthorized EPS service usage by using UE authentication provided by EPS Authentication and Key Agreement (AKA)
- User identity confidentiality with SAE Temporary Mobile Subscriber Identity (S-TMSI)
- User data and signalling confidentiality
- Origin authentication of signalling data with integrity protection
- Authentication of the network by the UE

Ciphering and integrity protection are performed in the MME for the Non Access Stratum (NAS) and in the eNB for the Access Stratum (AS). Refer to 33.401 [18] for more details on security architecture for SAE and 33.402 [19] for security aspects of non-3GPP accesses. Network interface physical link protection is performed in Network Domain Security (NDS) architecture as detailed in 33.210 [20]. The security protocols are Internet Engineering Task Force (IETF) defined IP Security (IPSec), specified in IETF RFC 2401 [21]. Encapsulating Security Payload (ESP) in tunnel mode is recommended with transport mode implementation optional.

5.2.1.4 Mobility Management

Mobility management comprises many functions.

UE reachability management within the ECM-IDLE state: Tracks the location of a UE in the ECM-IDLE state to the level of the Tracking Area (TA) list. All cells in the TA list are paged during a UE-terminated call session. An EMM-registered UE performs periodic TA updates. The MME maintains a similar UE-reachable timer as the periodic Tracking Area Update (TAU) timer, which is used to determine whether the UE is out of E-UTRAN coverage so that the appropriate network resource can be released.

Tracking area list management: Sends the TA list from an MME to the UE, which identifies the TAs that can be entered without performing a TA update procedure.

Inter-eNB mobility anchor: Anchors the user plane for E-UTRAN mobility (e.g., intra-LTE handovers). At the time of this writing, the functionality resides in the serving gateway.

Inter-3GPP mobility anchor: Anchors the user plane for mobility between 3GPP 2G/3G access systems and the E-UTRA access system. At the time of this writing, the functionality resides in the serving gateway.

Idle mode signalling reduction: Provides a mechanism to limit signalling during inter-RAT cell-reselection in idle mode (ECM-IDLE, EMM-IDLE, GPRS STANDBY states). In relation to Circuit Switched Fallback (CSFB) operations, the MME requests the Serving GPRS Support Node (SGSN) via the S3 interface to simultaneously page the UE within its Routing Area (RA).

Mobility restriction: Imposes restrictions on the handling of a UE in E-UTRAN access. This functionality is provided by the UE, the radio access network and the core network. In ECM-IDLE state, mobility restriction is executed in the UE based on information received from the core network: for example, various rejections of requests such as attach, tracking area update, service request or detach, or messages such as tracking area not allowed or not available for EPS services. Mobility restriction in ECM-CONNECTED state is executed in the radio network and the core network. In this state the core network EPS Mobility Management (EMM) provides the radio network (eNB) with a handover restriction list over the S1 interface and transferred within the E-UTRAN during X2-initiated handovers. The handover restriction list specifies PLMN roaming, TA, Location Area (LA), and access (inter-RAT) restrictions.

5.2.1.5 Radio Resource Management

Radio Resource Management (RRM) functions ensure efficient use of the available radio resources and provide mechanisms that enable the E-UTRAN to meet radio resource requirements identified in subclause 10 of 25.913 [7]. In particular, RRM provides the means to manage (assign, reassign and release) radio resources, taking into account single and multi-cell aspects.

RRM functions in the E-UTRAN include

- Radio bearer control — Establishes, maintains, and releases radio bearers and configures the associated radio resources.

- Radio admission control — Admits or rejects the establishment request of new radio bearers.
- Connection mobility control — Manages radio resources in connection with idle or connected mode mobility.
- Dynamic resource allocation/packet scheduling — Allocates and de-allocates resources for sending data over the air interface.
- Inter-cell interference coordination — Manages radio resources (especially radio resource blocks) and ensures that inter-cell interference is kept at a minimum.
- Load balancing — Handles uneven distribution of traffic loads over multiple cells, which may result in traffic re-distribution in cases of intra-eNB and inter-eNB (intra-E-UTRAN).
- Inter-RAT RRM — Manages radio resources in connection with inter-RAT mobility, especially handovers in consideration of target RAT resourcing, UE capabilities and operator policies. Inter-RAT RRM also includes inter-RAT load balancing from idle and connected mode UEs.
- Subscriber Profile ID (SPID) — The SPID for RAT/frequency priority parameters received by the eNB via the S1 interface is an index of user information (e.g., mobility profile, service usage profile and roaming restrictions). The information is UE-specific and applies to all its radio bearers. This index is mapped by the eNB to locally defined configurations in order to apply specific RRM strategies (e.g., to define RRC_IDLE mode priorities and control inter-RAT/inter-frequency handover in RRC_CONNECTED mode).

Refer to 36.300 [10] for further information on the RRM in the E-UTRAN.

5.2.1.6 Network Management

MME load balancing functionality permits UEs that are entering into an MME pool area to be directed to an appropriate MME in a manner that achieves load balancing. Each MME assumes a Weight Factor (WF), which typically is based on the capacity of the MME itself relative to other MME nodes within the same MME pool. This WF (also known as relative MME capacity) is transmitted to the eNBs associated with the MME via S1-Application Protocol (S1-AP) messages as defined in 36.413 [22] and is used by the eNBs for MME selection.

MME load re-balancing functionality permits UEs that are registered to a particular MME (EMM-REGISTERED) to be moved to another MME within the MME pool. To offload UEs in ECM-CONNECTED state (a session with an active S1 connection), the S1 and Radio Resource Control (RRC) connections are released, while requesting the UE to perform a TAU so that another MME can be selected via the MME selection function. Offloading UEs in ECM-IDLE state can be achieved either by transitioning the UEs to ECM-CONNECTED state (through paging procedures) or by awaiting the next TAU or attach procedures.

MME control overload functionality is used to handle potential overload conditions. This is done either by rejecting NAS requests from UEs or by restricting the load from associated eNBs via S1-AP overload control procedures. Overload actions may include rejecting all connection requests for EMM signalling, non-emergency mobile-originated data transfer, or permitting only emergency sessions when activated.

5.2.1.7 Network Entity Selection

Packet data network gateway selection functionality allocates a PDN-GW to provide the PDN connectivity for 3GPP access. This function uses subscriber information provided in the HSS, which includes the PDN subscription contexts, hence the associated PDN GWs. The UE provides the requested Access Point Name (APN) for the PDN GW selection function in order to establish connectivity with additional PDNs simultaneously.

Serving gateway selection functionality allocates an available S-GW for a UE session. Selection is based mainly on network topology, by determining the S-GW that serves the UE's location. The MME must ensure that all TAs in the TA list belong to the selected S-GW service area. Service area overlap between S-GWs can occur; for example, in load-balancing between S-GWs. In the case of integrated PDN-GW and S-GW nodes, the S-GW selected should preferably also be the PDN-GW for the UE. S-GW support for GPRS Tunneling Protocol (GTP) and Proxy Mobile Internet Protocol (PMIP) variants should also be part of the selection criteria, as subscribers of GTP-only networks can roam into PMIP networks.

MME selection functionality allocates an available MME for a UE session. Selection is based mainly on network topology, determining the MME that serves the UE's location. The MME must ensure that all TAs in the TA list belong to the selected S-GW service area. Service area overlaps can occur between MMEs; for example, in load-balancing between MMEs.

SGSN selection functionality allocates an available SGSN for a UE session. Selection is based mainly on network topology, determining the SGSN that serves the UE's location. Service area overlaps are possible between SGSNs; for example, in load-balancing between SGSNs.

Policy and Changing Rules Function (PCRF) selection functionality allocates an available PCRF for a UE session.

5.2.1.8 IP Network

Directory Name Service (DNS) functionality resolves logical names to IP addresses for EPS nodes, including the PDN-GWs. Dynamic Host Configuration Protocol (DHCP) functionality allows delivery of IP configuration information to the UEs.

5.2.1.9 S1-Flex

S1-flex defines a multi-to-multi relationship between the eNBs and the EPC nodes — in other words, a single eNB may connect to more than one MME or S-GW. In the EMM-REGISTERED state, a UE will be served by the same MME, unless relocated for various reasons such as being out of the pool area or for offloading purposes within the EPC pool.

The NAS node selection function is available in the eNB to determine the MME association and thus perform proper routing on the S1 interface via the Globally Unique Temporary Identity (GUTI) allocated by the serving MME. If the UE identifies itself with the GUTI and then changes serving MME, the new MME should initiate an identification request procedure with the old MME via the S10 interface to retrieve the UE's International Mobile Subscriber Identity (IMSI).

5.2.1.10 E-UTRAN Sharing

E-UTRAN sharing allows different core network operators to connect to a shared RAN. System information broadcast in each of the shared cells contains the Tracking Area Identity (TAI) consisting of the Tracking Area Code (TAC) and PLMN Id, which comprises the Mobile Network Code (MNC) and the Mobile Country Code (MCC).

The selected PLMN Id is sent by the UE to the eNB and is used for MME selection if the registered MME information is not available. Otherwise, the eNB routes the UE session to the registered MME.

5.2.2 EPS Connection and Mobility Management States

5.2.2.1 EPS Connection Management States

EPS Connection Management (ECM) states describe the signalling connectivity between the UE and the EPC. Two states are defined: ECM-IDLE and ECM-CONNECTED. These are also referred to as EMM-IDLE and EMM-CONNECTED modes, respectively, in 24.301 [23]. Table 5.2-1 summarizes some of the key differences between the two ECM states.

Table 5.2-1. EPS connection management states

ECM states	ECM-IDLE	ECM-CONNECTED
Signalling connection between MME and EPC	Disconnected S1/RRC and S101 tunneling interface connections do not exist	Connected S1/RRC or S101 tunneling interface connection exists
UE context in E-UTRAN	Does not exist	Exists
UE context in MME and UE	Limited	Exists
UE location status in MME (minimum resolution)	EMM-REGISTERED • Tracking area list resolution EMM-DEREGISTERED • Unknown	EMM-REGISTERED • Cell during initial connection establishment • eNB subsequently; e.g., MME might not be informed of intra-eNB handovers EMM-DEREGISTERED • Unknown
ECM State Transition	S1 and RRC Connection Establishment	S1 and RRC Connection Disconnection
Mobility	EMM-REGISTERED • Cell Re-Selection EMM-DEREGISTERED • PLMN, Cell Selection	EMM-REGISTERED • Intra-E-UTRAN Handover • Inter-RAT Handover EMM-DEREGISTERED • PLMN, Cell Selection
Mobility Restriction Execution	UE based on info from CN	E-UTRAN (Handover Restrict List) EPC
UE AS Security Context	No	Yes
EPS Bearer Context(s)	EMM-REGISTERED • Available (Maybe out of sync between UE and EPC) EMM-DEREGISTERED • Not Available	EMM-REGISTERED • Available (UE and EPC in-sync) EMM-DEREGISTERED • Not Available

5.2.2.2 EPS Mobility Management States

EPS Mobility Management (EMM) states describe the relationship between the UE and the MME resulting from mobility procedures. Two main states are defined, EMM-DEREGISTERED and EMM-REGISTERED. Table 5.2-2 summarizes some of the key differences between the two main EMM states. Note that additional EMM main and sub-states have been specified; see 24.301 [23] for more details.

Table 5.2-2. EPS mobility management states

EMM States	EMM-DEREGISTERED	EMM-REGISTERED
UE location status in MME (minimum resolution)	Unknown	ECM-IDLE • Tracking area list EMM-CONNECTED • eNB
Dependencies on ECM state for EMM state transition	ECM-CONNECTED state during transit to EMM-REGISTERED	No
Mobility	PLMN, cell selection	ECM-IDLE • Cell re-selection ECM-CONNECTED • Intra-E-UTRAN handover • Inter-RAT handover
Tracking area updates	No	Yes
EPS bearer contexts	Not available	Available with minimum default bearer ECM-IDLE • UE and EPC may be out of sync ECM-CONNECTED • UE and EPC in-sync

5.2.2.3 ECM and EMM State Transitions and Relationship

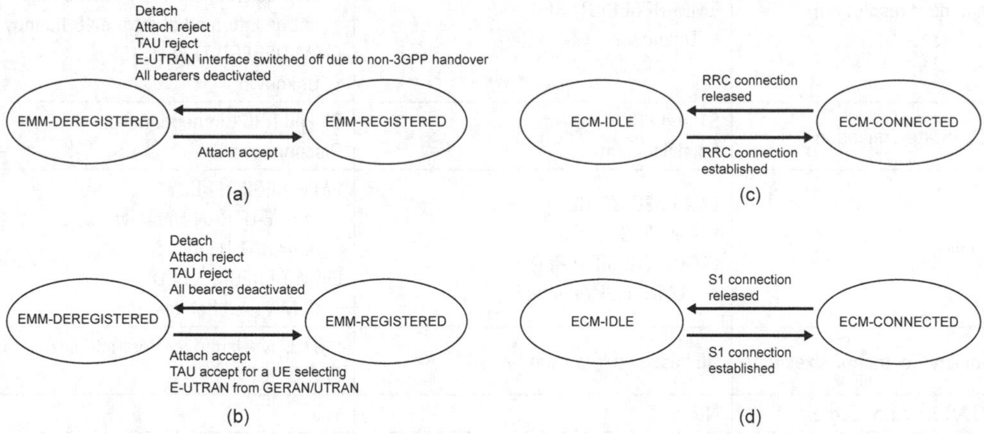

Figure 5.2-2. ECM and EMM state transition models (from 23.401 [1]):
(a) EMM state model in UE (Fig. 4.6.4-1); (b) EMM state model in MME (Fig. 4.6.4-2);
(c) ECM state model in UE (Fig. 4.6.4-3); (d) ECM state model in MME (Fig. 4.6.4-4)

Figure 5.2-2 shows the main ECM and EMM state transition models. Together the ECM and EMM form a multi-dimensional state model, specifying varying network and UE behaviors. For example, when the UE is in the ECM-IDLE and EMM-REGISTERED states, it performs a periodic TAU; however, the TAU is not performed if the UE is in the EMM-DEREGISTERED state.

The ECM and EMM have minimum dependencies on each other, apart from the state transitions summarized in Table 5.2-3.

Table 5.2-3. ECM and EMM state transition dependencies

EMM and ECM state independence	ECM-IDLE and EMM-REGISTERED (e.g., attached but non-active session)	
	ECM-IDLE and EMM-DEREGISTERED (e.g., detached)	
	ECM-CONNECTED and EMM-REGISTERED (e.g., attached and active)	
	ECM-CONNECTED and EMM-DEREGISTERED (e.g., detach in progress)	
State transition dependencies	**State Transition**	
	ECM State	**EMM State**
	ECM-IDLE to ECM-CONNECTED	EMM-REGISTERED/EMM-DEREGISTERED
	ECM-CONNECTED to ECM-IDLE	EMM-REGISTERED/EMM-DEREGISTERED
	EMM State	**ECM State**
	EMM-DEREGISTERED to EMM-REGISTERED	**ECM-CONNECTED**
	EMM-REGISTERED to EMM-DEREGISTERED	ECM-IDLE/ECM-CONNECTED

See 24.301 [23] for more details on ECM and EMM states and state transition models.

5.2.3 E-UTRAN

5.2.3.1 E-UTRAN Architecture

The E-UTRAN consists of evolved Node Bs (eNBs) that provide the E-UTRA user plane and control plane protocol terminations towards the UE. Note that the user plane protocols are the Packet Data Control Plane (PDCP), Radio Link Control (RLC), Medium Access Control (MAC) and Physical Layer (PHY) protocols; the control plane protocol is the Radio Resource Control (RRC) protocol. An eNB is a logical network component that serves one or more E-UTRAN cells. An eNB can support FDD mode, TDD mode or dual mode operation.

The eNBs are interconnected by means of the X2 interface, shown in Figure 5.2-3. They are connected to the Evolved Packet Core by means of the S1 interface. More specifically, they are connected to the MME by means of the S1-MME and to the Serving Gateway (S-GW) by means of the S1-U.

The E-UTRAN also may contain Home eNBs (HeNBs), which can be connected to the EPC either directly or via an HeNB GW, as shown in Figure 5.2-3. The HeNB GW provides additional support for a large number of HeNBs, primarily serving as an S1-MME concentrator to the HeNBs. The S1-U from the HeNB may be routed through the HeNB GW or S-GW via direct tunneling. S1 interface functions between the HeNB and EPC are the same whether the HeNB GW is in use or not.

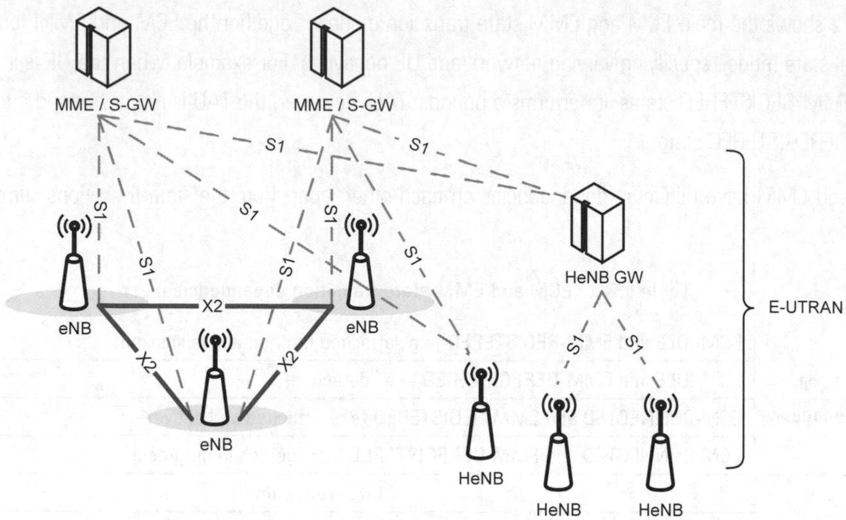

Figure 5.2-3. E-UTRAN architecture with deployed HeNB GW (from 36.300 [10] Fig. 4.6.1-2)

In Release 8, inter-connectivity of HeNBs is not supported. In other words, there are no X2 interfaces between HeNBs. The S1 interface supports many-to-many relationships between eNBs, HeNBs, and HeNB GWs and MME/S-GWs in the EPC. The HeNB can be connected to a single HeNB GW only as S1-flex is not at this time available for this element.

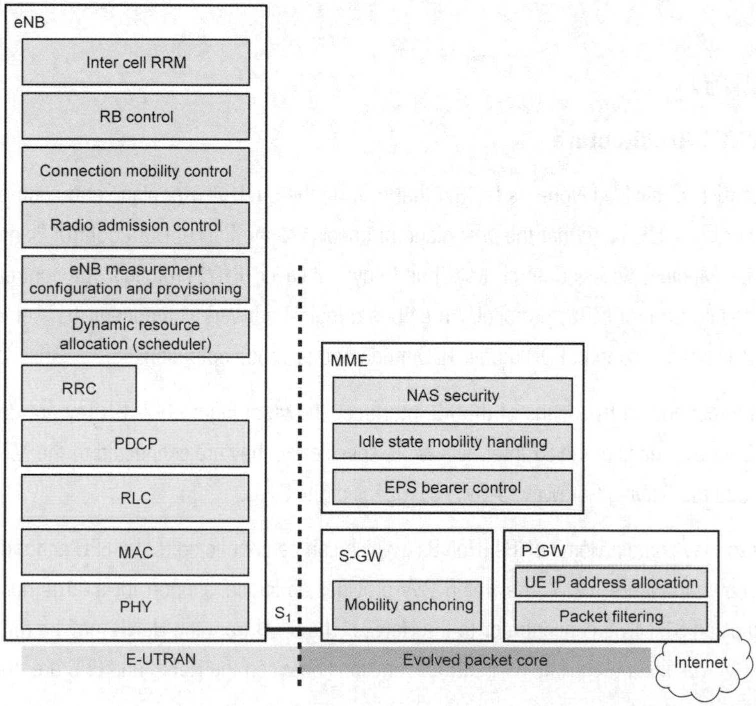

Figure 5.2-4. Functional split between E-UTRAN and EPC (from 36.300 [10] Fig. 4.1-1)

5.2.3.2 E-UTRAN Functions

Figure 5.2-4 shows the functional split between the E-UTRAN and the EPC in the EPS. The E-UTRAN hosts the following functions:

Radio resource management functions, described in Section 5.2.1.5, consist of radio bearer control, radio admission control, connection mobility control, dynamic allocation of resources to UEs in both the uplink and the downlink (scheduling), load balancing and Inter-Cell Interference Coordination (ICIC).

Compression and decompression of IP headers, which takes place at the PDCP protocol layer in the E-UTRAN and UE for the Data Radio Bearers (DRBs) using an RoHC technique, facilitating efficient transmission over the air interface. Signalling Radio Bearers (SRBs) are not subjected to RoHC compression.

Security feature provisioning, which includes (1) user to network security — confidentiality (ciphering/deciphering) and integrity protection of user data streams over the radio channel (SRBs and DRBs) and (2) network domain security — security protection for control and user plane data on the transport network layer of the E-UTRAN interfaces as outlined in 33.210 [20].

NAS node selection functionality, which is located in the E-UTRAN in order to determine the MME association of the UE based on (1) the UE temporary identifier assigned to the UE by the MME if the UE is already registered at a particular MME or (2) the MME selection function, which considers load balancing, when the serving MME cannot be determined.

User data transfer, which involves user plane data routing between the S-GW (via S1-U) and the UE (via the Uu air interface) with the following bearer level functions:

- Uplink bearer level rate enforcement based on UE Aggregate Maximum Bit Rate (UE-AMBR) and Maximum Bit Rate (MBR) via means of uplink scheduling (e.g., by limiting the amount of uplink resources granted per UE over time) for non-Guaranteed Bit Rate (GBR) and GBR bearers, respectively.
- Downlink bearer level rate enforcement based on UE-AMBR related to the UE's subscription profile for non-GBR bearers.
- Uplink and downlink bearer level admission control.

Transport level packet marking is performed in the uplink — e.g., setting the DiffServ Code Point — based on the QoS Class Identifier (QCI) of the associated EPS bearer.

Paging functions, which handle scheduling and transmission of paging messages originated by the MME and received over the S1-MME interface.

Information broadcast functions, which handle scheduling and transmission of broadcast messages related to the AS or NAS.

Mobility management, which is based on the following radio measurements: intra-E-UTRAN (intra- and inter-frequency), 3GPP inter-RAT (GERAN/UTRAN) and non-3GPP RAT (cdma2000 1xRTT, cdma2000 HRPD,

WiMAX, etc). Mobility can be performed in E-UTRAN connected (RRC_CONNECTED) or non-connected (RRC_IDLE) states.

In the RRC_CONNECTED state, mobility is network controlled. The handover decision is initiated by the network, typically based on UE assisted handover measurement reports as configured by the network. Handovers also can be performed as part of load balancing within the EPS (e.g., MME load re-balancing) or between RATs (e.g., offloading speech calls to 3GPP legacy RATs via CSFB).

In RRC_IDLE state, mobility is UE controlled. This typically involves network and cell selection/re-selection, based on the 3GPP PLMN selection principles. RRC state definitions, transitions and procedures are covered in 36.331 [24].

Intra-E-UTRAN mobility

Idle mode mobility such as cell selection is required upon transition from the EMM-DETACHED to EMM-REGISTERED state and from the ECM-IDLE to ECM-CONNECTED state. Connected mode (ECM-CONNECTED) mobility can be either an X2-initiated handover or S1-initiated handover. The latter is used most often in the case of no X2 connectivity between eNBs, an unsuccessful attempt of X2-initiated handover, or a handover involving a change in the EPC node.

The handover procedure consists of the following phases.

- Handover preparation and resource allocation
- Handover decision and execution including PDCP status transfers
- Handover completion including cleaning up of resources in the source cell

Preparation time and interruption time are split, as the latter should be minimized to reduce handover effects on service quality. Requirements are defined in 25.913 [7].

Data forwarding can be configured for Radio Link Control (RLC) Acknowledged Mode Data (AMD) and Unacknowledged Mode Data (UMD) bearers to avoid data loss. Path switch procedures over the S1 interface are used in X2-initiated handovers to request switching of user plane paths from the source eNB to the target eNB upon successful acquisition of the UE by the target cell. End markers are sent via the "old path" through the source eNB via the S1-U interface and propagated over the X2-User (X2-U) interface to mark the end of data forwarding in the downlink.

3GPP Inter-RAT (GERAN/UTRAN) mobility

Connected mode (ECM-CONNTECED) mobility is supported for handovers to and from the E-UTRAN and 3GPP legacy RANs, including the UTRAN and GERAN. Handover procedures consist of phases similar to that of Intra-E-UTRAN handovers and include support for Single Radio Voice Call Continuity (SRVCC).

Key interfaces used for 3GPP inter-RAT handovers include

- S3, MME and SGSN
- S4, S-GW and SGSN
- S12, S-GW and UTRAN via user plane direct tunneling
- Sv, MME and MSC/VLR for SRVCC support

Non-3GPP Inter-RAT (cdma2000 HRPD) mobility

Optimized handovers between E-UTRAN and cdma2000 HRPD access are split into two phases to reduce total service interruption time:

- Pre-registration
- Handover

The pre-registration phase involves the UE registering to the cdma2000 HRPD Access Network (AN) or MME, while remaining connected to the source RAN (E-UTRAN or HRPD AN). The actual handover phase involves the UE leaving the source RAN (E-UTRAN or HRPD AN) and joining the target RAN, while the resources on the source RAN and core network are released accordingly. The E-UTRAN and EPC support tunneling of cdma2000 signalling messages between the cdma2000 HRPD AN and UE over the S1 and S101 interfaces during both handover phases. The S103 interface is used for user plane data forwarding via Generic Routing Encapsulation (GRE) tunnels during the optimized handover procedure, and between the S-GW and HRPD GW during E-UTRAN to HRPD handovers. The S101 tunnel between the serving MME and HRPD AN can be redirected during a serving MME relocation.

Non-optimized handovers can be performed as well; for example, in cases in which pre-registration has failed, or if optimized handovers are not readily available, as when S101 or S103 functionality is lacking in the MME or HRPD AN.

Non-3GPP Inter-RAT (cdma2000 1xRTT) mobility

Handovers between E-UTRAN and cdma2000 1xRTT access are used to provide Single Radio Voice Call Continuity (SRVCC) and 1xRTT CSFB functionality. A cdma2000 1xRTT CS Interworking Solution (IWS) with an S102 interface can transfer tunneled signalling messages between the SRVCC UE and cdma2000 1xRTT Mobile Switching Center (MSC). In the cdma2000 1xRTT CSFB, pre-registration with cdma2000 1xRTT is supported. E-UTRAN and EPC support tunneling of cdma2000 signalling messages between the cdma2000 1xRTT and UE over the S1 and S102 interfaces during the SRVCC handover procedure.

Location reporting of the UE, which is requested by the MME. Reports are made directly or upon serving cell change, and reporting stops upon change of serving cell. This function is applicable only in the ECM-CONNECTED state. Location reports should include E-UTRAN Cell Global Id (ECGI), Tracking Area Id (TAI) and the request type that triggered the report.

Earthquake and Tsunami Warning System (ETWS) scheduling and transmission. ETWS messages originate from the MME. S1-AP procedures are used to configure the eNB to broadcast ETWS contents to a specific area (ECGI, TAI, or Emergency Area Id List) or to all cells of the eNB.

RAN sharing, which is based on support for multi-to-multi relationships between E-UTRAN nodes and EPC nodes (via S1-flex). The E-UTRAN broadcasts the TAIs of each shared cell, consisting of the PLMN Id of each operator and the TAC. The NAS Node Selection Function (NNSF) is used by the eNB to correctly route the messages over the S1 interface to the appropriate MME.

Self-configuration process pre-operational state, in which newly deployed nodes are configured by automatic installation procedures to a basic configuration for system operation. This support includes basic setup and initial radio configuration functions. Some of the use cases include dynamic configuration of S1-MME and X2 interfaces and the Automatic Neighbour Relation (ANR) function. See 36.902 [25] for more details on use cases and solutions for self-configuring networks.

Self-optimization process operational state, in which UE and eNB measurements and performance measurements are used to auto-tune the network. This support includes optimization and adaption functions. See 36.902 [25] for more details on use cases and solutions for self optimizing networks.

Subscriber and equipment trace support, which for LTE and EPS is covered in 32.421 [26], 32.422 [27], 32.423 [28], 32.441 [29], 32.442 [30] and 32.443 [31]. All traces are initiated by the core network, even if the trace is to be carried out in the radio network. Trace procedures in the eNB are configured by the MME and include trace control and configuration parameters (activation, deactivation), interfaces to be traced (Uu, S1, X2) and trace depth (minimum, medium, maximum and vendor-specific levels). The UE session associated signalling messaging has to be used in the ECM-CONNECTED state. Tracing is implicitly deactivated in the ECM-IDLE state. A trace setup in the radio network will be propagated on the X2 interface at handover and on the S1 interface if the handover is carried out between MMEs.

RAN Information Management (RIM) function, which is a generic mechanism that allows the request and transfer of information (e.g., GERAN system information) between two RAN nodes via the core network. In the EPS, RIM data is transferred between the E-UTRAN and GERAN through the MME and SGSN respectively over the S3 interface. RIM information is transferred from the E-UTRAN to the MME over the S1 interface via S1-AP procedures.

5.2.4 EPC Elements

The functional split in the EPS moves important control plane and gateway functions to the EPC, as shown in Figure 5.2-4.

5.2.4.1 Mobility Management Entity

The Mobility Management Entity (MME) is the control plane entity in the EPS and hosts the following functions, which are defined in 36.300 [10].

- NAS signalling and security
- AS security control
- Inter-core-network node signalling for mobility between 3GPP access networks
- Idle mode UE reachability (including control and execution of paging retransmission)
- Tracking area list management (for UE in idle and active mode)
- PDN GW and Serving GW selection
- MME selection for handovers with MME change
- SGSN selection for 3GPP handovers to 2G or 3G access networks

- Roaming (S6a towards home HSS)
- Authentication
- Bearer management functions including dedicated bearer establishment
- Support for ETWS message transmission
- Lawful Interception of signalling traffic

5.2.4.2 Serving Gateway

The Serving Gateway (S-GW) is the gateway that terminates the EPC interface towards the E-UTRAN via the S1-U interface. For each UE associated with the EPS, at any given point in time there will be a single S-GW hosting the following functions, which are defined in 36.300 [10].

- Local mobility anchor point for inter-eNB handover
- Mobility anchoring for inter-3GPP mobility
- E-UTRAN idle mode downlink packet buffering and initiation of network triggered service request procedure
- Lawful Interception
- Packet routing and forwarding
- Transport level packet marking in the uplink and the downlink
- Accounting on user and QCI granularity for inter-operator charging
- Uplink and downlink charging per UE, PDN and QCI

5.2.4.3 Packet Data Network Gateway

The PDN-GW is the gateway that terminates the SGi interface towards the PDN. If a UE accesses multiple PDNs, it may be assigned more than one PDN GW. The following functions are supported as defined in 36.300 [10].

- Per-user based packet filtering (by deep packet inspection, for example)
- Lawful Interception
- UE IP address allocation
- Transport level packet marking in the downlink
- Uplink and downlink service level charging, gating and rate enforcement
- Downlink rate enforcement based on AMB

Other network elements are central to EPS functionality — for example, the HSS, SGSN, PCRF, etc. See 23.002 [32] for more details.

5.2.4.4 Definitions

The following terms are important for understanding EPC functionality and processes.

MME area is the part of the network served by an MME. An MME area consists of one or several TAs. All cells served by an eNB are included in an MME area. There is no one-to-one relationship between an MME area and an MSC/VLR area. Multiple MMEs may share the same MME area, and MME areas may overlap each other.

MME pool area is an area where intra-domain connection of RAN nodes to multiple core network nodes is applied. Within a pool area, a UE may be served without needing to change the serving MME. An MME pool area is served by one or more MMEs (a "pool of MMEs") in parallel. MME pool areas are also a collection of complete TAs. MME pool areas may overlap each other.

S-GW service area is defined as an area within which a UE may be served without needing to change the S-GW. An S-GW service area is served by one or more S-GWs in parallel. S-GW service areas are a collection of complete TAs, and S-GW service areas may overlap each other. There is no one to one relationship between an MME area and an S-GW service area.

Tracking Area (TA) includes one or several E-UTRAN cells. The network allocates a list with one or more TAs to the UE. In certain modes of operation, the UE may move freely in all TAs in the list, without updating the MME, via EMM TA update procedures. A single physical cell may belong to more than one TA.

5.2.5 Reference Points (Interfaces)

This section describes the new reference points (interfaces) in the EPS and their key functions in the network.

5.2.5.1 S1 Interfaces

Two S1 interfaces have been defined between the E-UTRAN and the EPC as shown in Figures 5.2-5 and 5.2-6.

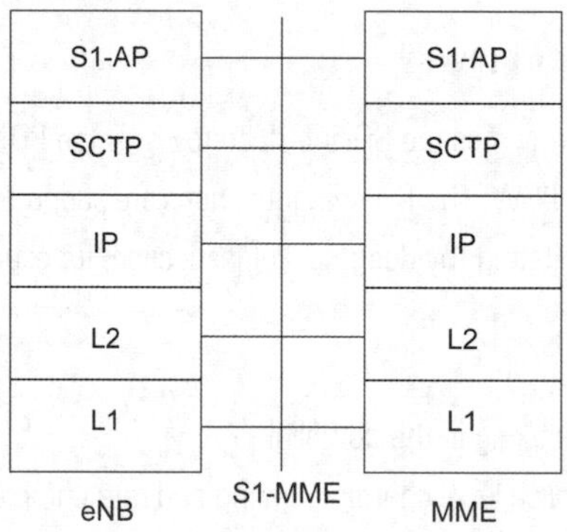

Figure 5.2-5. S1-MME reference point between E-UTRAN and MME

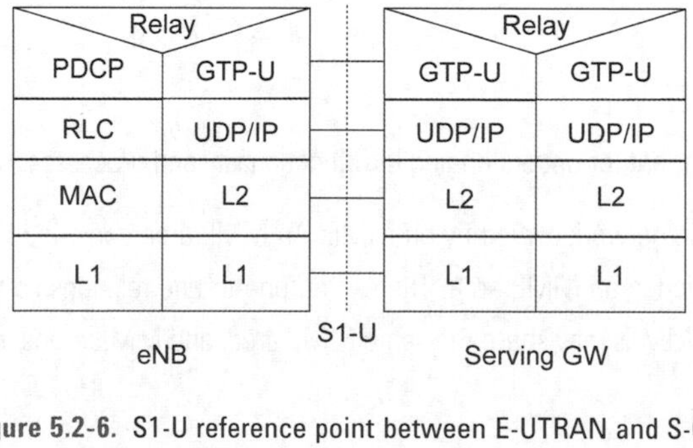

Figure 5.2-6. S1-U reference point between E-UTRAN and S-GW

S1-MME Interface

S1-MME is defined between the eNB and the MME for the control plane protocol, S1-AP, in 36.413 [22]. The EPS NAS, defined in 24.301 [23], is transported transparently over S1-AP, terminating at the MME. The S Common Transport Protocol (SCTP) transport layer provisions the network for guaranteed S1-AP delivery.

A UE-associated logical connection over the S1-MME interface is uniquely identified using the eNB UE S1-AP Id and MME UE S1-AP Id pair. These identifiers will be allocated and maintained throughout the duration of the UE-associated logical S1 connection with the UE, and will be included in all UE-associated S1-AP signalling procedures exchanged over the S1-MME interface.

The eNB UE S1-AP Id and MME UE S1-AP Id are unique within the eNB and MME logical nodes that have allocated these Ids. During the path switch operation — the X2-initiated handover completion phase at the target eNB — the source MME UE S1-AP Id, as received in the X2-AP handover request message, is forwarded from the target eNB to the serving MME to allow the MME to locate the related UE context. Note that there is no MME relocation as part of the X2-initiated handover procedure, although S-GW relocation is possible. The target eNB (with the new cell) will, however, allocate a new eNB UE S1-AP Id from its own unique logical pool. The new eNB UE S1-AP Id from the target eNB shall replace the old eNB UE S1-AP Id from the source eNB in the MME.

Multiple S1-MME logical interfaces may exist between the eNB and the MMEs, with the latter from one or multiple MME pools. This is defined as S1-Flex. The NAS node selection function is used for routing of messages onto the associated S1-MME interface.

S1-MME Functions

Context management is responsible for setting up, modifying and releasing the S1 UE context and the associated E-UTRAN radio and S1 resources for one or more Enhanced Radio Access Bearers (E-RABs). These are used for user data transport in both the serving MME and the eNB. The UE context also includes E-RAB QoS and transport parameters, security context (cipher key), handover restriction, trace activation, CSFB, SRVCC ops status, UE radio and security capabilities. Establishment and modification of UE context is initiated by the MME. The E-RAB management function (described next) can be performed as part of the context management function requirements; e.g., a default E-RAB can be set up as part of the initial context request procedure.

UE trace and location reporting, if active for the current UE context in the source eNB, are also activated if supported in the target eNB. UE trace procedures are further described in 32.421 [26], 32.422 [27] and 32.423 [28]. Either the MME or eNB can initiate the UE context release procedure, upon which the S1 logical connection, UE context and associated network and radio resources for signalling and user data transport are released. UE context release procedures can be used for MME load re-balancing purposes.

E-RAB management is responsible for setting up, modifying and releasing E-UTRAN radio and S1 resources for one or more E-RABs that are used for user data transport. Establishment and modification of E-RAB resources is initiated by the MME. Establishment of E-RABs can be performed through E-RAB management, context management or handover resource allocation procedures. UE AMBR, if included, is used for UE non-GBR bearers. Each E-RAB to be set up or modified is uniquely identified with an E-RAB Id, which is identical to the EPS Bearer

Id used at the NAS layer. E-RAB associated resources are configured with the E-RAB QoS parameters provisioned by the MME, which include the QoS Class Identifier (QCI), Allocation and Retention Priority (ARP) and optional bi-directional MBR and GBR for the GBR bearer. Transport layer tunneling information for the S1-U is also exchanged between the eNB and MME, as the S-GW uses the MME as a relay via the S11 interface. Either the MME or eNB can initiate the E-RAB release procedure.

Mobility for UEs in ECM-CONNTECED state to enable the following handovers:

- **Intra-LTE**, a change of eNBs within the EPS via the S1 interface with EPC involvement. This is also known as an S1-initiated handover. The MME and S-GW can be relocated through this procedure.
- **Inter-3GPP RAT**, a change of RAN nodes between different RATs via the S1 interface with EPC involvement. This is also known as an inter-3GPP-RAT handover.

Handover preparation is initiated by the source eNB to the serving MME to request resource preparation at the target cell. The handover type specifies the target RAT (E-UTRAN, GERAN or UTRAN), and the target Id uniquely identifies the target cell (e.g., for intra-LTE, the globally eNB Id and selected TAI are used). A source-to-target transport container with RAN radio related information is also relayed to the target RAN. Note that in the case of intra-LTE mobility, MME and S-GW relocation may be possible — e.g., the selected TAI indicates that the eNB is served by a different MME and requires an MME relocation via the S10 interface.

The source eNB indicates the SRVCC type via the SRVCC handover indication, for either Dual Transfer Mode (DTM) CS and PS, or CS only. For more details on SRVCC, see 23.216 [33]. In the case of intra-LTE handovers, the source eNB can indicate the availability of the direct forwarding path, which can be used for direct user plane data forwarding between the source and target eNBs via the X2-U interface.

Handover resource allocation for E-UTRAN handover operation to the E-UTRAN is initiated by the serving MME to request resource reservation and allocation at the target cell. The handover type specifies the source RAT (E-UTRAN, GERAN or UTRAN). The MME specifies the E-RABs and associated parameters to be established for RAB management functionality. The MME informs the target eNB of the S1-U tunnel parameters — transport layer address and Tunnel Endpoint Identifier (TEID) — of the selected S-GW for each of the E-RABs to be established. The MME indicates the DL forwarding status for each E-RAB as applicable. For each E-RAB admitted for handover, the eNB allocates (a) an eNB tunnel for S1-U operation upon handover completion, (b) a DL tunnel for the proposed DL forwarding option and (c) a UL tunnel for request of UL forwarding.

The eNB stores the UE security capabilities and handover restriction list, which specifies the supported encryption and integrity algorithms in the UE, and the restricted roaming areas and access restrictions, respectively. Indication of UE and MME SRVCC support status is to be stored and used in the eNB. Security context is used by the eNB to derive the AS security configuration as outlined in 33.401 [18]. UE trace and location reporting, if active for the current UE context in the source eNB, is also activated if supported in the target eNB. The UE trace procedures are further described in 32.421 [26], 32.422 [27] and 32.423 [28].

Handover confirmation/execution begins with completion of the handover preparation phase by an S1-AP handover command message to initiate the E-UTRAN hand-out operation. (It is also possible for a preparation failure message to be received from the MME at this stage.) The eNB forwards the NAS downlink count value to the UE via RRC procedures in the case of inter-RAT handover for security procedures outlined in 33.401 [18]. E-RAB tunnels are established for all E-RABs to which UL or DL forwarding is applied during the handover session. Any E-RAB not admitted in the target system is marked for release in the S1-AP handover command message. For intra-LTE handovers, target eNB and S-GW destination tunnel information is included for direct (via X2-U) or indirect forwarding, respectively. Inter-RAT to UTRAN/GERAN procedures for direct and indirect forwarding are not fully defined at the time of this writing. However, a direct tunnel for this purpose can exist between the UTRAN and S-GW via the S12 interface without routing the data through the SGSN.

The PDCP receiver and transmitter status are transferred from the source to target eNB via the MME for each E-RAB with PDCP status preservation.

Handover cancellation can be used by the source eNB to cancel an ongoing handover, after which handover procedures are terminated in the source eNB and the MME. The MME also releases the associated resources allocated for this handover in the target system (target eNB, S-GW, etc.).

Handover completion for intra-LTE handovers begins when the target eNB acquires the UE and the MME is notified. The MME then allocates the S-GW to the new (target) eNB. The notification of successful UE acquisition in the target eNB is done using different S1-AP procedures for S1-initiated and X2-initiated handovers, with handover notify and path switch procedures, respectively. The UE context and associated radio resources are released in the source eNB, and the S1-MME/S1-U association between the source eNB and the EPC is terminated. For more details on 3GPP intra-LTE and inter-RAT handover procedures see 23.401 [1].

Paging procedures give the EPC the ability to page the UE through the eNBs that have one or more cells belonging to the TA in which the UE is registered. The UE can be paged for EPS services or non-EPS services (in a CSFB mobile terminated session), indicated through the CN Domain Id (PS/CS). Paging using IMSI triggers the UE to perform a detach and reattach procedure to the EPC.

NAS signalling transport is used to transfer NAS signalling related information between the UE and serving MME. An S1 UE context may be established as part of this functionality if one does not already exist. NAS protocol information is further discussed in 24.301 [23].

S1 Interface Management Functions

Error indication procedures are used by the MME and eNB to indicate self-detected errors, which may or may not be related to the UE S1 context. The S1-AP Ids are tagged with error indication messages if the errors are related to the UE S1 context.

Reset procedures are used by the MME and eNB to request that all or part of the S1 interface context be reset. In the case of partial reset, the initiating node indicates the S1-AP Ids for the connections to be reset.

Overload procedures are used by the MME to tell the eNBs to reduce the signalling load. The MME stops the overload control operation via an overload stop procedure. Overload actions include (1) rejecting RRC connection requests for non-emergency mobile originated data transfer, (2) rejecting all new RRC connection requests for signalling or (3) permitting RRC connection establishments for emergency causes only.

S1 Setup procedures are used by the MME and eNB to exchange application level data for S1 interoperability. S1 setup is initiated by the eNB, which sends the Global eNB Id, name and supported TAs while the MME responds with the list of served PLMNs and Globally Unique MME Identities (GUMMEIs). The relative MME capacity used for MME load balancing at the eNB is also transferred.

eNB and MME configuration update procedures are used by the MME and eNB to update application level data for S1 interoperability, similar to S1 setup procedures, but can be initiated by nodes over the S1-MME interface. Note that the global eNB Id cannot be updated using this procedure.

UE capability information indication is used to provide UE radio capability information when received from the UE by the MME, as initiated by the eNB.

Trace is used to configure UE trace procedures for UEs in the ECM-CONNECTED state. Each activated trace is associated with a trace reference, interfaces to be traced, and trace depth for each of the traced interfaces. Trace activation and deactivation is initiated by the serving MME. UE trace procedures are further described in 32.421 [26], 32.422 [27] and 32.423 [28].

Location reporting enables the MME to request that the eNB for a given UE either (1) directly report the current serving cell or (2) report or stop reporting upon change of the serving cell.

S1 cdma2000 tunneling is used to carry cdma2000 signalling between the UE and cdma2000 RAT over the S1 interface. This function comprises signalling for (1) UE preregistration with the cdma2000 HRPD network, (2) UE preregistration and paging with the cdma2000 1xRTT network and (3) handover preparation signalling for handovers from the E-UTRAN to cdma2000 HRPD/1xRTT. See 23.402 [2] for more details on inter-RAT non-3GPP handover procedures.

Warning message transmission provides the means to start and overwrite warning message broadcasts. The MME merely forwards this procedure as received from the Cell Broadcast Center (CBC) over the SBc interface. See 29.168 [34] for more details.

S1-U Interface

S1-U is defined between the eNB and the S-GW. It is used for user plane (per bearer) GTP User (GTP-U) tunneling and inter-eNB path switching during S1 and X2-initiated handover. The UDP transport layer provisions the network for non-guaranteed S1-AP delivery. User plane tunneling information (GTP-U IP addresses and TEIs) between the S-GW and eNB is coordinated by the MME as part of the S1-AP E-RAB management procedures.

An end marker message, which is a GTP-U message, is initiated by the S-GW and sent across the S1-U and X2-U interface for each of the GTP-U tunnels, marking the termination of these tunnels for user data transfer. Any G-PDU (carrying user plane data) received after the end marker message are deemed invalid and discarded silently by the receiving nodes.

Multiple S1-U logical interfaces may exist between the eNB and the S-GW, for which the latter can be from one or multiple S-GW pools (defined as S1-Flex). The S-GW selection function is performed by the MME. See 29.281 [35] for more details on GTP-U functions, noting that GTP-U remains on GTPv1 (a variant of the GPRS tunneling protocol) and is common across user plane interfaces Iu-U, Gn, Gp, S1-U, S4, S5, S8, S12 and X2-U.

5.2.5.2 X2 Interfaces

Two X2 interfaces have been defined between the eNBs, as shown in Figures 5.2-7.

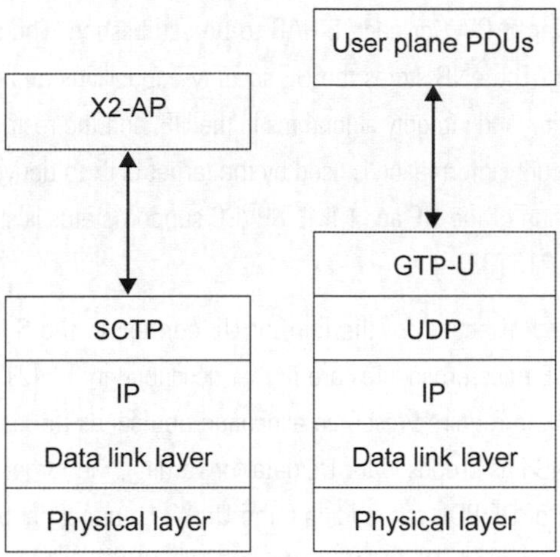

Figure 5.2-7. X2 reference points between eNBs

X2-C Interface

The X2-Control (X2-C) interface is defined between the eNBs for transport of the X2-Application Part (X2-AP) control plane protocol, in 36.423 [36]. The E-UTRAN RRC defined in 36.331 [24] is transported over X2-AP for handover information transfer. The SCTP transport layer provisions the network for guaranteed X2-AP delivery.

UE-associated logical connections over the X2-C interface are uniquely identified using the old and new eNB UE X2-AP Id pairs. These identifiers are allocated and maintained throughout the duration of the UE-associated logical X2 connection with the UE, and they are included in all UE associated X2-AP signalling procedures exchanged over the X2-C interface. Old and new eNB UE X2-AP Ids are unique within the source and target eNBs logical nodes that have allocated the Ids.

X2-C Functions

Mobility management for UEs in the ECM-CONNECTED state enables intra-LTE handovers within the EPS (also known as X2-initiated handovers) via the X2 interface without EPC involvement, up to the handover completion phase, when the S1 path switch is required for the target eNB and S-GW to sync up to the new S1-U user path. S-GWs can be relocated through the mobility management function.

Handover preparation is initiated by the source eNB to the target eNB to request resource preparation at the target cell, specifying the Target Cell Id (an ECGI). The Serving MME Id (a GUMMEI) is used by the target eNB to uniquely identify the MME that serves the UE context to be handed in. The MME UE S1-AP Id is used by the MME to uniquely identify the UE context during the path switch procedure.

The source eNB specifies the E-RABs and associated parameters to be established for RAB management functionality in the eNB. The source eNB informs the target eNB of the S1-U tunnel parameters (transport layer address and TEID) of the serving S-GW for each E-RAB to be established. The source eNB also indicates the E-RAB status for DL forwarding. The eNB stores the UE security capabilities and handover restriction list, which specifies the supported encryption and integrity algorithms in the UE, and the restricted roaming areas and access restrictions, respectively. AS security information is used by the target eNB to derive the AS security configuration, outlined in 33.401 [18]. Indication of the UE and MME SRVCC support status is stored and used in the eNB. For more details on SRVCC, see 23.216 [33].

UE trace and location reporting, if active for the current UE context in the Source eNB, is also activated if supported in the Target eNB. UE trace procedures are further described in 32.421 [26], 32.422 [27] and 32.423 [28]. The target eNB performs the required resource allocation and sends the handover preparation status. For each E-RAB that the source eNB has proposed for DL data forwarding, the target eNB may include the DL X2-U tunnel endpoint for forwarding of DL PDUs. In addition, the UL X2-U tunnel endpoint may be included for each E-RAB target that the eNB requests for UL PDU forwarding. The RRC handover information is sent to the UE transparently over the X2-AP with a handover request acknowledge message.

Status transfer is sent from the source eNB to the target eNB to transfer the uplink receiver and downlink transmitter PDCP status for each E-RAB for which PDCP Sequence Number (SN) and Hyper Frame Number (HFN) status preservation applies during X2-initiated handover. After the transfer status is sent, PDCP status in the Source eNB is considered frozen and any out of sequence packets received for the E-RABs will be forwarded to the target eNB if UL forwarding is enabled or else be discarded. In cases in which status preservation does not apply, packets will be sent to the S-GW.

UE context release is sent from the target eNB to the source eNB to indicate successful handover and trigger release of resources at the source eNB. The source eNB releases the radio and control plane resources including the S1-MME related to the UE context. Release of DL forwarding resources is implementation-dependent; potential options include utilizing guard timers, sending end marker GTP PDUs over S1-U and subsequently X2-U interfaces, etc.

Handover cancel can be used by the source eNB to cancel an ongoing handover. The target eNB removes all associated references and releases any resources previously reserved as part of the handover preparation phase.

Inter-cell interference coordination is used by the eNB to transfer load and inter-cell inference coordination information between the intra-frequency neighbour eNBs. This allows receiving eNBs to make radio resource assignments to reduce interference. Information includes interference levels, sensitivity experienced by the sending eNB, and DL power restriction status at the cell resource block level.

Load management is used by the eNB to exchange load measurements, whereby an eNB requests reporting from another eNB. This allows the receiving eNB to better control load conditions and potentially make better handover decisions.

X2 Interface Management Functions

Error indication procedures are used by the eNB to indicate to its neighbours any detected errors, which may or may not be related to UE X2 contexts. The X2-AP Ids are tagged with the error indication messages if the errors relate to the UE X2 contexts.

Reset procedures are used by the eNB to indicate to its neighbours that a failure has occurred, and all active X2 interface contexts are to be reset and related resources removed.

X2 setup procedures are used by the eNB to exchange application level data with its neighbours for X2 interoperability. This data includes served cell information, neighbour information and the MME pool list consisting of Globally Unique (GU) Group Ids.

eNB configuration update procedures are used by the MME and eNB to update application level data for X2 interoperability, similar to the X2 setup procedures, providing updates for served cell information, neighbour information, and MME pool list (GU Group Ids).

Trace is used to configure UE trace procedures for UEs in the ECM-CONNECTED state. Each trace activated is associated with a trace reference, interfaces to be traced, and trace depth for each interface. Trace activation and deactivation are initiated by the serving MME. UE trace procedures are further described in 32.421 [26], 32.422 [27] and 32.423 [28]. Applicability to X2 is initiated by the source eNB during the handover preparation procedure, if trace activations exist for the UE context to be handed over to the target eNB.

X2-U Interface

X2-User (X2-U) interface is defined between the eNBs that provide user plane per bearer GTP-U (29.281 [35]) tunneling for data forwarding during X2-initiated handover. The UDP transport layer provisions the network for non-guaranteed S1-AP delivery. User plane tunneling information (GTP-U IP addresses and TEIs) between the source and target eNBs is coordinated as part of the X2-AP mobility management procedures.

An end marker message, which is a GTP-U message initiated by the S-GW and sent across the S1-U, is forwarded across the X2-U interface for each of the GTP-U tunnels, marking the termination of these tunnels for user data transfer. Any G-PDUs (carrying user plane data) received after the end marker message are deemed invalid and discarded silently by the receiving nodes. See 29.281 [35] for more details on GTP-U function, noting that GTP-U remains on GTPv1 and is common across user plane interfaces Iu-U, Gn, Gp, S1-U, S4, S5, S8, S12 and X2-U.

5.2.5.3 Other Interfaces

S3 is the reference point between the MME and SGSN, shown in Figure 5.2-8. It enables the exchange of user and bearer information for inter-3GPP access network (UTRAN/GERAN) mobility in idle or active state. S3 is based on GTP version 2-Control plane (GTPv2-C) defined in 29.274 [37].

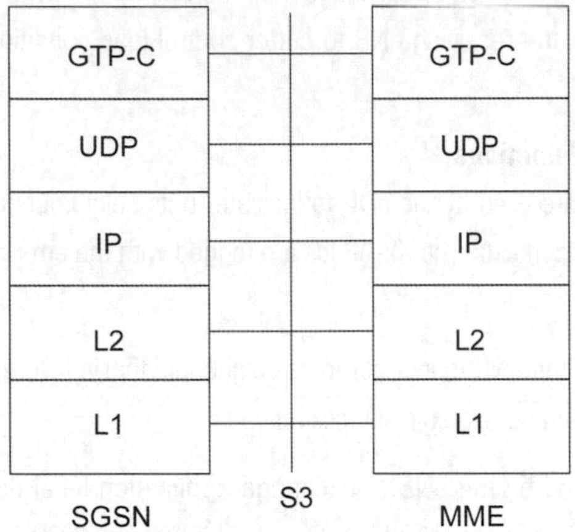

Figure 5.2-8. S3 interface

S4 is the reference point between the S-GW and SGSN. Two S4 paths — S4-C and S4-U — are based on GTPv2-C defined in 29.274 [37] and GTPv1-U defined in 29.281 [35], respectively. They are shown in Figure 5.2-9. S4 provides control and mobility support between the GPRS core and the 3GPP anchor function of the S-GW. It also provides user plane tunneling between the EPC and SGSN if direct tunneling is not enabled through the S12 interface.

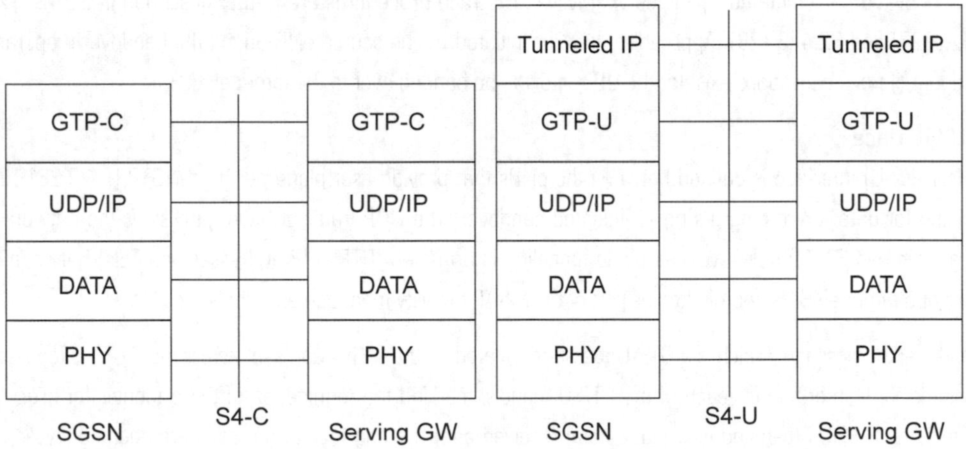

Figure 5.2-9. S4 interfaces

S5/S8 is the reference point between the S-GW and the PDN GW, providing user plane tunneling and tunnel management. S8 is the inter-PLMN variant of the S5 interface. S5/8-C and S5/8-U versions are based on GTPv2-C defined in 29.274 [37] and GTPv1-U defined in 29.281 [35], respectively, for the GTP variant. These are shown in Figure 5.2-10. A PMIP variant is not shown.

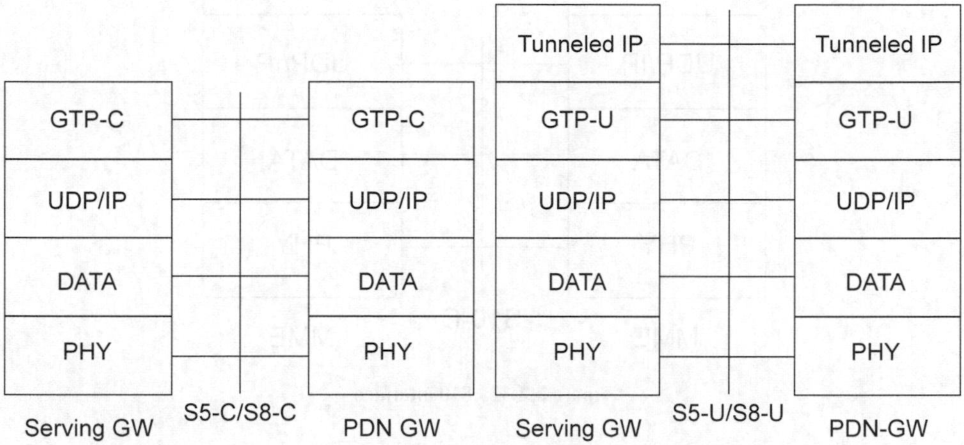

Figure 5.2-10. S5/S8 interfaces

S6a is the reference point between MME and HSS used to transfer subscription and authentication data for authenticating and authorizing user access to EPS services. It is based on the Diameter application with required extensions defined in 29.272 [38], as shown in Figure 5.2-11.

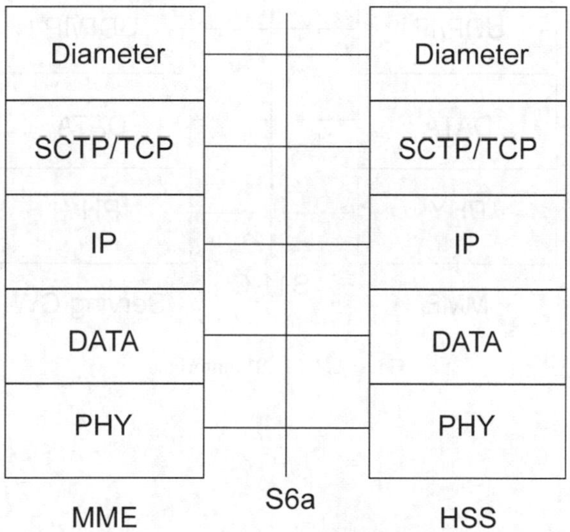

Figure 5.2-11. S6a interface

S10 is the reference point between MMEs used for user information transfer and MME relocation support. S10 is based on GTPv2-C defined in 29.274 [37] and is shown in Figure 5.2-12.

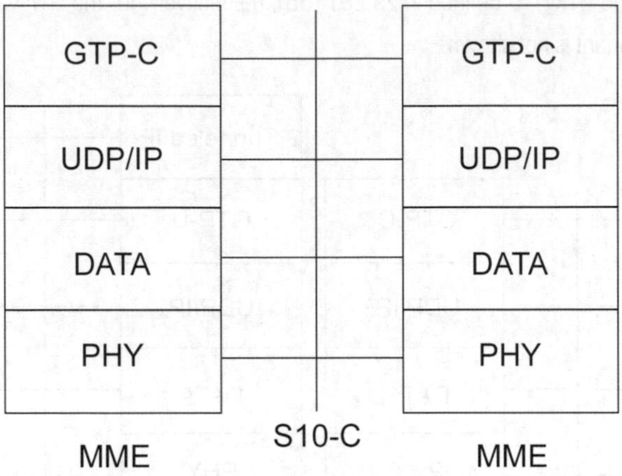

Figure 5.2-12. S10 interface

S11 is the reference point between the MME and S-GW used to support mobility and bearer management. S11 is based on GTPv2-C defined in 29.274 [37] and is shown in Figure 5.2-13.

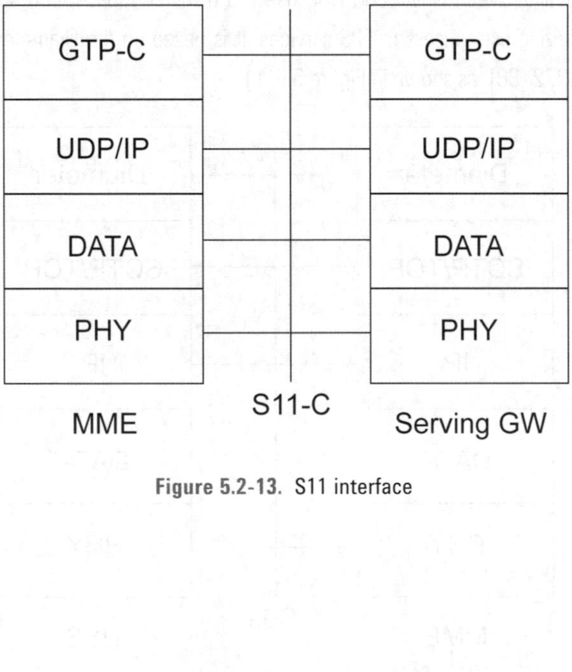

Figure 5.2-13. S11 interface

S12 is the reference point between the S-GW and UTRAN used for direct user plane tunneling during E-UTRAN and UTRAN handovers. S12 is based on GTPv1-U defined in 29.281 [35] and is shown in Figure 5.2-14.

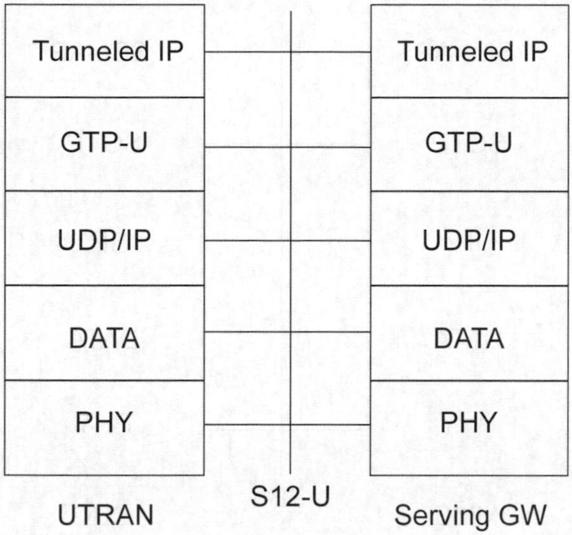

Figure 5.2-14. S12 interface

S13 is the reference point between the MME and the Equipment Identity Register (EIR) used for UE identity validation. S13 is based on the Diameter application with required extensions defined in 29.272 [38]. It is shown in Figure 5.2-15.

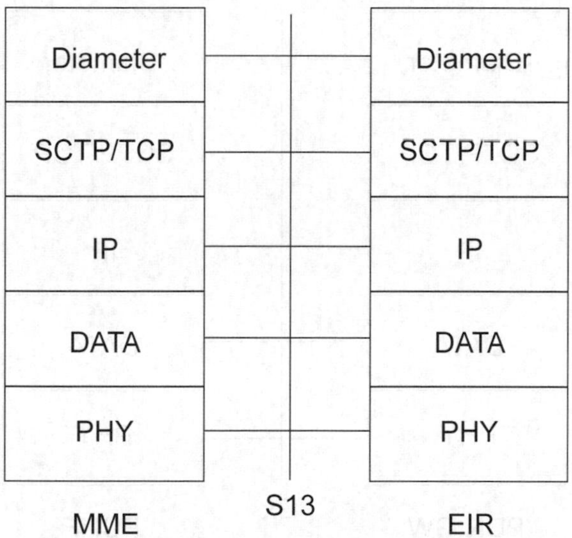

Figure 5.2-15. S13 interface

SBc is the reference point between the MME and the CBC used for warning-message delivery and control functions. It is shown in Figure 5.2-16. The SBc-AP protocol is defined in 29.168 [34].

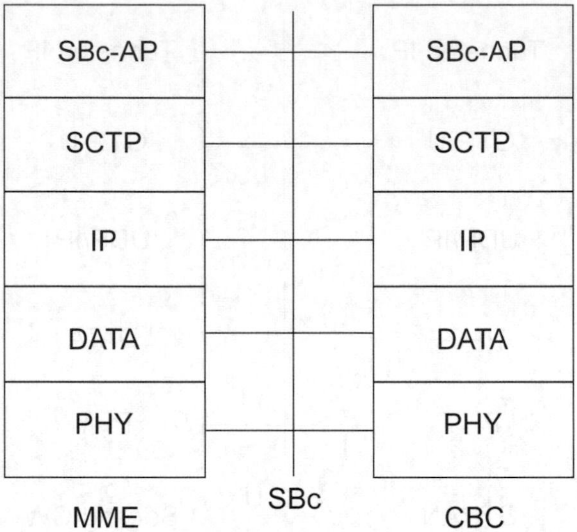

Figure 5.2-16. SBc interface

Gx is the reference point between the PCRF and the Policy Enforcement and Charging Function (PECF), providing transfer of policy and charging rules from PCRF to PECF in the PDN GW in the EPS. Gx is based on the Diameter application with required extensions defined in 29.212 [39] and is shown in Figure 5.2-17.

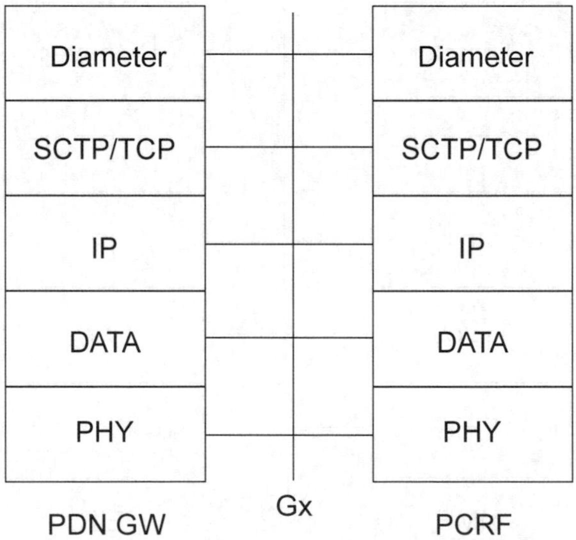

Figure 5.2-17. Gx interface

Rx is the reference point between the Authentication Framework (AF) and PCRF defined in 23.203 [13]. Rx is based on the Diameter application with required extensions defined in 29.214 [40]. It is shown in Figure 5.2-18.

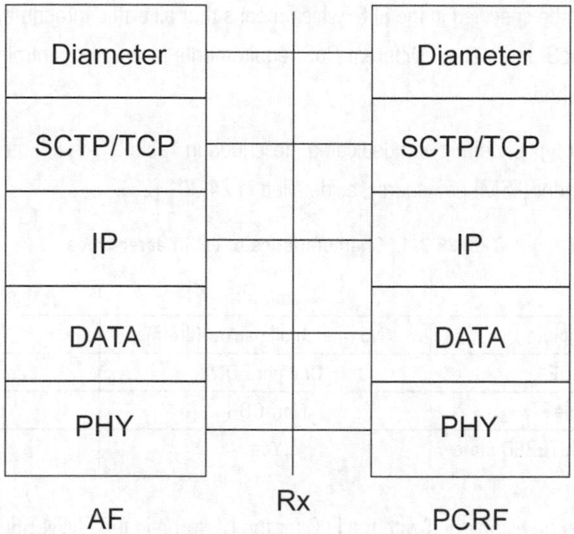

Figure 5.2-18. Rx interface

SGi is the reference point between the PDN and PDN-GW.

5.3 Quality of Service in EPS

Quality of Service (QoS) in the EPS is based on the EPS bearer service layered architecture shown in Figure 5.3-1.

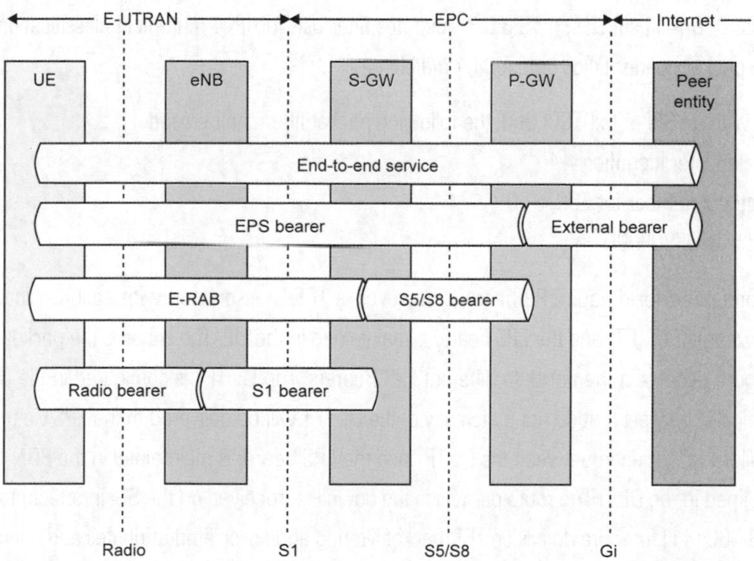

Figure 5.3-1. EPS bearer service architecture (from 36.300 [10] Fig. 13.1-1)

5.3.1 EPS Bearer

The EPS bearer provides PDN connectivity service to the UE via EPS access. The EPS bearer defines the bearer level QoS control that can be specified in the EPS, which means that all traffic through a particular EPS bearer has to use the same set of QoS parameters. Different QoS requirements for bearer controls would require additional EPS bearers to be established.

There are two EPS bearer types, default and dedicated, described in Table 5.3-1. EPS bearer contexts are handled by EPS Session Management (ESM) procedures, as detailed in 24.301 [23].

Table 5.3-1. Characteristics of EPS bearer types

EPS Bearer	Default	Dedicated
Traffic flow template	No (match all packet filters)	Yes
Quantity per UE	One per PDN	Zero or more per PDN
Resource type	Non-GBR	GBR or non-GBR
Required for EMM-REGISTERED state	Yes	No

A default EPS bearer must be established with the EPC for the UE to be in the EMM-REGISTERED state and hence able to access EPS services. Additional default bearers can be established with additional PDNs if simultaneous access to multiple PDNs is required. Dedicated EPS bearers are defined as additional EPS bearers established with any PDN after the default EPS bearer has been established with that PDN. Dedicated EPS bearers are linked to the default bearer via the Linked EPS Bearer Identity (LBI) at the NAS ESM layer.

The Traffic Flow Template (TFT) consists of one or more packet filters, each identified with a unique packet filter identifier. Each packet filter has an evaluation precedence index, which is unique among all the packet filters associated with PDN contexts that share the same PDN address and Access Point Name (APN). The following example from 23.060 [41] subclause 15.3.3.3 illustrates filter use for IPv4 multi-field classification for IPSec data (more than one packet header fields required for matching).

If IPSec is used with an SPI of 0x0F80F000, the following packet filter can be used:

- Packet filter identifier = 4
- Protocol number for ESP = 50
- SPI = 0x0F80F000

TFTs are not configured for default EPS bearers; however, a TFT is associated with each dedicated EPS bearer. Association between an UL TFT and the EPS bearer is maintained in the UE. The UE uses the packet filters defined in the UL TFT to route packets in the uplink to different EPS Bearers. The UL TFT is configured in the UE via NAS ESM procedures. Typically, packets that do not match any of the UL TFT will be delivered to the EPS via the default bearer (match all). Similarly, association between the DL TFT and the EPS bearer is maintained in the PDN-GW, which uses packet filters defined in the DL TFT to route packets in the downlink (received on the SGi interface) to associated EPS bearers. See 23.060 [41] for more details on TFT, packet filtering and associated attributes and operations.

The EPS Bearer has a one-to-one relationship with the following lower layer bearers: E-RAB, a composite of the S1 bearer and Data Radio Bearer (DRB); and the S5/S8 bearer.

5.3.1.1 E-UTRAN Radio Access Bearer

The E-RAB is used to transport packets of an EPS bearer between the UE and the EPC, and has a one-to-one relationship with a single EPS bearer. The E-RAB is defined as the concatenation of the S1 bearer and the corresponding DRB (described below). An E-RAB management function resides in the MME and eNB. The E-RAB Id is used between the eNB and the EPC to provide a unique identity to the E-RAB allocated to the UE. This identity has the same value as the EPS Bearer Id that is used between the UE and EPS.

5.3.1.2 S5/S8 Bearer

The S5/S8 bearer is used to transport packets of an EPS bearer between the S-GW and the PDN-GW, and has a one-to-one relationship with the EPS bearer. The S-GW and PDN-GW bind the EPS bearer to the S5/S8 bearer by allocating one dedicated GTP-U tunnel (TEID-identified) per EPS bearer. S5/S8 tunnel management functions are provided by GTP-Cv2 procedures specified in 29.274 [37]. Transport level packet marking in the uplink and downlink based on the QoS Class Identifier (QCI) associated with the EPS bearers is performed on the packets transferred through the S5/S8 GTP-U tunnels. QCI will be discussed in greater detail later in this section.

The PDN-GW maintains the association between the DL TFT and the S5/S8 bearer. Note that PMIP-based S5/S8 is not discussed in this section. See 23.402 [2] for more on that subject.

5.3.1.3 S1 Bearer

The S1 bearer is used to transport packets of an EPS bearer between the eNB and the EPC, specifically the S-GW over S1-U interface. The S1 bearer has a one-to-one relationship with the E-RAB. The eNB and S-GW bind the EPS bearer to the S1 bearer by allocating one dedicated GTP-U tunnel (TEID-identified) per EPS bearer. S1 tunnel management functions are provided by S1-AP and X2-AP E-RAB management procedures specified in 36.413 [22] and 36.423 [36], respectively. Note that S1-AP is used by the MME to relay UL and DL tunnel information allocated by the S-GW, via the S11 interface and eNB, respectively.

Transport level packet marking in the UL and DL based on the QCI associated with the EPS bearers is also performed on the packets transferred through S1 GTP-U tunnels.

5.3.1.4 Data Radio Bearer

The DRB is used to transport packets of an EPS bearer between the eNB and the UE, and has a one-to-one relationship with a single EPS bearer. The eNB and UE map the EPS bearer QoS received from the MME via the S1-MME and NAS ESM, respectively, to the Radio Bearer QoS, which in turn is used to configure the related E-UTRAN and UE resources. Some examples are Semi-Persistent Scheduling (SPS) and uplink rate control with the DRB logical channel priority, Prioritized Bit Rate (PBR), and bucket size duration signalled to the UE via RRC. For more details see 36.331 [24].

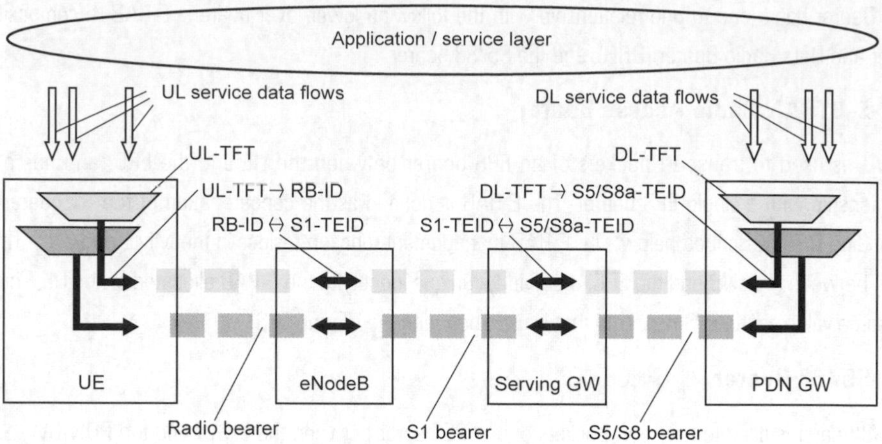

Figure 5.3-2. Layered architecture and binding relationships for various elements of EPS bearers (from 23.401 [1] Fig. 4.7.2.2-1)

The UE maintains the association between the UL TFT and the DRB, as each DRB has an Id that is mapped to the EPS Bearer Id via RRC procedures signalled from the eNB to UE. Each DRB is associated with one PDCP entity, which in turn associates with one or two RLC entities, one in each direction. That means each PDCP and RLC PDU is associated with the EPS bearer and bearer QoS profile. See 36.323 [42] and 36.322 [43].

Figure 5.3-2 depicts the binding relationships between the different layer bearers with GTP-based S5/S8. See 23.402 [2] for information on the EPS bearer with PMIP-based S5/S8.

5.3.2 QoS Profile and Parameters

The EPS bearer and E-RAB QoS profile includes service level QoS parameters defined by the following:

- QoS Class Identifier (QCI)
- Allocation and Retention Priority (ARP)
- Guaranteed Bit Rate (GBR), applicable only for GBR bearer
- Maximum Bit Rate (MBR), applicable only for GBR bearer

QCI is a scalar value. It is used as a reference to node-specific parameters that handle bearer level packet forwarding behavior in order to meet a set of performance characteristics required by applications and services for which these bearers are utilized. QCI provides a consistent QoS identification used extensively in various ways through every node along the path within the EPS and with the UE.

Some sample usage scenarios of QCI are the following:

- Transport level packet marking by setting the DiffServ code point for classification and differentiating treatments of user data flows
  - eNB: uplink on S1-U, between neighbouring eNBs via X2-U
  - S-GW: uplink on S5/S8 and downlink on S1-U
  - PDN-GW: uplink on SGi and downlink on S5/S8

- Scheduling prioritization in the eNB
- Link layer protocol configuration such as RLC AMD mode for TCP-based services while in UMD mode for Voice over IP Multimedia Subsystem (VoIMS) services
- Semi-persistent scheduling for VoIMS services
- Downlink and uplink rate control function in the eNB and UE for GBR and non-GBR bearers, respectively

Table 5.3-2. Standardized QCI characteristics (adapted from 23.203 [13] Table 6.1.7)

QCI	Resource type	Priority	Packet delay budget	Packet error loss rate	Example services
1	GBR	2	100 ms	10^{-2}	Conversational voice
2	GBR	4	150 ms	10^{-3}	Conversational video (live streaming)
3	GBR	3	50 ms	10^{-3}	Real time gaming
4	GBR	5	300 ms	10^{-6}	Non-conversational video (buffered streaming)
5	Non-GBR	1	100 ms	10^{-6}	IMS signalling
6	Non-GBR	6	300 ms	10^{-6}	Video (buffered streaming) TCP-based (e.g., www, e-mail, chat, ftp, p2p file sharing, progressive video, etc.)
7	Non-GBR	7	100 ms	10^{-3}	Voice Video (live streaming) Interactive gaming
8	Non-GBR	8	300 ms	10^{-6}	Video (buffered streaming) TCP-based (e.g., www, e-mail, chat, ftp, p2p file sharing, progressive video, etc.)
9	Non-GBR	9	300 ms	10^{-6}	Video (buffered streaming) TCP-based (e.g., www, e-mail, chat, ftp, p2p file sharing, progressive video, etc.)

Table 5.3-2 shows the standardized QCI values and standardized characteristics specified in 23.203 [13]. The objective of this standardization is to ensure QoS requirement interoperability between multi-vendor nodes, shared networks and roaming scenarios, independent of access systems.

The following performance characteristics are specified along with each of the QCI values:

- Resource type, which differentiates between GBR and non-GBR Service Data Flows (SDFs)
- Priority, which is associated with every QCI, with 1 as the highest value
- Packet delay budget, which supports the configuration of scheduling and link layer functions by defining the maximum amount of time that packets are allowed to be delayed between the UE and PDN-GW
- Packet error loss rate, which defines the upper bound for packets lost through non-congestion related causes. By definition these are packets processed by the link layer protocol or the sender but not successfully received at the upper layer of the receiver. This specification supports the appropriate link layer protocol configurations (e.g., L1 HARQ and RLC ARQ).

ARP contains information that is used for bearer admission control in a resource-level network:

- Priority level used to differentiate the relative importance between different bearers, especially during setup, modification or replacement decisions (potentially replacing other bearers).
- Pre-emption capability, indicating whether the bearer should be allowed to preempt other bearers.

- Pre-emption vulnerability, indicating whether the bearer can be preempted (i.e., eligible for a request to be replaced by other bearers).

Note that ARP has no effect on run-time QoS control of the EPS bearers and the associated lower layered bearers.

GBR indicates the guaranteed EPS bearer and E-RAB bit rates for a GBR type bearer, defined for uplink and downlink directions.

MBR indicates the maximum EPS bearer and E-RAB bit rates for a GBR type bearer, defined for uplink and downlink directions.

In addition to the QoS parameters just described, 3GPP defines parameters for bit rates of data per groups of bearers.

UE-AMBR sets the limit for the aggregate bit rate that can be expected to be provided across all non-GBR bearers per UE. Enforcement of the UE-AMBR in both the uplink and downlink is performed in the eNB.

APN-AMBR sets the limit for the aggregate bit rate that can be expected to be provided across all non-GBR bearers over all PDN connections of the same PDN. Enforcement of the APN-AMBR in the uplink is performed in the UE and PDN-GW, while downlink is performed in the PDN-GW.

Table 5.3-3 summarizes the availability of the various EPS QoS parameters in the UE and various user plane handling Network Elements (NEs) in the EPS. The interface and protocol through which these QoS parameters are transferred are indicated as well.

Table 5.3-3. Availability of QoS parameters in UE and user plane NEs

EPS related QoS parameters	UE	eNB	S-GW	PDN-GW
EPS bearer Id (per EPS bearer)	Yes NAS (ESM) and RRC	Yes (E-RAB Id) S1-AP (S1-MME) X2-AP (X2-C)	Yes GTP-C (S11)	Yes GTP-C (S5/S8)
QCI (per EPS bearer)	Yes NAS (ESM)	Yes S1-AP (S1-MME) X2-AP (X2-C)	Yes GTP-C (S11/S5/S8)	Yes GTP-C (S5/S8)
ARP (per EPS bearer)	No	Yes S1-AP (S1-MME) X2-AP (X2-C)	Yes GTP-C (S11/S5/S8)	Yes GTP-C (S5/S8)
GBR (GBR only) (per EPS bearer)	Yes NAS (ESM)	Yes S1-AP (S1-MME) X2-AP (X2-C)	Yes GTP-C (S11/S5/S8)	Yes GTP-C (S5/S8)
MBR (GBR only) (per EPS bearer)	Yes NAS (ESM)	Yes S1-AP (S1-MME) X2-AP (X2-C)	Yes GTP-C	Yes GTP-C (S5/S8)
APN-AMBR (non-GBR only) (per APN)	Yes NAS (ESM)	No	No (Routing)	Yes GTP-C (S5/S8)
UE-AMBR (non-GBR only) (per UE)	No	Yes S1-AP (S1-MME) X2-AP (X2-C)	No	No

TFT uplink (per EPS bearer)	Yes (dedicated) NAS (ESM)	No	Yes (dedicated) GTP-C (S11/S5/S8)	Yes (dedicated) GTP-C (S5/S8)
TFT downlink (per EPS bearer)	No	No	Yes (dedicated) GTP-C (S11/S5/S8)	Yes (dedicated) GTP-C (S5/S8)

Table 5.3-4 summarizes the availability of the various QoS parameters in various control plane handling Network Elements (NEs) in the EPS. The interfaces through which these QoS parameters are transferred either directly or via routes are indicated as well.

Table 5.3-4. Availability of QoS parameters in control plane NEs

<table>
<tr><th>EPS related QoS parameters</th><th>HSS</th><th>MME</th><th>S-GW</th><th>PDN-GW</th></tr>
<tr><td>EPS bearer Id
(per EPS bearer)</td><td>No</td><td>Yes
Allocated by the MME</td><td>Yes
Forwarded by MME (S11)</td><td>Yes
Forwarded by S-GW
(S5/S8)</td></tr>
<tr><td>QCI
(per EPS bearer)</td><td rowspan="4">Yes
Default subscribed
Stored as part of PDN subscription profile</td><td rowspan="4">Yes
Default subscribed
received/modified from HSS (S6a)

Default and Dedicated
in use received/modified from HSS via S6a and PDN-GW via S-GW (S11)</td><td rowspan="4">Yes
Default and Dedicated
in use received/modified from HSS routed via MME (S11) and PCRF routed via PDN-GW (S5/S8)</td><td rowspan="4">Yes
Default and Dedicated
in use received/modified from HSS routed via MME/S-GW (S5/S8) and PCRF (Gx), or local policy</td></tr>
<tr><td>ARP
(per EPS bearer)</td></tr>
<tr><td>GBR
(GBR only)
(per EPS bearer)</td></tr>
<tr><td>MBR
(GBR only)
(per EPS bearer)</td></tr>
<tr><td>APN-AMBR
(non-GBR only)
(per APN)</td><td>Yes
Stored as part of PDN subscription profile</td><td>Yes
Subscribed received from HSS (S6a)

In use maintained by the PDN GW routed via S-GW (S11)</td><td>No</td><td>Yes
received/modified from HSS routed via MME/S-GW (S5/S8) and PCRF (Gx), or local policy</td></tr>
<tr><td>UE-AMBR
(non-GBR only)
(per UE)</td><td>Yes
Stored as part of UE profile</td><td>Yes
Subscribed received from HSS (S6a)

In use maintained by the MME</td><td>No</td><td>No</td></tr>
<tr><td>TFT uplink
(per EPS Bearer)</td><td rowspan="2">No</td><td rowspan="2">Yes (dedicated)
PMIP option</td><td rowspan="2">Yes (dedicated)
received/modified from HSS routed via MME (S11) and PDN-GW (S5/S8)</td><td rowspan="2">Yes (dedicated)
received/modified from HSS routed via MME/S-GW (S5/S8) and PCRF (Gx), or local policy</td></tr>
<tr><td>TFT downlink
(per EPS bearer)</td></tr>
</table>

See 23.401 [1] and 23.203 [13] for more on dynamic Policy and Charging Control (PCC) with PCRF.

5.4 Security in the Network

The security aspects of LTE and SAE are not fully defined in Release 8 as of this writing. The reader is encouraged to study forthcoming updates to the 3GPP specifications to understand this critical topic and the modifications that are anticipated. A clear harmonization of the Stage 2 and Stage 3 standards development process is expected.

Briefly, service access in the PS domain requires a security association to be established between the UE and the PLMN. A separate security association must be established between the UE and the IMS Core Network Subsystem (IMS CN SS) before access can be granted to multimedia services hosted.

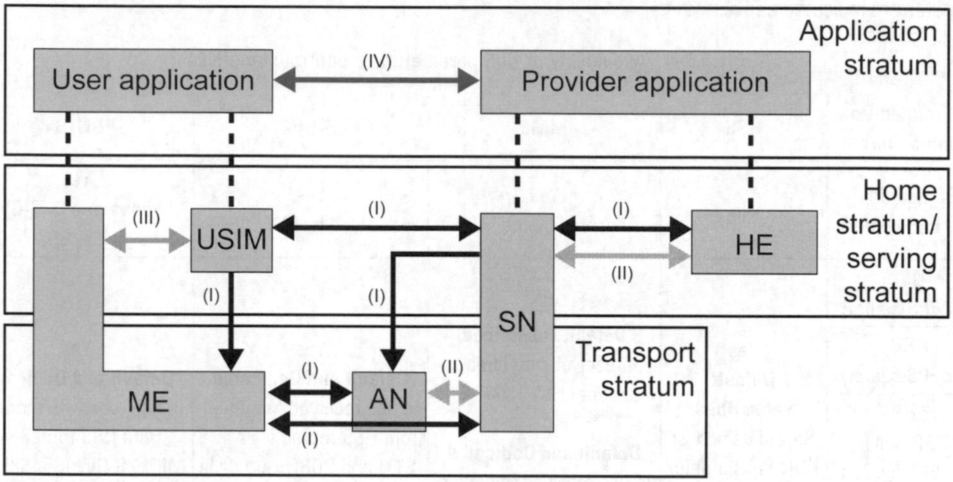

Figure 5.4-1. Security features in the network (from 33.401 [18] Fig.4-1)

As shown in Figure 5.4-1, five security feature groups are defined in 33.401 [18]

(I) **Network access** provides users with secure access to services and protects against attacks on the access interfaces.

(II) **Network domain** enables nodes to securely exchange signalling data and user data, and protects against attacks on the wire line network.

(III) **User domain** provides secure access to mobile stations.

(IV) **Application domain security** enables applications in the user and provider domains to securely exchange messages.

(V) **Visibility and configurability of security** allow the user to learn whether a security feature is in operation or not and whether the use and provision of services should depend on the security feature.

A more detailed description of security features (I) and (II) is available at www.agilent.com/find/ltebook. Details on (III), (IV) and (V) are available in 33.102 [44]. Security architecture for non-3GPP accesses to EPS is covered in 33.402 [19].

5.5 Services

For an end user the EPS will in many aspects behave much like current fixed access networks. The services deployed on the EPS will not be limited to a single access technology such as E-UTRAN but will more likely be part of a larger overall service framework. As the EPS and E-UTRAN access have been designed for much more cost effective operation, it is anticipated that much wider use of data services will be made in the future, not limited to but including an ample amount of machine-to-machine communication possibly without the direct interaction of a human end user.

This section does not intend to provide any examples of so-called killer applications or any breakthrough inventions; rather it examines some common services offered on today's networks to understand how they can be maintained in an EPS. Indeed, a significant portion of this section will be dedicated to traditional circuit-switched voice calls, a service that has not yet been standardized for the EPS.

5.5.1 End to End Service Concept

What constitutes end-to-end service is very much in the eye of the beholder. In other words, what are considered the end points of a communication can vary greatly depending on who the observer is. Figure 5.3-1 depicts the concept, presenting as part of the overall QoS picture the different aspects of the EPS that are involved in delivering services across the end-to-end chain.

Depending on what service is used and what bearer is set up over the EPS, the resulting end user experience can vary greatly in different instances, even when network conditions are similar. Thus the price charged for the service might depend on the QoS achieved. End-to-end service concepts must be well understood by network design and implementation teams and by the teams that develop and deploy new services. A solid understanding of the underlying technology is perhaps more important than ever to develop proper marketing, including pricing of the different services that can be deployed on the EPS. Without such an understanding, implementing a service such as CS voice via CSFB, for example, could result in a poor end-user Quality of Experience (QoE). All parties involved in delivering the service must know the tradeoffs, and not only on an engineering level. The International Telecommunications Union (ITU) has established conventions about the relationship between QoS and QoE that includes non-technical factors such as the end user's subjective expectations of service quality.

Figure 5.5-1 shows how QoE is built not only from technical QoS attributes but also from non-technical QoS attributes. These merge with the customer expectations that are derived from many external factors. The contributions of network and terminal performance will be considered here.

Section 5.3 described how the EPC and E-UTRAN categorized different high level services by QoS Class Identifier (QCI). Each of these services could then be managed properly. The MAC process discussion of Chapter 4 suggested that the scheduler could effectively manage a real time service and deliver a high level of QoS because the traffic is fully deterministic and resources can be granted proactively rather than by request only. By taking care to properly manage both services and the QCI allocation of services, an improved end user QoE based on the highly efficient allocation and use of resources can be achieved.

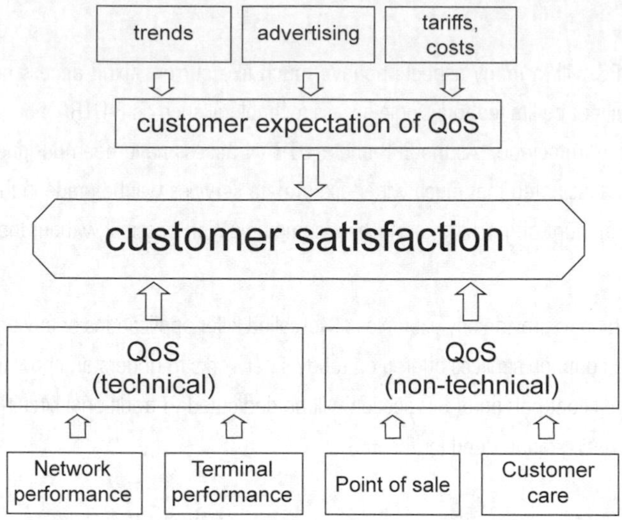

Figure 5.5-1. Relationship between customer satisfaction (QoE) and QoS

5.5.2 Circuit Switched Services for EPS

One item that is yet to be defined for the EPS at the time of this writing is how circuit-switched services — e.g. voice, CS Unrestricted Digital Information (UDI) video, Short Message Service (SMS), Location Service (LCS) and Unstructured Supplementary Service Data (USSD) — will be managed. Several options exist, including the following:

- Circuit Switched Fall-Back (CSFB)
- Generic Access Network (GAN)
- Voice over IP Multimedia Subsystem (VoIMS)
- Proprietary options

Of these, CSFB and GAN are both standardized and could be readily implemented.

Another item that is not yet specified in Release 8 is the use of voice codecs. Again, several options are available but because a choice has not yet been made, this part of the standard could be delayed until Release 10. One reason for the delay is a lack of agreement on the objective: should the codec be chosen to improve voice quality or network capacity? It is likely that the codec chosen for initial EPS deployments will be based on mutual bi-lateral agreements between the UE vendors, the operators and the EPS providers. It appears likely that Adaptive Multi-Rate (AMR) and AMR-Wideband (AMR-WB) will be used initially.

It is crucial to note that the ITU has already moved ahead with the definition of the G.718 codec. G.718 is built on AMR-WB and provides at 12.65 kbps a 57% increase of capacity over AMR at 7.95 kbps with only a very limited effect on speech delay. The reader is encouraged to study ITU-T Rec. G.718 [45] in full to better understand this topic.

5.5.2.1 CS Fallback in EPS

CSFB in EPS enables the provisioning of voice and other CS-domain services (listed above) by reuse of the CS infrastructure when the UE is served by the E-UTRAN and the E-UTRAN coverage overlaps those of 3GPP legacy access networks (GERAN/UTRAN) or non-3GPP cdma2000 1xRTT. This means that if CSFB is implemented the E-UTRAN will not support the CS service as such but will hand over any CS call initiated or received to either a GERAN/UTRAN or a non-3GPP cdma2000 1xRTT access. A CSFB-enabled terminal may establish one or more CS-domain services via these legacy access networks.

CSFB can co-exist with IMS-based services in the same operator's network, with IMS-based services (VoIMS, SMS over IP, etc.) taking precedence over the CSFB option.

Functional Entities

A CSFB-capable UE supports access to E-UTRAN and EPC as well as access to the CS domain over GERAN or UTRAN. It also supports combined procedures for EPS/IMSI attach, update and detach, as well as CSFB and SMS procedures for using CS domain services. A UE using CSFB supports Idle-mode Signal Reduction (ISR) according to 23.401 [1].

A CSFB-enabled MME supports the following functions:

- Deriving a Visitor Location Register (VLR) number and Location Area Identity (LAI) from the GUTI received from the UE or from a default LAI
- Maintaining Security Gateway (SG) association towards the MSC/VLR for EPS/IMSI attached UE
- Initiating IMSI detach at EPS detach
- Initiating specified paging procedures towards eNB when the MSC pages the UE for CS services
- Supporting specified SMS procedures
- Rejecting CSFB call request (e.g., for O&M reasons)

An MME that supports CSFB uses the LAI and a hash value from the IMSI to determine the VLR number as defined in 23.236 [46] when multiple MSC/VLRs serve the same LAI. The same hash value/function is used by the SGSN to determine the VLR number.

The CSFB-enabled MSC supports the following functions:

- Maintaining SG association towards the MME for the EPS/IMSI attached UE
- Paging on SG and Iu/A interface in parallel
- Supporting SMS procedures

The CSFB-enabled E-UTRAN supports the forwarding of paging requests and SMS to the UE, and directs the UE to the target CS-capable cell.

If the SGSN supports ISR, then the SGSN follows the rules and procedures described in 23.401 [1] and 23.060 [41] with the following clarification: the SGSN will not send the ISR activated indication at a combined Routing Area Update/Location Area Update (RAU/LAU) procedure. An SGSN that supports Gs uses LAI and a hash value from the IMSI to determine the VLR number as defined in 23.236 [46] when multiple MSC/VLRs serve the same LAI. The same hash value/function is used by MME to determine the VLR number.

Reference Points

S3 is defined in 23.401 [1] with the additional functionality to support CSFB with ISR activated.

SGs is the reference point between the MME and VLR/MSC server. The SGs reference point is used for the mobility management and paging procedures between the EPS and CS domain, and is based on the Gs interface procedures. The SGs reference point is also used for the delivery of both mobile-originating and mobile-terminating SMS via NAS tunneling procedures.

Mobility Management

The combined EPS attach procedure is used by a CSFB-enabled UE to attach for both EPS and non-EPS services. It is performed according to 24.301 [23], after which the attach procedure for non-EPS services will be performed. The detach procedure can be initiated by the network (MME/HSS) or UE. In event of a detach with an active SGs association, the MME will always notify the VLR, and the related SGs association will be deactivated.

Other mobility management functions include TA and LA updates, mobile-originated and mobile-terminated calls, and interaction with ISR. The latter aims to reduce the frequency of TAU and RAU procedures resulting from the UE reselecting between E-UTRAN and GERAN/UTRAN, which are operated together. Effectively, ISR reduces the related update signalling between the UE and the network and within the network. See 23.060 [41] for more details.

5.5.2.2 Generic Access Network

GAN was developed to allow the GSM user and control plane to be transmitted over Wireless LAN. It has been integrated into 3GPP and today is part of the baseline 3GPP specifications in 43.318 [47]. Note that GAN supports both CS and PS services, although in the context of this discussion the PS aspects of GAN are not used.

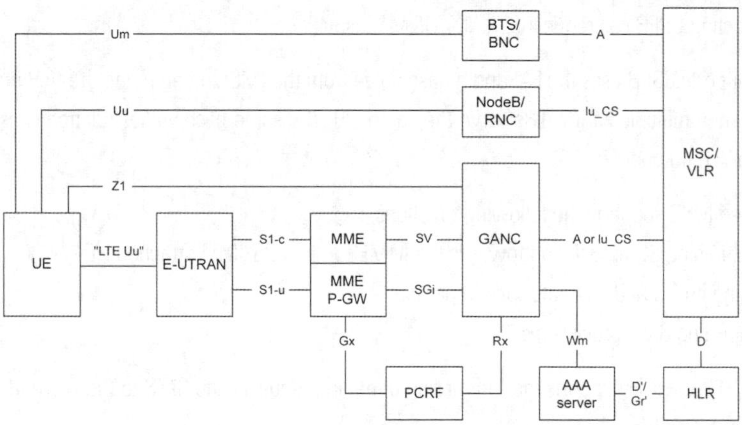

Figure 5.5-2. GANC interfaces to traditional NEs (from 43.318 [47])

The generic network diagram in Figure 5.5-2 outlines how the GAN Controller (GANC) interfaces with the traditional MSC/VLR node over the Z1, Sv and SGi interfaces. As can be seen from the basic protocol stack in Figure 5.5-3, the traditional NAS signalling specified in 24.008 [48] is transparent between the UE and the MSC, but adaption layers are added between the NAS layer and the IP transport layer and are terminated in the GANC.

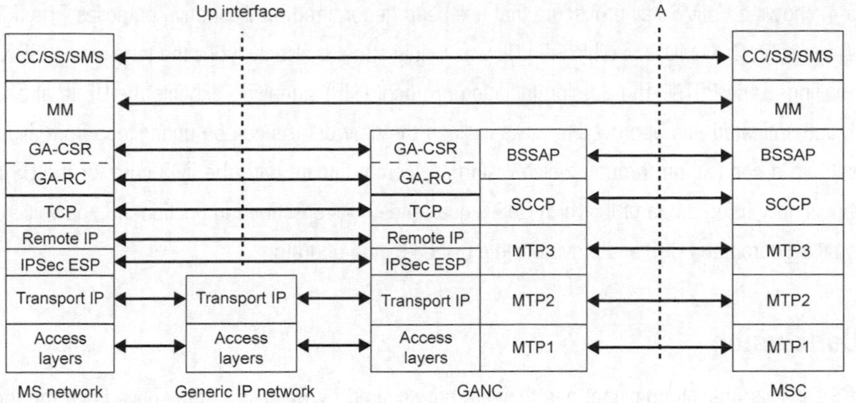

Figure 5.5-3. Uplink GANC CS control plane signalling architecture (43.318 [47] Figure 2)

The GANC can interface with the MSC on either the A or the IuCS (circuit switched) interface, although the reference stack in the figure is simplified to show only the A interface alternative.

5.5.2.3 Voice Over IMS

Full support for IMS into the EPS requires detailed description that is beyond the scope of this book. A single example of VoIMS is given in Figure 5.5-4.

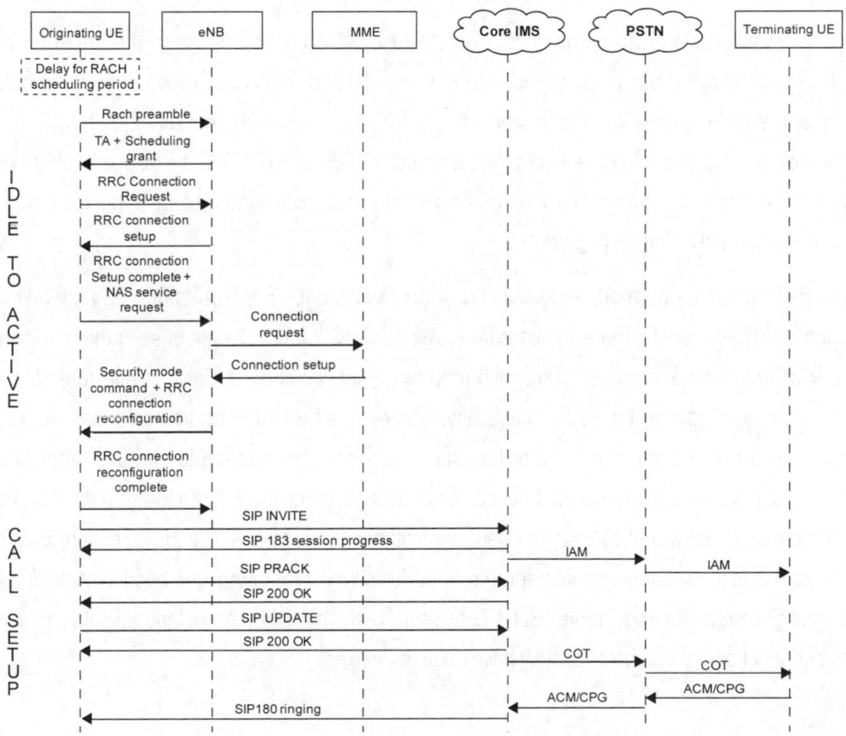

Figure 5.5-4. VoIMS call procedure

Figure 5.5-4, shows a VoIMS call procedure that has been generalized for illustrative purposes. The figure shows a Mobile Originating Call (MOC) in which the UE was in Idle state. It also includes the terminating ISDN User Part (ISUP) signalling in the PSTN. The Session Initiation Protocol (SIP) signalling expects the UE to already be fully registered, authenticated and approved to make calls on the network. As can be understood from this figure, the network sets up a connection through which it starts to communicate with the IMS core for the CS call setup. The network is now using a bearer in which QoS is guaranteed. As described in Section 5.3, the voice call quality depends on the guaranteed QoS and provisioning provided by the operator.

5.5.3 Conclusion

Because CS services are still dominant and they are not covered by Release 8, they have been the focus of this section, which ends with some concluding remarks about the possible voice service options. In general, CSFB will enable delivery of CS services in an E-UTRAN environment but the user will be restricted to the services of the traditional UTRAN or GERAN. Call setup will be delayed compared to what is experienced today in the UTRAN and GERAN. In other words, with CSFB at best the user will get a service similar to what is available today.

GAN is a stable and working solution already used in the network today. Drawbacks of GAN are the increased cost of deploying the GANC and the fact that the UE has to support extra protocol stacks. Battery life of the GAN-enabled UE is affected as the UE has to maintain an IP connection with the network all of the time. A further limitation, not discussed here, is reduced effectiveness in the LTE transport network.

The main issue related to VoIMS is the cost structure of the IMS subsystem and the uncertainty about its scalability. IMS uptake so far has been limited, and thus only limited real world experience is available to tell us whether IMS and VoIMS can deliver an effective solution for voice over E-UTRAN and EPS. VoIMS technology is readily applicable to other access technologies including the UTRAN and GERAN. It is expected that VoIMS, or an evolution thereof, will become the final solution to the overall circuit switched problem, although it may take some time to become fully stabilized and integrated.

It is highly likely that some operators and service providers will launch E-UTRAN and EPS networks using non-3GPP CS solutions. These could include solutions from Skype, MSN, Yahoo, Google or any other traditional Internet IM or voice supplier. A major result of using such propriety solutions is the lack of an end-to-end, standardized means of call control, media and encoding capability. However, as with the Internet of today, solutions can be found to all these problems that are more or less stable, scalable, maintainable and cost effective. The ever increasingly competitive landscape makes it difficult to predict whether the adaptation of a solution that has not been standardized by 3GPP would allow for a significant first mover advantage. One possibly significant obstacle to proprietary solutions is the security requirement to provide full support for lawful interception, including adaptation to possible local governmental regulations. But it does seem likely that some non-standard solutions will find their way onto the connections of end users as they have done in the past.

5.6 References

[1] 3GPP TS 23.401 V8.4.0 (2008-12) General Packet Radio Service (GPRS) enhancements for Evolved Universal Terrestrial Radio Access Network (E-UTRAN) access

[2] 3GPP TS 23.402 V8.4.1 (2009-01) Architecture enhancements for non-3GPP accesses

[3] Next Generation Mobile Alliance, Next Generation Mobile Networks Beyond HSPA and EVDO, V3.0, December 5, 2006: www.ngmn.org/uploads/media/White_Paper_NGMN_Beyond_HSPA_and_EVDO.pdf

[4] 3GPP TS 22.278 V9.2.0 (2008-12) Service requirements for the Evolved Packet System (EPS)

[5] 3GPP TR 21.905 V8.7.0 (2008-12) Vocabulary for 3GPP specifications

[6] ETSI TS 102 250-1 V1.1.1 (2003-10) Speed Processing, Transmission and Quality Aspects (STQ); QoS aspects for popular services in GSM and 3G networks: Part 1: Identification of Quality of Service aspects

[7] 3GPP TR 25.913 V8.0.0 (2008-12) Requirements for Evolved UTRA (E-UTRA) and Evolved UTRAN (E-UTRAN)

[8] 3GPP TS 22.115 V8.3.0 (2008-03) Service aspects; Charging and billing

[9] 3GPP TS 23.122 V8.4.0 (2008-12) Non-Access-Stratum (NAS) functions related to Mobile Station (MS) in idle mode

[10] 3GPP TS 36.300 V8.7.0 (2008-12) Evolved Universal Terrestrial Radio Access (E-UTRA) and Evolved Universal Terrestrial Radio Access Network (E-UTRAN); Overall description; Stage 2

[11] 3GPP TS 43.022 V8.1.0 (2008-06) Functions related to Mobile Station (MS) in idle mode and group receive mode

[12] 3GPP TS 25.304 V8.4.0 (2008-12) User Equipment (UE) procedures in idle mode and procedures for cell reselection in connected mode

[13] 3GPP TS 23.203 V8.4.0 (2008-12) Policy and charging control architecture

[14] 3GPP TS 32.240 V8.5.0 (2008-12) Telecommunication management; Charging management; Charging architecture and principles

[15] 3GPP TS 33.106 V8.1.0 (2008-03) Lawful interception requirements

[16] 3GPP TS 33.107 V8.6.0 (2008-12) 3G security; Lawful interception architecture and functions

[17] 3GPP TS 33.108 V8.5.0 (2008-12) 3G security; Handover interface for Lawful Interception (LI)

[18] 3GPP TS 33.401 V8.2.1 (2008-12) 3GPP System Architecture Evolution (SAE); Security architecture

[19] 3GPP TS 33.402 V8.2.1 (2008-12) 3GPP System Architecture Evolution (SAE); Security aspects of non-3GPP accesses

[20] 3GPP TS 33.210 V8.2.0 (2008-12) 3G security; Network Domain Security (NDS); IP network layer security

[21] Internet Engineering Task Force (IETF) Request For Comments (RFC) 2401

[22] 3GPP TS 36.413 V8.4.0 (2008-12) Evolved Universal Terrestrial Radio Access (E-UTRA) ; S1 Application Protocol (S1AP)

[23] 3GPP TS 24.301 V8.0.0 (2008-12) Non-Access-Stratum (NAS) protocol for Evolved Packet System (EPS); Stage 3

[24] 3GPP TS 36.331 V8.4.0 (2008-12) Evolved Universal Terrestrial Radio Access (E-UTRA); Radio Resource Control (RRC); Protocol specification

[25] 3GPP TR 36.902 V1.0.1 (2008-09) Evolved Universal Terrestrial Radio Access Network (E-UTRAN); Self-configuring and self-optimizing network (SON) use cases and solutions

[26] 3GPP TS 32.421 V8.4.0 (2008-12) Telecommunication management; Subscriber and equipment trace; Trace concepts and requirements

[27] 3GPP TS 32.422 V8.3.0 (2008-12) Telecommunication management; Subscriber and equipment trace; Trace control and configuration management

[28] 3GPP TS 32.423 V7.4.0 (2006-12) Telecommunication management; Subscriber and equipment trace; Trace data definition and management

[29] 3GPP TS 32.441 V8.1.0 (2008-09) Telecommunication management; Trace Management Integration Reference Point (IRP): Requirements

[30] 3GPP TS 32.442 V8.0.0 (2008-12) Telecommunication management; Trace Management Integration Reference Point (IRP): Information Service (IS)

[31] 3GPP TS 32.443 V8.0.0 (2008-12) Telecommunication management; Trace Management Integration Reference Point (IRP): Common Object Request Broker Architecture (CORBA) Solution Set (SS)

[32] 3GPP TS 23.002 V8.4.0 (2008-12) Network architecture

[33] 3GPP TS 23.216 V8.2.0 (2008-12) Single Radio Voice Call Continuity (SRVCC); Stage 2

[34] 3GPP TS 29.168 V8.0.0 (2008-12) Cell Broadcast Centre interfaces with the Evolved Packet Core; Stage 3

[35] 3GPP TS 29.281 V8.0.0 (2008-12) General Packet Radio System (GPRS) Tunnelling Protocol User Plane (GTPv1-U)

[36] 3GPP TS 36.423 V8.4.0 (2008-12) Evolved Universal Terrestrial Radio Access Network (E-UTRAN); X2 Application Protocol (X2AP)

[37] 3GPP TS 29.274 V8.0.0 (2008-12) 3GPP Evolved Packet System (EPS); Evolved General Packet Radio Service (GPRS) Tunnelling Protocol for Control plane (GTPv2-C); Stage 3

[38] 3GPP TS 29.272 V8.1.1 (2009-01) Evolved Packet System (EPS); Mobility Management Entity (MME) and Serving GPRS Support Node (SGSN) related interfaces based on Diameter protocol

[39] 3GPP TS 29.212 V8.2.0 (2008-12) Policy and charging control over Gx reference point

[40] 3GPP TS 29.214 V8.3.0 (2008-12) Policy and charging control over Rx reference point

[41] 3GPP TS 23.060 V8.3.0 (2008-12) General Packet Radio Service (GPRS); Service description; Stage 2

[42] 3GPP TS 36.323 V8.4.0 (2008-12) Evolved Universal Terrestrial Radio Access (E-UTRA); Packet Data Convergence Protocol (PDCP) specification

[43] 3GPP TS 36.322 V8.4.0 (2008-12) Evolved Universal Terrestrial Radio Access (E UTRA); Radio Link Control (RLC) protocol specification

[44] 3GPP TS 33.102 V8.1.0 (2008-12) 3G security; Security architecture

[45] International Telecommunications Union Telecommunication Standardization Sector (ITU-T) Rec. G.718

[46] 3GPP TS 23.236 V8.0.0 (2008-12) Intra-domain connection of Radio Access Network (RAN) nodes to multiple Core Network (CN) nodes

[47] 3GPP TS 43.318 V8.3.0 (2008-09) Generic Access Network (GAN); Stage 2

[48] 3GPP TS 24.008 V8.4.0 (2008-12) Mobile radio interface Layer 3 specification; Core network protocols; Stage 3

Links to all reference documents can be found at www.agilent.com/find/ltebook

Chapter 6

Design and Verification Challenges

6.1 Introduction

The material in this chapter was the motivation for writing this book. Agilent and our partner Anite are actively involved in developing the design and measurement tools the LTE industry needs to efficiently turn LTE and the Evolved Packet Core (EPC) network concepts into deployed and operational systems. Although the process of developing the radio equipment for a new standard is complex and no one model captures everything, Figure 6.1-1 is an attempt to define the product development lifecycle and provides the outline for this chapter.

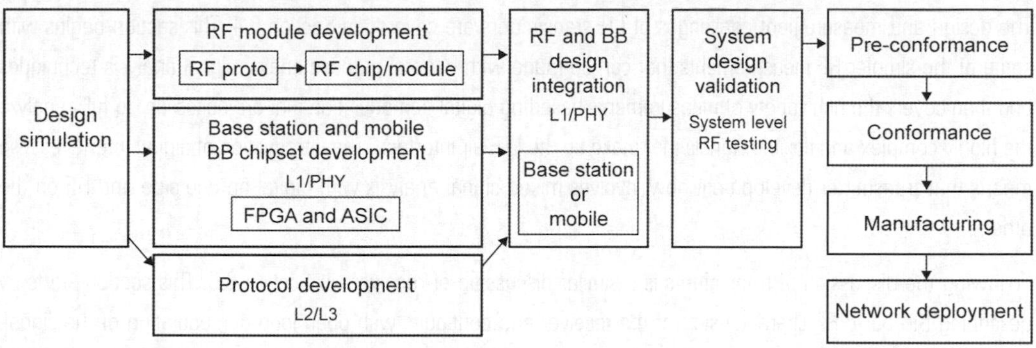

Figure 6.1-1. Example development lifecycle

This chapter is divided into ten major sections, shown in Table 6.1-1, each addressing different aspects of the lifecycle.

Table 6.1-1. Design and measurement sections

Section	Title
6.2	Simulation and Early R&D Hardware Testing
6.3	Testing RFICs With DigRF Interconnects
6.4	Transmitter Design and Measurement Challenges
6.5	Receiver Design and Measurement Challenges
6.6	Design and Verification Challenges of MIMO
6.7	MIMO Closed Loop Operation
6.8	Signalling Protocol Development
6.9	Network Troubleshooting
6.10	Battery Drain Testing

The chapter starts in Section 6.2 with design simulation. The complexity of systems is continuing to rise, and therefore the value of simulation early in the lifecycle is increasingly important. The ability to integrate Electronic Design Automation (EDA) tools with instruments to stimulate, measure and emulate hardware subsystems extends the reach of simulation tools further into the design lifecycle. This section offers numerous examples of how Agilent's EDA tools and other instruments can be used to overcome design and verification challenges in the earliest phases of product development.

Section 6.3 addresses the challenges created by the increasing use of high-speed serial interconnect between subsystems within User Equipment (UE) and the evolved Node B (eNB or base station). Traditional interconnect between the baseband and IF or RF subsystems has been analog, with some use of parallel digital systems, both of which come with a long history of probing and measurement techniques. With the peak data rates in wireless systems continuing to increase, the analog and parallel digital interconnect methods cannot keep pace and high-speed serial interconnect is taking over. However, the use of serial interconnect, which can include embedded control, presents an entirely new domain for stimulation and measurement that demands a new generation of test equipment. Section 6.3 investigates the development of the DigRF standard for interconnecting baseband and RF subsystems within the UE.

The design and measurement challenges of LTE transmitters are covered in Section 6.4. This section begins with some of the simpler RF measurements that can be made with general purpose analog signal analysis techniques and then covers the rich variety of measurements based on digital demodulation that are necessary to fully analyze the highly complex and flexible signals that make up the LTE air interface. The introduction of digital interfaces also means that transmitter development now involves mixed signal analysis with digital on one side and RF on the other.

Following the discussion of transmitters is a similar discussion of receivers in Section 6.5. This section starts by describing the basic RF characteristics of the receiver and continues with open loop demodulation of the signal. The section next looks at the most complex of receiver performance verification challenges: closed loop analysis of a MIMO receiver in a faded channel. This requires real time feedback of the channel conditions to enable adaptive modulation control and frequency selective scheduling, in addition to the use of incremental redundancy for damaged packets and retransmission for lost packets. The section finishes with an overview of methods for analyzing performance at the application layer.

Section 6.6 focuses on the RF challenges presented by multi-antenna systems including MIMO. The theoretical gains possible from such systems are well documented; however, the practical gains that will be seen in realistic conditions are influenced by many factors that involve new methods for analyzing antenna design, the channel propagation conditions and the received signals.

To obtain optimal performance from MIMO systems requires perfect knowledge of the channel. Section 6.7 investigates the performance implications that result from non-ideal feedback caused by several factors including the rate of feedback, quantization effects caused by use of codebooks, the affects of UE speed, channel estimation errors, and the impact of reporting delays.

The chapter changes focus in Section 6.8 by moving from RF aspects to consider the challenges of signalling protocol development. This section is contributed by Agilent's partner for LTE, Anite Telecoms Ltd. The different phases of development from early development testing through conformance testing to interoperability testing are discussed along with the tools available to facilitate this aspect of the product lifecycle. A more formal discussion of conformance testing for both RF and signalling is provided in Chapter 7.

The chapter continues with Section 6.9 that considers test challenges of the Evolved Packet Core (EPC) network, which together with the LTE air interface makes up the overall Evolved Packet System (EPS). The flatter architecture of the EPC presents both opportunities for cost savings and new challenges for testing and monitoring due to the removal of the physical interfaces previously available for such purposes. Aspects covered in this section include building the network for testability, managing multi-site test activities, the challenges of duplicating real world scenarios, and benchmarking performance. The section ends with the role of drive test in the deployment phase of new networks.

The chapter ends with a twist in Section 6.10 by considering the challenges of battery drain testing. With the ever-increasing demands being put on high end mobile devices, power consumption is often a limiting factor. This section takes a look at some of the tools available to help measure and optimize battery current drain.

6.2 Simulation and Early R&D Hardware Testing

LTE presents a number of design and test challenges for system designers:

- Evaluating existing designs, algorithms and hardware (for example, those based on W-CDMA, HSPA or WiMAX) to determine if they can be reused in LTE systems.
- Defining design requirements and specifications for new hardware.
- Developing and verifying new algorithms as the wireless specification evolves.
- Designing, verifying and testing the performance of RF and mixed-signal designs and hardware independent of the baseband hardware and firmware (for example, coded Bit Error Ratio (BER) or Block Error Ratio (BLER) designs in which baseband coding functionality such as turbo coding impacts RF BER and BLER performance).
- Verifying the interoperability of LTE designs with multiple signal formats (including WiMAX, WLAN, W-CDMA and HPSA).

This section discusses physical layer simulation to assist in meeting the design challenges of 3GPP LTE RF systems and circuits. It also covers early R&D testing of these hardware designs by combining simulation software tools with test equipment in an integrated environment.

The LTE Wireless Library for Agilent's system design software, which includes a rich set of LTE FDD and TDD downlink and uplink models and simulation examples, is used to illustrate simulation benefits. Examples show how the LTE Wireless Library can be applied for LTE design requirement partitioning, algorithm development and RF and mixed signal transmitter and receiver design. The effect of Local Oscillator (LO) phase noise on OFDMA BER performance — a key area of interest — is examined by comparing LTE and Mobile WiMAX OFDMA BER in a simulated receiver design. Also covered are the benefits and technical considerations of combining simulation with test equipment to address R&D testing challenges. Several LTE hardware BER test examples are included.

The complexities of LTE, along with time-to-market pressures, make it critical to minimize system integration risk whenever possible to avoid costly design turns and product delivery delays. The concepts and simulation techniques presented in this section can help minimize integration risk throughout the product development lifecycle, beginning with the initial design and extending through R&D hardware testing.

This section discusses physical layer simulation and test and does not address the protocol layer, which is covered in Section 6.8.

6.2.1 Physical Layer Simulation Tools

The LTE Wireless Library is a collection of standards-based simulation models and examples for designers working at the LTE physical layer. In addition to simulation models, the LTE Wireless Library includes a number of pre-configured examples for simulating LTE metrics such as Error Vector Magnitude (EVM) and BER. Please note that the features of the LTE Wireless Library may have changed since this printing. To highlight Agilent's simulation design and verification capabilities, Figure 6.2-1 shows how an LTE system can be modeled and tested.

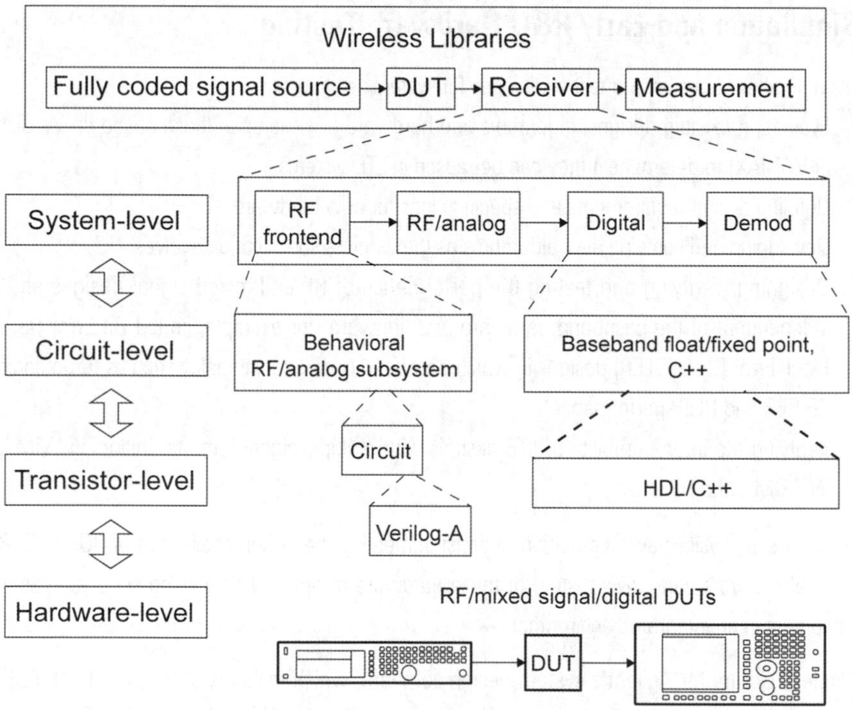

Figure 6.2-1. Simulation conceptual overview

Radio frequency system designs are constructed using parameterized behavioral block models (components) such as amplifiers, filters and mixers. Component performance is specified using parameters such as gain, 1 dB compression point and third order intercept point. These parameters can be varied until the system design meets specification; then they serve as the basis for the circuit design requirements.

As the design cycle progresses, the parameterized behavioral models are replaced by transistor-level circuit designs. Co-simulation is performed with Agilent's Circuit Envelope simulator so that circuit-level effects are included in the system-level simulation. Verifying a system design with circuit effects included in the simulation helps minimize risk as the design cycle moves from the system level to the circuit level. Greater modeling fidelity is provided as the design process moves from concept to implementation.

In the baseband domain, floating and fixed point behavioral models are used to construct baseband algorithm functionality. Co-simulation with external simulators can be used to replace these blocks with custom algorithms written in Hardware Description Language (HDL). Custom models defined by the user also can be written and simulated.

To help mitigate RF/baseband integration risks and unexpected behavior late in the system testing phase, RF and baseband designs are simulated and verified together using the parameterized behavioral models, co-simulating with transistor-level circuit designs and with external simulators for algorithms written in HDL.

As the design cycle transitions to the hardware testing stage, Agilent's design software can be combined with test equipment to verify LTE system-level performance. With this approach, some portions of the design are modeled in simulation and other portions are represented as hardware Devices Under Test (DUTs). This approach allows simulated signals to be downloaded to an arbitrary waveform signal generator to turn simulated signals into "real world" physical test signals. The test signals are then used as stimuli for hardware DUTs during R&D testing. The DUT outputs are captured with signal analyzers and read back into the design software for simulation post-processing.

The power of this approach is demonstrated in examples that show how LTE BER measurements can be made on RF and mixed-signal hardware using simulated baseband capability to represent missing baseband hardware functionality. The use of simulation enables the RF and mixed-signal hardware to be tested independent of the baseband hardware. It also helps isolate issues between the baseband and RF sections if problems arise later in the hardware integration phase.

6.2.1.1 LTE Downlink Simulation Example

The LTE Wireless Library contains a number of LTE Downlink (DL) simulation examples that system engineers use to accelerate design activities. An example of a downlink coded BER simulation is shown in Figure 6.2-2.

The left side of the diagram shows six LTE User Equipment (UE) data sources in which the data pattern and modulation type (QPSK, 16QAM or 64QAM) are specified. Coded BER simulations for UE1 are illustrated in this example, and the channel coding is performed by the LTE downlink channel coding block. The downlink source accepts UE1-6 data and performs the physical channel mapping, OFDMA modulation, up-sampling and spectral shaping required to generate a modulated RF downlink signal. A Gaussian noise source is used to sweep the E_b/N_0 at the input of the downlink receiver block. The downlink receiver block down-samples the data and performs the OFDMA demodulation and physical channel de-mapping. A downlink channel decoder performs the channel decoding to extract the data bits, and a BER measurement sink on the far right then performs a coded BER simulation measurement, comparing the extracted UE1 data bits to the UE1 reference data bits.

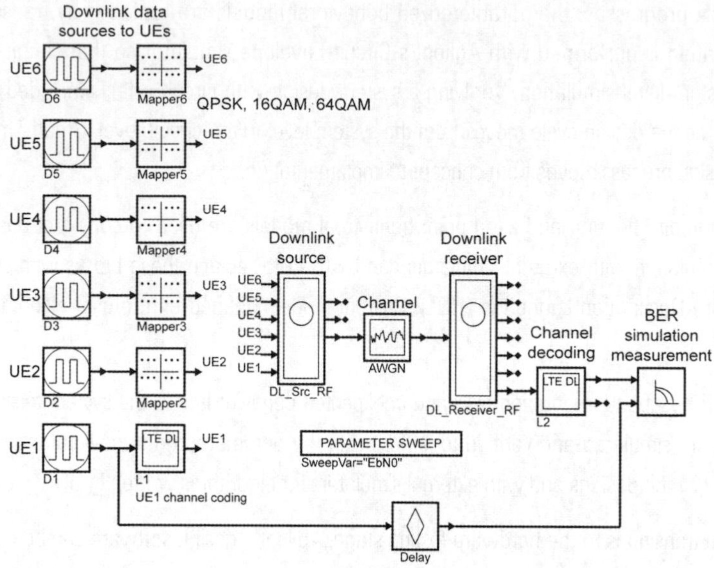

Figure 6.2-2. LTE downlink BER schematic

Part of the LTE Wireless Library downlink channel coder block is shown in Figure 6.2-3. The use of double lines on the channel coder symbol indicate that it is hierarchical: moving down a level reveals the algorithm blocks. The DL-SCH transport channel processing is shown on the left, and the corresponding algorithm blocks for the LTE Wireless Library downlink channel coder are shown on the right.

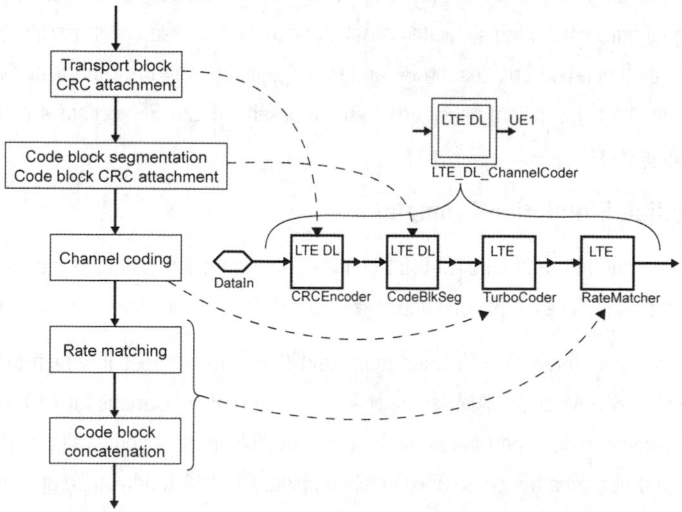

Figure 6.2-3. Part of LTE Wireless Library downlink channel coder (DL-SCH transport processing from 36.212 [1] Figure 5.3.2-1)

An overview of LTE downlink channel processing according to 36.211 [2] is shown in Figure 6.2-4, along with the corresponding LTE Wireless Library simulation blocks.

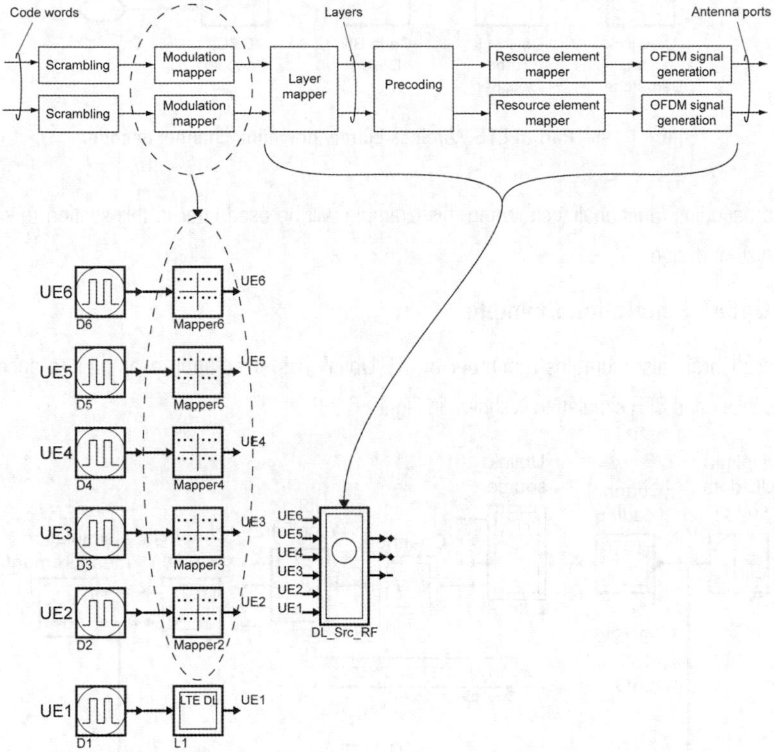

Figure 6.2-4. 3GPP LTE downlink channel processing and corresponding LTE Wireless Library downlink channel processing (downlink channel processing from 36.211 [2] Figure 6.3-1)

The LTE mapper, as Figure 6.2-4 shows, sets the modulation type to QPSK, 16QAM or 64QAM. For UE1, modulation mapping is performed in the LTE downlink channel coder block. For UEs 2-6, it is performed at the top-level schematic. The Reference Signal (RS), primary synchronization signal, secondary synchronization signal, Physical Broadcast Channel (PBCH) and Physical Downlink Control Channel (PDCCH) are multiplexed together with the Physical Downlink Shared Channel (PDSCH) UE 1-6 data inside the DL_Src_RF block. This block performs the OFDMA modulation, slot and frame multiplexing, and it up-samples and filters the data for spectral shaping. The resulting IQ data is then modulated on an IF/RF carrier to use at the top level for RF system design.

The LTE downlink receiver RF block in the top level schematic performs time and frequency synchronization, channel estimation, slot and frame de-multiplexing and OFDMA demodulation.

The LTE Wireless Library downlink receiver then decodes the signal to remove the channel coding from the downlink source side so that the coded BER simulation can be performed. Figure 6.2-5 shows part of the LTE Wireless Library downlink channel decoder block.

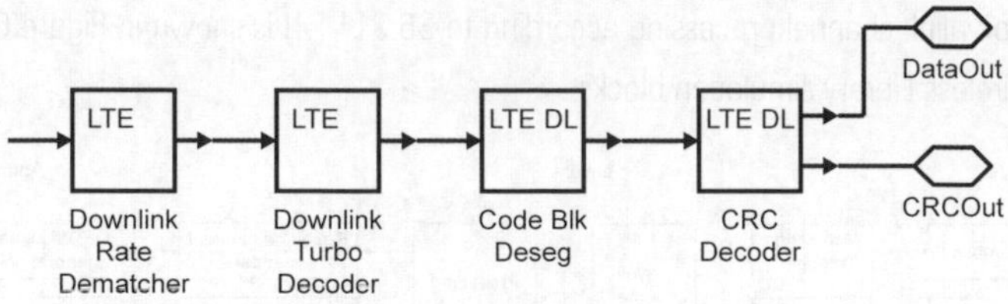

Figure 6.2-5. Part of LTE Wireless Library downlink channel decoder

The coding and decoding functionality shown in this example will be used later in this section to simulate coded BER in an LTE system design.

6.2.1.2 LTE Uplink Simulation Example

The LTE Wireless Library also contains a number of LTE Uplink (UL) simulation examples to accelerate design activities. An uplink coded BER simulation is shown in Figure 6.2-6.

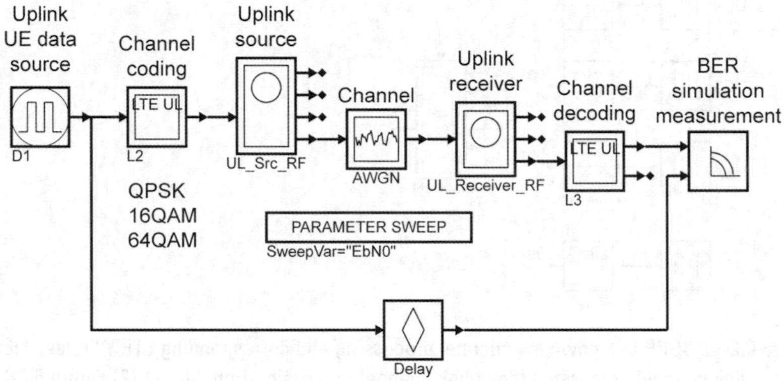

Figure 6.2-6. LTE uplink coded BER schematic

In this example an LTE uplink UE data source is shown on the left side, and coded BER simulations for this UE are shown on the right. The channel coding is performed by an uplink coder block, and the uplink source block accepts UE data and performs the multiplexing, SC-FDMA modulation, up-sampling and spectral shaping required to generate a modulated RF uplink signal. A Gaussian noise source is used to sweep the E_b/N_0 into the uplink receiver block. The uplink receiver down-samples the data and performs the SC-FDMA demodulation and de-multiplexing. An uplink channel decoder extracts the data bits, and a BER measurement sink on the far right performs the coded BER simulation measurement, comparing the extracted UE data bits to the UE reference data bits.

The LTE Wireless Library uplink channel coder block is shown in greater detail in Figure 6.2-7. The use of double lines on the channel coder symbol indicate that this function is hierarchical: moving down a level shows the algorithm blocks. The transport channel processing according to 36.212 [1] is shown on the left, and the corresponding algorithm blocks for the LTE Wireless Library uplink channel coder are shown on the right. The channel coding performed by these numeric simulation blocks is multi-rate; that is, a varying number of samples will be output from each block for an output sink that sets the simulation length (for example, a frame of data).

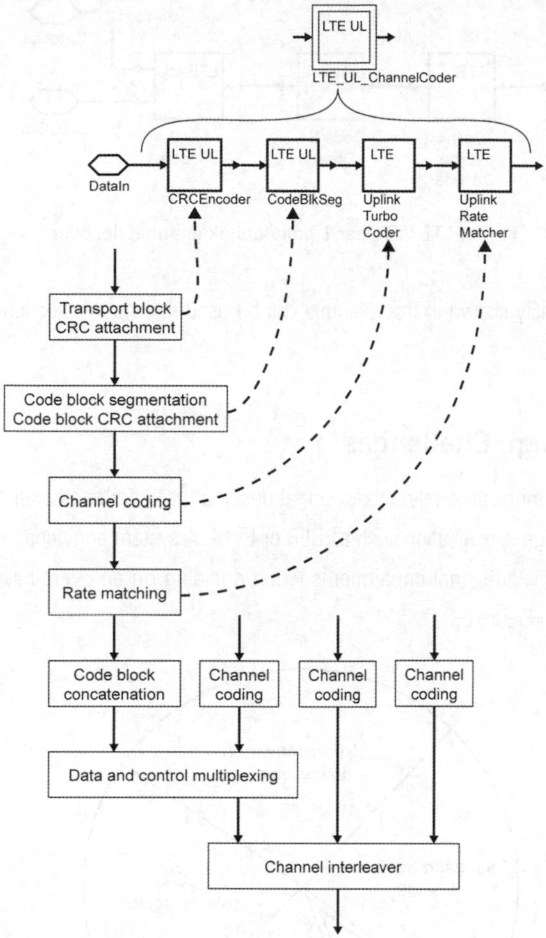

Figure 6.2-7. Part of LTE Wireless Library uplink channel coder
(uplink transport channel processing from 36.212 [1] Figure 5.2.2-1)

The RS, Physical Uplink Shared Channel (PUSCH), Physical Uplink Control Channel (PUCCH) and Physical Random Access Channel (PRACH) are multiplexed together with the PUSCH UE data inside the LTE uplink source RF block. This block performs the SC-FDMA modulation and multiplexing, and up-samples and filters the data for spectral shaping. The resulting IQ data is then modulated on an IF/RF carrier to use at the top level for RF system design.

The uplink receiver RF in the top-level schematic performs time and frequency synchronization, channel estimation, de-multiplexing, and SC-FDMA demodulation. The LTE Wireless Library uplink receiver then decodes the signal to remove the channel coding from the uplink source side so that the coded BER simulation can be performed. The LTE Wireless Library uplink channel decoder block is shown in Figure 6.2-8.

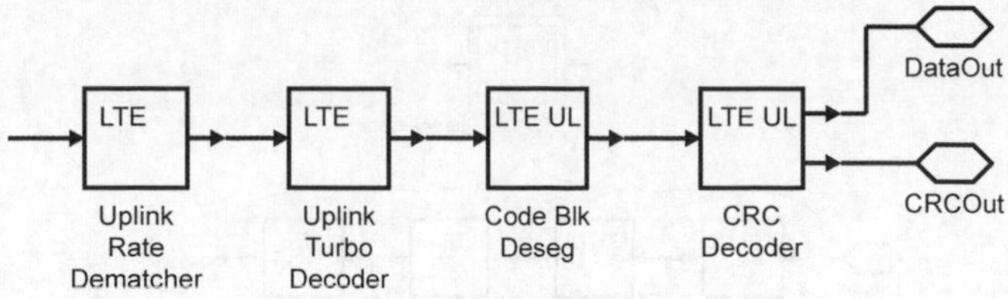

Figure 6.2-8. Part of LTE Wireless Library uplink channel decoder

The coding and decoding functionality shown in this example will be used later in this section to simulate coded BER on an LTE system design.

6.2.2 Mixed-Signal Design Challenges

Today's system-level designs are, more precisely, mixed-signal designs that combine baseband/digital, analog and RF to meet a system-level design specification such as BER or EVM. A system engineer typically has to make tradeoffs among various RF and mixed-signal impairments when deciding on an overall system performance budget such as the one illustrated in Figure 6.2-9.

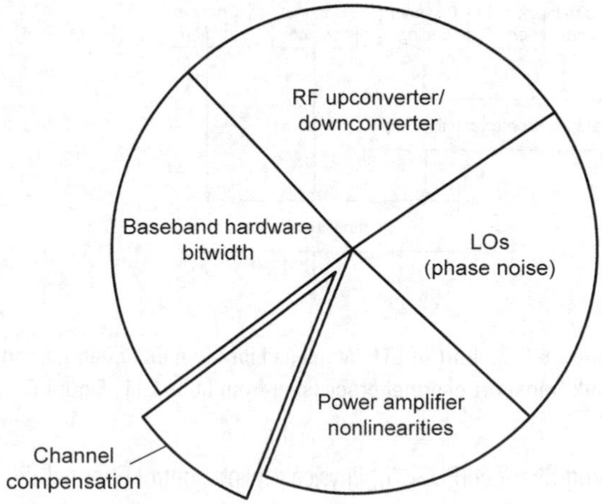

Figure 6.2-9. Partitioning for a system performance budget

A simplified RF/mixed-signal system design is shown in Figure 6.2-10.

Figure 6.2-10. RF/mixed-signal system design

In digital communication systems such as LTE, channel impairments are a major concern. Channel coding is applied to the data bits to improve system performance and robustness in the presence of these impairments. In the LTE downlink, for example, the data bits are processed with a CRC encoder and channel coding is applied with a turbo coder. Code block segmentation and rate matching are also applied to achieve the desired coding scheme. The LTE uplink processing and coding functions are similar, but channel interleaving is also added to combat the effects of channel fading.

In Figure 6.2-10, the term "coding algorithms" is used for this processing and coding functionality, which typically is provided by baseband hardware and firmware. The hardware implementation of the baseband functionality is usually fixed-point and can introduce signal impairments to the signal path.

Examples of fixed-point impairments for a Root Raised Cosine (RRC) filter are shown in Figure 6.2-11. Transmitter and receiver filters for LTE are not defined in the specifications so for illustrative purposes an RRC filter will be used to indicate the simulation issues associated with filtering. Once the RRC-filtered waveform is modulated on an IF carrier, fixed-point impairments can be observed as out-of-channel spectral impairments. These impairments can affect the in-channel system EVM as well. In the examples shown here, the bit-width of a fixed-point, Finite Impulse Response (FIR) RRC is swept from 6 bits to 12 bits.

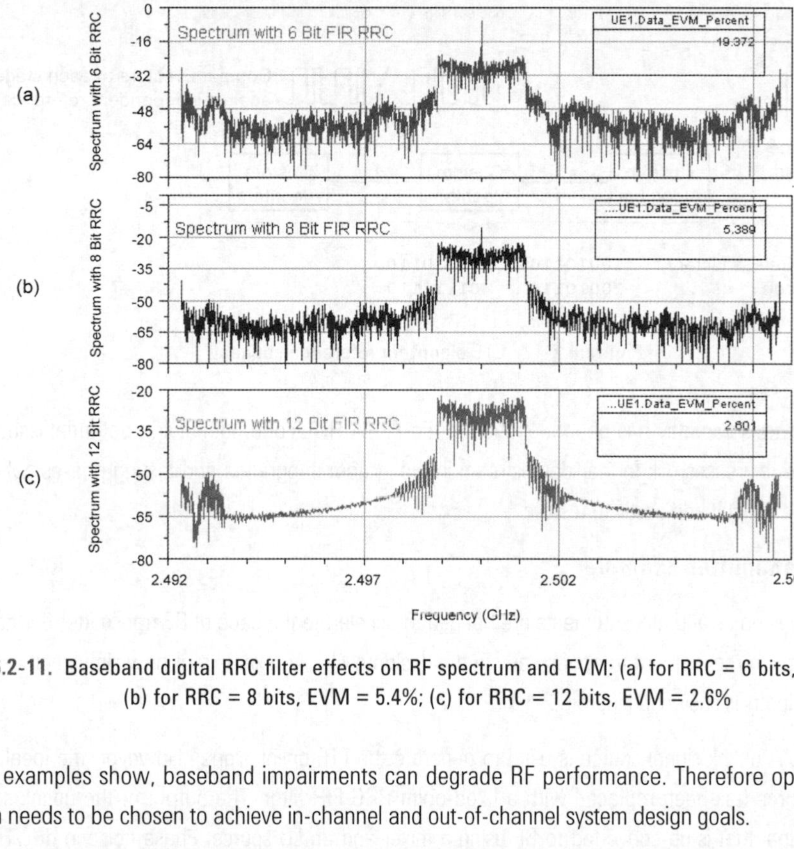

Figure 6.2-11. Baseband digital RRC filter effects on RF spectrum and EVM: (a) for RRC = 6 bits, EVM = 19.4%; (b) for RRC = 8 bits, EVM = 5.4%; (c) for RRC = 12 bits, EVM = 2.6%

As these examples show, baseband impairments can degrade RF performance. Therefore optimal baseband resolution needs to be chosen to achieve in-channel and out-of-channel system design goals.

In addition to the baseband section of the system design, the Transmitter (TX) and Receiver (RX) sections introduce impairments. For example, mixers used for up-conversion from IF to RF introduce intermodulation products, which degrade spectral spurious performance. Also, gain compression and phase distortion from non-linear power amplifiers, phase noise from LOs used for up- and down-conversion, filter group delay, and ADC/DAC performance can affect EVM and BER.

The next set of examples shows how simulation is used to evaluate LTE system design performance and to partition design requirements for the various sections and components that make up the design.

6.2.2.1 Baseband Example

One challenge of designing to an evolving standard such as LTE is that the specifications are subject to interpretation, which can lead to uncertainty during early system development. The LTE Wireless Library is useful in verifying LTE algorithm functionality by providing an independent reference against which algorithm test vectors can be compared. Figure 6.2-12 illustrates this scenario. Reference data bits are sent to the LTE Wireless Library uplink coding chain and test vectors are compared between the LTE Wireless Library algorithms and custom algorithms — which may be written, for example, in HDL for an FPGA implementation.

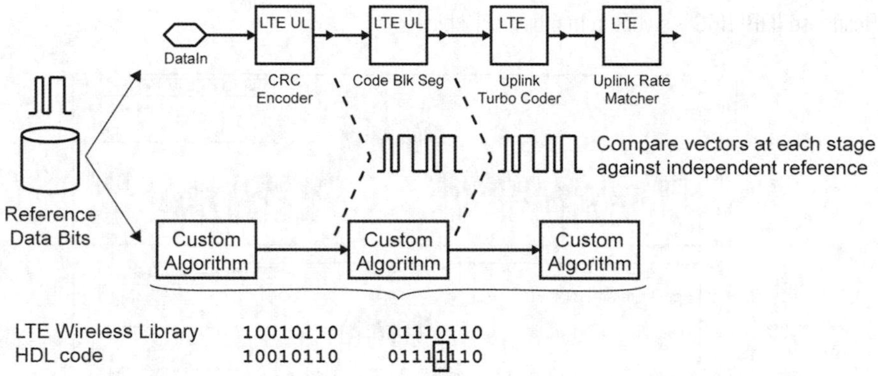

Figure 6.2-12. LTE algorithm reference concept

In this example, a discrepancy has been identified in the FPGA HDL code. Identifying potential issues early in the design phase decreases risk further downstream in the system integration and testing phases, when design problems become difficult and costly to resolve.

6.2.2.2 RF Transmitter Example

Simulation signal sources and measurements are needed to accelerate the pace of RF transmitter design activities and to enable design requirement tradeoffs early in the design cycle. An example of how simulations are used in making such tradeoffs is shown in Figure 6.2-13.

The LTE SC-FDMA uplink signal source is used to generate the LTE uplink signal. However, the ideal RRC filter in the uplink source has been replaced with a fixed-point RRC FIR filter. The output of the uplink source is a modulated IF signal that is up-converted to RF using a mixer and an LO source. Phase noise in dBc/Hz is set at various frequency offsets for the LO source. A non-linear power amplifier is modeled by specifying the gain in dB and the output 1 dB compression point in dBm. The output signal is then filtered and EVM is measured using the LTE EVM sink.

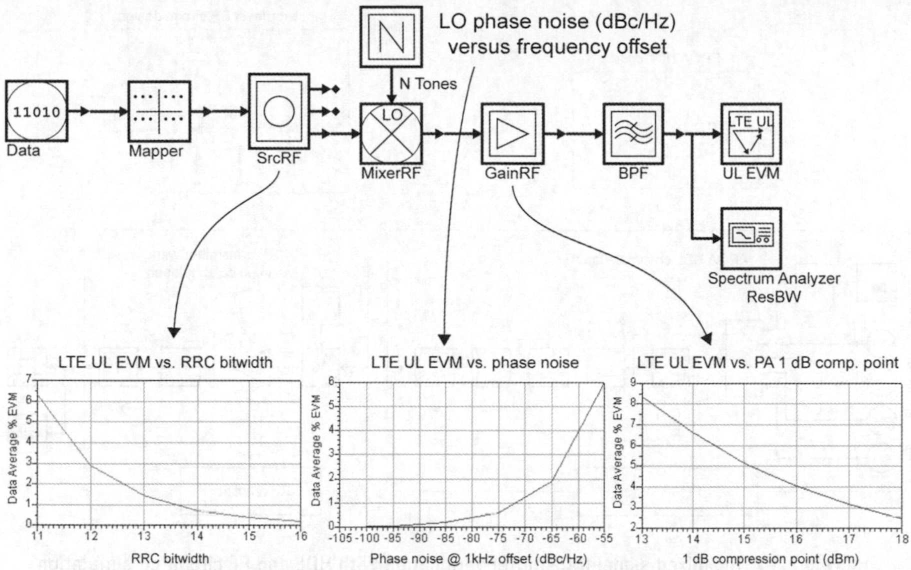

Figure 6.2-13. **Transmitter baseband/RF design tradeoffs vs. RRC bit-width, phase noise and power amplifier 1 dB compression point**

The effective bit-width of the fixed-point FIR RRC is swept, as is the LO phase noise at a 1 kHz offset and the Power Amplifier (PA) output 1 dB compression point. The resulting plots of EVM versus swept design impairments are shown. These types of simulation enable system engineers to gain insight into design sensitivities so that informed decisions can be made for design requirements. System engineers gain visibility into the performance required for each section and can consider the effect on schedule and cost of optimizing performance just enough so that the system specifications can be met without over-designing.

Simulations similar to the example here are valuable early in the design cycle to determine design requirements. However, once the cycle advances to the detailed phases of design, simulation can be used to verify system-level RF and mixed-signal design performance to mitigate baseband/RF integration risks. For the RF sections, this could involve co-simulating the transistor-level circuit designs with the rest of the RF system design. For baseband sections, it could involve co-simulating the HDL written for an FPGA implementation with the rest of the RF system design.

The example in Figure 6.2-14 illustrates the concept of co-simulation for system-level verification. HDL for an FPGA implementation is co-simulated together with a transistor circuit-level design to verify the system-level performance. RF circuit-level effects, rather than mathematical polynomial curve-fit modeling, provide an added level of RF modeling fidelity to this simulation relative to the parameterized 1 dB compression point modeling performed earlier. Thus simulation modeling fidelity is improved as the project advances from concept to detailed design.

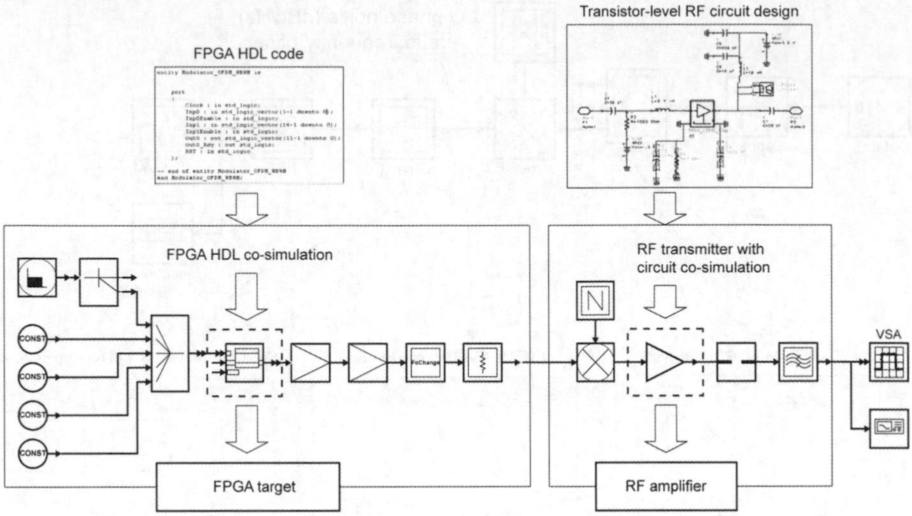

Figure 6.2-14. RF/mixed-signal transmitter verification with HDL and RF circuit co-simulation

An Agilent Vector Signal Analyzer (VSA) simulation measurement element — the 89601A VSA Measurement Software — is used at the output of the mixed-signal transmitter design to evaluate the simulation performance. See Figure 6.2-15.

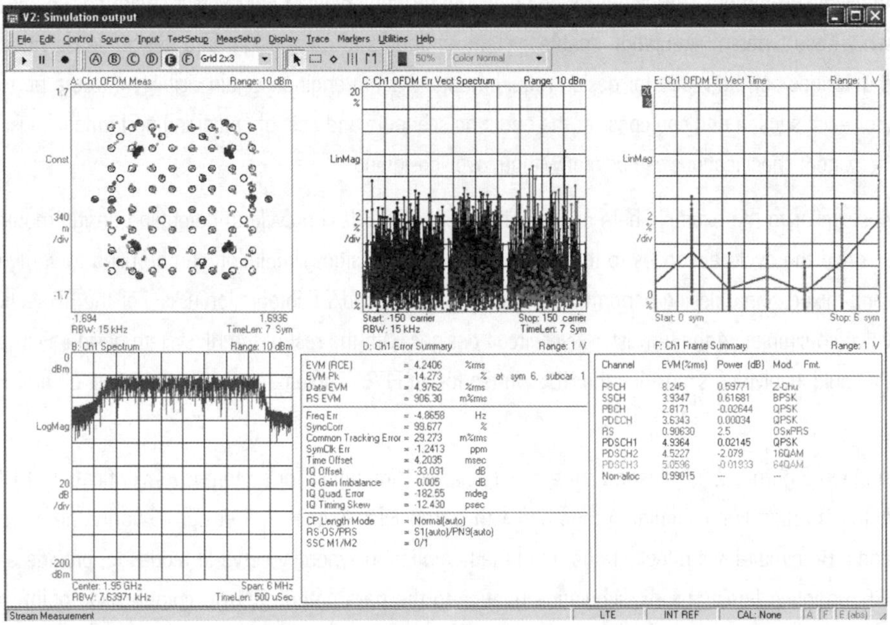

Figure 6.2-15. RF/mixed-signal transmitter simulation results with Agilent 89601 VSA measurement software

The simulation results in Figure 6.2-15 are shown in six different traces as follows: the constellation (upper left), RF spectrum (lower left), EVM versus subcarrier (upper center), modulation error summary (lower center), EVM versus symbol (upper right), and frame summary (lower right). Note that the same 89601 VSA software can be used in conjunction with digital and RF signal acquisition hardware to measure real signals from the DUT. The ability to use this software for both design simulation and testing of real hardware provides unique measurement-algorithm and user-interface consistency across the entire product development cycle. Examples of R&D LTE hardware testing are included later in this section.

6.2.2.3 Receiver Mixed-Signal Design Challenges

Similar to transmitter design, receiver design presents a set of mixed-signal design challenges. Typically, wireless standards define receiver performance metrics in terms of receiver coded BER sensitivity, or coded BER at a minimum RF input power level into the receiver. In addition, the receiver's BER can be specified with in-band interferers present, adjacent channel interferers present or both.

A significant challenge for LTE RF receiver design and verification is that baseband coding and decoding functionality is required to measure the coded BER performance of a receiver, both for simulated designs and for R&D DUT hardware. Furthermore, baseband and RF designs often need to progress in parallel to meet the objectives of development schedules. These requirements can impede LTE RF receiver design and test, since baseband coding/decoding algorithms and baseband hardware may not be available until later in the product development cycle.

Simulated LTE baseband capability is used to overcome this impediment so that LTE RF receiver design and test activities can begin. For example, an uncoded BER using the LTE Wireless Library to evaluate LO phase noise requirements is shown in Figure 6.2-16. Phase noise is of key interest in OFDMA systems, because the close subcarrier spacings can make OFDMA system performance susceptible to phase noise and frequency error. An RF receiver design is inserted between the LTE downlink simulation signal source and downlink simulation receiver, and the E_b/N_0 into the RF receiver is swept, along with the downconverter LO phase noise.

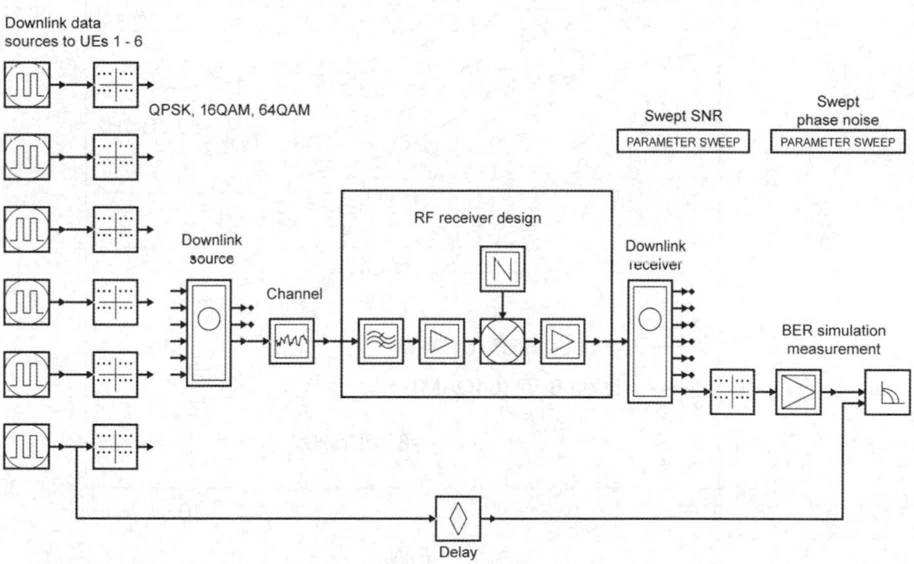

Figure 6.2-16. Schematic to measure BER of RF receiver vs. swept E_b/N_0 and phase noise

The E_b/N_0 is swept from 0 dB to 12 dB in 1 dB steps, and the LO phase noise is swept from –60 dBc/Hz to –80 dBc/Hz in 10 dB steps at a 10 kHz frequency offset. Note that the 10 kHz frequency offset is within the LTE 15 kHz subcarrier spacing. The simulation results are shown in Figure 6.2-17.

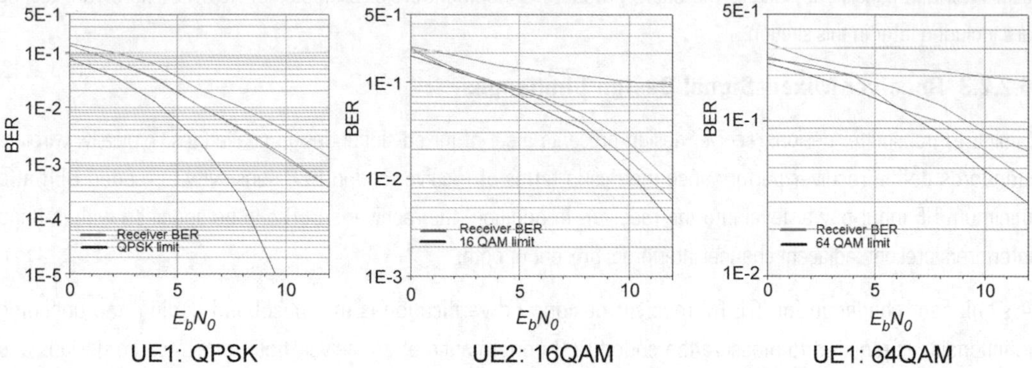

Figure 6.2-17. Uncoded BER simulation results for RF receiver

The LTE uncoded BER simulations are performed for three different UE1 modulation types: QPSK, 16QAM and 64QAM, shown from left to right, respectively. Each plot has three traces resulting from the swept LO phase noise.

The plots show that the LO phase noise impacts BER performance more significantly for 64QAM than for 16QAM or QPSK. This result is expected, as noise margin is lower when higher order modulation is used. It is just one example of the many tradeoffs to consider when designing for higher order modulation and the associated higher data throughputs.

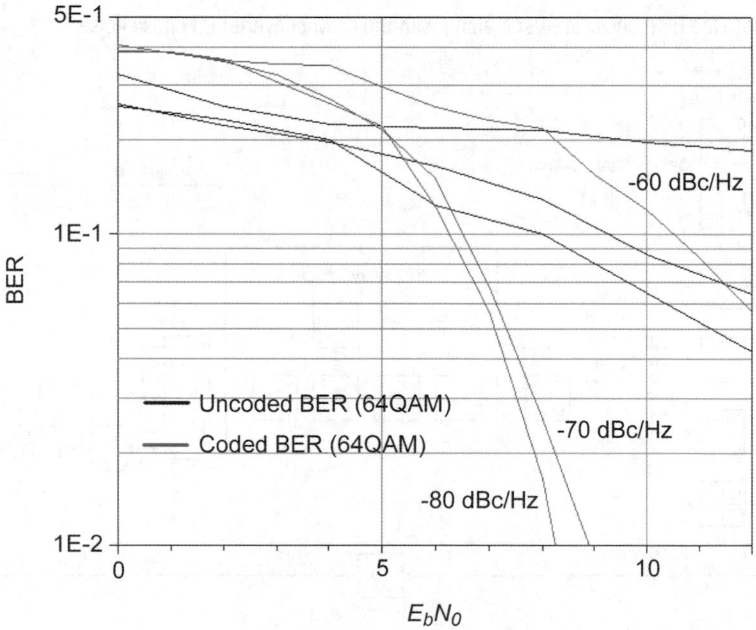

Figure 6.2-18. Comparison of coded BER and uncoded BER results for RF receiver

The LTE Wireless Library LTE downlink coded BER schematic (Figure 6.2-2) can be used to evaluate coded BER performance of the simulated RF receiver design. A comparison of uncoded versus coded LTE BER results for the 64QAM case is shown in Figure 6.2-18.

The coded LTE BER performance is significantly better than the uncoded BER at higher values of E_b/N_0 as a result of the LTE downlink coding. However, at lower values of E_b/N_0 the coded BER performance is degraded relative to the uncoded BER performance.

6.2.2.4 Design Re-Use and Convergence

When a new standard such as LTE emerges, it is often necessary to evaluate existing designs to determine what, if anything, can be reused. For example, an existing Mobile WiMAX RF system design might be considered for possible reuse in an LTE system.

A simulation example that evaluates the performance of an existing design for both WiMAX and LTE is created by replacing the LTE signal source and measurements shown previously in Figure 6.2-16 with a WiMAX signal source and measurements.

The results, shown in Figure 6.2-19, compare the LTE coded BER to the WiMAX coded BER for swept LO phase noise values of –80 dBc/Hz, –70 dBc/Hz and –60 dBc/Hz at a 10 kHz frequency offset.

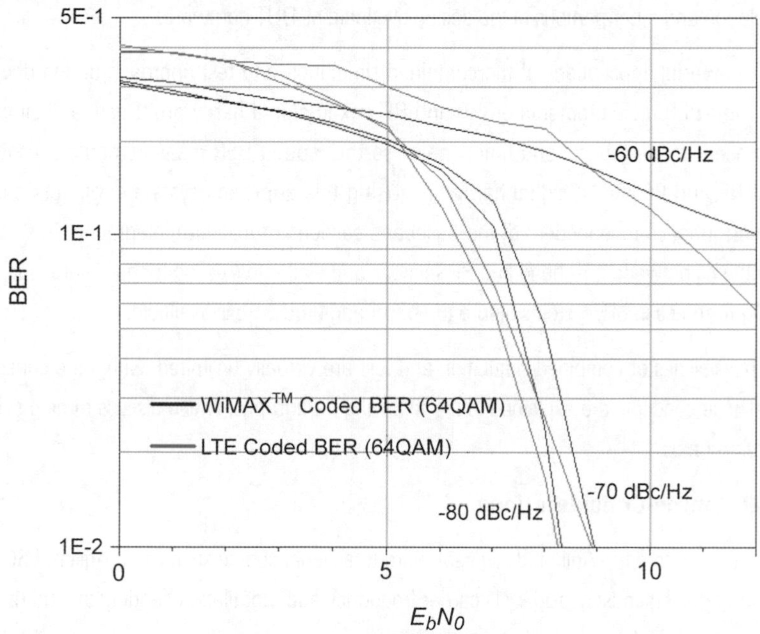

Figure 6.2-19. Comparison of LTE coded BER vs. WiMAX coded BER for RF receiver

The simulation results show that coded BER is similar for the LTE downlink and the Mobile WiMAX downlink for this particular RF receiver design.

6.2.3 Combining Simulation and Test to Address LTE R&D Hardware Testing

Combining simulation with test offers a number of benefits for an emerging wireless standard such as LTE. The examples thus far have shown that simulation is powerful and flexible in its ability to model baseband coding and decoding functionality. In addition, simulation can be used to model impairments such as multipath, thus enabling the creation of test signals with channel impairments. By combining simulation with test instruments, system engineers can extend the test functionality of their equipment, adding pre-processing and post-processing of test signals using flexible simulation models.

One simple example of this approach is the use of simulation and test instruments together to set the frequency mask of an LTE spectrum for a hardware DUT test signal. The task can be accomplished easily by simulating a baseband filter, such as an FIR RRC, and then downloading the IQ waveforms to an arbitrary waveform generator (arb) to create the user-defined test signal.

A more complex example is to generate LTE hardware DUT test signals with multipath fading to test an LTE receiver design. The multipath fading environment can be simulated and the impaired IQ waveforms then downloaded to the signal generator arb to create an LTE receiver test signal. The downloaded waveforms can include modeled system design impairments such as LO phase noise, simulated PA gain and phase distortion, or FIR RRC fixed point impairments. This technique enables system-level testing to begin with portions of the design modeled in simulation and other portions of the design available as DUT hardware.

One of the most powerful applications of the combined simulation and test approach during development is to perform R&D coded BER measurements on RF and RF/mixed-signal hardware. Baseband simulation models are used to represent missing baseband functionality so that coded BER measurements can be made during development of RF and RF/mixed-signal hardware. Using this approach system engineers can evaluate RF hardware BER performance independent of the baseband sections to minimize integration risks, isolate potential performance problems between baseband and RF sections and evaluate existing RF hardware (such as W-CDMA, HSPA or WiMAX) for reuse in LTE systems before the baseband hardware is available.

The application possibilities of combined simulation and test are virtually unlimited, within the constraints of a few basic concepts. These concepts are explained in the following paragraphs, which discuss turning simulated signals into real-world test signals.

6.2.3.1 Signal Source Considerations

To support a signal flow from the Agilent design software to a signal source such as an Agilent ESG or MXG signal generator, system engineers must consider (1) carrier frequency and modulation bandwidth, and (2) the number of IQ data-pair samples required for the application.

Generation of real-world signals is supported by Agilent design software ESG sink models such as the one shown in Figure 6.2-20. To create a real-world test signal, simulated IQ data pairs are automatically downloaded to the ESG or MXG arb and then modulated onto an IF, RF or microwave carrier using the IQ modulator in the signal generator.

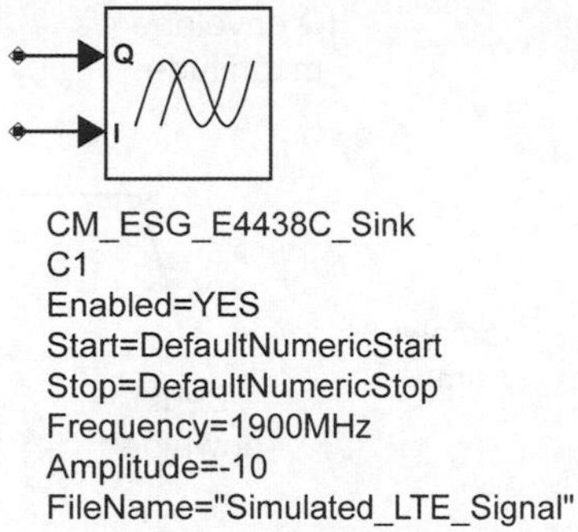

Figure 6.2-20. Generating a real-world test signal

The complex envelope that is represented by the Agilent design software simulator is expressed as follows:

$$s_l(t) = I(t) + j * Q(t)$$

The carrier frequency and amplitude are set directly on the ESG sink as parameters. The simulated IQ data pairs are auto-scaled inside the sink model before they are downloaded. Thus to perform a swept-power LTE BER measurement, for example, the simulated LTE IQ pairs have to be downloaded to the arb only once, and a command can then be sent to the signal generator's RF/IF power for each point in the BER measurement waterfall curve.

Several constraints imposed by the test instrument must be considered when simulated IQ pairs are downloaded to an arb. One is the signal generator's IQ modulator bandwidth and its ability to support the simulation bandwidth used to generate the simulated IQ data. The simulation bandwidth is defined by the simulation *time step* used to sample the I and Q envelopes, where time step is the time step used to sample $I(t)$ and $Q(t)$ for the complex envelope expression as defined above.

$$simulation\ bandwidth = 1/(time\ step)$$

Note that the time step does not sample the modulated carrier frequency itself. So, for example, the MXG signal generator's 100 MHz IQ modulator bandwidth sets a simulation bandwidth constraint of 100 MHz for a given application with the Agilent design software and the MXG. However, this is well above the bandwidth required for any LTE application. For example, an LTE configuration with a 5 MHz bandwidth requires a time step of 1/(15.36 MHz) and correspondingly an IQ modulator bandwidth of 15.36 MHz with 2X oversampling.

Arb depth is another instrument constraint. Typically, a signal generator allows a finite number of simulation samples to be downloaded and stored within the arb. For example, the MXG with Option 019 has an arb depth of 64 MSa and allows up to 64 M IQ waveform samples to be downloaded from the Agilent design software to the signal generator.

It is also important to consider delays in the simulated design — for example, delays from filters — so that the first sample downloaded corresponds to the start of the frame. This is shown in Figure 6.2-21.

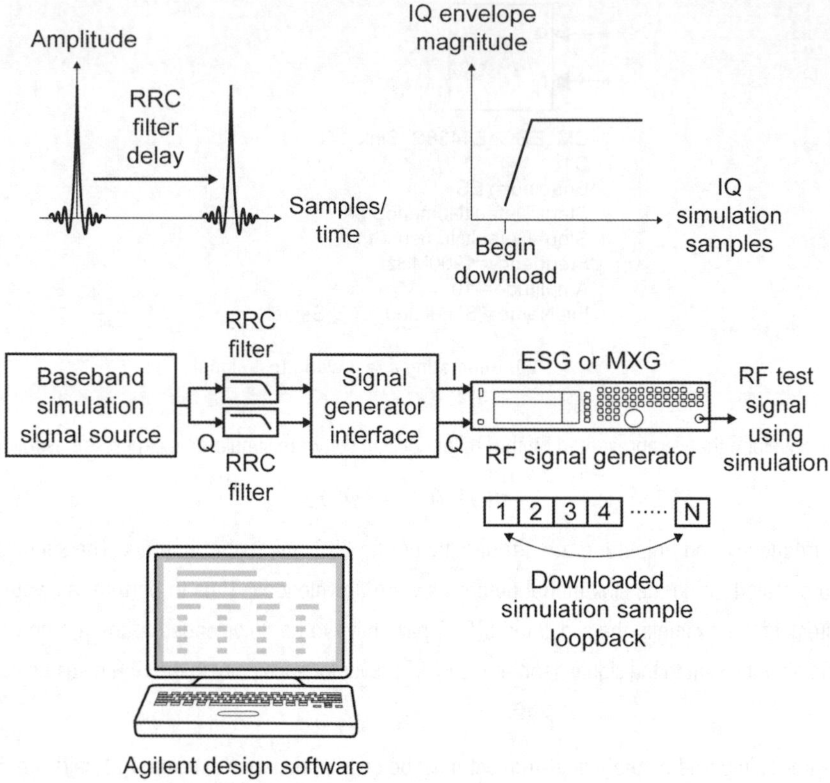

Figure 6.2-21. Downloading simulated IQ pairs to RF signal generator

Note that N simulation samples are downloaded from Agilent's design software to the arb. Typically, the N simulation samples are repeated in a loopback mode in the signal generator, and the simulation data record is repeated when the last simulation sample has been played. If the first and last samples are not carefully considered and well-conditioned, the loopback mode can cause discontinuity between the last sample and the first sample, which may degrade waveform quality, performance and spectral dynamic range. For signal formats such as LTE, this issue is addressed by ensuring that the first sample of data downloaded from Agilent's design software corresponds to the beginning of a frame, and the total number of simulation samples downloaded corresponds to an integer number of frames.

The maximum number of IQ data pairs to be downloaded from the Agilent design software to the signal generator arb is an important consideration, particularly for receiver BER measurements. To obtain a statistically meaningful result, enough data must be downloaded from the simulator to the signal generator. The number of data bits required for the BER measurement translates to the number of required IQ data pairs to be downloaded from Agilent's design software to the signal generator arb. General considerations include (1) coding structure of the signal format — for example, LTE, WiMAX or W-CDMA; (2) sampling rate needed for sufficient waveform quality — for example, 2X or 4X oversampling; and (3) number of frames/bit that must be measured to achieve a statistically meaningful result or meet a given specification. As a result of these considerations, an arb memory depth may appear sufficient for BER measurements of one signal format but not another.

6.2.3.2 Coded LTE BER Arb Depth Calculation

The arb depth requirements for a coded LTE BER measurement are given in Table 6.2-1.

Table 6.2-1. Arb depth requirements for a coded LTE BER measurement

LTE configuration	LTE uplink with Type 1 frame structure, normal Cyclic Prefix (CP) 5 MHz bandwidth, 25 RB, QPSK modulation 2X oversampling
Samples per frame	SamplesPerFrame = 10ms/frame * 7.68MHz sampling frequency * 2x oversampling = 153,600 samples/frame
ESG/MXG arb depth	64 MSa
Maximum number of frames to be downloaded	64 MSa/153,600 samples/frame = 416 frames
PUSCH bits per subframe (TTI)	2 bits/subcarrier (QPSK) * 12 subcarriers/RB * 25 RB/symbol * 12 symbols/subframe (without RS symbols)= 7200 PUSCH bits/subframe
Coding rate	For TransBlockSize = 3600 bits, the coding rate is now R = 3600/7200 = ½
Maximum number of bits to be downloaded	With R = ½, the maximum number is 3600 bits/subframe * 10 subframes/frame * 416 frames = 14,976,000 bits

Note: At 0.1% BER operating condition, or 0.001, estimate 1 error for every 1000 bits (1/0.001).
Estimate counting approximately 29,952 errors if operating at 0.1% coded BER condition for 416 frames (14,976,000 bits/64MSa arb * 0.001 BER= 14,976 errors on average).

6.2.3.3 Signal Analysis Considerations

As previously described, simulation can be used to create test signals for device testing. The DUT outputs can also be captured and analyzed within the simulation. The following examples describe how measured signals from hardware DUTs can be captured using signal analyzers and post-processed in simulation using the LTE Wireless Library receiver. This capability allows a complete signal flow that begins in simulation, transitions to the signal generator, passes in and out of the DUT and then transitions from the signal analyzer back into simulation.

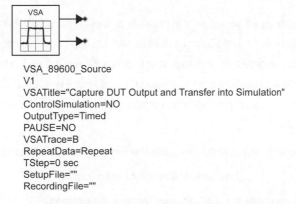

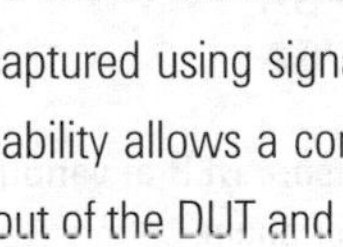

Figure 6.2-22. Capturing and transferring DUT output

Agilent's design software includes instrumentation links that enable the DUT output to be captured with test equipment and transferred into simulation. For example, the 89601 VSA software (part of the 89600 VSA source) can capture digital and RF DUT outputs using a variety of different instruments and transfer the data into Agilent's design software for simulation post-processing. The 89600 VSA source element used for this procedure is shown in Figure 6.2-22.

To capture RF DUT output, the 89601 VSA software can be used with the Agilent signal analyzers such as the VSA, PSA or MXA. For analog IQ DUT outputs, the VSA software can be used with the Agilent Infiniium series oscilloscopes. And for digital DUT outputs, the VSA software can be used with Agilent logic analyzers.

Signal analysis is used extensively throughout the product development cycle. For example, a useful technique for testing RF/mixed signal receivers is to measure BER and EVM at the various stages of the block diagram, as shown in Figure 6.2-23.

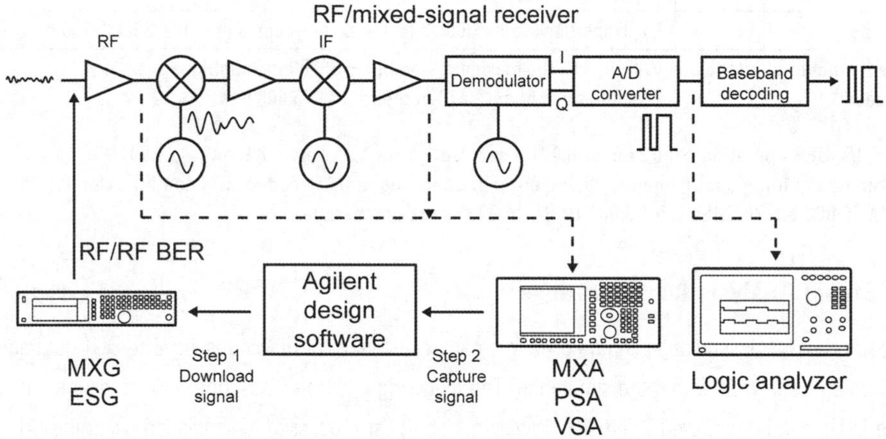

Figure 6.2-23. Combining simulation and test to measure BER at various stages along the RF/mixed-signal receiver chain

The signal analyzer, like the signal generator, must be able to support the carrier frequency and modulation bandwidth of interest. Ideally, the signal analyzer should be able to support a measurement bandwidth defined by the Agilent design software simulation time step used to create the signal downloaded to the arb. This helps maintain a consistent sampling rate between the simulator, signal source and signal analyzer, and it mitigates simulation complexities such as up-sampling and down-sampling when the signals flowing in and out of a DUT are compared in BER measurements.

The RF signal analyzer frequency span and the simulation time step are inversely related as follows:

$$simulation\ \ bandwidth = 1/(time\ step)$$

where time step is the time step used to sample $I(t)$ and $Q(t)$ for the expression

$$S(t) = I(t) + j * Q(t).$$

Therefore the frequency span of the RF signal analyzer should be set to the inverse of the simulation time step that was used to create the signal downloaded to the arb. This helps maintain the sampling rate consistency described above. Also, note that the capture depth of the selected analyzer must be set, at a minimum, to the number of IQ data pairs downloaded to the arb.

6.2.3.4 Time Synchronization for BER Applications

An additional consideration for BER measurement applications is the time synchronization of the simulation-generated LTE signal between the signal generator arb and the signal analyzer.

LTE BER measurements require comparing DUT output bits to the input bits to compute BER. This implies that the bits being compared are aligned in time. Furthermore, it implies that the IQ waveforms are aligned in time when the signal generated by the simulator is output from the signal generator arb and is subsequently captured by the signal analyzer.

Figure 6.2-24 illustrates these time-alignment considerations. Note that in this conceptual representation, the I and Q waveforms out of the signal analyzer do not show any magnitude or phase differences relative to the I and Q waveforms downloaded to the signal generator.

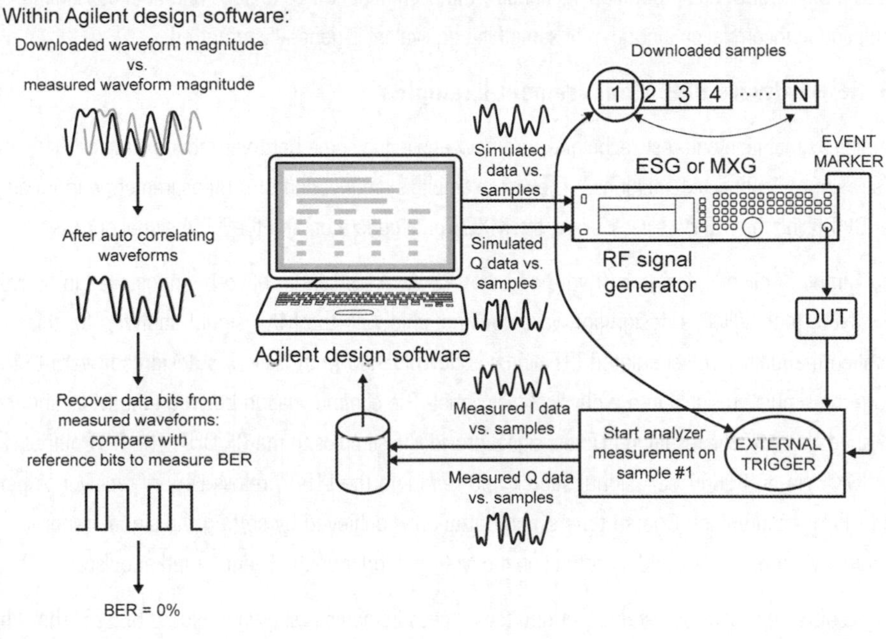

Figure 6.2-24. Time synchronization considerations for the simulator, signal source and signal analyzer

In this example there are two levels of time synchronization represented: (1) synchronization of the IQ waveform playback in the signal generator with the signal analyzer measurement and (2) removal of any residual physical delays from the DUT prior to performing a measurement such as BER with the LTE Wireless Library receiver.

To accomplish the first level of time synchronization, it is important to have an event marker output on the signal generator that produces a marker pulse when the first sample of the simulation IQ data is generated (which corresponds to the beginning of the arb sweep). The marker pulse stimulates the signal analyzer's external trigger, which then starts the measurement and the measurement-data capture. Figure 6.2-24 depicts this relationship as a physical connection between the signal generator's event marker and the signal analyzer's external trigger.

Even when the first level of time-synchronization has been carried out, additional physical delay from the DUT and cables may need to be accounted for. To accomplish this second level of time-synchronization, the simulated LTE IQ waveforms downloaded to the signal generator need to be time-aligned with the measured IQ waveforms captured by the signal analyzer. To illustrate this, the graph at the upper left of Figure 6.2-24 shows two superimposed traces: one representing the magnitude of the simulated waveform created in Agilent's design software and downloaded to the signal generator's arb, called the reference waveform, and a second representing the magnitude of the waveform captured from the DUT and read back into simulation from the signal analyzer, called the test waveform. The two traces are misaligned in time, reflecting the physical delay of the DUT and cables. Time alignment of the reference and test waveforms must therefore be performed in simulation, either manually or automatically, prior to recovering the data bits from the test waveform and comparing them to the reference data bits for BER computation. A manual time alignment can be tedious and time consuming, so the use of a simulation autocorrelation algorithm or something equivalent is generally preferred.

6.2.3.5 RF Hardware BER Measurement Examples

The combined simulation and test techniques are now applied in some hardware test examples that make use of Agilent's range of "connected solutions." The first example is an uncoded BER measurement performed on an RF amplifier DUT using the LTE Wireless Library, the MXG signal generator, and the MXA signal analyzer.

For this example, Agilent's design software and the LTE Wireless Library have been installed in an MXA signal analyzer. (Note that Agilent's design software does not ship with the MXA signal analyzer; for this example, it was installed manually.) The simulated LTE signal is downloaded from Agilent's design software to the MXG's arb to turn the simulated signal into a physical test signal. The communication between the MXA and the MXG is accomplished via LAN. The resulting LTE test signal provides a stimulus to the RF DUT. The DUT output is captured with the MXA via an 89600 VSA signal source and read into the LTE Wireless Library receiver to perform the uncoded BER measurement. Coarse time synchronization is achieved by setting the signal generator's Event1 marker output via the ESG sink and by setting up the MXA to trigger on the Event 1 marker pulse.

The design software schematic used to perform these measurements is shown in Figure 6.2-25. The sub-network on the left generates and downloads the simulated LTE signal to the MXG arb using the ESG sink. The sub-network on the right captures the DUT output with the MXA and the VSA software in the Agilent design software and then transfers the captured signal into the LTE Wireless Library receiver for the BER measurement. A sequencer element is used in Agilent design software to perform the signal generation and download first, followed by the signal capture and analysis. Note that the BER measurement is performed in batch mode rather than real time. The results of the DUT uncoded BER versus RF input power are shown in Figure 6.2-26.

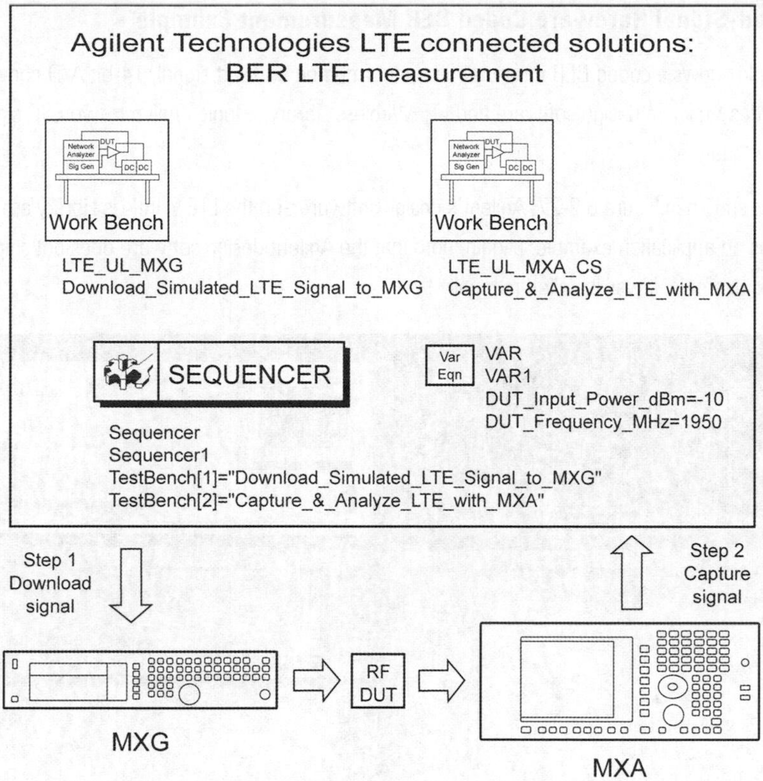

Figure 6.2-25. Agilent design software schematic used to perform BER measurement

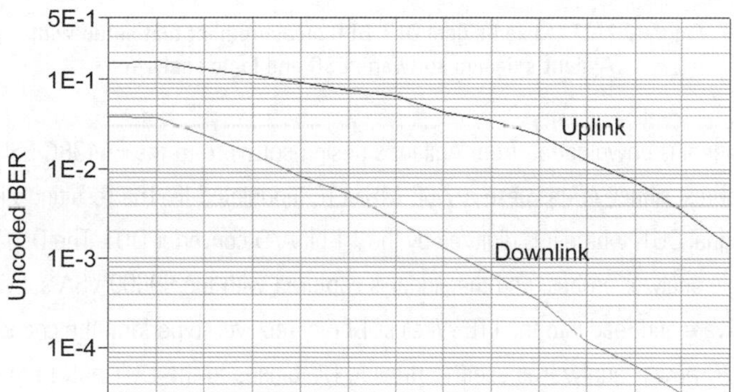

Figure 6.2-26. RF DUT BER measurement results

A web video that shows the Agilent design software being used with the MXG and MXA to perform similar BER measurements can be found at http://wireless.agilent.com/vcentral/viewvideo.aspx?vid=329.

6.2.3.6 Mixed-Signal Hardware Coded BER Measurement Example

The next example shows a coded BER measurement performed on a mixed-signal, 14-bit A/D converter DUT. The test setup includes Agilent's design software and LTE Wireless Library, a logic analyzer, two ESG signal generators and a DC power analyzer.

The test setup is shown in Figure 6.2-27. Agilent's design software and the LTE Wireless Library are installed in the logic analyzer as an application example. (Again, note that the Agilent design software does not ship with the logic analyzer; for this example, it was installed manually.)

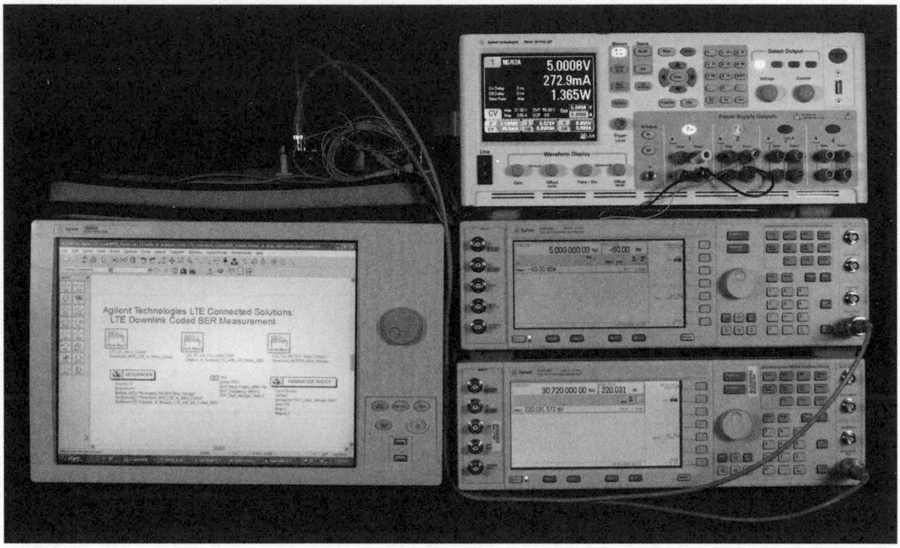

Figure 6.2-27. Mixed-signal DUT BER measurement test setup with Agilent's design software, ESG and logic analyzer

The simulated LTE signal is downloaded from Agilent's design software to the E4438C ESG's arb to be turned into a "real" physical test signal; in this case a 7.68 MHz LTE-modulated IF. The resulting LTE test signal is then input to the mixed-signal DUT, where it is digitized by the 14-bit A/D converter DUT. The DUT's digital outputs are connected to the logic analyzer probes, and the signal is captured with the 89600 VSA software signal source in Agilent's design software and read into the LTE Wireless Library receiver to perform the coded BER measurement. An Agilent N6705 DC power analyzer is used to provide DC biases to the DUT and to monitor current draw. A second ESG provides a clock signal to the DUT. Figure 6.2-28 illustrates these connections.

Note that a LAN connection between the logic analyzer and the E4438C ESG allows the simulated LTE signal to be downloaded from Agilent's design system (installed in the logic analyzer) to the ESG's arb. Coarse time synchronization is achieved by setting the Event1 marker on the ESG sink and by setting up the logic analyzer to trigger on the occurrence of this marker. The N6705 is connected to the logic analyzer via a USB-GPIB connector so that Agilent's design software can programmatically set the dc bias voltages.

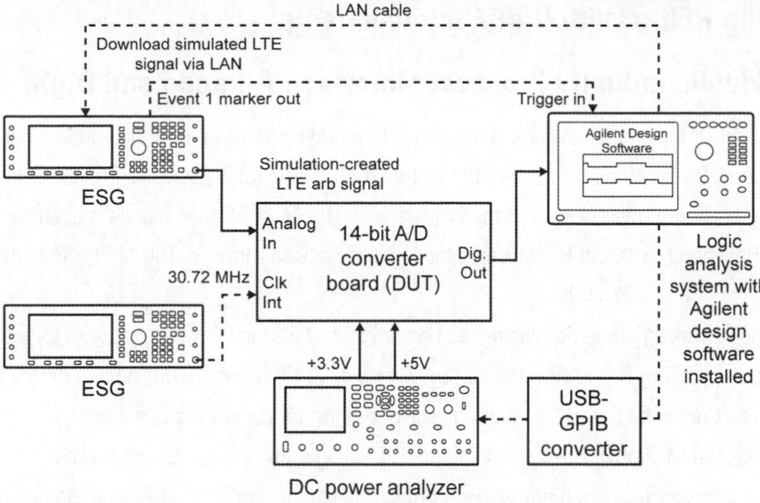

Figure 6.2-28. Connection diagram for mixed-signal DUT BER test setup

The DUT coded BER versus IF input power and DC bias are shown in Figure 6.2-29.

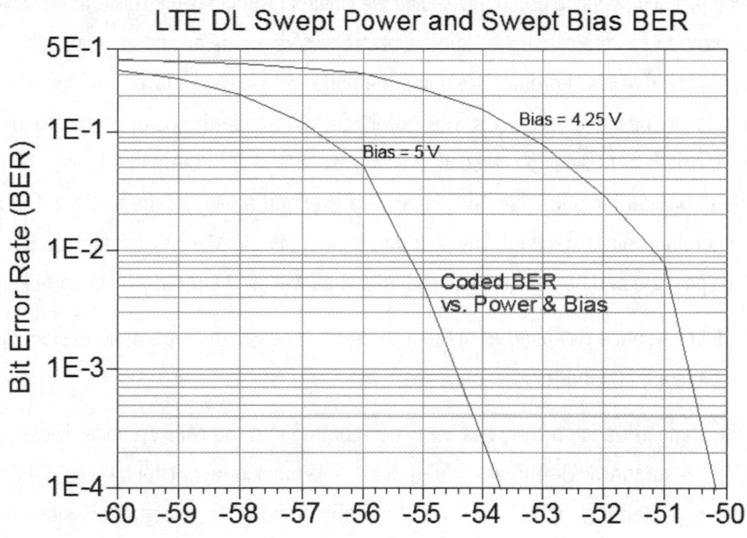

Figure 6.2-29. Mixed-signal DUT coded BER results vs. swept DC bias and IF input power

The DUT's coded BER versus IF input power was measured at two different biases, 4.25 V and 5 V.

6.2.4 Summary

The simulation concepts and examples described in this section can be applied to help accelerate development and minimize risk throughout the LTE product development cycle. The synergy that is achieved by combining simulation with test provides even greater power and flexibility for hardware testing.

6.3 Testing RFICs With DigRF Interconnects

6.3.1 The Mobile Industry Processor Interface Alliance and DigRF

The introduction of LTE brings architectural change to virtually every subsystem in the wireless network, from IP-based infrastructure to the chipsets used in mobile handsets. The Mobile Industry Processor Interface (MIPI) Alliance is driving several of the changes at the chipset level. The MIPI Alliance has developed several standards that affect both Baseband (BB) and RF chipsets used in mobile cellular devices. The MIPI standards work is in the following areas:

- Camera working group developing the Camera Serial Interface 2 (CSI 2) physical layer protocol.
- Display working Group developing the Display Serial Interface (DSI) packet protocol carrying the Display Command Set (DCS) application layer support for display management.
- Low-speed Multipoint Link working group developing audio and control interfaces.
- System Power Management working group developing the System Power Management Interface (SPMI) using a master/slave approach to handle the increasing challenge of power management in complex mobile devices
- DigRF working group developing the DigRF v4 standard for BB to RFIC connectivity
- Unified protocol working group developing the Unified Protocol (UniPro) standard, which is a transport layer protocol for interconnecting application processors, modems and peripherals
- Physical layer working group developing the underlying physical layer interconnect that carries the higher level application protocols. The current D-PHY standard runs at up to 1 Gbps with up to four lanes giving 500 MBytes per second, which explains the D in the name coming as it does from the Roman numeral for 500. The D-PHY standard is aimed mainly at the DSI and CSI-2 protocols and the emerging UniPro standard. The next development is the M-PHY standard, which will run at up to 6 Gbps per lane and be able to support DigRF v4 as well as the protocols supported on D-PHY.

The efforts of the MIPI Alliance will bring to the mobile device industry the type of subsystem interchangeability that has existed in the computer industry for many years.

Recently the DigRF standardization activity has been incorporated into the MIPI Alliance. There are three existing versions of the DigRF standard. DigRF v4 is the newest and most relevant for LTE as the link bandwidth is appropriate for the expected data rates. However, the DigRF standard is a proprietary standard available only to MIPI Alliance members. Therefore the details of the standard will not be covered here. Instead, this section examines the challenges of integrating and testing DigRF v4 in LTE designs.

6.3.1.1 Why DigRF?

DigRF has been designed to address several issues. By making the baseband to RF link fully digital, baseband IC design can now become a less expensive, digital-only process. DigRF v4 specifies a serial link, reducing pin count and further simplifying designs. DigRF v4 also incorporates low-power modes that can reduce standby power consumption. With a standard baseband to RFIC interface, it now becomes theoretically possible to have interchangeable subsystems allowing a mobile cellular device vendor to "mix and match" baseband and RFICs based on the performance attributes desired. As a practical matter, true interchangeability of ICs will likely await further standardization efforts to ensure that all relevant physical and protocol standards exist.

6.3.1.2 Testing Baseband and RFICs With DigRF

The multi-gigabit DigRF v4 standard removes the potential inter-chip communication bottleneck resulting from the higher data rates implicit in LTE. However, this fourth version of the DigRF standard introduces multiple levels of design and test complexity due to changes such as a new link protocol and the high-speed serial link.

From a test perspective, the integration of DigRF into the baseband IC is relatively straightforward. This is because the baseband IC is now completely digital and can be tested with standard digital test tools. Straightforward does not imply easy, however, as the DigRF v4 interface is a gigabit-speed interface requiring special care and test to integrate. The testing issues of the baseband interface are a subset of the issues encountered on the RFIC and are not covered further here.

6.3.2 New Challenges in Building and Testing RFICs

The move to a digital baseband interface introduces a number of new challenges to designing and testing the RFIC. These challenges exist in the physical and protocol layers of the digital and RF domains and they include the following:

- The formerly analog baseband to RFIC communication link is now a high-speed serial digital interface that requires special design and test techniques.
- Because analog sources can no longer be used to stimulate the RFIC on the baseband interface, testing requires different equipment and a different methodology than used in previous generation chipsets.
- Unlike other serial interfaces, the DigRF has a protocol stack encapsulated within the digital interface and this "dual protocol stack" complicates characterization and validation.
- The information flowing on the interface between the baseband and RFICs includes data and control traffic.
- Information transfers must comply with strict time constraints (time determinism).

These challenges and the associated considerations for testing will now be examined more closely.

6.3.2.1 Digital Serial Link

To provide the data rates needed for LTE implementations, the DigRF interface runs at gigabit per second rates. Under these conditions, high-speed analog effects can impair signal quality and degrade link Bit Error Ratio (BER).

Similar to other high-speed serial buses, the current DigRF standards employ data-encoding mechanisms along with embedded clocks and state machines for link and transaction operations. To analyze the data, the embedded clock must be extracted before the data can be decoded and fully analyzed. A clear understanding of clock recovery, encode/decode protocols and real-time measurements is critical for success. Most general-purpose measurement tools cannot understand signals encoded for DigRF v4 and information encoding so therefore provide only raw information about the digital data.

6.3.2.2 RFIC Test Methodology

Digital IQ data and control information is now packetized and transferred between the baseband and RFICs over the DigRF interface. Previously, RF engineers and validation teams used analog sources to stimulate the RFIC on the IQ analog interface. Now the analog interface is gone, so new tools are needed to enable the same RF physical measurements through the DigRF digital serial interface.

6.3.2.3 Dual Protocol Stack

Like many other serial buses, the DigRF interface is described as a stack of multiple layers in which each layer has a specific function and mode of operation. These layers grow from the physical layer to the application or software layer, and they include the link layer (or mode of operation of the bus), the data-encoding scheme, the frame structure, the flow control, the error handling mechanism and others.

Ensuring that an RFIC properly interoperates with a baseband IC requires verification that all layers of the digital protocol stack are designed and operate in accordance with the DigRF v4 specification. A suitable test environment must provide analysis and stimulus capabilities on the entire digital protocol stack.

DigRF is designed to be used in mobile devices and is unlike most serial buses because there is another protocol stack "encapsulated" within the digital interface — this stack representing the mobile device's wireless protocol (e.g., GSM, W-CDMA, LTE, WiMAX). As with other protocols, this stack extends from the RF physical layer to the RF application layer.

Things can become confusing as the physical and protocol layers of the two stacks are intermixed. Because the RF physical-layer information is encapsulated in the payload of DigRF frames, it is seen as existing "above" the DigRF protocol layer. This is different from typical layering schemes in which the physical layer resides at the bottom of the stack.

The characterization and validation of a DigRF-enabled RFIC requires separate measurement of each layer of the digital and RF protocol stacks. This in turn requires a test infrastructure that provides insight to all layers (Figure 6.3-1). From a stimulus point of view, the ability to test an RFIC under real-world conditions requires a test environment that can encapsulate IQ stimulus data within DigRF traffic to create the required dual-stack stimulus model.

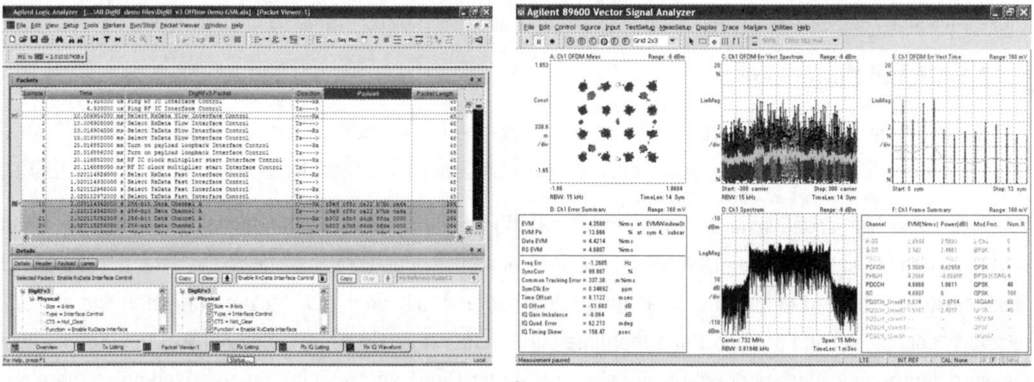

Figure 6.3-1. Agilent DigRF test dual interface presenting information from the digital protocol layers (bit-and packet-level view, left) and the RF physical information (modulation analysis, right) from the same measurement

6.3.2.4 Mixed Traffic

The information flowing between RF and baseband ICs consists of IQ data encapsulated in DigRF frames as well as control information that is sent from the baseband IC to the RFIC. This control information stays within the RFIC. Here are some examples of control traffic:

- Turning on and configuring the RFIC in loopback mode
- Changing transmit output power level
- Changing the RF output frequency

When an RFIC is tested, proper validation requires test equipment that can configure and create this mix of control and data traffic. To test an RFIC, the stimulus environment must be able to insert RFIC control information within the IQ data flow.

6.3.2.5 Time Determinism

Information transfers between the RF and baseband ICs must comply with strict time constraints. Therefore, it is important for the test environment to precisely measure when each frame is sent from one IC to the other and provide real-time detection of time-constraint violations.

6.3.3 Addressing the Cross-Domain Issues

To address the need to test in both the digital and RF domains, Agilent has combined traditional RF measurement tools with digital and protocol analysis and stimulus tools in a complete test environment for cross-domain RFIC test.

This new test platform enables DigRF protocol debugging as well as comprehensive stimulus and analysis across the digital and RF domains to enable and accelerate the turn-on, validation and integration of DigRF v4-based devices.

The DigRF test environment incorporates testing of both the transmitter and receiver paths. For transmit path testing, the typical environment includes three major elements:

- A signal analyzer for modulation analysis on the antenna side of the RFIC. Advanced signal-analysis tools, such as the 89601A Vector Signal Analysis (VSA) software, enables detailed signal analysis including digital demodulation of the IQ data according to the radio protocol being transmitted.
- A DigRF exerciser/analyzer provides digital and RF stimulus on the baseband side of the RFIC.
- Signal generation software, such as Agilent design software or Signal Studio, generates the IQ data to be sent to the RFIC. See Section 6.2 for more information on how the design software is used to generate signals. The signal generation software is hosted on the DigRF exerciser as an analog signal source and cannot be used on the DigRF interface.

For receiver path testing, the typical environment includes four key elements:

- A vector signal generator provides an appropriate RF signal on the antenna side of the RFIC.
- Signal generation software, such as Agilent design software or Signal Studio, provides baseband modulated data for the vector signal generator.
- A DigRF exerciser/analyzer enables analysis of received DigRF packets.
- Signal analysis software such as the 89601A VSA software, which enables analysis of the resulting IQ data carried by the DigRF interface.

The 89601A VSA software can run inside the DigRF exerciser. With the DigRF analyzer and VSA software, both the digital and RF paths can be examined and analyzed in parallel from the same measurement.

Since RF designers are used to connecting test equipment directly to the IQ port between the RF and baseband ICs, the test methodology and tools are now changed to connect with the digital interface. Fortunately, many of the tools can still be used; they are just hosted on different hardware. See Figure 6.3-2 for a before and after illustration of the test configuration for TX testing. For TX testing of the RFIC, the Agilent Radio Digital Cross Domain (RDX) test system connects to the DigRF interface and hosts the signal creation software which acts as a kind of "virtual signal generator." For RX testing, the RDX tester hosts the VSA software acting as a "virtual signal analyzer." The RDX tester inserts and extracts the IQ data to and from the DigRF data stream while interleaving any control or timing packets as part of the DigRF control stream.

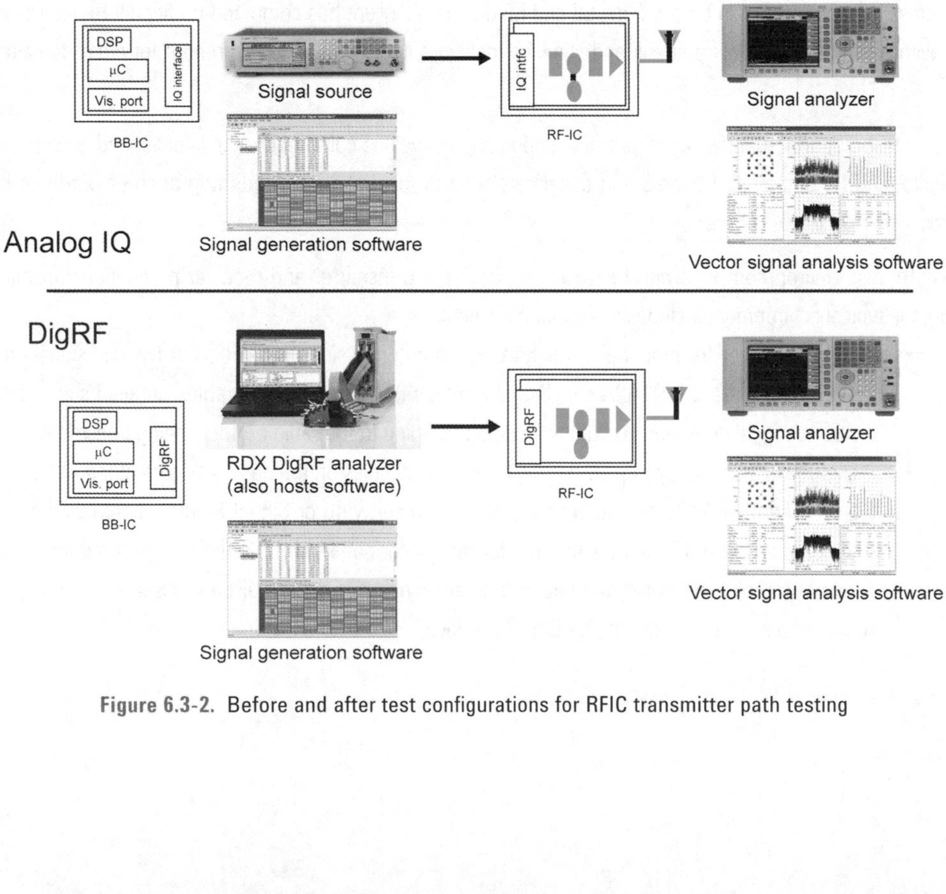

Figure 6.3-2. Before and after test configurations for RFIC transmitter path testing

6.3.4 Stepping Through the Layers

A typical design process will progress from left to right as shown in Figure 6.3-3. Digital designers are accustomed to working with one set of tools in the digital domain; RF designers are used to working with another set of tools in the RF domain. With DigRF in the picture, a unified set of tools will benefit both digital and RF designers.

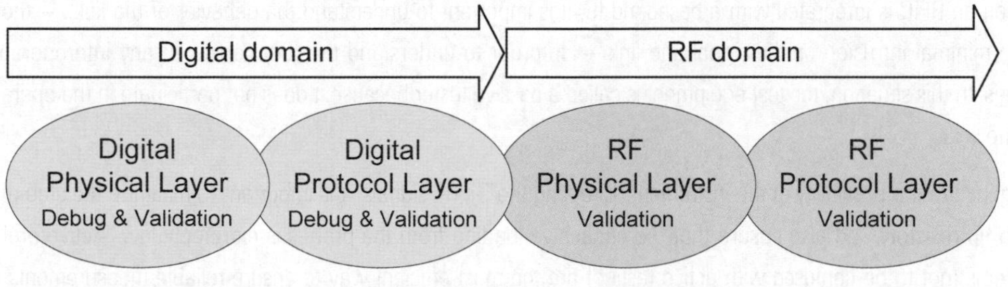

Figure 6.3-3. Working through the four layers is an efficient way to characterize and validate an LTE device.

6.3.4.1 Digital Physical Layer

Because the baseband-side interface to the RFIC is digital, it is necessary to ensure proper DigRF operation before testing the RF sections of the IC. The RFIC design may integrate "legacy" inputs with analog IQ inputs that are separate from the DigRF interface. This offers multiple ways to access the RF subsections. In such cases, it might be possible to simultaneously test the DigRF interface and the RF subsections.

Because the DigRF v4 interface is a high-speed, multi-lane, bidirectional link — with edge rates operating at sub-nanosecond intervals — the signal's rise time, pulse width, timing, jitter and noise must all be measured and controlled. Specialized tools for testing high-speed serial interfaces include high-performance oscilloscopes and Bit-Error-Ratio Testers (BERTs). To minimize possible signal disruption, specialized probing solutions are also needed for testing high-speed serial links. The combination of a high-performance oscilloscope and an advanced probing system is the primary tool used to test the transmit lines of the DigRF interface. A multilane BERT is the primary tool used to test the receive lines of the DigRF interface.

6.3.4.2 Digital Protocol Layer

Testing in this layer involves seven distinct activities:

- Active and passive testing of the DigRF link
- "Stateful" exercising of the DigRF link
- Exercise and analysis of bus-mode transitions
- Testing of 8b/10b encoding mechanisms
- Verification of RFIC responses
- Testing of RFIC responses to DigRF errors
- Checking of the RFIC initialization sequence

Test considerations for each of these activities are discussed next.

Active and Passive Testing of the DigRF Link

There are two ways to test a DigRF v4 link: active and passive. During the turn-on of an IC, the test environment must emulate a peer device communicating with the device under test (DUT). This environment is called an active tester because it is an active "citizen" of the link.

When an RFIC is integrated with a baseband IC, it is important to understand the behavior of the link — though with minimal intrusion on the signal and link — in order to understand the root causes of any interoperability issues. In this situation, the test equipment is called a passive tester because it does not participate in the operation of the link.

To minimize the possibility of the instrument disrupting the DigRF signals, it is important to minimize the stub effect with tip resistors and also ensure that the capacitive loading from the probes is extremely low. Active probing systems (not to be confused with active testing) are the most efficient way to ensure reliable measurements and minimize signal degradation.

Because the root cause of link problems may be either a physical or protocol defect, the use of a common probing system with oscilloscopes and DigRF analyzers can minimize the chances of misleading results. Figure 6.3-4 shows a common set of tip resistors that can be connected to both types of instruments. The active probe adds just 150 fF of capacitive loading.

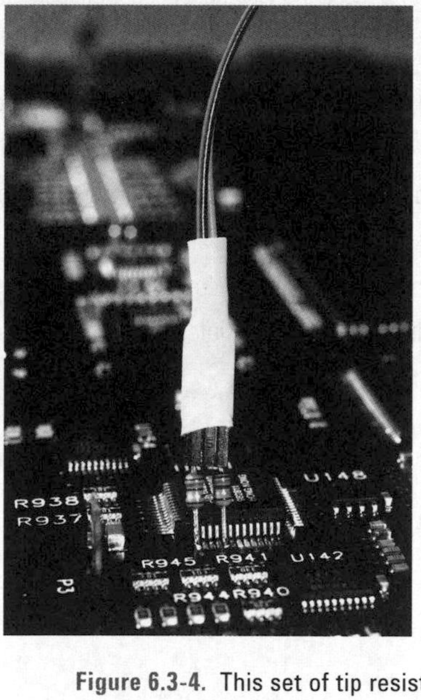

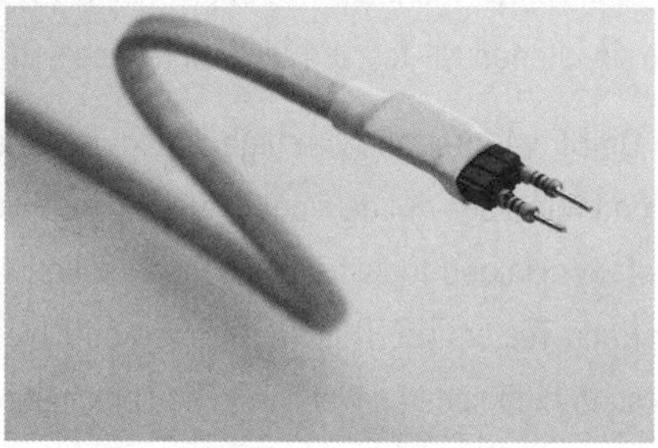

DigRF v4 analyzer probe

Plug-on socket connection for E2678A differential probe head

Figure 6.3-4. This set of tip resistors helps to minimize the stub effect and can be connected to either an oscilloscope or a DigRF analyzer.

Stateful Exercising of the DigRF Link

To perform the DigRF link layer test of an RFIC requires an active test system that mimics a peer device connected to the DigRF port of the DUT. The nature of active test equipment can be divided into two categories: "stateless" and "stateful" test devices.

The stateless test environment generates a stimulus with limited or no knowledge of the protocol state machines of the DUT.

The stateful test environment (or "exerciser") incorporates the DigRF protocol state machines and acts much more like a real device. A typical example in which a retry sequence is tested illustrates the benefits of an exerciser. Most digital protocol stacks include a packet resend mechanism: A receiver can require the sender to retransmit a packet if the packet was not received properly the first time it was sent. A stateful test platform will recognize the request to resend the packet and act according to the resend sequence definition. A stateless device, however, will simply ignore the request.

A stateful test environment allows testing of the following bus modes:

- Transitions from sleep mode to active mode
- Retry sequences
- Flow-control mechanisms that require the sender to slow down or speed up the traffic
- Emulation of the dynamic physical characteristics of a bus that may change in response to protocol events (e.g., termination or voltage level)

Exercise and Analysis of Bus-Mode Transitions

To optimize both power consumption and performance, the DigRF v4 bus has been designed to operate in multiple high speed and low power modes. When no data is being sent, the bus shifts into a sleep mode that requires very little power. When data must be transferred, the bus can quickly wake up and start transferring data.

The DigRF test environment should support power management features and the associated bus transitions. From a stimulus point of view, the test platform must support these modes deterministically so that it can check DUT mode transitions and verify specification-compliant execution.

From an analysis point of view, it is necessary to perform two types of measurements with one analysis module: track the transitions and then capture the data between the transitions, especially just after the bus has woken up. In this application, instrumentation lock time is critical because the test needs to capture data from the embedded clock. To reliably measure the DUT behavior and capture the initial data transmission while the bus is waking up, the tester's lock time must be faster than that of the DUT. The Agilent RDX tester includes a multipath clock-recovery mechanism to capture data during very fast bus mode transitions.

Testing of 8b/10b Encoding Mechanisms

The 8b/10b coding converts a byte-wide data stream of random ones and zeros into a DC-balanced stream of ones and zeros. The code also provides sufficient signal transitions to enable reliable clock recovery. The average number of ones and zeros in the serial stream must be maintained at nearly-equal levels.

It is important to ensure that the DUT properly encodes and decodes the data. It is also essential to properly identify disparity errors to determine how the DUT detects and recovers from such exceptions. Disparity errors tend to occur infrequently and the analyzer triggering mechanisms must include real-time detection of such errors.

Verification of RFIC Responses

At this point in the development process, it is important to confirm that the RFIC is responding properly to commands. To validate RFIC responses — and to activate loopback mode — it is necessary to send a customized command sequence to the RFIC. The exerciser Graphical User Interface (GUI) shown in Figure 6.3-5 illustrates commands that can be used to build one or more custom frames to enable verification of the RFIC response.

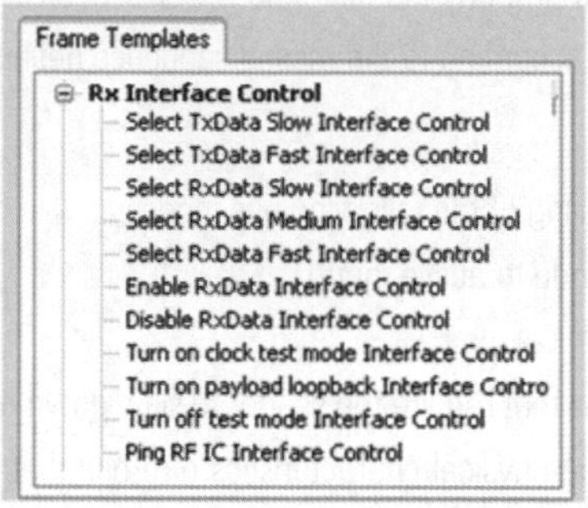

Figure 6.3-5 Control commands can be generated from a template list to manage the state of the RFIC.

Testing of RFIC Responses to DigRF Errors

It is useful to create errors in order to validate (1) how well the DUT detects each error and recovers from it and (2) whether the error recovery mechanism is compliant with the specification. Testing with known errors also increases the test coverage of the protocol state machines by analyzing exceptional transitions between each state. There are multiple error categories, including low level errors such as disparity or symbol errors, and higher level errors such as Cyclic Redundancy Check (CRC) errors in a packet. Figure 6.3-6 shows how errors can be selected from a template list and added into the main stimulus file.

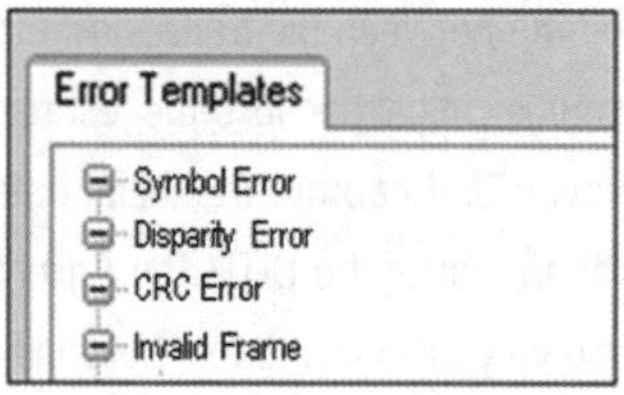

Figure 6.3-6. One or more frames with errors can be created and sent to the DUT to analyze how well it recovers from them.

Checking of the RFIC Initialization Sequence

Before each operation, the RFIC must be initialized with a sequence of control commands that set up its internal registers and configure its mode of operation. This sequence is executed only once, after which the desired operation is initiated. If the initialization sequence is short — for example, to put the DigRF port in loop-back mode — the custom frame GUI can be used to configure the initialization sequence. In some cases this sequence includes a large number of configuration parameters that cannot be created manually. Figure 6.3-7 shows how the stimulus software can get a large command sequence from a file and executes it once before the test.

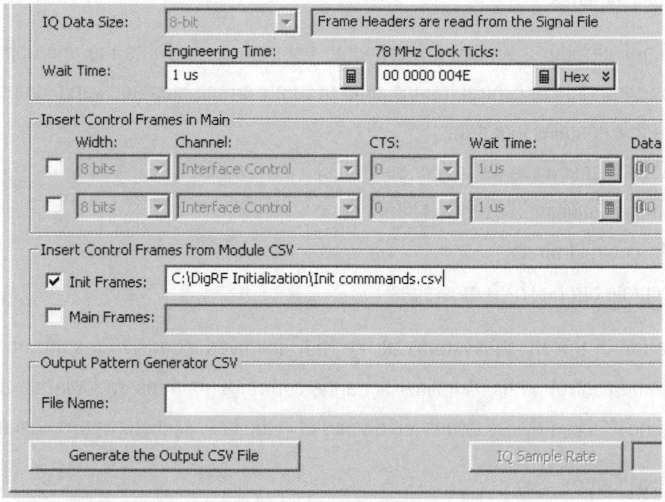

Fig 6.3-7. Inserting a complex command sequence from a file

6.3.4.3 Transitioning From Digital to RF Domains

Once the DigRF link itself appears to be working properly, testing of the RF transmit path can be started. Data is sent to the RFIC by embedding digitized IQ data into DigRF frames. One of the advantages of the Agilent RDX tester is its ability to insert IQ data generated by standard tools into the DigRF data stream.

Conversely, to test the RF receive path, the RDX tester has the ability to separate the command and data frames so the data can be routed to VSA software. This allows detailed analysis and characterization of the received IQ data without the need for a connected baseband IC or special IQ port that bypasses the DigRF interface (though a direct IQ port can also be very useful for debug). Figure 6.3-1 showed simultaneous displays of the VSA software's RF physical analysis along with packet analysis showing digital protocol information. Other sections in this chapter discuss the actual RF physical layer tests appropriate for LTE designs.

6.3.4.4 RF Physical Layer

The RF physical layer tests are performed through the antenna interface and either the DigRF interface or a special IQ port on the baseband side of the RFIC. To perform tests via the DigRF interface, a test instrument must be able to insert IQ data into the DigRF bitstream (for transmitter test) or extract IQ information from the bitstream (for receiver test). This is a key feature of the Agilent RDX tester.

A variety of tools can be used to create and generate the IQ waveforms. For example, design packages such as Agilent design software make it possible to generate waveforms based on design models. Another common tool is Agilent's Signal Studio software, which provides waveform creation capabilities for a variety of modulation formats including LTE. MATLAB® or other analysis tools (or programming languages) can also be used to create custom waveforms.

Tools such as Signal Studio for 3GPP LTE can create the standards-based LTE signals needed to verify RF uplink and downlink performance. These signals can include transport channel coding for receiver testing using Block Error Ratio (BLER) measurements.

The RDX tester for DigRF includes a signal inserter tool to translate IQ data into the appropriate DigRF-compliant bitstream. It also allows insertion of control frames, time-accurate strobe messages and status messages. The end result is a stimulus file that contains four items:

- The RFIC initialization sequence (control traffic)
- Data frames containing digitized IQ information
- On-the-fly control frames
- Time-Accurate Strobe (TAS) messages

Debug and qualification of the RF subsystems of the RFIC involves extensive testing and verification of the transmitter, receiver and control paths. Amplifier linearity, control algorithms, modulation quality and a host of other items must also be checked. These issues are discussed in the later sections of this chapter.

6.3.4.5 RF Protocol Layer

Testing this layer generally begins later in the process of designing and integrating the chipset and the overall system. As a result, it has relatively little bearing on the DigRF subsystem and so is not covered here.

6.3.4 Conclusion

The multi-gigabit DigRF v4 standard is rapidly emerging as the next-generation serial interface between mobile baseband and RFICs because it removes the inter-chip communication bottleneck. However, it also creates measurement challenges that exist in — and span — the physical and protocol layers of the digital and RF domains. For more information on DigRF test, see www.agilent.com/find/digrf.

6.4 Transmitter Design and Measurement Challenges

From the perspective of the RF engineer, LTE promises a dauntingly wide range of design and measurement challenges, arising from a number of factors:

- The requirement to handle six channel bandwidths from 1.4 to 20 MHz.
- The use of different transmission schemes for the downlink (OFDMA) and uplink (SC-FDMA).
- Flexible transmission schemes in which the physical channel configuration has a large impact on RF performance — much more so than in CDMA systems.
- Specifications that include both FDD and TDD transmission modes. While the examples in this section focus on FDD, the general principles described apply equally to TDD, with the added complexities of "time-sliced" signal generation and analysis.
- Challenging measurement configurations resulting from the spectral, power and time variations due to traffic type and loading.

- Further challenges resulting from the need to support multi-antenna techniques such as TX diversity, spatial multiplexing (MIMO) and beamsteering.
- The need for making complex tradeoffs between in-channel, out-of-channel and out-of-band performance.

As with the development of other modern communication standards, the design task involves troubleshooting, optimization and design verification with an eye toward conformance and interoperability testing. Since the number of possible measurements and operating permutations is virtually infinite, this section will focus on representative examples of impairments and the associated measurements, along with a discussion of the essential aspects of measurement setup and interpretation.

6.4.1 General Design and Verification Challenges for LTE Transmitters

This section discusses general challenges of transmitter design and some basic verification techniques, starting with basic characteristics and then moving on to LTE-specific aspects.

6.4.1.1 Output Power and Power Control

Accurate average power measurement of time-invariant signals is not a major challenge for LTE. Accurate broadband power measurements can be made using power meters, signal and spectrum analyzers or Vector Signal Analyzers (VSAs). However, due to the nature of the downlink and uplink signal characteristics, the more typical case for LTE involves output power measurements that are much more specific. These involve measurement all the way down to the Resource Element (RE) level, which is one OFDMA or SC-FDMA symbol lasting 66.7 μs on one subcarrier. For such measurements a power meter is of no value, but a spectrum or signal analyzer or a VSA is essential. In particular, power measurements associated with specific portions of the signal often require the digital demodulation capabilities of VSAs, described further in Section 6.4.6.

6.4.1.2 Out-of-channel and Out-of-band Emissions

Out-of-band emissions are regulated to ensure compatibility between different radio systems. The primary requirement is for control of spurious emissions from very low (9 kHz) frequencies to very high (13 GHz) frequencies. LTE in this respect is no different than any other radio system and spurious emissions will not be discussed further. LTE gets more interesting at the band edges, however, where the signal has to meet the out-of-channel requirements as well as the out-of-band requirements, which are often tighter. With LTE supporting channel bandwidths up to 20 MHz, and with many bands too narrow to support more than a few channels, a large proportion of the LTE channels are also at the edge of the band.

Controlling transmitter performance at the edge of the band requires careful filter design to trade off the required out-of-band attenuation without affecting the in-channel performance of the channels near the band edge. This tradeoff must also consider costs (in terms of financial cost, power or power efficiency, physical space, etc.), which must be balanced with optimization of the in-channel and out-of-band performance and the location in the transmitter block diagram where this tradeoff is achieved. Requirements for out-of-channel emissions are covered by Adjacent Channel Leakage Ratio (ACLR) and Spectrum Emission Mask (SEM) measurements, as was the case for UMTS. These measurements are generally made with spectrum or signal analyzers using built-in routines for ACLR and SEM. The measurements can be done using either swept analysis in a signal or spectrum analyzer or using FFT analysis in a VSA. The swept approach offers higher dynamic range and faster measurements.

6.4.1.3 Power Efficiency

Power efficiency is a critical design factor for both eNB and UE transmitters and the design must meet power consumption targets while ensuring that the transmitter meets the output power, modulation quality and emission requirements. There are no formal requirements for power efficiency although this may change in the future with increased environmental awareness. Instead, power efficiency remains an ever-present design challenge to be met through design choices and optimization. The subject of battery drain testing is covered in Section 6.10.

6.4.1.4 Strategies for Handling High Peak Power

As discussed in Section 2.2, OFDMA signals can have a high Peak to Average Power Ratio (PAPR) and eNB power amplifiers must have a high degree of linearity to avoid producing out-of-channel distortion products. Power amplifiers with high linearity for the eNB are expensive and modest in their power efficiency. Two complementary methods exist to counteract this challenge: Crest Factor Reduction (CFR), which attempts to limit the signal peaks, and predistortion, which attempts to match the signal to the non-linear characteristics of the amplifier. Both methods are DSP-intensive, with predistortion being the more advanced method with the best performance but also the more difficult method to implement. For this reason CFR is usually the method used first.

For the UE it is still necessary to control PAPR, but the use of SC-FDMA in the uplink rather than OFDMA means that the PAPR of the signal is no worse than that of the underlying modulation depth for QPSK or 16QAM. These are, respectively, 4 dB and 2 dB better at 0.01% probability than the Gaussian peaks typical of OFDMA. When requirements for 64QAM are introduced in the future, the UE design may need to include CFR to limit the PAPR. The more sophisticated predistortion technique is less suitable for use in the UE.

Crest Factor Reduction

CFR was first widely used with CDMA signals and is also an important technique for LTE, although the specifics of the implementation will be somewhat different. CFR is distinct from predistortion in that it attempts to limit the peaks in the signal before it reaches the amplifier rather than shaping the input signal to compensate for amplifier nonlinearity. As such, CFR is a general technique that can be applied to any amplifier design. CFR improves headroom at the cost of degraded in-channel performance. OFDM signals without CFR have RF power characteristics similar to that of Additive White Gaussian Noise (AWGN), with peak power excursions more than 10 dB above the average power. It is impractical to design and operate power amplifiers with this level of headroom. Careful use of CFR can substantially reduce peak power requirements while maintaining acceptable signal quality.

All CFR techniques involve balancing PAPR improvements to alleviate out-of-band distortion versus the detrimental impact on in-channel distortion and the cost and power associated with the increased baseband processing overhead. Perhaps the simplest type of CFR is clipping or signal compression, in which intermittent RF power peaks are either removed (by means of a simple clipping algorithm) or scaled (in the case of compression). Because of the dramatic effects of clipping and compression on signal quality and the availability of increased processing power, more advanced techniques are also used.

An example of a more sophisticated CFR technique is tone reservation, which is possible only on the downlink since the eNB can control the resource allocation for every RB. A dummy transmission is allocated on the reserved tones, which cancels out the peaks generated by the composite signal. Although tone reservation promises to accomplish CFR without degrading signal quality, it has several disadvantages that need to be considered, including a loss of spectral efficiency (due to the loss of some subcarriers), loss of useful power and the increased computational overhead.

The effectiveness of CFR can be evaluated using the Complementary Cumulative Distribution Function (CCDF) applied to a series of instantaneous power measurements. See Section 6.4.5.2 where this measurement technique is described.

The CCDF can be measured after the CFR operation and compared with either the actual or predicted CCDF of the signal without CFR. The CCDF measurement will yield a family of direct measurements of the reduction in PAPR, along with an associated probability of a specific PAPR. Measuring the power CCDF of a signal can be misleading if the signal is not stable; for instance, if some or all of the signal is not continuously transmitted. In such cases, CCDF measurements should be made time-specific.

The positive consequence of applying CFR is to increase the headroom available within the amplifier. This headroom can either be used to drive the amplifier harder or to improve the out-of-channel performance as measured by ACLR or SEM, or some combination of the two. To choose the correct operating point for CFR, it is essential also to measure the in-channel quality (EVM, etc.) since in all cases, this quality will be degraded.

Predistortion

Predistortion enables the use of amplifier technologies that are both more power-efficient and less costly, although predistortion also adds design and operational complexity. Predistortion is a more advanced power management technique than CFR because it requires tight coupling to a specific amplifier design. Predistortion maintains the in-channel performance while operating in the non-linear region of the amplifier. This minimizes signal compression so that out-of-channel performance does not degrade at the higher operating level. A number of analog and digital predistortion techniques are available, from analog predistortion to feed-forward techniques and full adaptive digital predistortion. These techniques operate with varying degrees of effectiveness over varying bandwidths, and the eNB design may use a combination of techniques including CFR to optimize overall cost and performance.

6.4.1.5 Phase Noise

Optimizing designs for sufficient phase noise performance is particularly challenging in OFDM systems for two reasons. First, excessive phase noise degrades the orthogonality of the closely spaced subcarriers causing frequency domain Inter-Carrier Interference (ICI) leading to impaired demodulation performance. This is discussed in Section 2.2 and in "Vector Modulation Analysis and Troubleshooting for OFDM Systems" [3]. Second, phase noise reduction can be expensive in terms of system cost and power efficiency. These costs are, relatively speaking, a larger issue for the UE as opposed to the eNB.

6.4.1.6 In-channel Signal Quality

Many factors influence in-channel signal quality, from baseband signal processing to modulation, filtering, up-conversion, CFR and predistortion techniques, and the power amplification process. For LTE one of the most significant of these factors is filtering. Section 2.1.5.1 introduced the fact that the LTE specifications do not define a transmit filter for either the UE or the eNB. In UMTS, an RRC filter is specified for both the transmitted signal and for its measurement, giving the designer an exact target at which to aim. For the LTE designer there is no standardized filter. This fact can be viewed both as an opportunity to optimize the in-channel and out of channel performance and as a challenge because there is no longer a fixed target.

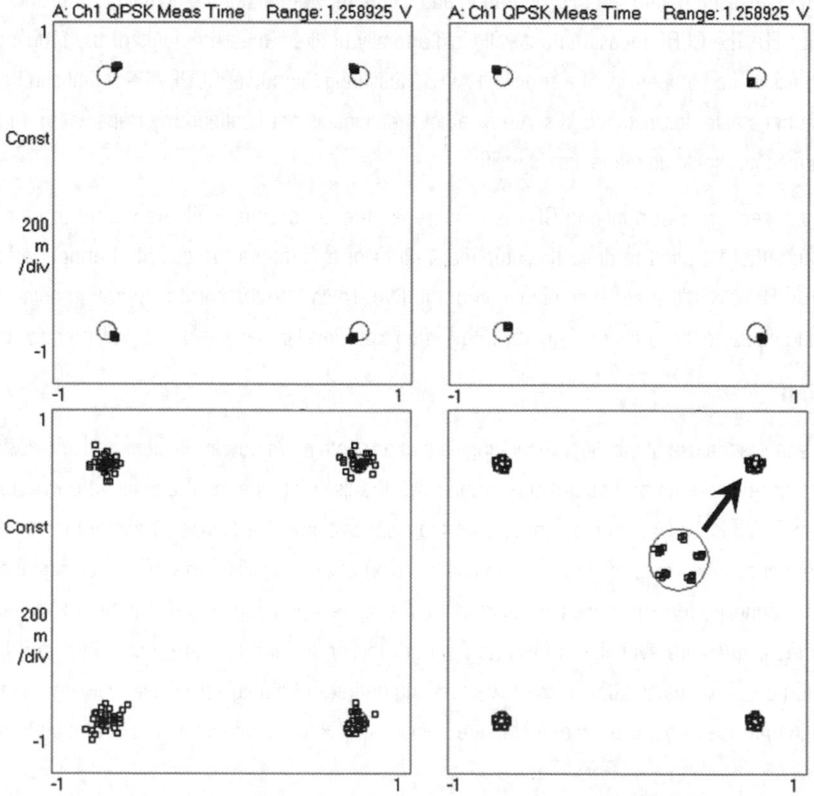

Figure 6.4-1. Constellation diagram examples of single carrier impairments in the IQ plane

One of the most useful indicators of signal content and some types of in-channel distortion is the constellation diagram. From this it is possible to tell if the demodulator is locked to the signal, what signals and modulation types are present and whether specific types of distortion are indicated. There are seven primary types of distortion, and most have a distinct constellation pattern when viewed with single carrier modulation. The distortions are white noise, phase noise, IQ gain imbalance, quadrature error, phase error, AM to AM (linear compression) and AM to PM (non-linear compression). Figure 6.4-1 shows examples of four impairments. Clockwise from the top left they are 1 dB IQ gain imbalance, 5 degree quadrature error, in-channel interference from a frequency spur 36 dB below the carrier, and general state spreading that would be characteristic of problems such as white noise, improper filtering, small amounts of compression or a symbol rate error.

A signal generator can be used to generate a single carrier digitally modulated signal at the appropriate bandwidth to test for component or subsystem IQ impairments. A skilled engineer can look at an IQ constellation and quickly determine which distortion mechanisms are present. If more than one distortion is present, it becomes harder to identify the individual components. At the other extreme, a numeric EVM measurement will indicate only the amount of distortion, giving no indication of the mechanism that created it. Thus while EVM is necessary to evaluate signal quality for conformance testing, the IQ constellation can be an essential tool for troubleshooting the source of distortion, particularly when a simple multi-level stimulus such as single carrier 16QAM is used.

In a multicarrier system such as OFDMA, the uncorrelated relative phase relationships of the subcarriers turn many of these distortions into state spreading, masking the underlying error. State spreading is a term used to describe the spreading of energy from the ideal constellation point. Some impairments do produce a distinctive constellation with multicarrier signals, but most just result in state spreading. Further reading on this subject can be found in [3] and "Effects of Physical Layer Impairments on OFDM Systems" [4].

Impairments such as AM-AM and AM-PM are sometimes best measured with dedicated distortion analysis tools such as Agilent Distortion Suite. Such general purpose tools offer the advantage of not requiring LTE-specific stimulus and demodulation. These methods can be used on components or subsystems and provide an estimate of EVM contribution.

6.4.2 A Systematic Approach for Verifying LTE Transmitter Performance

When complex digitally modulated signals are verified and optimized, it is tempting to go directly to advanced digital demodulation measurements such as those described in Section 6.4.6 using vector signal analysis. However, it is usually more productive and sometimes necessary to follow a verification sequence that begins with basic spectrum measurements and continues with vector measurements (combined frequency and time) before switching to digital demodulation and modulation analysis. This sequence is shown in Figure 6.4-2 and will be used as a way of partitioning the measurements discussed in the remainder of section 6.4.

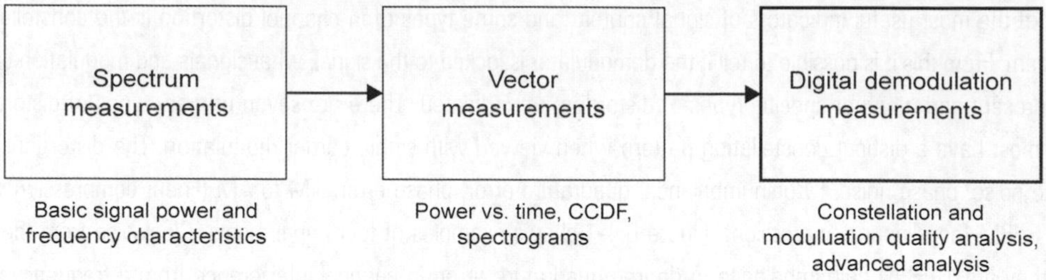

Figure 6.4-2 Sequence for verification of LTE transmitter performance

This sequence is useful because it improves the chance that underlying signal problems will be identified at the earliest stages of design before possibly being masked when complex signals are measured. In particular, the frequency and time domain measurements at the beginning of the sequence enable the verification of many signal parameters (including some associated with the digital modulation itself) without the need to perform digital demodulation. This is an advantage in early development when fully coded signals may not be available or are in some way questionable. The use of simpler measurements also means that development progress can be made using less sophisticated test equipment than is needed for the more advanced measurements.

6.4.3 Measuring Signals at Different Locations in the Transmitter

Before discussing the process of verifying transmitter performance it is necessary to address the growing use of digital interfaces, which are starting to replace traditional analog interfaces between modules within the UE and eNB. This trend leads to the need for new probing techniques and mixed domain signal analysis. Many transmitter measurements are a straightforward matter of connecting the transmitter RF output directly to an RF signal analyzer input and measuring signal characteristics and content. Some measurements, however, will require connecting, probing and measuring at early or intermediate points in the transmitter signal chain. Figure 6.4-3 shows a typical UE block diagram and the possible ways in which signals can be injected or probed at different points.

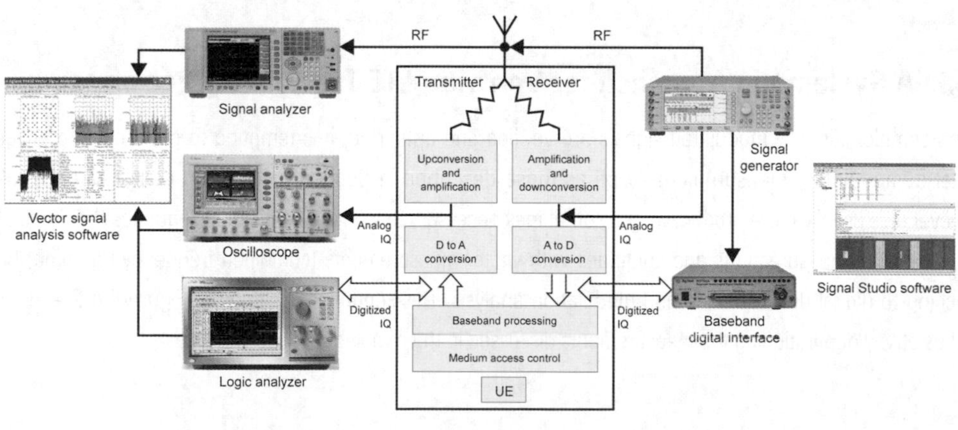

Figure 6.4-3. Stimulus and analysis of different points in the UE block diagram

6.4.3.1 Measuring the RF Output at the Antenna Connector

The RF output or antenna connector is the traditional point for signal analysis. For the critical maximum power requirements defined at the antenna connector, some modern spectrum and signal analyzers now have an accuracy approaching that of power meters [5], although achieving high accuracy depends on careful selection and use of cables, connectors and adapters. Testing the high output power of an eNB requires the use of external attenuators to protect the analyzer inputs. For more information on best practices for RF signal analysis see Agilent application notes AN-150 [6] and AN-1303 [7].

Spectrum and signal analyzers have the added benefits over power meters of time and frequency selectivity, often found in combination. With appropriate software this time and frequency selectivity can be extended into digital demodulation in which individual OFDM subcarriers or groups of subcarriers can be separately measured, and individual symbols or groups of symbols can be separately measured as well. These selective measurements are invaluable for troubleshooting and system optimization.

RF analysis at the antenna connector is used to evaluate the complete transmission system, but RF analysis is also used to evaluate subsystems and components such as upconverters, filters, local oscillators and power amplifiers, requiring probing at different parts of the system. The increasing use of DSP techniques such as CFR and predistortion in the baseband stages of transmitters adds complexity to the interpretation of RF measurement results, whether they involve spectrum or time domain measurements or digital demodulation analysis. For evaluation of components or subsystems an incremental approach is often used in which the transmitter system is stimulated with a signal generator or its own baseband/IF, and successive measurements are made at later points in the signal chain to quantify the distortion, spurious emissions and other impairments contributed by individual stages and elements of the transmitter.

6.4.3.2 Measuring IF Signals

Signal analysis at the IF is used to determine the quality of signals after the first stage of up-conversion or to determine the signal quality of an IF signal generated directly from baseband. IF analysis also provides a baseline for understanding the relative contributions of up-conversion and RF amplifier circuits. Quantifying the individual distortions that make up the overall transmitter signal quality allows the system designer to isolate problems and make necessary design tradeoffs for power, cost and board real estate.

In some transmitters the IF signal is generated directly by an all-digital baseband section feeding a single Digital to Analog Converter (DAC), whose output is the analog IF signal. While this analog IF signal can be measured directly, it may be useful to also understand the quality and content of the input to the DAC. Indeed, it may be beneficial to compare the signal quality of the DAC output to its digitized input. For this type of mixed signal analysis VSA software can be used with logic analyzers to capture digital rather than RF input data prior to analysis using the same algorithms and user interface as traditional RF measurements. Mixed signal analysis is discussed in Sections 6.2.2 and 6.3.3.

6.4.3.3 Measuring Analog and Digital Baseband Signals

The situation with measuring analog and digital Baseband IQ (BBIQ) signals is similar to that for the analog and digital IF signals described above. Signal analysis begins with data acquisition and the method depends on the system design.

For systems using analog BBIQ the signals may be in dual single-ended or dual differential form, and probing is often necessary, along with probe calibration and compensation, for accurate analysis. Modern spectrum and signal analyzers such as the Agilent X-Series offer the option of analog BBIQ inputs in single-ended and differential form, along with software to assist in probe identification, calibration and compensation. A discussion of IQ probing, compensation and calibration is beyond the scope of this book, but these topics are discussed in "Analysis of Baseband IQ Signals" [8].

Modern designs increasingly use digital rather than analog baseband approaches and, as with the digital IF described above, analysis starts by acquiring the digital signal using an appropriate tool such as a logic analyzer. The baseband signal can then be analyzed with VSA software as if the signal had been captured as an analog or RF waveform. The ability to capture a signal in analog or digital form at any point in the block diagram and then analyze it with the same software provides the ability to precisely analyze the quality of the signal as it progresses through the transmit chain, making design optimization and troubleshooting more productive and less complicated.

Such measurement requires generation of a digital baseband or IF signal to stimulate later sections of the transmitter for signal analysis. Digital signal generation solutions are available such as the Agilent ESG series, which offers a digital output connector driven by the same signal generation software as is used for analog signal generation. The digital connector, known as a Digital Signal Interface Module (DSIM), provides flexible data formats, clocking, and physical interfaces for IQ, serial and parallel data streams, including digital IF signals. To match circuit requirements, DSIMs may also perform resampling and provide adjustable clock phase and skew.

6.4.4 Spectrum Measurements

6.4.4.1 Channel Power, Amplitude Flatness, Central Frequency and Occupied Bandwidth

The following are basic spectrum measurements that can be made on an LTE signal:

- Channel power
- Amplitude flatness
- Center frequency
- Occupied Bandwidth (OBW)

The center frequency and amplitude flatness measurements are indicative results since the formal definition of these requires digital demodulation of the signal.

As with most digitally modulated signals, LTE signals are significantly noise-like in their power and spectral characteristics. Traditional spectrum analyzers are not designed for noise-like and bursted signals, although with care spectrum analyzers can be used to make useful measurements. Fortunately many modern spectrum and signal analyzers as well as vector signal analyzers are designed to accurately measure signals such as these, implementing true RMS detection and appropriate averaging rather than the traditional video bandwidth filtering. For more information see "Spectrum Analyzer Detectors and Averaging for Wireless Measurements" [9].

In most cases the best way to measure the power of an LTE signal is to use the power calculations available in demodulation applications. The time synchronization and time selectivity of demodulation (selecting which part of the frame to measure) are important for ensuring that the desired portion of the signal is measured. In addition, demodulation provides a way to separately measure the relative power of the LTE channels and signals as discussed in Section 6.4.6.1. If time synchronization is not required or if timing is available from a trigger or a power on/off event, power can be accurately measured without demodulation by averaging spectrum or RF envelope measurements and using band power markers to select the signal of interest. Signal power may also be measured by dedicated LTE measurement applications as part of the measure of ACPR and SEM. An important issue for all of these measurement approaches is the use of consistent or equivalent signals (signal content) since LTE IF and RF power levels vary with signal content and other parameters.

Figure 6.4-4 shows an example measurement of a fully allocated 5 MHz downlink signal made with a large FFT block size to provide a high resolution spectrum measurement with averaging of 100 traces. The trace provides an accurate power measurement and any significant amplitude flatness errors can be seen. It is also possible to approximate the center frequency and the OBW. Band power markers are used to integrate and measure the power over the desired bandwidth, which is typically the same as the occupied bandwidth of the signal. Note, however, that this spectrum measurement is not time-selective and indicates only the power of the averaged spectra. The center frequency can be calculated from the centroid of the occupied bandwidth markers, but this can be of questionable accuracy because the subcarrier allocation is not always symmetrical about the center frequency.

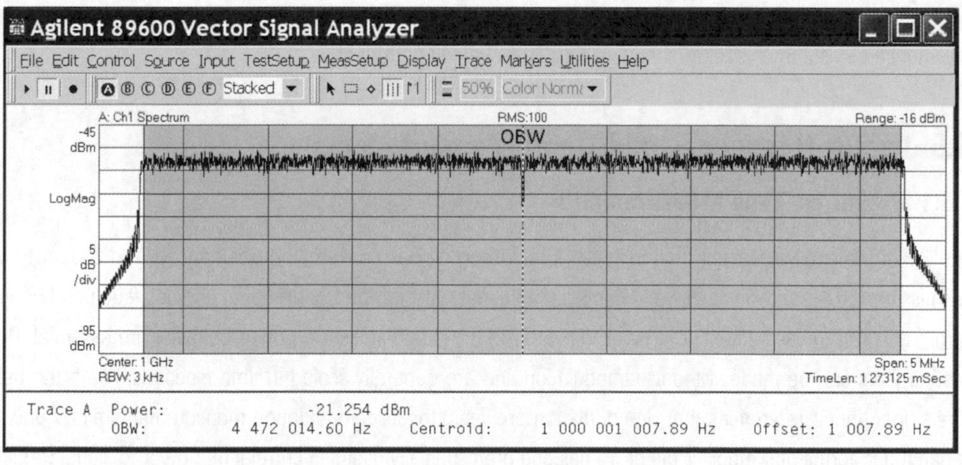

Figure 6.4-4. Spectrum of 5 MHz downlink showing power, OBW, and center frequency

A more accurate measurement of center frequency that is not affected by asymmetry in the subcarrier allocation can be made for the downlink by identifying the spectral minimum associated with the central subcarrier, which is not transmitted. This subcarrier is used to accommodate any LO leakage caused by impairments in the transmitter such as IQ offset, so that this distortion does not degrade the wanted part of the signal. The accuracy using this method is significantly better than 1 ppm. The required frequency accuracy for the downlink is ±0.05 ppm and is measured using digital demodulation as part of the EVM measurement process. For the uplink, the central subcarrier is not reserved and so cannot be used to estimate the center frequency.

6.4.4.2 Filtering and Spectral Shape

Some fine details of the signal spectrum can provide insight into system optimization, although they are not essential in terms of conformance testing. For example, different choices of baseband filter parameters may optimize in-band flatness versus computational efficiency, or load versus Signal to Noise Ratio (SNR). An example is shown in Figure 6.4-5.

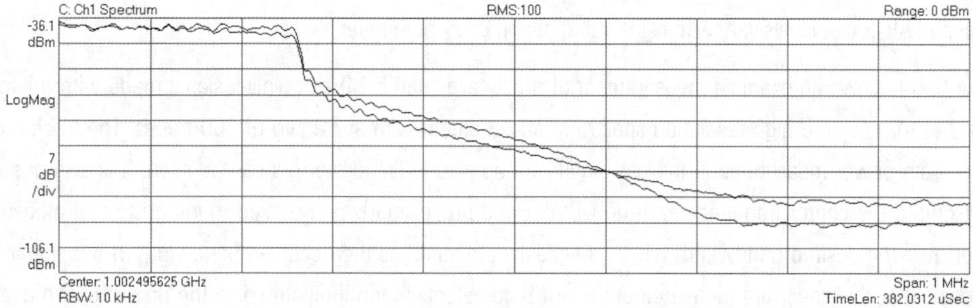

Figure 6.4-5. Comparison of different baseband filter choices on OFDMA signal roll off

A high resolution averaged spectrum measurement can show the effect of different baseband filter choices on the signal's transition band and stop band. The formal implications of such choices have to be evaluated using the conformance measurements for in-channel and out-of-channel performance.

6.4.5 Vector (Frequency and Time) Measurements

6.4.5.1 Power vs. Time Measurements

Since RF signal power varies due to factors including signal content, power control and Discontinuous Transmission (DTX), and since power affects signal quality, design and operational choices (such as UE power control), accurate measurements of Power Versus Time (PVT) and statistical power behavior are essential. Power measurements can be made without demodulation and are generally scaled in time (seconds). With the benefit of the signal timing references that demodulation provides, these demodulation measurements allow power to be analyzed in terms of symbols, slots or frames and are especially useful in correlating power to signal traffic and control actions. Examples are discussed in section 6.4.6.

Basic PVT measurements can be made through direct analysis of the RF envelope using a spectrum analyzer in a zero-span mode, although the accuracy of this approach is limited due to the fact that the Resolution Bandwidth (RBW) filters are not rectangular channel filters and may not have the bandwidth (up to 20 MHz) to measure wider LTE signals. PVT measurements and power statistics measurements (see Section 6.4.5.2) are more typically made with vector signal analyzers, which can implement wide, flat channel filters for accurate measurements. VSAs also provide band power markers, which are useful in making some time-specific power measurements.

PVT measurements made without demodulation can be performed simply and quickly, without the setup and processing needed for demodulation. Such measurements can be performed even on signals that have not been successfully demodulated. The measurements provide confirmation of absolute power levels and some visual indications of signal structure, but typically not frame timing. In making PVT measurements the VSA digitizes the entire channel bandwidth (as its FFT span) and reports the power in this span as log magnitude versus time. Band power markers are used to integrate the power over a particular region in time. Depending on the signal structure and power behavior it can be useful to measure over periods ranging from one or more frames to a single slot. An example PVT measurement of a half frame (5 ms) of a downlink signal is shown in figure 6.4-6. Band power markers are used to indicate the average power over a 1 ms interval.

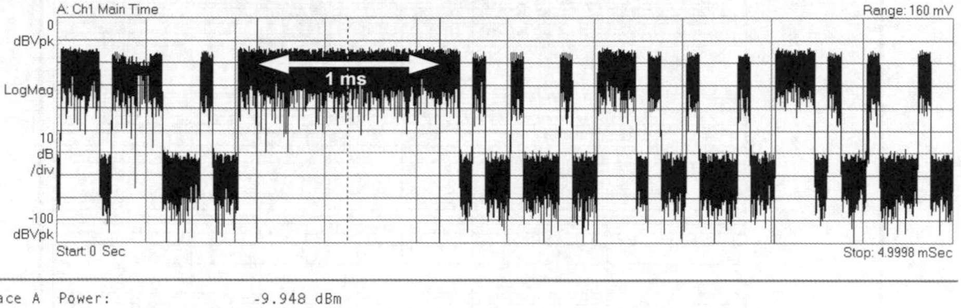

Figure 6.4-6. PVT measurement of one half frame of a downlink signal with band power markers to indicate average power over 1 ms

For the FFT techniques used in vector signal analyzers there is an inverse relationship between settings for frequency span and length of the maximum time record. In measurements such as PVT over 10 ms on a 5 MHz signal it is necessary to have both a 5 MHz frequency span and a relatively long (10 ms) time record. This results in a very large FFT block size of 50,000 points or more. A frame of a 20 MHz signal would require a 200,000 point FFT time record. Once a longer duration measurement has been made, the average power of any portion can be easily measured using band power markers.

6.4.5.2 Power Statistics CCDF Measurements

CCDF measurements provide a broad quantitative measurement of signal power behavior and are useful in evaluating the operating points and efficiencies of transmitters. CCDF measurements are particularly important for evaluating OFDMA (and to a lesser extent SC-FDMA) systems in which high PAPR makes it impractical to amplify the signal in unmodified form due to the excessive headroom required.

An example of a CCDF power measurement is given in Figure 6.4-7. The X-axis of the CCDF measurement is log power (dB) referenced to the average power of the signal during the selected measurement interval. The Y-axis of the measurement is a logarithmic scale of probability, commonly from 0.001% to 100%. A point on the CCDF curve indicates the probability (as a percentage of individual power measurements) that the signal will reach a given peak level above the measured average power level.

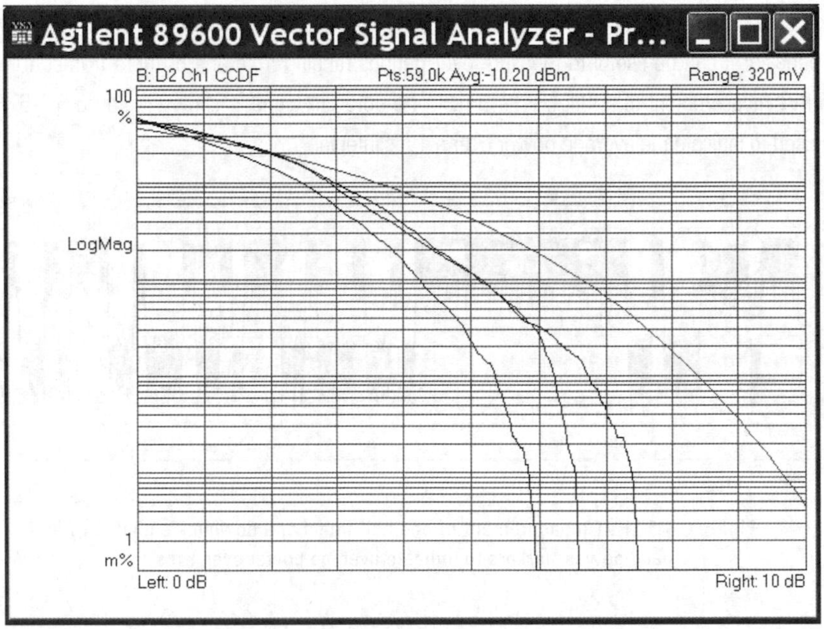

Figure 6.4-7 CCDF measurements of uplink signals: from left to right, QPSK, 16QAM and 64QAM

So that CCDF measurements will not be misinterpreted, they must be made with knowledge of the signal under test. For example, removing power from the signal by turning it off for periods of time (discontinuous transmission) can dramatically increase the apparent level of the peaks since the average signal power is lower. However, from the perspective of the power amplifier, such a signal is not any harder to amplify since the absolute level of the peaks has not changed.

Provided care is taken not to measure CCDF during the periods when the signal is off, CCDF is a relatively straightforward measurement to interpret because it is automatically normalized for average amplitude, and modern analyzers can quickly compile the statistics for a large number of power measurements. This provides accurate average power and low variance for the statistics of the relatively rare peak power events.

The example shown in figure 6.4-7 is from an uplink signal containing a PUSCH with SC-FDMA precoding and three different modulation formats. The three curves in the measurement were obtained using time gating to isolate each modulation format and represent, from left to right, QPSK, 16QAM and 64QAM. Note that for all modulation formats this SC-FDMA signal shows significantly lower peaks than the AWGN reference curve that is furthest to the right. Downlink LTE signals prior to any CFR are generally very close to the AWGN curve and more challenging to amplify.

Section 6.4.1.4 discusses how CCDF measurements can be used along with in-channel and out-of-channel measurements to evaluate the effectiveness of CFR techniques.

6.4.5.3 Spectrum vs. Time: The Spectrogram

One of the most useful general spectrum measurements for LTE signals is the spectrogram. The spectrogram provides a means of interpreting the signal structure at a glance. Specifically, the spectrogram can simultaneously present hundreds of contiguous or overlapping spectra revealing underlying detail of the frame structure.

Spectrograms are made up of a sequence of ordinary spectrum measurements, each of which is compressed to a height of 1 pixel row on the display with the amplitude values of the spectra encoded in color. This produces a display of spectrum versus time containing hundreds or even thousands of spectrum measurements. The spectrogram enables an entire LTE uplink or downlink frame to be shown. All of the spectrum data is preserved and individual spectrum measurements can be selected from the spectrogram for more detailed analysis using a spectrogram marker.

The spectrogram allows easy visual recognition of the major signal characteristics in the downlink including channel types and symbol transitions based on subcarrier allocation. These measurements all occur without the need for digital demodulation. For uplink signals the frame structure is simpler, but the spectrogram remains a very useful tool to show the position in time and frequency of any dynamic RB allocation, and it can provide an indication of the images created by IQ errors. An example is shown in Section 6.4.6.9.

To show the LTE frame structure the spectrogram should be made with the analyzer operating in real time mode — that is, the spectra for the measurement should be produced from time records in which no data from the input signal is missing from the spectrum calculations, and the time records for each spectrum overlap. A typical overlap figure for these measurements is 75 – 95%.

In order to make such heavily overlapped, real time measurements of signals that can be up to 20 MHz wide, it is necessary to use time capture, a feature of many vector signal analyzers. During time capture, the sampled data is streamed directly to memory, without gaps and without performing analysis that would interrupt gap-free recording. After capture, spectrum/spectrogram measurements are made during playback of the recording, and the overlap percentage is varied to adjust both the effective "speed" of the playback and the time increment represented by each new spectrum in the display. Figure 6.4-8 shows a spectrogram of part of an LTE downlink frame in which the channel allocations are clearly visible. Also seen are the fine horizontal lines indicating the spectral spreading that occurs at each symbol transition where the collective phase and amplitude of the subcarriers change abruptly, resulting in a discontinuity in the transmitted signal.

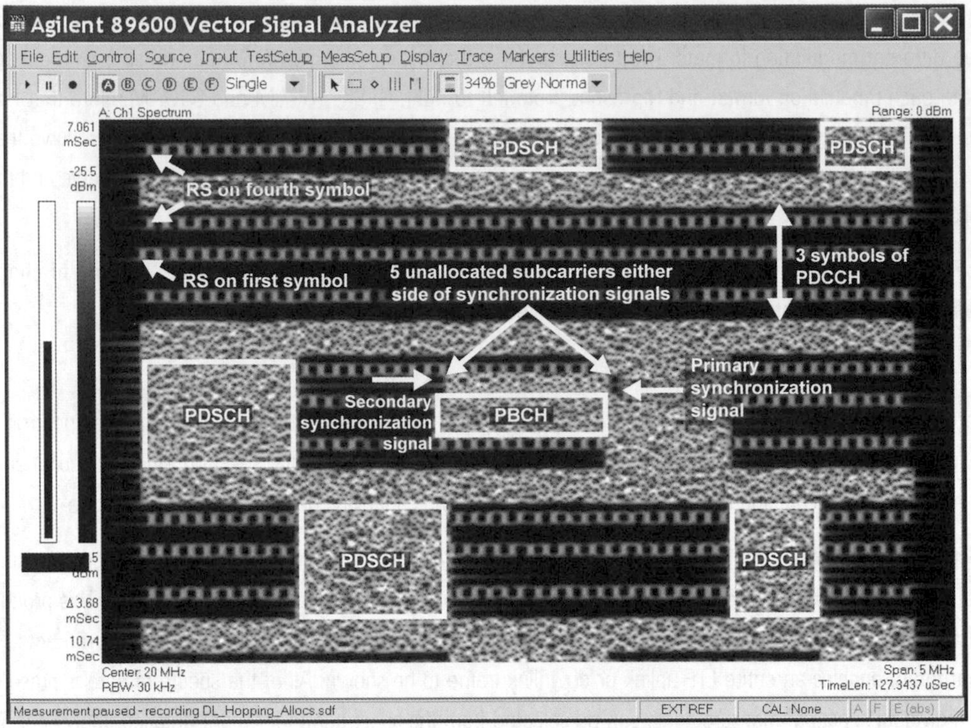

Figure 6.4-8. Spectrogram of 3.7 ms duration from a 5 MHz downlink signal

In this spectrogram the Y-axis is time, progressing from top to bottom over a time period of approximately 3.7 ms, which is just over 50 symbols. The X-axis is frequency and signal power is represented in shades of gray, although on the actual instrument the power variations are represented in color. The most obvious patterns in the signal are the RS subcarriers, which are allocated to the first and fourth symbol of every seven symbol slot. The RS are allocated every sixth subcarrier, which creates a ladder effect across the entire channel bandwidth. The definition of the RS subcarrier allocation for this single antenna example (see also Figures 2.4-3 and 3.2-9) is that for the first symbol of each slot the RS starts from the first subcarrier, whereas on the fourth symbol of the slot the RS starts from the fourth subcarrier. A left-right alternating pattern is thus created that can be seen clearly in the spectrogram. The first RS allocations appear near the top of the spectrogram with no power at the lowest subcarrier, indicating that this symbol is the fourth symbol of the slot rather than the first.

The first five symbol periods of the spectrogram show allocations in the central part of the channel and a block at the upper end. These allocations are likely to be the Physical Downlink Shared Channel (PDSCH) carrying the user data. This allocation is followed by three symbol periods in which the entire channel bandwidth is allocated. The periodicity of this allocation, which occurs every 14 symbols (one subframe), suggests that it is the Physical Downlink Control Channel (PDCCH), as seen in Figure 3.2-9. The next period of activity is at the center of the channel, which shows the pattern created by the primary and secondary synchronization signals followed by the Physical Broadcast Channel (PBCH). Recall from Figure 3.2-9 that the synchronization signals occupy only the central 62 subcarriers and that the five subcarriers on either side are unallocated. This small gap can clearly be seen in the spectrogram. The next symbol contains the PBCH, which occupies 72 subcarriers along with the RS across the rest of the channel. The following three symbols for the central 72 subcarriers contain the rest of the PBCH. Any other allocation in the spectrogram is most likely to be more PDSCH.

The time capture recordings used for spectrograms can also be used for signal demodulation. For troubleshooting purposes it can be useful to compare both spectrum and demodulation measurements of the same captured signal.

6.4.6 Analysis of Signals After Digital Demodulation

By performing digital demodulation according to the radio specifications using a vector signal analyzer it is possible to analyze the structure and quality of signals in the domain for which they were designed. This analysis provides a low level interoperability test. In addition to these basic tasks it is also possible to perform more advanced analysis. Here are some examples:

- Separately measure the characteristics of individual components of the signal right down to the Resource Element (RE) level of one symbol for one subcarrier.
- Understand how modulation quality varies over time to identify periodic or single shot effects.
- Measure subtle effects of different operating conditions (average signal power, battery voltage and impedance, operating temperature, number of transmitters driven, etc.).
- Isolate the source of signal impairments.
- Evaluate tradeoffs of modulation quality versus design or operational parameters (CFR or predistortion techniques, amplifier operating points, component choices, etc.).
- Validate correct coding of physical signals and physical channels.

The procedure for basic demodulation will be discussed first before moving on to the more advanced demodulation techniques that reveal the full nature of the signal structure. Digital demodulation and subsequent signal analysis is generally carried out using vector signal analysis software such as the Agilent 89601A VSA software coupled with some form of signal capture, which can be from a variety of sources such as those described in Section 6.4.3. An alternative is to use a dedicated signal analyzer with built-in measurement applications such as the Agilent X-Series signal analyzers with LTE measurement personality. The digital demodulation examples and associated measurements used in the remainder of this section are illustrated using the Agilent 89601A VSA software. The power of this tool is not fully conveyed here due to the limitations of two color printing. Color is used in the VSA software to great effect, highlighting aspects of the complex LTE signal structure for purposes of identifying and isolating specific signal and channel effects and impairments.

6.4.6.1 Procedure for Basic Digital Demodulation

Figure 6.4-9 shows a typical display of a digitally demodulated signal. The VSA user has complete flexibility to choose (1) at what point in the demodulation process the signal will be analyzed and (2) the format and number of simultaneous displays. This particular example is a downlink LTE signal with a 5 MHz channel bandwidth. Each of the six displays shows an orthogonal view of the signal, and many more views are possible depending on the purpose of the analysis. Before detailed analysis can begin, however, the first priority is to configure the analyzer correctly to obtain demodulation lock to the signal.

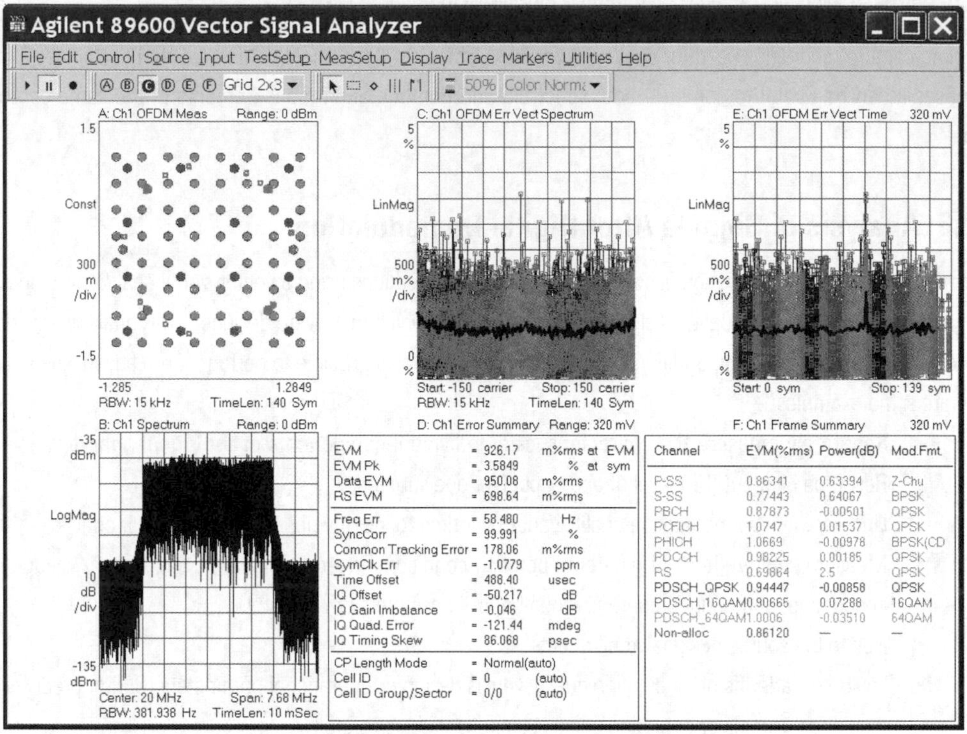

Figure 6.4-9. Example analysis of digitally demodulated 5 MHz LTE downlink signal using Agilent 89601A VSA software

The spectrum and vector measurements described earlier in this section are relatively easy to make since they require few analyzer parameter settings: once the signal frequency, bandwidth and input range (level) have been established, not much can go wrong. However, to successfully perform digital demodulation requires many more settings. Fortunately, most of these can be configured automatically using preset demodulation parameters.

For situations in which the signal frequency is not known precisely or its stability is suspect, the frequency lock range of the analyzer can be extended. This extended lock range increases the amount of data processed and reduces the measurement update rate with no reduction in accuracy. After demodulation lock has been achieved, a precise frequency error measurement as reported in the Figure 6.4-9 Trace D error summary will be available to set the analyzer center frequency more accurately.

After frequency and input range, the next important demodulation parameter that must be set is the uplink or downlink selection. This selection is critical because unlike some other systems, the LTE uplink and downlink synchronization reference signal structure and modulation formats are quite different. It would be nearly impossible to make sense of a downlink signal using uplink demodulation parameters and vice versa. Similarly the choice of FDD or TDD frame structure is important because again the differences in synchronization reference signal structure between the two are large.

The next important parameter is the channel bandwidth, and LTE has six to choose from: 1.4 MHz, 3 MHz, 5 MHz, 10 MHz, 15 MHz and 20 MHz. For analysis of IQ signals obtained directly from supported front-end acquisition hardware, selecting the appropriate channel bandwidth from the demodulation properties will also preset an appropriate front-end hardware acquisition span and IQ sample rate. While span is typically thought of as a display parameter, the VSA acquisition span is closely related to the signal acquisition bandwidth. If the bandwidth is too wide, unwanted noise and interference could impact measurement accuracy. Wider spans also required higher sample rates, which could negatively affect measurement speed, without providing any benefit. For analysis of signals coming from a simulation environment or a recording file, it is also necessary to specify the correct IQ sample rate. In this case the IQ sample rate will be used as part of the VSA recording file header information, enabling the IQ samples to be interpreted correctly.

The final parameter to consider is the appropriate sync type, which determines the specific downlink or uplink reference signal component to be used for initial synchronization of the VSA to the LTE signal being measured. For downlink analysis, valid choices include Primary Synchronization Signal (P-SS) or Reference Signal (RS). (The acronym P-SS is not formally defined in the 3GPP specifications but is used for convenience in the VSA software.) For uplink analysis, valid sync type choices include PUSCH Demodulation Reference Signal (DMRS), PUCCH DMRS, Sounding Reference Signal (SRS) or Physical Random Access Channel (PRACH). Selecting between different synchronizing methods allows fuller verification of the signal being tested. For example, coding errors in the downlink P-SS may not prevent measurements using the RS, but would leave a problem to be resolved when operating with the UE. Note that for uplink signals some additional, higher layer configuration parameters are required in order to achieve reliable VSA synchronization. These parameters can be configured under the demodulation properties profile allocation editor within the VSA software.

Depending on where in the upconversion or downconversion process the signal is being probed, the frequency spectrum may be reversed. There is a setting within the demodulator properties that takes this into account so that demodulation is still successful. The mirrored spectrum is corrected before demodulation by performing a complex conjugate on the time-domain representation of the signal. This setting can also compensate for swapped I and Q signals.

If these steps are followed, it should be possible to view the demodulated signal. Each of the traces in Figure 6.4-9 will now be described as an introduction to basic digital demodulation. This particular set of displays is not the default for the 89601A but has been chosen to represent a broad range of basic capabilities.

Description of Basic Digital Demodulation Traces

Figure 6.4-9 Trace B (bottom left) shows the classic spectrum analyzer view of signal power versus frequency, calculated from a single FFT over the whole time interval being used for demodulation. This view, although it does not show digital demodulation, is often comforting during the early stages of the digital demodulation process because it confirms that the two most important parameters of frequency and input range are consistent with the signal. From the trace it can be determined that the occupied bandwidth is around 4.5 MHz, which indicates a fully allocated 5 MHz downlink signal. The power spectral density for the 380 Hz resolution bandwidth is around –45 dBm. This power spectral density should not be confused with the aggregate signal power, which can be measured using band power markers across the entire 4.5 MHz occupied bandwidth.

The spectrum analyzer view establishes that the signal is generally at the correct frequency and power. The next important trace to consider is the error summary shown in Trace D (bottom middle). Important metrics to verify initially include SyncCorr, which indicates the observed initial synchronization correlation quality level. Ideally this level would approach 100%. The SyncCorr metric is a useful, quick indicator of how well the VSA is locked to the received signal's previously selected sync type parameter signal component. Other useful, quick checks include EVM, frequency error, auto-detected Cyclic Prefix (CP) length and cell ID metrics.

After the initial synchronization quality check and other summary metric checks have been made, the next important trace to examine is Trace A (top left). This trace shows an IQ constellation of the demodulated signal in which, for OFDMA, each point represents the amplitude and phase of one subcarrier in the frequency domain. From this trace it should be immediately apparent whether the analyzer has successfully locked to and demodulated the signal. If the trace has a regular pattern, then lock has almost certainly been achieved. If the pattern is unstable or just shows noise, then lock has not been achieved and a check of the demodulation setup and signal quality will be required to trace the cause. Trace A also reveals the different modulation depths detected in the signal. In this example the most obvious is 64QAM, followed by 16QAM and then by QPSK, all of which are allocated for the Physical Downlink Shared Channel (PDSCH) used in this example. The QPSK modulation points also represent subcarrier allocations for the Physical Broadcast Channel (PBCH), Physical Control Format Indicator Channel (PCFICH), Physical Downlink Control Channel (PDCCH) and Reference Signal (RS). A closer look reveals BPSK modulation points representing the Secondary Synchronization Signal (S-SS). (As with P-SS, S-SS is not an official 3GPP acronym.) Additional points on the unity circle represent the P-SS modulated with a Zadoff-Chu phase sequence. The signal in this example was chosen because it represents, simultaneously, all the modulation types available on the downlink.

The dots in Trace A, representing each physical channel or physical signal, are color-coded with the same colors used in the other displays. The key to the color coding is provided in Trace F (bottom right), the frame summary display. This display lists all the physical signals and physical channels in the signal. For each entry there is an assigned color, and four measurement results are displayed: EVM, detected signal or channel power relative to the un-boosted RS power level (0 dB unity circle), the allocated RB and modulation format.

Trace D (bottom middle) is the error summary. The top section provides quality statistics for the composite signal including overall EVM, peak EVM, EVM of the PDSCH data and EVM of the RS pilot signals. In the middle section of Trace D is the frequency error (which is a residual error subtracted from the signal prior to calculating EVM), and various statistical metrics that indicate the types of error that make up the overall EVM. These include the IQ gain imbalance, IQ quadrature error and IQ timing skew. Apart from the frequency error and the IQ offset, the other error terms do not have definitions in the specifications. Rather, to the skilled designer, they are troubleshooting tools that can help pinpoint the underlying errors that make up the overall EVM. The bottom section of Trace D shows the auto-detected OFDMA symbol CP length, as well as the auto-detected cell ID and the cell ID group or sector derived from demodulation of the P-SS and S-SS.

Further insight into the nature of the signal errors can be found in the two remaining traces. Trace C (top middle) is the error vector spectrum, which shows the EVM as a function of subcarrier in the frequency domain. The value of analyzing EVM in this domain is to determine if there are frequency-specific elements in any observed error. Typical errors that are discernable in this trace are spurious signals — which could elevate the EVM of subcarriers located near the spur — as well as baseband modulation errors and IF or RF filter responses, both of which can shape the error spectrum. In any practical signal it is expected that the EVM will degrade at the channel edges due to effects of channel and band filters. Maintaining the optimal balance between in-channel and out-of-channel performance is one of the biggest challenges for the LTE transmitter designer, and tools such as the VSA can be invaluable for that purpose. This particular signal has an almost flat EVM spectrum with only a slight increase at the channel edges. The heavy dark trace is the average EVM per subcarrier over the measurement period, which for this example is one radio frame (10 ms or 140 symbols). There is a third dimension to this trace that explains the solid nature of the data. For any one subcarrier there will be one EVM result for every measured symbol. In this case 140 data points will be overlaid horizontally on the vertical axis for each of the 301 subcarriers. From visual inspection it can be seen that the peak EVM is just over 3% with most of the peaks around 2% and the average just under 1%. This aligns with the rms EVM and peak EVM statistics in the error summary of Trace D. It is also possible to change the X-axis units to RBs rather than subcarriers; this averages the data for each set of 12 adjacent subcarriers to derive a single rms EVM value per RB.

The final view of this signal is error vector time, in Trace E (top right). This trace shows EVM in the time domain as a function of the OFDMA symbol. In this example, the errors are generally evenly spread in time, although there is a noticeable jump in the average EVM at the end of the sixth subframe, which could indicate a problem somewhere that needs further investigating. The color coding is more evident here than in Trace C and shows that the allocation of the different PDSCH modulation formats is sequential in time. As with Trace C, there is an additional dimension to this trace. For each of the 140 OFDMA symbols in time, 301 data points will be overlaid on the vertical axis, indicating the EVM of each subcarrier during that symbol period. It is also possible to configure the X-axis in units of slots rather than symbols; this averages the data for each set of seven adjacent OFDMA symbols (assuming normal CP) within a given slot to derive a single rms EVM value per slot. Common errors visible in this trace include amplifier gain instability, particularly for TDD signals in which thermal settling can be a factor. This trace can also be useful for other problems that are temporal in nature, such as timing glitches or interference from logic signals. Large single-symbol errors could indicate amplifier clipping due to a symbol interval with particularly high peak amplitude.

It should be evident from this introductory view of digital demodulation just how powerful a vector signal analyzer can be for understanding the structure and quality of LTE signals.

6.4.6.2 Coupling Measurements Across Domains

One of the most powerful VSA tools used in modulation analysis is the coupling of markers across different measurements, traces and domains. This tool is particularly effective for analyzing LTE signals, which can have a high symbol content (large number of symbols per frame, burstiness, etc.) and a large number of different signal elements (channels, reference signals, OFDM subcarriers, etc.). Coupled markers allow the user to understand the identity and characteristics of a symbol simultaneously in time, frequency, power and error. To make this analysis even more specific, coupled markers can be combined with the selection or de-selection of individual LTE physical signals and physical channels for display and analysis.

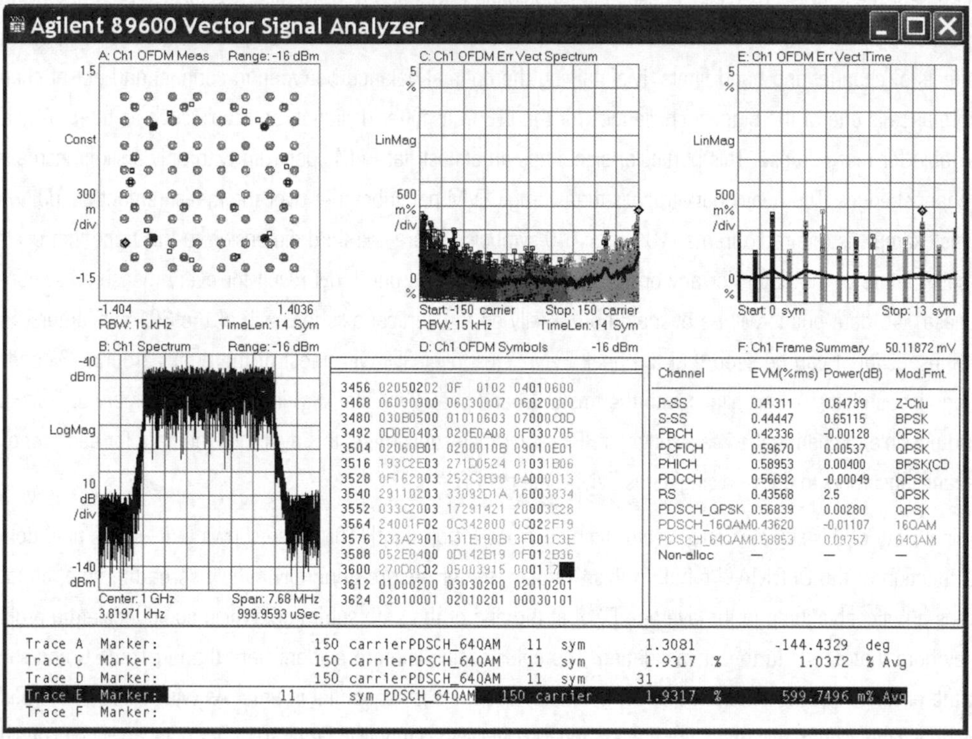

Figure 6.4-10. Example of using coupled markers across four different measurement domains

An example of the use of coupled markers across multiple measurement displays is shown in Figure 6.4-10. This downlink demodulation measurement takes advantage of the VSA software's ability to simultaneously show multiple color-coded displays and a complete marker table. With markers coupled and all LTE physical signals and physical channels selected for analysis, a peak search in either the error vector spectrum or error vector time mode indicates the largest error during the measurement interval of one subframe (14 symbols for normal CP). The exact symbol associated with this error can now be understood in terms of time domain OFDMA symbol index, frequency domain subcarrier number, IQ magnitude and phase values, physical channel type, encoded modulation format, decoded symbol table bit value and other parameters. Note that in this case the highest detected error involves a 64QAM PDSCH physical channel symbol from OFDMA symbol index 11, located on the outermost edge subcarrier index 150 and modulated using one of the highest power outer IQ constellation states, which was decoded as 64QAM state bit value 0x1F (see the Trace A, C, D and E marker values at the bottom of Figure 6.4-10). This example identifies the important fact that the highest error is located at the edge of the channel spectrum, which is consistent with the rest of the error vector spectrum display in Trace C. Although this characteristic of the signal error appears obvious in the error vector spectrum display, it would not be clear from examination of either the error vector time or error summary trace displays. Therefore a flexible measurement tool that provides many different views into the measured signal across different domains is extremely valuable in troubleshooting, providing a much fuller understanding of the underlying causes of observed impairment.

The Trace C error vector spectrum shows a more pronounced degradation (increase in EVM) at the channel edges than was the case with the equivalent Trace C of the previous example in Figure 6.4-9.

6.4.6.3 Measuring With and Without Equalization

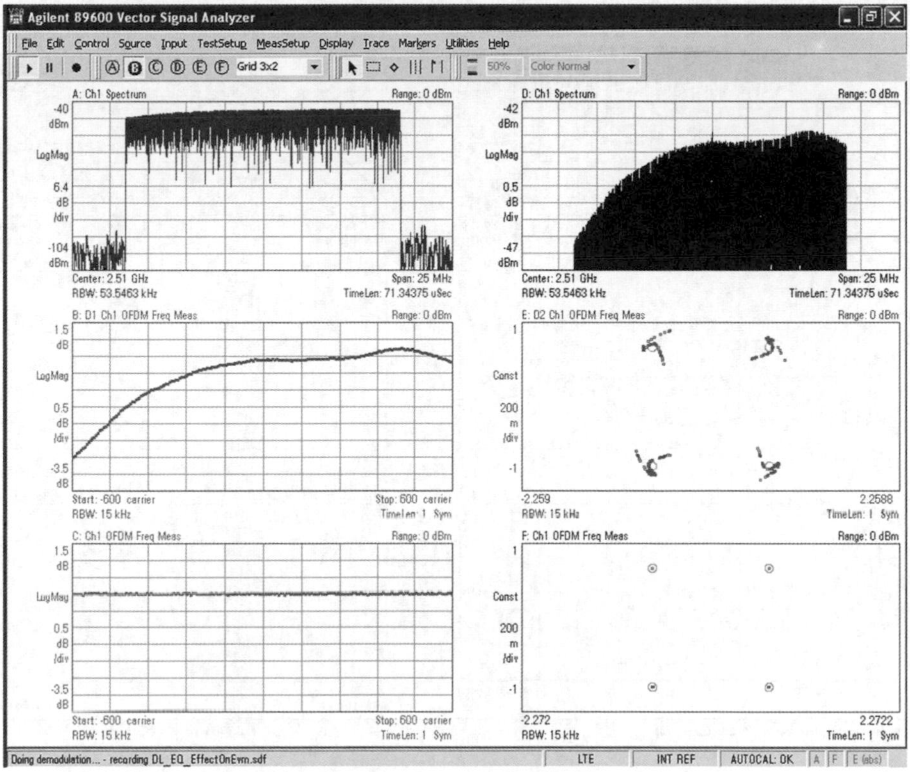

Figure 6.4-11. Example of impact of equalization on RS power

Figure 6.4-11 shows a simple QPSK downlink signal. Trace A (top left) is the non-demodulated spectrum, which reveals a 20 MHz channel bandwidth. Some slight unflatness is evident. Trace D (top right) is the same measurement but with an expanded scale to show the detail of the unflatness, which is about 3 dB peak to peak. The VSA's ability to display the same measurement in different views with different display attributes is especially convenient.

Trace B (middle left) shows the demodulated downlink RS subcarrier power observed in the third last symbol of slot index 1. In this example, slot index 1 (the second slot of radio frame) contains no data allocations, so only the RS subcarriers are active, and their magnitude follow the same shape as the RF spectrum in Traces A and B. Trace E (middle right) shows the constellation of the RS subcarriers. The shape of the distortion is simple enough that it can be mapped visually onto the unflatness in Trace B. The lower frequencies start at the lower power nearer the center of the constellation, and then the power rises with nearly constant phase. This rise is followed by a small counterclockwise phase error, which changes direction with the power and then remains nearly constant to the highest frequency. In Trace F (bottom right) the VSA's equalizer has been turned on and the constellation is now corrected to the ideal values, and the RS power and phase response are now normalized. This is seen in Trace C (bottom left), where the RS power is now constant across the channel.

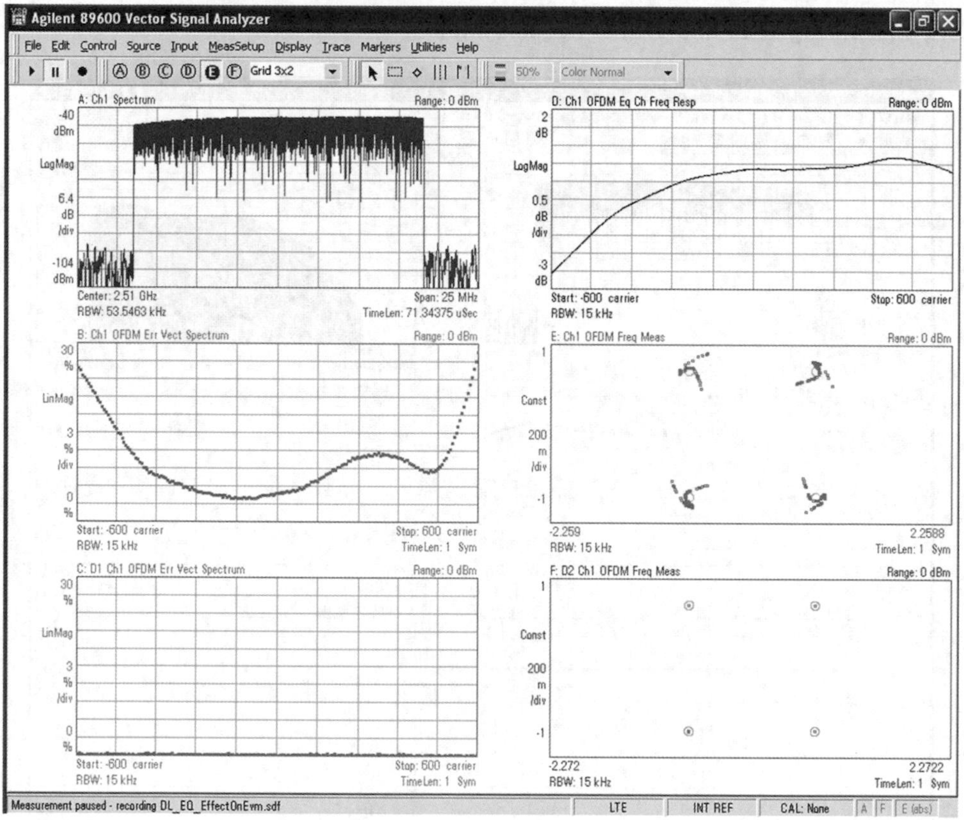

Figure 6.4-12. Impact of the equalizer on EVM

Figure 6.4-12 shows further analysis of the same signal. Trace A (top left) is the same spectrum shown in Figure 6.4-11. Trace D (top right) is the frequency response of the equalizer coefficients. This matches the pattern of the RS power in Trace B of Figure 6.4-11. It would also be possible to display the phase or group delay component of the equalizer coefficients (not shown in this example). Trace E (middle right) shows the same unequalized constellation that appears in Figure 6.4-11. Trace B (middle left) shows the unequalized EVM spectrum. Note how EVM rises at the channel edges and reaches around 27%. Without equalization the EVM spectrum response reflects not only the un-compensated frequency magnitude response of Trace D, but also the corresponding un-compensated phase or group delay distortion component (not shown in this example). This explains why EVM at the channel edges is similar in value even though the amplitude error at the upper frequencies is small. It is the phase error at the higher frequencies that contributes this EVM. The requirements for UE spectral flatness in 36.101 [10] subclause 6.5.2.4 apply only for the amplitude component. This example indicates why phase is just as important as amplitude error.

When the equalizer is applied to the signal, the constellation in Trace F (bottom right) returns to the ideal points and Trace C (bottom left) shows how the equalized EVM spectrum is flat and reduces to nearly zero.

6.4.6.4 Measuring EVM at Different Points in the CP

As discussed in Section 2.1.5.1, the EVM definition requires that measurements be made at two different points in time during the CP. The reasons are discussed extensively in Section 2.1.5.1 and will not be repeated here other than to say that EVM is an important aspect of transmitter design that needs analysis beyond a simple pass-fail result. The 89601A VSA makes EVM measurements at the required positions within the CP and returns the largest result. However, so that LTE designers can investigate how much of the CP has been used up by time domain distortions in the signal, it is possible to modify the default window lengths used to make EVM measurements. Figure 6.4-13 shows some of the flexibility built into the VSA to allow evaluation of EVM at different points in the CP. There are also other parameter selections for turning on and off the equalizer along with various RS pilot tracking options to allow in-depth analysis of the source of errors in the signal.

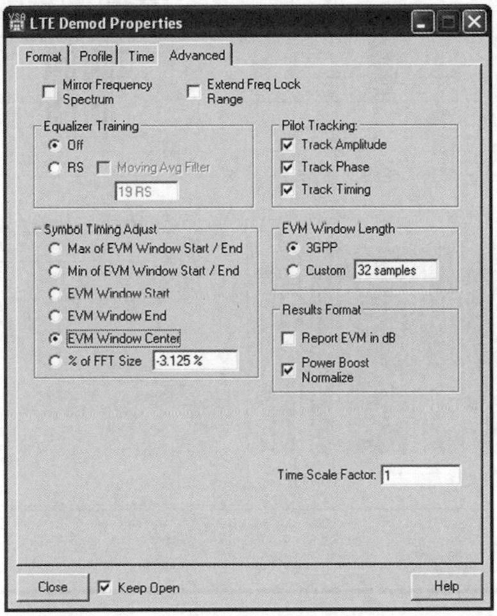

Figure 6.4-13. Advanced demodulation properties

6.4.6.5 Time-based Measurements Across the Radio Frame

An example of three different time-domain views for one frame of a 5 MHz downlink signal is shown in Figure 6.4-14. Trace B (bottom left) shows the detected allocations versus time, and is a demodulated version of the spectrogram shown in Figure 6.4-6. Note that time is now on the X-axis rather than the Y-axis. Figure 6.4-14 can be compared easily to Figure 3.2-8. The regular PDCCH three-slot allocation is evident across the entire channel at the beginning of every subframe, with the RS showing up in between.

Within the first subframe the primary and secondary synchronization signals as well as PBCH can all be clearly seen occupying the central 62 and 72 subcarriers (see Section 3.2.5.1). The remainder of the first subframe allocation consists of a 16QAM PDSCH. This can be identified by the consistent color coding used across the demodulation traces, including the color key within the frame summary Trace D (bottom right). The frame summary also reports that 16QAM PDSCH is the only active data modulation format present in the measured radio frame (10 ms or 140 symbols), occupying a total of 150 allocated RB. From Traces A, B and C we can clearly see that these PDSCH RB allocations occur in subframes 0, 3 and 6 with RB allocations extending across the entire 5 MHz transmission BW. The 16QAM PDSCH is allocated for 6 of the 10 slots during the 10 ms radio frame, with each allocation being the full 25 RB in the frequency domain. This gives a total of 150 RB as reported in the frame summary.

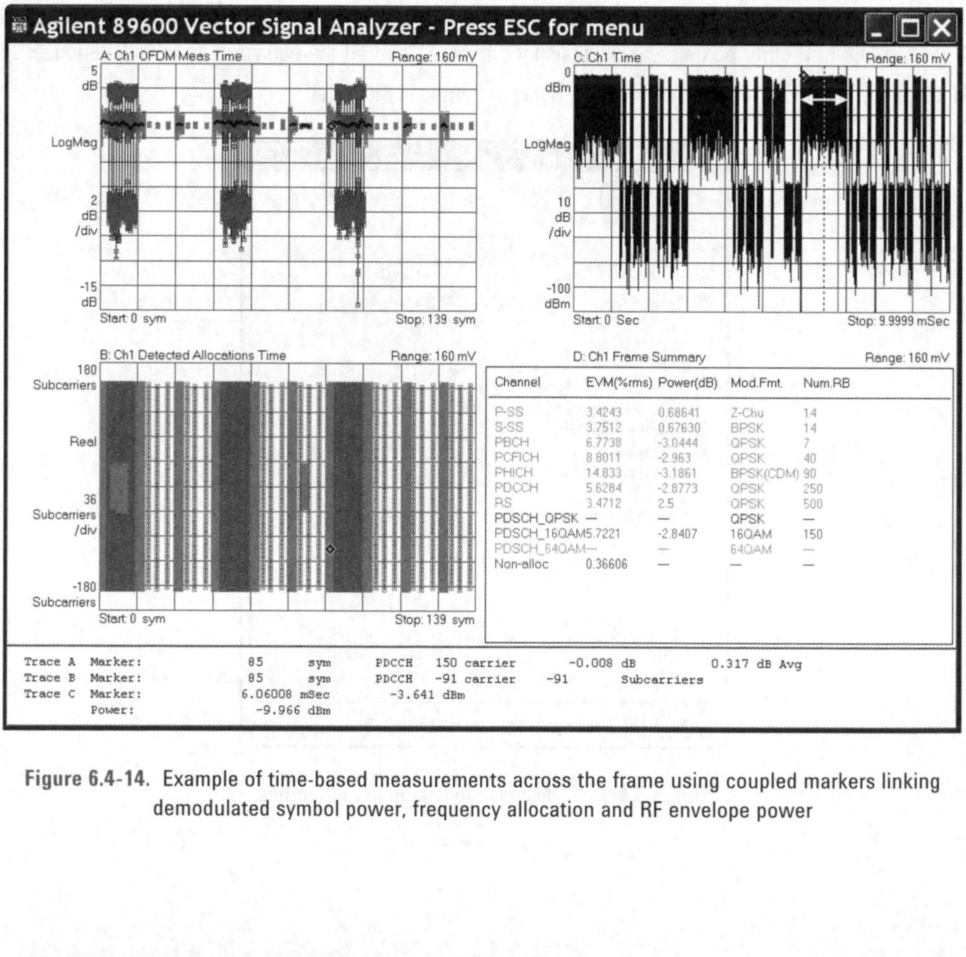

Figure 6.4-14. Example of time-based measurements across the frame using coupled markers linking demodulated symbol power, frequency allocation and RF envelope power

In Trace A (top left) the demodulated IQ subcarrier power is displayed on a Y-axis scale of 2 dB per vertical division, for each of the 140 measured OFDMA time symbols along the X-axis. The first three time symbols show very little variation in power since this is the QPSK of the PDCCH along with some power boosted RS subcarrier activity in the first time symbol. The next eleven symbols represent the 16QAM PDSCH and there is a much larger power spread of around 10 dB. The power is clustered in three horizontal bands, which represent the three different ideal power levels present in a 16QAM signal. Since this is a 301 subcarrier signal, for every symbol in time on the X-axis there will be 301 vertical data points representing the power of every subcarrier. The average of this power for each subcarrier across the measurement interval is shown by the horizontal dark line through the middle. The final observable pattern is the RS, which shows up as a tight burst of power on the first and fourth symbol of each slot. The variation in the RS power is very low since this is the reference used to equalize the signal.

The results in Trace A and Trace B (bottom left) are linked by coupled markers to Trace C (top right), which shows the RF envelope power versus time. A peak search in Trace C identifies the peak power at 6.06 ms, while a band power calculation indicated by the white arrow for 11 symbols centered on the dotted line at 6.6 ms calculates the average power of –10 dBm for that particular PDSCH allocation. This particular signal uses full allocation across the channel so the peak power in Trace C is constant for all allocated symbols. If the allocations had been for less than the whole channel bandwidth, Trace C would have shown appropriate step changes in the peak power.

The detected allocations and symbol power versus time traces can be used to understand the effect of channel loading on power, and to establish appropriate and consistent conditions for the measurement of peak and average power. Without a full understanding of the symbol structure in the frame, the power measurements needed for design and optimization will be inconsistent and potentially misleading.

6.4.6.6 Controlling the Measurement Interval

To view the signal with more precision, measurement offsets and intervals can be set in the time domain. Any time-specific portion of the signal can be isolated for analysis, as shown in the example demodulator setup of Figure 6.4-15.

The terms used to describe the timing control are as follows:

- Result length, which determines the length (in slots) of the acquired IQ time-continuous capture buffer aligned to the start of the user-specified analysis start boundary event.
- Measurement offset, which determines the delay offset (in slots and symbols) from the start of the user specified result length from where the measurement interval processing starts.
- Measurement interval, which determines the measurement interval duration (in slots and symbols) starting from the user specified measurement offset to be used for the measurement analysis.

By definition, the measurement offset plus the measurement interval cannot exceed the result length. The following section uses this ability to isolate a particular part of the signal for more detailed analysis.

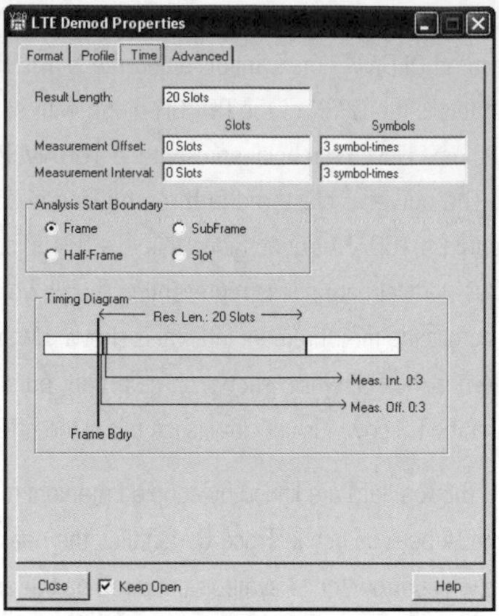

Figure 6.4-15. Configuration of measurement interval and offset within the capture interval (result length)

6.4.6.7 Measuring Power Across the Subframe

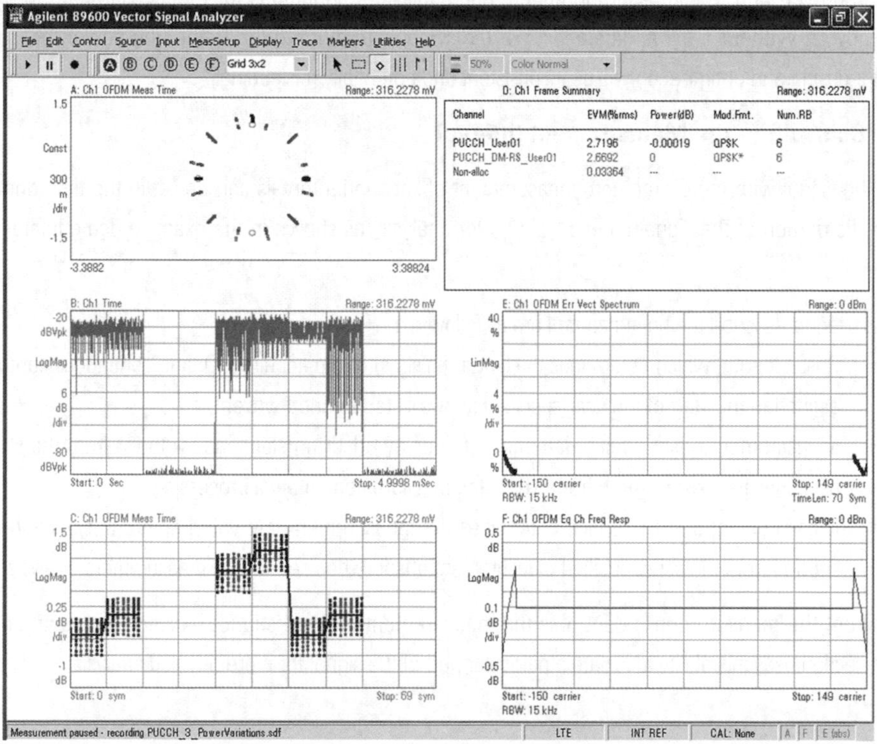

Figure 6.4-16. Hopping PUCCH Format 1b showing amplitude error across the channel

Figure 6.4-16 is a 5 MHz uplink signal with only the PUCCH allocated. The PUCCH format chosen is Format 1b in which the PUCCH is allocated for one RB at the lowest frequency followed by one RB at the highest frequency. See Figures 3.2-12 and 3.2-13. Three different PUCCH subframes (indexes 0, 2 and 3) are allocated with a gap of one subframe. In the time domain this means for the first subframe there is one slot at the lowest RB followed by one slot at the highest RB. The next subframe is empty and then the pattern of the first subframe is repeated twice. Each slot consists of two PUCCH symbols followed by three Demodulation RS (DMRS) symbols followed by two more PUCCH symbols as was shown in Figure 3.2-12.

PUCCH and DMRS structure

Before describing the power dynamics in this example, the constellation in Trace A (top left) containing the PUCCH and DMRS requires explanation. The measurement interval of five subframes contains three active subframes. Each subframe transmits just one PUCCH Format 1b control data useful QPSK symbol. In this example each subframe transmits a different PUCCH useful QPSK symbol value and these are represented by three clusters of dots at the left, top and right of the 45-degree rotated QPSK grid. Each subframe's PUCCH control data useful QPSK symbol value is carried by eight PUCCH symbols: two on either side of the three DMRS symbols in the first slot and the same again in the second slot. Each PUCCH symbol comprises 12 subcarriers, each with a phase offset. The unmodulated base subcarrier phases are calculated from a cyclically shifted base reference sequence with further scrambling and orthogonal spreading. The result is a subcarrier sequence of 12 phase values on a 30 degree raster. The base reference sequence component varies depending on the slot index, and the cyclic shift component varies depending on the symbol index within the slot. One subframe contains eight PUCCH symbols, each with 12 subcarriers, resulting in a basis function of length 96 subcarriers per subframe. The PUCCH control data useful QPSK symbol value is then modulated onto this basis function to determine the actual subcarrier phase to be transmitted per subcarrier.

Rather than display the complexity of the underlying signal structure, the VSA removes the nominal reference rotation introduced by the basis function. As a result all 96 points distributed around the 30 degree raster are de-mapped onto one of the four rotated QPSK points in the grid, revealing the original PUCCH control data useful QPSK symbol value. The purpose of this complex PUCCH coding is (1) to introduce robustness to the PUCCH in the presence of interference and (2) to deal with the fact that the PUCCH RB is a shared resource, and several UEs can be allocated to the same frequency and time. The orthogonal coding included in the basis function allows the eNB receiver to separate out each individual UE.

Should any one of the underlying subcarrier amplitudes or phases contain an error, it would be seen in Trace A as a point lying outside the nominal rotated QPSK grid. Trace A shows clearly that the 96 points, which represent the PUCCH control data useful QPSK symbol values, are tightly clustered, indicating that the signal contains few errors.

The remaining 12 states that do not lie on the rotated QPSK constellation points represent the PUCCH Format 1b DMRS symbol subcarrier magnitude and phase values. The phase values for the DMRS subcarriers are defined using methods similar to those used to generate the basis function used for the PUCCH, the main difference being the use of a different orthogonal sequence. Each slot contains three DMRS symbols, each symbol comprising

12 subcarriers. With two slots per subframe the DMRS are represented in Trace A by 72 data points per subframe. Unlike the PUCCH symbols, the DMRS symbol data points are displayed exactly as they are transmitted without removing the basis function rotation of each subcarrier.

Analyzing the Power Variation Across the Frame

The constellation in Trace A shows amplitude distortion, which creates a starburst effect. This is because both the VSA receiver equalizer and pilot amplitude tracking settings are both disabled, resulting in the observed IQ constellation magnitude variations. These variations are due to an uncompensated 1 dB power boost applied to the middle subframe and a 0.3 dB channel flatness error revealed by the frequency hopping.

Trace B (middle left) shows the unsynchronized power versus time of the signal. Small variations can be seen between the slots, but at 6 dB per division the unflatness is not obvious. Trace C (bottom left) shows the demodulated power versus symbol, which is a much more sensitive measurement than the unsynchronized power versus time in Trace B. This highlights the limitations of general purpose measurements for LTE. In Trace C the six transmitted slots can clearly be identified. Looking first at the average power (solid line) per symbol, four discrete levels can be identified. The first slot is at –0.20 dB and the second slot is about 0.3 dB higher. Then a gap of one subframe occurs, and the next slot is at +0.8 dB followed by another about 0.3 dB higher. The next subframe repeats the first. This measurement is made without any pilot amplitude tracking, so the observed 0.3 dB power steps are due to the uncompensated level unflatness of the transmitted signal when it hops from the lowest RB to the highest RB.

The average power per symbol measurement is also made without any equalization, resulting in a vertical spread of subcarrier power at each symbol. The PUCCH is a single RB so it has 12 subcarrier points per symbol. The magnitude spread is about 0.5 dB peak to peak and can also be seen in Trace A. Note that this 0.5 dB magnitude spread is directly attributable to the un-compensated equalizer frequency response shown in Trace F (bottom right) for both the low frequency and high frequency PUCCH RB. There is equalizer information only for the outer PUCCH RBs since nothing is transmitted anywhere else in the frequency domain. By applying the equalizer to the signal, it is possible to remove almost all the amplitude spreading error.

Trace E (middle right) shows the un-equalized EVM versus subcarrier. Note again that no information is shown except for the outer RB since the rest of the signal is unallocated. The dark line for the lower RB starting at 6% and dropping to 1% represents the lower PUCCH, which gives an average EVM of around 3%. The upper PUCCH has an average EVM closer to 2%. This is summarized in Trace D (top right) in which the PUCCH average EVM is 2.7%. A similar analysis can be done for the DMRS.

6.4.6.8 Measuring Power Across the Symbol

The VSA software can be used to look in even more detail at the signal. Figure 6.4-17 is an analysis of just two adjacent symbols in an SC-FDMA uplink. The first symbol is a PUCCH followed by a PUCCH DMRS. The IQ constellation is shown in Trace A (top left) and follows the same rules explained in detail in Section 6.4.6.7.

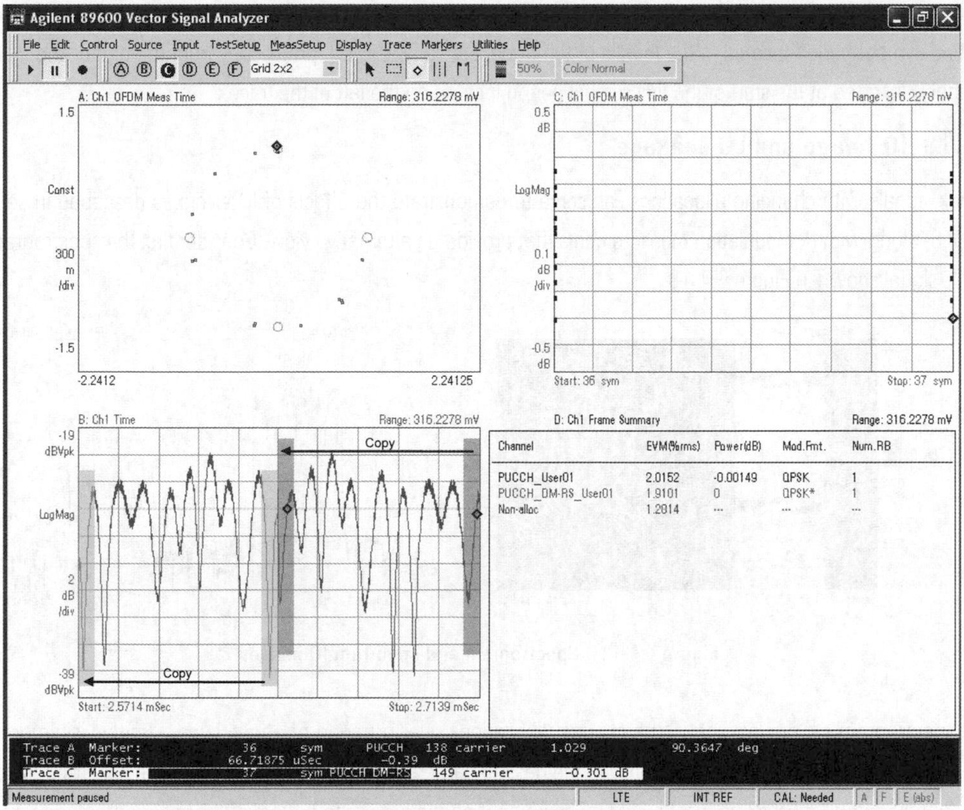

Figure 6.4-17. Analyzing power across the symbol showing the CP

Trace C (top right) plots the amplitude versus time of the constellation points shown in Trace A. The X-axis shows the measurement interval to be two symbols with an offset of 36 symbols, which means only two sets of data will be displayed, representing symbol index 36 and 37 (or the 37th and 38th symbols) within the captured signal. The results on the left of Trace C show the amplitude of the 12 subcarriers that make up symbol index 36, which is a PUCCH symbol. The spread is just over 0.5 dB, so this symbol is well-behaved. On the right hand side are the 12 subcarrier amplitudes that make up the adjacent PUCCH DMRS symbol.

Trace A has an un-coupled marker enabled and placed on one of the symbol index 36 PUCCH control data useful QPSK symbol points. Note that the Trace A marker readout (bottom of screen) clearly identifies the selected symbol point as belonging to the PUCCH. Trace C also has an un-coupled marker enabled and placed on one of the symbol index 37 PUCCH DMRS symbol points. Similarly, the Trace C marker readout (bottom of screen) clearly identifies the selected symbol point as belonging to the PUCCH DMRS.

Trace B (bottom left) is the time domain waveform of the PUCCH and adjacent PUCCH DMRS symbols. The most interesting aspect of this trace is that it shows the CP prepended to each symbol. Note that two time markers have been placed across the tail end of the PUCCH DMRS symbol period. From the Trace B marker readout (bottom of screen), it can be observed that the two time markers are actually separated by the nominal 66.7 μs symbol period. A cyclic prefix copy of the final 4.69 μs of the PUCCH DMRS symbol is inserted at the start of the same second symbol period located in the middle of the trace. Similarly, a cyclic prefix copy from the end of the PUCCH symbol is inserted at the start of the first symbol period located on the left of the trace.

6.4.6.9 IQ Image and LO Leakage

Uplink signals with changing allocations can serve to demonstrate the effects of IQ errors as described in section 6.4.2.8, along with demodulation measurements that provide an alternative view. Consider first the spectrogram of an UL signal shown in Figure 6.4-18.

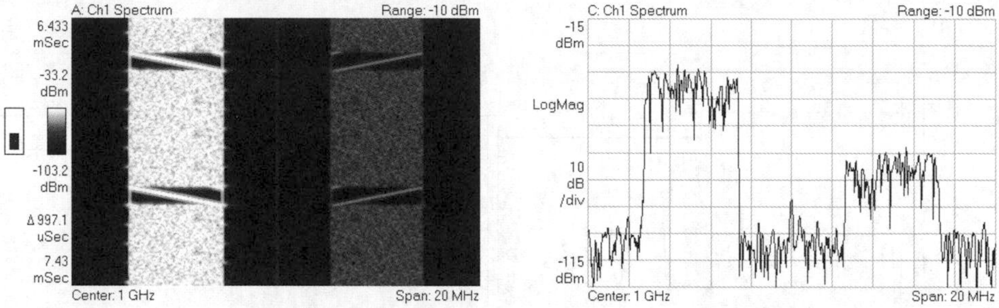

Figure 6.4-18. Spectrogram and spectrum IQ images

The spectrogram on the left shows the channel allocations over a period of about 1 ms. Clearly visible are the mirror images around the center frequency of the desired carriers — the result of IQ errors. The spectrum trace on the right by default reflects the most recent measurement appearing at the bottom of the spectrogram; however, a "trace select" marker from the spectrogram display can be used in the trace on the right for analysis of any single spectrum from the spectrogram buffer. In that spectrum, trace band power markers can be used to compare the power of the allocated carriers and their images.

The spectrogram clearly reveals the symmetrical signal-duplicating effect of IQ distortion about the center frequency without the need for demodulation. These measurements can also indicate the suppression of unwanted subcarrier energy of more than 30 dB for this signal.

A more accurate analysis of IQ image requires demodulation of the signal. Figure 6.4-19 analyzes three adjacent symbol periods from a 5 MHz uplink 16QAM PUSCH. The three symbols chosen for analysis are a PUSCH DMRS symbol in the center of the slot along with a single PUSCH data symbol on either side. In order to demonstrate typical IQ image and LO leakage distortions, the signal was deliberately impaired using the features in the MXG signal generator. To emulate LO leakage a 0.1% IQ offset was added, and to emulate the IQ image a 1 dB IQ gain imbalance was added. Given the richness of the information in Figure 6.4-19, it will be used to provide further explanation of the uplink signal structure prior to explaining how the IQ image and LO leakage measurements are made.

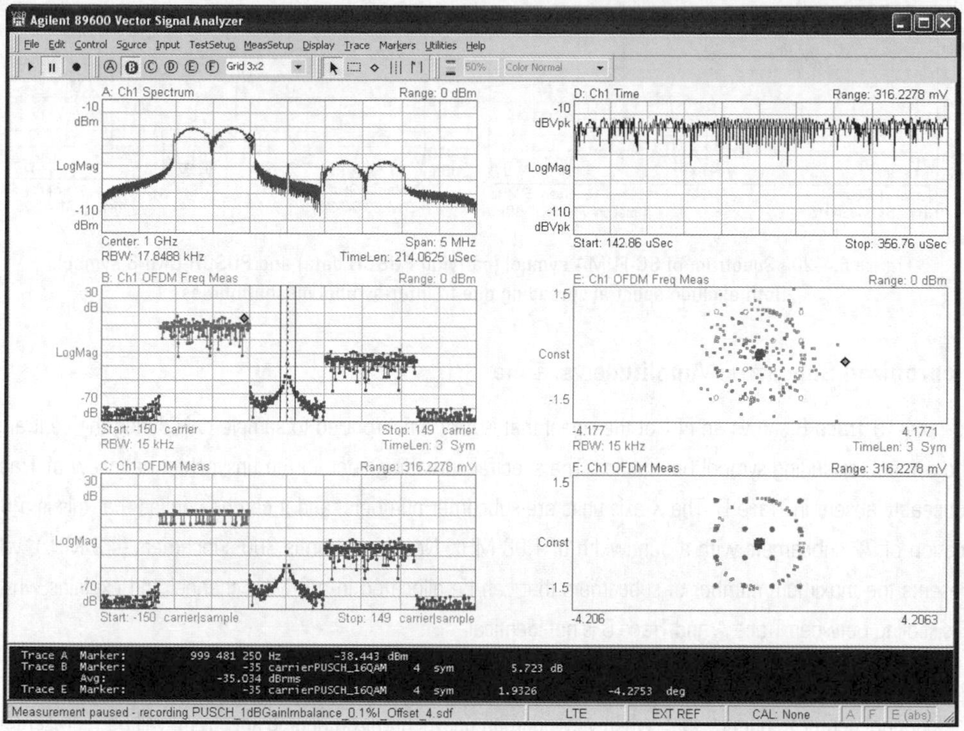

Figure 6.4-19. Example of IQ image and LO leakage distortion on uplink signal

Unsynchronized Frequency Spectrum

Trace A (top left) shows the frequency spectrum of the signal in a 5 MHz span. From this trace the approximate allocation bandwidth of 1 MHz and the presence of an image about 30 dB below the wanted signal can be determined. An LO leakage spike at the channel center frequency can be seen as well. The high level of spectral spreading of the wanted signal almost engulfs the LO leakage spur. This spreading is generated by the discontinuity at the SC-FDMA symbol boundaries and was discussed in Section 6.4.5.3. To see the signal in the same way that an uplink receiver sees it, each symbol, excluding the symbol boundary transients, must be analyzed separately. Figure 6.4-20 shows such an analysis. On the left is the spectrum of one SC-FDMA symbol carrying PUSCH data and on the right is the spectrum of one symbol of DMRS. Since the symbol transitions have been excluded, the LO leakage is no longer partially obscured by the spectral spreading. Note how the spectra are very different and the reversed spectrum of the image is very clear. The distinctive spectrum in Figure 6.4-19 Trace A is the combination of two symbols of SC-FDMA plus one symbol of DMRS.

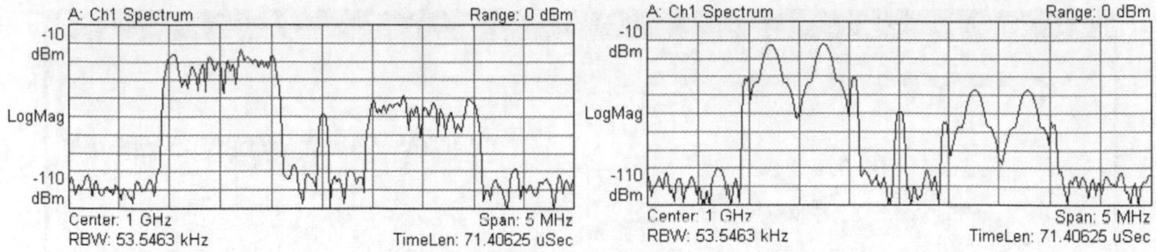

Figure 6.4-20. Spectrum of SC-FDMA symbol (carrying PUSCH data) and PUSCH DMRS symbol. Both exclude spectral spreading due to inter-symbol discontinuities.

Synchronized Subcarrier Amplitude vs. Time

Figure 6.4-19 Trace B shows an FFT of the signal that is fully synchronized to sample only during the central part of the symbol, excluding symbol boundaries. The spectral spreading seen in the unsynchronized view of Trace A is noticeably absent in Trace B. The X-axis units are subcarrier numbers, and it can be verified that this is a 6 RB allocation of 72 subcarriers with a bandwidth of 1.08 MHz. Note the span is 300 subcarriers (4.5 MHz), which represents the maximum number of subcarriers that can be allocated in a 5 MHz channel and explains why the X-axis scaling between Trace A and Trace B is not identical.

Another difference between Trace A and Trace B is the representation of the LO leakage. LO leakage is a CW tone at the channel center frequency that, when viewed in an unsynchronized analog spectrum, will be represented as a single tone with a shape matching the RBW of the analyzer. The CW nature of LO leakage is partially obscured in Figure 6.4-19 Trace A due to the inclusion of symbol discontinuities, but is more evident in Figure 6.4-20.

In contrast, the synchronized FFT spectrum of Figure 6.4-19 Trace B shows the LO leakage energy spread across many subcarriers. The reason is that the raster for the subcarrier frequencies in the uplink is offset by one half subcarrier (7.5 kHz) from the channel center frequency. The spreading seen in Figure 6.4-19 Trace B is an artifact of the FFT process. Any energy falling on a frequency that is not exactly aligned with the FFT bin spacing will result in energy being spread (or leaked) into adjacent bins according to the sin(x)/x function roll off described in Section 2.2.1.

The Y-axis in Figure 6.4-19 Trace B represents the amplitude of each subcarrier in the frequency domain. For each subcarrier in the X-axis there will be as many data points displayed as there are symbols in the chosen measurement interval. In this example three symbols are being analyzed so for the allocated part of the signal there are 72 x 3 = 216 discrete subcarrier data points. Two distinct patterns are visible in the allocated part of the signal. There is a line of constant amplitude data points around 0 dB and another set of what look like noisy data points above and below 0 dB.

Synchronized Subcarrier Constellation (Frequency Domain)

It is easier to see what is going on in Figure 6.4-19 Trace B by looking at Trace D (middle right). This is the same subcarrier amplitude data as Trace B but with phase replacing frequency to form an IQ constellation display.

Each data point represents the amplitude and phase of one subcarrier for the duration of each measured 66.7 µs symbol period. A cluster of points around the unity circle can clearly be seen (magnitude level 1.0 equivalent to 0 dB). This represents the Zadoff-Chu phase modulation of the DMRS subcarriers. On Trace B these subcarriers are represented by the flat line of data points around 0 dB in the allocated part of the signal.

Also represented in Trace D are the amplitude and phase of the unallocated subcarriers. These are at very low levels and form a noisy ball at the center of the display. This energy represents the unwanted LO leakage and image responses. The remainder of the data points in Trace D can be considered random, having no observable pattern. These data points represent the subcarriers carrying the PUSCH data encoded with SC-FDMA modulation. The reason these subcarriers have no regular pattern is explained in the definition of SC-FDMA, given in Section 2.3.1 and specifically in Figure 2.3-1. During the period of each SC-FDMA symbol, there are as many PUSCH data time symbols transmitted as there are subcarriers in the allocation. In this example there are 72 allocated subcarriers.

On the downlink, the mechanism for transmitting 72 PDSCH data symbols within one 66.7 µs OFDMA symbol is to assign each data symbol to its own subcarrier and transmit all data symbols simultaneously, which creates a high PAPR composite signal that is difficult to transmit. However, on the uplink with SC-FDMA the 72 PUSCH data symbols are transmitted sequentially in time using one broadband carrier. In this example each PUSCH data symbol is represented as one point on a 16QAM constellation. Within the period of one 66.7 µs SC-FDMA symbol, a time domain waveform is generated by transitioning from one PUSCH data time symbol to the next. This single carrier waveform, which has a PAPR no worse than 16QAM, is then converted from the time domain to the frequency domain using a Discrete Fourier Transform (DFT) prior to subcarrier allocation mapping.

By sampling at the correct rate this transformation results in 72 DFT subcarrier bins with a spacing of 15 kHz, each with its own amplitude and phase held constant for the duration of the SC-FDMA symbol. The fact that each subcarrier is constant for 66.7 µs explains why it is then possible to insert the 4.69 µs CP on each subcarrier, even though the PUSCH data time symbols encoded by the 72 subcarriers are 72 times shorter in length and are not constant during the SC-FDMA symbol period. By using SC-FDMA modulation, the relationship between the original PUSCH data time symbols and each individual allocated subcarrier is lost. Only when the entire 72 subcarriers are summed in the time domain within the eNB receiver is it possible to recreate the original transmitted PUSCH data time symbol in the 16QAM constellation.

Trace E shows another example of using coupled markers. One of the outlying subcarriers on the right hand side is identified with a marker. By coupling the markers between Trace E and Trace B it is possible to identify which subcarrier this outlying point in the constellation represents in the frequency domain. In this example the outlying subcarrier identified in Trace E is seen in Trace B as being near the high end of the allocation.

It is worth summarizing key points regarding the definition of OFDMA and SC-FDMA. On the downlink, all data, control and reference symbols have a period of 66.7 µs, and a 1:1 relationship to the 66.7 µs OFDMA symbols is allocated to each subcarrier. On the uplink, the same frequency domain modulation and mapping technique is used to generate PUSCH reference symbols and PUCCH control and reference symbols. The SC-FDMA modulation technique is used only on the uplink for the PUSCH data symbol generation process. For an SC-FDMA allocation of M subcarriers, M PUSCH data time symbols are transmitted sequentially during the 66.7 μs SC-FDMA symbol period. The period of a PUSCH data time symbol is therefore 66.7 μs/M. A PUSCH data time symbol is defined by all its M subcarriers that make up the SC-FDMA symbol. An individual subcarrier in an SC-FDMA modulated signal has no meaning.

Time Domain

The amplitude component of the time domain waveform for the three symbol periods is shown in Figure 6.4-19 Trace D (top right). During the first SC-FDMA symbol period the waveform appears random, but in fact it is the amplitude component of a precisely controlled trajectory around the points in a 16QAM constellation representing the PUSCH data time symbols. By simply changing the displayed data from Log Magnitude (LogMag) to phase, a similar trace can be shown for the phase component of the time domain waveform. The phase trace would also appear to be random, but like the amplitude waveform; the phase is also entirely deterministic. The middle symbol representing the DMRS looks much more ordered. The DMRS consists of 72 subcarriers, each with a specified phase following a sequence across the frequency domain.

The time domain waveform for the DMRS has a very distinctive pattern comprising some 36 discrete peaks during the 66.7 μs period leading up to the right hand end of the symbol. There are additional peaks at the start of the symbol, which represent the 4.69 μs of the CP. The 36 peaks are to be expected, because the summation of 72 discrete subcarriers at the same amplitude and different phase creates a 72nd order time domain waveform that has 36 peaks.

The third symbol period is a further example of the SC-FDMA modulated PUSCH, except that the PUSCH data time symbol values and hence the details of the resulting time domain waveform are naturally different from the first symbol.

Full Uplink Digital Demodulation Constellation (Frequency and Time)

The full picture of the signal is most powerfully described in Figure 6.4-19 Trace F. This constellation represents the information content of the signal as observed after the full digital demodulation process has been performed by the uplink receiver. Since the uplink modulation contains both frequency domain (OFDMA) and time domain (SC-FDMA) components, this constellation is also mixed domain containing both frequency and time domain elements. The frequency domain DMRS unity circle in Trace E is repeated in Trace F. The big difference between Trace E and Trace F is the transformation of Trace E's apparently random SC-FDMA subcarriers into the 16QAM time domain constellation of Trace F. The 16QAM constellation is the result of performing an Inverse Discrete Fourier Transform (IDFT) on the PUSCH frequency domain subcarriers to recreate the original 16QAM time domain representation of 144 transmitted PUSCH data time symbols.

A final view of the signal is shown in Figure 6.4-19 Trace C (bottom left). This view is an alternative representation of the same signal in Trace F, but the phase information has been replaced with frequency information. If Trace

B is compared to Trace C, the DMRS information remains unchanged, similar to the unity circle remaining unchanged between Trace E and Trace F. Also note that the non-allocated subcarrier regions including both the IQ image and LO leakage distortion energy impairments remain unchanged. A new thing to note in the Trace C mixed domain results is that the apparently random allocated subcarriers from the Trace B frequency domain are now replaced by a regular pattern of three discrete levels. These levels represent the three discrete magnitude state sets in the 16QAM constellation of Trace F.

Note that the X-axis has now changed from being a "carrier" in Trace B frequency domain to a "carrier¦sample" in Trace C mixed domain. Thus the allocated region 16QAM amplitude data points can be read from left to right as the time domain sequence of the original 72 PUSCH data symbols. By coupling a marker in Trace C to a marker in Trace F, it is possible to scroll from left to right through the individual PUSCH data symbols in Trace C, matching them to their corresponding constellation points in Trace F. A tabulated demodulation display of the signal is available and is discussed in Section 6.4.6.10.

Measuring LO Leakage (Relative Carrier Leakage Power)

The definition of LO leakage is given in Sections 2.1.5.2 and 2.1.5.3 and is based on 36.101 [10] subclause 6.5.2.2. The first reference defines requirements for LO leakage from the perspective of wanted signal quality and the second reference considers IQ impairments including LO leakage in terms of how they impact other users when the allocation does not occupy the full channel bandwidth. Many names are used to describe the LO leakage phenomenon including IQ component, Relative Carrier Leakage Power (RCLP), IQ offset and IQ origin offset. There is also a class of requirements in 36.101 [10] subclause 6.5.2.3 for "in-band emissions" (which are actually in-channel emissions) and these include a "DC component," which is the same thing as LO leakage. To use the formal term, the RCLP requirement for signal power above 0 dBm is –25 dBc. At lower powers the requirement is relaxed as described in Section 2.1.5.2.

The measurement of RCLP is calculated as part of the EVM process according to 36.101 [10] Annex F. The RCLP (IQ offset) error is removed from the signal prior to measuring EVM but the quantity removed must meet the requirement limits for RCLP. If the center of the signal has not been allocated, it is possible to measure RCLP using band power markers. Figure 6.4-21 Traces A and B are used to illustrate such a measurement, with rms band power markers set to encompass both the allocated PUSCH RBs and the unused center RB, respectively. The Trace A rms band power marker result shows that the mean allocated subcarrier power is –0.2 dB, measured over the full 6 RB PUSCH frequency domain allocation. The Trace B rms band power marker result shows that the equivalent mean unused subcarrier power is –34.7 dB, measured over just the center unused RB. From these two results the RCLP (IQ offset) is calculated to be:

$$(-34.7) - (-0.2 + 10\log(6)) = -42.3 \text{ dB}.$$

Note the 10 log(6) total power adjustment factor accounts for the 6 RB PUSCH allocation used in this example.

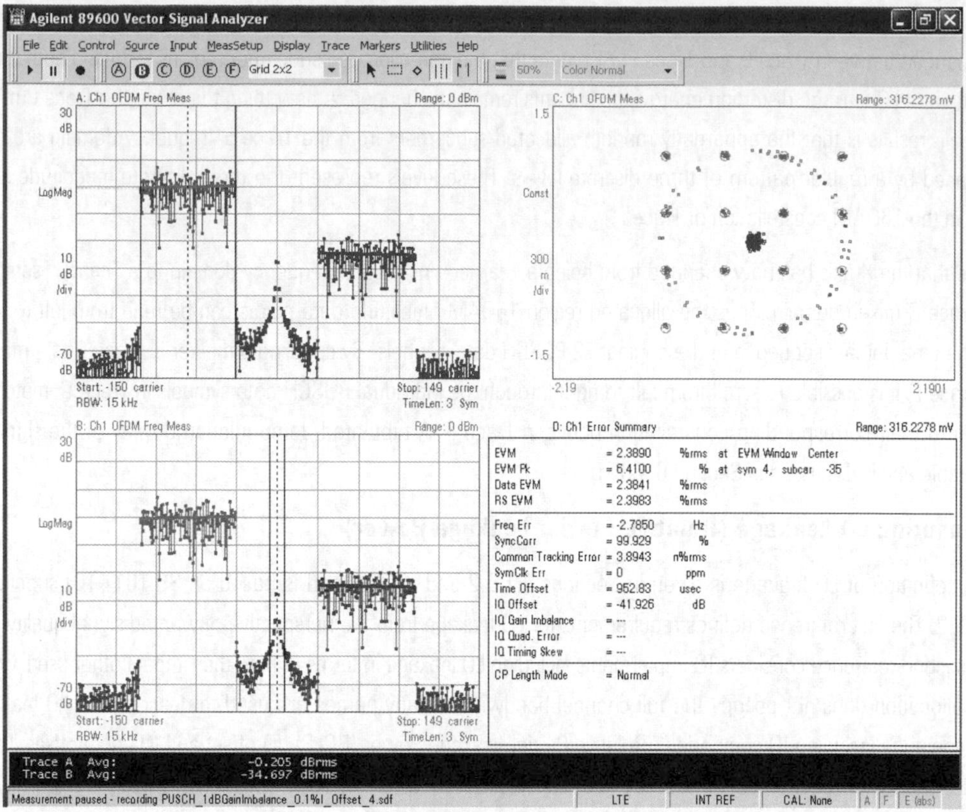

Figure 6.4-21 Example of IQ image and LO leakage distortion on uplink signal

The requirements for RCLP apply to all signal allocations, and if the center of the signal has been allocated, then the only way to measure RCLP is as part of the EVM process. The measured IQ offset is also provided as a result metric in the error summary display in Trace D. As shown the reported IQ offset metric value of –41.9 dB closely matches the RCLP result calculated above using the rms band power marker method.

Measuring In-band Emissions (DC component and IQ Image)

The definition of the DC component for in-band emissions in 36.101 [10] subclause 6.5.2.3 differs slightly from the RCLP definition. The in-band requirements are defined for a partially allocated signal so that the DC component and IQ image falling on unallocated subcarriers can be assessed in terms of their interference with other users. The measurement of in-band emissions is performed directly at the output of the receiver FFT step, prior to any equalization being applied.

The DC component is defined as the power of the RB containing the center frequency divided by the total power of the allocated RBs. If the maximum number of RBs for the channel bandwidth is even rather than odd, then the DC component is measured for the RB on either side of the center frequency, excluding any allocated RB.

The IQ image requirement is –25 dBc and is defined as the power in a non-allocated image RB relative to the average power of all the allocated RBs. In Figure 6.4-21 Trace B, this can be estimated as being near the limit of –25 dBc. This image is due to the 1 dB IQ gain imbalance impairment that was added using the MXG signal generator IQ adjustment feature to emulate real distortion in the UE. The IQ image measured value can be verified more accurately by further use of band power markers.

The 0.1% IQ offset applied to this signal has created an LO leakage 17 dB better than the requirements, while the 1 dB IQ gain imbalance has created an image level that is close to failing the requirements. These results give some indication of the level of IQ impairments that can be tolerated.

For the downlink, the LO leakage is not a problem since there is one subcarrier intentionally left unused. This was not an option for the uplink because the use of SC-FDMA requires a continuous transmission bandwidth and will always incorporate the LO leakage when the allocation exceeds half of the available RB. Given this situation, it was decided to offset the uplink subcarrier raster from the center frequency by a one half subcarrier so that the LO leakage would fall between the subcarriers and be spread out accordingly.

6.4.6.10 Verifying Demodulated Symbol Values

The demodulation measurements discussed in this section have focused on modulation quality results in various forms. Another important demodulation result is the symbol table trace data, which displays the values of the demodulated symbols. The symbol table includes only the user-selected physical signals and physical channels within the specified measurement interval, and thus it can be used to narrow the analysis to as little as a single symbol. For example, synchronization problems can be caused when the RS are incorrectly coded or when the coding (the symbol sequence) is generated according to one version of the standard while the demodulation is performed according to another. In the two symbol tables shown in Figure 6.4-22 the analyzer is set to display only the complex QPSK-like RS symbol values observed on every sixth subcarrier from a single downlink antenna port. A previously stored set of good symbol table trace data (stored in register D1) can be compared to the currently measured data in which the downlink RS sync is not found due to an error.

A: Ch1 OFDM Symbols — Range: 0 dBm — SYNC NOT FOUND

0	00	00	02	01
24	03	03	00	02
48	01	01	03	01
72	00	03	03	02
96	00	01	03	02
120	00	01	03	00
144	01	01	01	02
168	00	03	01	00
192	01	00	03	00
216	01	02	02	01
240	01	03	02	01
264	03	01	02	01
288	02	02		
312				
336				
360				

C: D1 Ch1 OFDM Symbols — Range: -16 dBm

0	00	02	01	00
24	01	02	03	00
48	02	01	03	00
72	02	02	00	02
96	01	03	01	00
120	03	03	03	01
144	00	02	03	02
168	01	03	01	00
192	03	03	03	01
216	00	02	03	02
240	03	01	00	00
264	03	03	03	01
288	00	02		

Figure 6.4-22. Example of RS demodulation

With the VSA set to display only the RS symbol values, the mismatch between the symbol table for the current measurement (left) and a stored measurement (right) indicates a possible cause for synchronization failure and can be used to diagnose the failure's root cause and to fix it.

6.4.6.11 Digital Demodulation Summary

The range of possible digital demodulation measurements is far greater than those described here. More examples and LTE-specific information are provided in references [11], [12], [13] and [14] at the end of this chapter.

6.5 Receiver Design and Measurement Challenges

6.5.1 Introduction

This section focuses on the design issues and challenges associated with testing LTE receivers from RF through baseband. The principles apply to both FDD and TDD access modes although the examples here are FDD. This section takes a systematic approach to testing the various receiver components in order to facilitate testing of the fully assembled receiver.

Open loop receiver testing is discussed first. In this case the DUT does not send feedback information to the source. Open loop testing is sufficient to test the fundamental characteristics of the individual components in the receiver and also is a first step in validating the demodulation algorithms in the baseband section. However, full verification of the overall receiver performance in real world conditions requires closed loop testing through a faded channel, a method that is discussed later in this section. In closed loop testing lost packets are retransmitted using incremental redundancy based on real-time packet acknowledgement feedback from the DUT. The modulation and coding used for transmission are similarly based on real-time feedback from the DUT. This feedback may be optimized for subbands within the overall channel bandwidth to enable frequency-selective scheduling.

A block diagram of a classical receiver, shown in Figure 6.5-1, provides a basis for the discussions in this section. Modern transmitters and receivers utilize the same blocks shown here; however, today there is a higher degree of integration with single components such as RFICs performing multiple functions. The concepts embodied in the classical block diagram still apply although there may be fewer places at which signals can be injected or observed for testing.

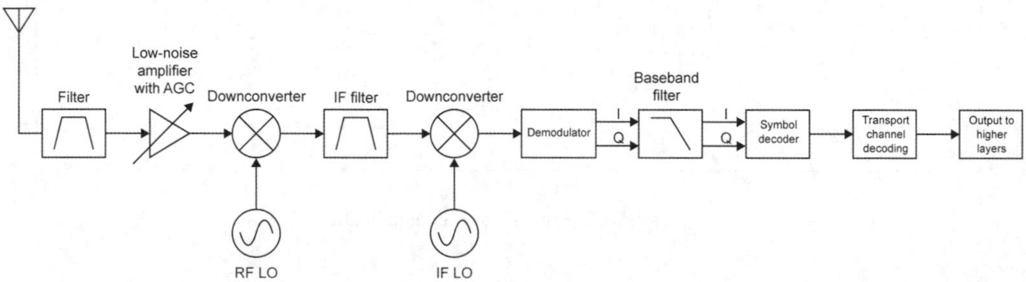

Figure 6.5-1 Classical receiver block diagram

6.5.2 Verifying the RF Receiver

The main objective of receiver testing is to make performance measurements on the entire receiver. However, many factors can influence receiver performance, so the basic receiver sub-blocks are considered first and uncertainty contributions eliminated or quantifiably reduced.

6.5.2.1 Amplitude Flatness

One of the unique aspects of LTE is that it supports six channel bandwidths ranging from 1.4 MHz to 20 MHz. To simplify system operation and roaming, the UE is mandated to support all of these bandwidths, even though actual deployment in any one area may be restricted to fewer bandwidths. The LTE 20 MHz bandwidth is significantly wider than the maximum bandwidths of today's other cellular systems; therefore, special attention to phase and amplitude flatness is required during receiver design. Filters, amplifiers and mixers in particular now have to operate correctly over multiple channel bandwidths. One benefit of the LTE signal structure is that the Reference Signals (RS) are spread in both frequency and time over the entire LTE signal. The UE and eNB receivers can use these signals along with Digital Signal Processing (DSP) techniques to compensate for amplitude and phase linearity errors in the receiver and radio channel. Relying on the receiver to correct these errors based on the RS ultimately comes at the price of degrading the Signal to Interference plus Noise Ratio (SINR), so a well behaved frequency response in the receiver is still important. Channel flatness needs be tested across each supported bandwidth and band, particularly at the band edges where the duplex filter attenuates the edge of the signal.

A simple way to verify receiver flatness is to use a broadband signal at the front of the receiver and measure the response at later stages. An actual LTE signal, such as one of the downlink test models, can be used. Care must be given to the signal configuration, however, because the flexibility of LTE means that the signal may not be fully occupied at the same power level over the entire bandwidth. An example of a simpler test signal is band-limited noise, which most signal generators can create. Averaging several hundred samples in a spectrum analyzer gives a good approximation of the receiver amplitude flatness. Caution is necessary, though, because the results are dependent on the flatness of the signal generator. This flatness varies with frequency and the signal should be checked prior to measuring the DUT. Typical signal generator flatness over 20 MHz is a few tenths of a dB but is better at the narrower LTE bandwidths. A technique for correcting flatness errors in the test equipment is described later in this section.

Another way of verifying receiver flatness is to create a multi-tone signal with a sufficient number of tones spaced over the 20 MHz bandwidth. In the downlink this can be simulated using an LTE signal composed of only the RS; however, since the RS are not present in every symbol, the bursty nature of the signal makes it harder to measure. A good representation of the RF front end frequency response can be made with 20 or 30 Continuous Wave (CW) tones spaced over the LTE bandwidth being tested. More tones can be added to increase the resolution of the test results. There are solutions available today that use a signal generator and spectrum analyzer in conjunction with software to automatically create, measure and correct a user-defined multi-tone signal for testing amplitude flatness and intermodulation distortion products. As already indicated, a signal generator is flat to within a few tenths of a dB over a 20 MHz bandwidth without the use of correction techniques; however, after corrections are applied; the signal generator output will be flat to within a few hundredths of a dB.

Figure 6.5-2 shows a multi-tone test system using a signal generator and spectrum analyzer in conjunction with Agilent Signal Studio for Multitone Distortion software. A benefit of this solution is that any part of the measurement setup included between the signal generator and spectrum analyzer RF path — for example, cables, connectors or amplifiers — can be corrected for both amplitude flatness and intermodulation distortion products. Figure 6.5-3 shows the amplitude flatness of tones spaced over a 100 MHz bandwidth before and after corrections. Although this example uses a bandwidth that is wider than the 20 MHz bandwidth supported for LTE, in the future LTE Advanced will support bandwidths up to 100 MHz, possibly aggregated from more than one band. Note in Figure 6.5-3 that the scale per division in the multi-tone traces is 0.2 dB per division.

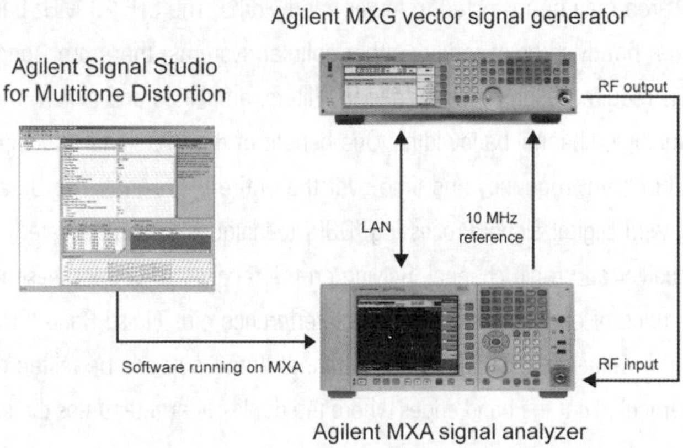

Figure 6.5-2. A calibrated, multi-tone system to measure amplitude flatness and intermodulation distortion

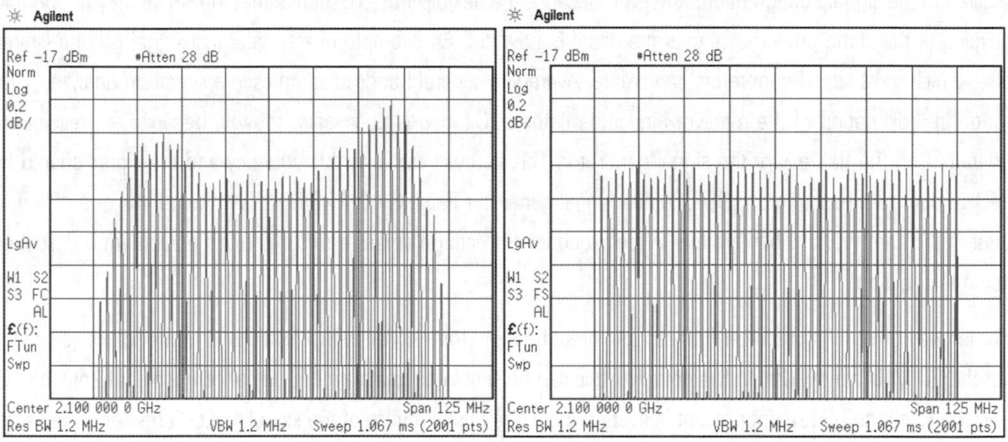

Figure 6.5-3. Amplitude flatness of tones spaced over a 100 MHz bandwidth before and after correction

6.5.2.2 Phase Linearity

The phase linearity of the receiver front end is just as important as the amplitude flatness. The receiver can compensate for phase linearity in the received signal using the RS in a manner similar to that used for correcting the amplitude flatness. Poor phase response results in degraded Error Vector Magnitude (EVM) and lowers the margin of error for determining the correct location on the constellation diagram of a given symbol. The phase linearity of a system cannot be measured directly with a traditional signal generator and spectrum analyzer. A network analyzer can be used if there are directly accessible components in the RF front end; however, this approach may be hard to realize with the high degree of integration in designs today. Another approach is to measure the phase by creating modulated LTE signals and then demodulating them in a vector signal analyzer, which has the added benefit of providing the amplitude response at the same time. How to create, demodulate and analyze these signals is addressed in the following sections.

Trace A (top left) and Trace B (bottom left) in Figure 6.5-4 show amplitude flatness and phase linearity of a 5 MHz downlink LTE signal. The error vector time and error vector spectrum of the signal are shown in Trace C (top middle) and Trace D (bottom middle). Trace E (top right) and Trace F (bottom right) show the constellation diagram and frame summary of the signal as another way to identify and isolate problems.

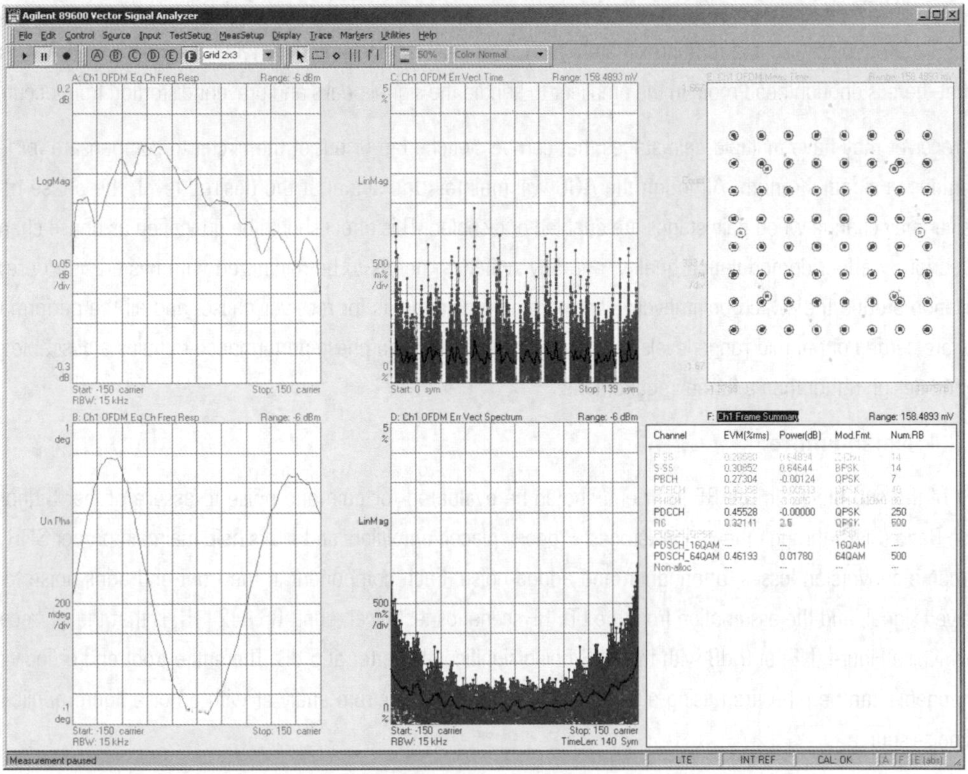

Figure 6.5-4. Amplitude flatness and phase linearity measurements of an LTE signal derived from digital demodulation of reference signals

6.5.2.3 Automatic Gain Control

The receiver's RF front end contains Automatic Gain Control (AGC) circuitry to maintain the proper signal levels at the various receiver stages. AGC is necessary since the operating range for the received signal is around 75 dB. Traditional analog receivers measure the average power level of the received signal and adjust gain blocks and the output of variable gain amplifiers to maintain the signal at a constant level for processing by following stages. The LTE radio system is more sophisticated, making use of the reference signals (rather than the average power) in conjunction with the RF AGC circuitry to set the gain. The task of the UE is limited to receiving transmissions from one eNB at a time; however, the eNB receives signals from multiple UEs arriving at different levels. The eNB therefore has to set the receiver input level for the strongest signal and use a wide dynamic range to capture the weaker signals.

Basic RF AGC operation can be tested with a band limited Additive White Gaussian Noise (AWGN) signal by varying the input over the expected range of amplitudes and then monitoring the output of the AGC for the correct level using a spectrum analyzer. The overall AGC operation is required to be tested with an LTE signal that has been modulated with the reference signals to determine if the baseband processing is providing the correct feedback to the AGC circuitry. Creating modulated LTE signals will be addressed later in this section.

The downlink PAPR is similar to Gaussian noise and can exceed 10 dB at 0.001% probability; however, in the eNB the peaks are typically limited to approximately 7 dB. This must be accounted for when the gain of the AGC is set so that there is enough head room in the amplifier to handle the signal peaks and prevent distortion from occurring.

The receiver may have multiple gain stages that can be switched in or out of the circuit to compensate for large variations in signal strength. Although the AGC will maintain the signal at the desired level, the phase of the receiver may change when gain stages are enabled or disabled. This effect should be quantified as phase changes can seriously affect demodulation quality, and any switching needs to be minimized with hysteresis to prevent oscillation around the switch point levels. There are no requirements for receiver phase, and all the performance tests are carried out at mid-range levels or at reference sensitivity, so phase performance remains a desirable goal of good design rather than a formal requirement.

6.5.2.4 Noise Figure

Each of the sub-blocks in the RF front end should be evaluated for gain and noise to assure proper Signal-to-Noise Ratio (SNR) through the various stages. Properly placed amplifiers and filters help maintain proper SNR and overcome conversion losses, attenuation and added noise. Each component in the front end adds noise to the received signal, and the assumption from the LTE RF scenarios technical report 36.942 [15] is that the UE receiver has a Noise Figure (NF) of 9 dB with the eNB being significantly better at 5 dB. The entire front end or individual components can be measured using a noise figure meter or a spectrum analyzer with a noise figure application and noise source.

6.5.2.5 Receiver Error Vector Magnitude

Error Vector Magnitude (EVM) is a measure of signal impairment normally applied to transmitted signals. However, it is equally useful in verifying receiver performance although no specific EVM requirements are defined in the specifications for receivers. Impairments in the RF front end — such as a non-ideal amplitude and phase response, noise, IQ imbalances, phase noise and compression — can cause the symbols to be in the wrong location relative to the ideal IQ constellation. Such errors become more important with higher-order modulation such as 64QAM, in which the vector distance between symbols is reduced, lowering any margin for error. The margin for error in the receiver is further reduced in real world conditions in which fading and interference are present.

The EVM is a singular metric that provides a gauge of how well a given signal matches the ideal signal and it gives good insight into the ways each component in the system may be distorting the received signal. However, as a singular metric, EVM masks the cause of the errors created by individual components. Therefore, detailed IQ analysis is usually required to locate to root cause. IQ analysis is covered in detail in Section 6.4.1.6. Although there are no requirements in the specifications that call for IQ measurements in receivers, it is still useful from a design and troubleshooting standpoint to understand the characteristics and performance of individual receiver components and also the overall RF front end.

EVM measurements are made by demodulating the signal in a vector signal analyzer, which requires a modulated signal as the stimulus to the input of the receiver or individual component. EVM can be measured with many types of signals; however, a modulated LTE signal should ultimately be used to verify performance. For a discussion on digital demodulation see Section 6.4.6. A useful source of standard downlink test signals (test models) is found in the eNB conformance test specification 36.141 [16]. These may be of some use for testing the UE receiver, but it should be noted that the purpose of these signals is to test the eNB transmitter performance, and these signals do not directly represent configurations that are used for the UE receiver tests, which are based on closed loop reference measurement channels. Test signals are discussed further in Section 6.5.4.

6.5.3 Verifying the Baseband Receiver

6.5.3.1 Analog-to-Digital Converter (ADC)

Traditionally, the analog signal from the RF section can be demodulated into the I and Q components using analog techniques, normally with an IQ demodulator. However, in an age of software-defined radios, the downconverted IF signal is usually digitized by an ADC and then fed to the baseband section for demodulation and decoding. It is possible to test the baseband receiver independent of the RF section by generating an appropriate IF signal. An IF signal can be created easily by simply setting the signal generator output frequency to the desired IF frequency.

Measuring the output of the ADC poses a challenge because the output is now in the digital domain while standard spectrum analyzers make measurements on analog signals. One solution is to analyze the digital bits from the ADC directly, and a logic analyzer is a natural choice for capturing this digital data. The difficult part of this solution is processing the captured data into a meaningful result since most logic analyzer applications are not focused on generating RF metrics. Using the Agilent 89601A Vector Signal Analysis software is one way to solve this challenge. The VSA software is commonly run in Agilent spectrum analyzers for demodulating various modulation formats; however, it can be run in the logic analyzer, too. The software offers a unique way to analyze the ADC performance by being able to make traditional RF measurements directly on digital data. This approach gives a designer the ability to quantify the ADC contribution to the overall system performance and compare it to RF measurements made earlier in the block diagram using the same measurement algorithms.

The output of the ADC may be converted to a high speed serial interface such as Common Public Radio Interface (CPRI) in the eNB or DigRF in the UE. In some cases the topology of the receiver may allow access to the digital data only via one of these industry standard buses, complicating the data analysis process. However, industry standard solutions are available that accept these high speed serial data streams. For example, Agilent offers a DigRF analyzer that can either analyze the digital data (as a logic analyzer would) or pass the data to the 89601A Vector Signal Analysis software, enabling vector measurement of the demodulated data. Refer to Section 6.3 for a more detailed discussion of DigRF.

6.5.3.2 Baseband Demodulation

The digitized signals from the ADC are transferred to the baseband section where FPGAs or ASICs perform signal demodulation. Up to this point the measurements have been relatively straightforward because test equipment has been used for both the generation and analysis of the LTE signals. Now the receiver in either the eNB or UE must demodulate the signal and indicate the result.

One challenge associated with testing the baseband section of the receiver is how to physically deliver the test signals to the DUT. Depending on where the receiver is in the development cycle, the test signal could be injected into the receiver as an RF, IF, analog IQ or digital IQ signal in the baseband section. Most signal generators can create signals directly for testing each of the different sections of a receiver. The digital outputs of signal generators are generally raw I and Q samples with highly configurable physical characteristics including logic type, numeric format, number of bits, bit order, sample rate and clock options. However, most baseband LTE radio designs are expected to use a dedicated industry-standard digital interface such as CPRI in the eNB or DigRF in the UE. As noted above, solutions are available today for analyzing these industry-standard buses as well as stimulating them. See Section 6.3 for more details. The rest of this section focuses on different test signals and how they can be used and assumes that the signal is physically delivered to the receiver in the appropriate format.

Signal generators can provide timing signals or accept trigger signals to facilitate synchronizing to either the UE or eNB receivers. To facilitate synchronization, information about the LTE signal being generated can be preprogrammed into the DUT; for example, when a UE is tested, the UE can be forced via preprogramming to use the physical layer cell ID group and sector generated by the signal generator. It may be helpful to configure a vector signal analyzer to demodulate the same signal that the receiver is configured to demodulate. The demodulation and decoding algorithms in the baseband section can be verified with physical layer coded LTE signals, which can be easily configured using a signal generator with an application such as Agilent Signal Studio for 3GPP LTE. The RBs configured at the channel and band edges are of particular interest because band and channel filters are likely to distort and attenuate part of the signal.

Although test signals are easily measured and interpreted using a vector signal analyzer with its multiple displays, the interface to a real LTE receiver is likely to be a simple terminal interface with proprietary commands and results. Thus a useful feature of a receiver is the ability to write the demodulated data from each channel to a file for post analysis to ensure that the received bits match the transmitted bits. The payload data in Signal Studio can be set to be a pseudorandom sequence, a regular pattern or a user-defined file.

Basic demodulation is verified at the subframe level. Once this step is complete, the next step is to check the transport channel decoding. The specifications define Fixed Reference Channels (FRCs) that are used as reference configurations for defining receiver requirements. These signals are a good starting point for initial verification of the transport channel decoding algorithms. An example using Signal Studio of an uplink FRC for testing an eNB is shown in Figure 6.5-5.

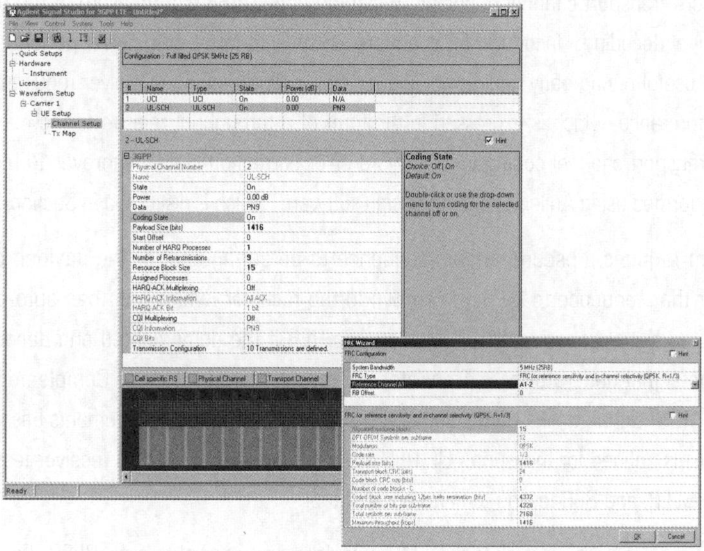

Figure 6.5-5. Example from Agilent Signal Studio of a QPSK R=1/3 uplink FRC used for making eNB sensitivity and in-channel selectivity measurements

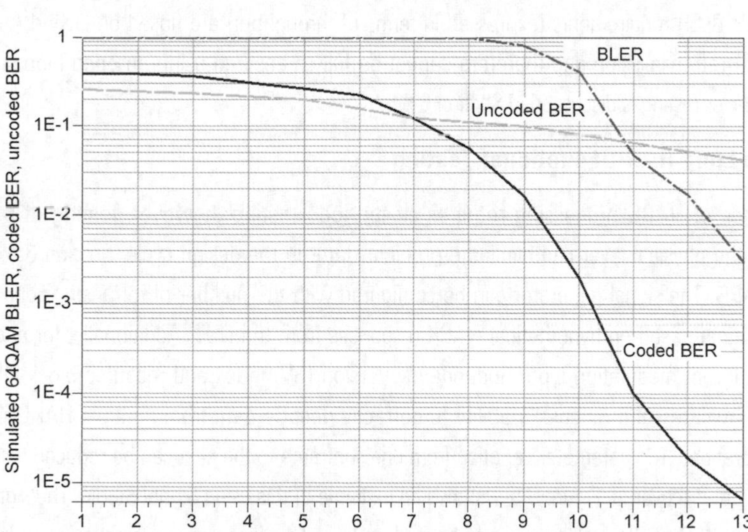

Figure 6.5-6. Simulation of UE receiver performance for 64QAM PDSCH showing the relationships between uncoded BER, coded BER and BLER

Once the receiver has been verified and is correctly demodulating and decoding the signal, Bit Error Ratio (BER) and Block Error Ratio (BLER) measurements can be performed. Figure 6.5-6 shows a simulation of UE receiver demodulation performance for a 64QAM Downlink Shared Channel (DL-SCH) as a function of E_b/N_0, which is the energy per bit divided by the noise power spectral density. This gives a general idea of the relationships between uncoded BER, transport channel coded BER and BLER. The uncoded BER is a measure of the bit error ratio at the physical layer before transport channel decoding, while the coded BER is a measure of the bit error ratio after the transport channel decoding. Uncoded BER is a more sensitive measure of receiver performance than BLER or coded BER and is useful during early phases of receiver characterization. The receiver requirements use BLER as the metric for performance, which is expressed in the form of a throughput relative to the maximum throughput of the FRC. The transport channel coding with forward error correction clearly improves BER performance. The simulation was performed using Agilent's system design software, which is discussed in Section 6.2.

BER measurement requires a pseudorandom sequence to be configured for the payload data in the signal generator and for that sequence to be made known to the receiver, which can then auto-correlate to it and calculate BER. Some signal generators can calculate the BER if the demodulated and decoded signal can be routed back to the signal generator as a Transistor to Transistor Logic (TTL) or Complementary Metal Oxide Semiconductor (CMOS) signal. Unlike UMTS and earlier systems, LTE has no requirements based on BER, and the loopback mechanisms defined for measuring UE BER are not supported in LTE. All receiver tests for both UE and eNB are based on BLER, and BER testing remains an R&D tool.

The eNB conformance tests require that the eNB calculate and report its own BLER. For the UE this is an option for proprietary testing but the conformance tests calculate BLER independent of the device by counting Acknowledgement (ACK) and Negative Acknowledgement (NACK) reports transmitted by the UE on the uplink. The UE and eNB BLER requirements (expressed in terms of throughput) are based on Hybrid Automatic Repeat Request (HARQ) retransmission and therefore cannot be fully measured using an open loop signal generator. Closed loop receiver testing is discussed in Section 6.5.5.

6.5.3.3 Open Loop HARQ Functional Testing

The performance of HARQ processing requires closed loop testing; however, testing of basic open loop functionality at the physical layer can eliminate problems later in the design cycle. Section 3.4.1 discusses the definition of HARQ. The signal generator can be configured with the number of retransmissions that is required to generate a signal based on hypothetical NACK responses from the DUT. Additionally, for each of the HARQ processes, a different modulation type, Redundancy Version (RV) index and resource block allocation can be configured. This will test the receiver's ability to correctly decode data from multiple HARQ processes using different configurations. The parameter variation from one subframe to the next can be reduced for troubleshooting when problems are discovered. Figure 6.5-7 shows an example of this using Signal Studio. The signal is configured to transmit a single DL-SCH with transport channel coding. The first transmission is in subframe 0 and the retransmission is in subframe 8 with different coding due to a simulated NACK response from the DUT.

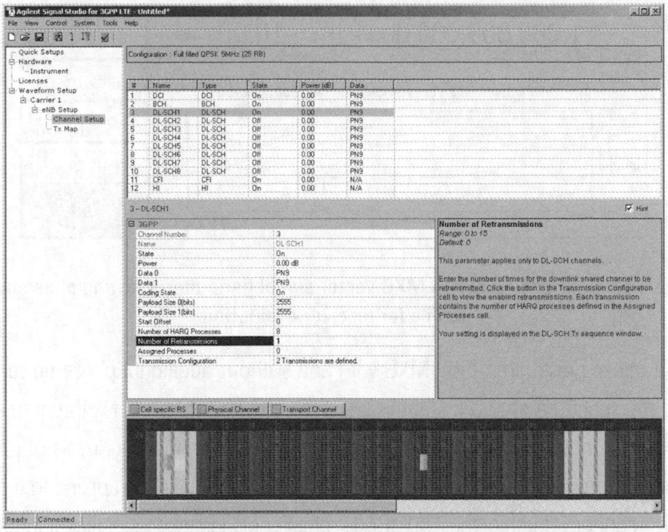

Figure 6.5-7. Example from Agilent Signal Studio showing the original transmission (subframe 0) and the retransmission (subframe 8) in response to a simulated NACK response from the DUT

6.5.4 Receiver Performance Under Impaired Conditions

The receiver test discussions up to this point have focused on verifying and testing receiver performance using highly accurate reference signals created by a signal generator. However, it is essential to be able to degrade these near-perfect signals in a known and controlled way to gain additional insight into the characteristics of the receiver after it has been shown to work with the unimpaired signals.

6.5.4.1 Phase Noise Impairments

The first impairment that will be examined is phase noise, and it can be used to investigate several receiver performance factors. LTE uses OFDMA and SC-FDMA modulation schemes based on either 7.5 kHz (eNB only) or 15 kHz subcarrier spacing. This makes receiver demodulation performance very sensitive to phase noise impairments. A signal generator can be used as a substitute for the Local Oscillator (LO) in the receiver to investigate demodulation performance. The default phase noise of a signal generator typically is much better than that of the DUT receiver; however, by degrading the phase noise, the performance of the receiver can be evaluated over a range of different operating conditions. This ability to emulate different phase noise levels is useful in determining the optimum LO phase noise requirements for a given receiver design. Figure 6.5-8 shows a screen image of the Agilent N5182A MXG vector signal generator with adjustable phase noise capability. The start and stop frequencies of the "pedestal" region can be set along with the level of the pedestal itself.

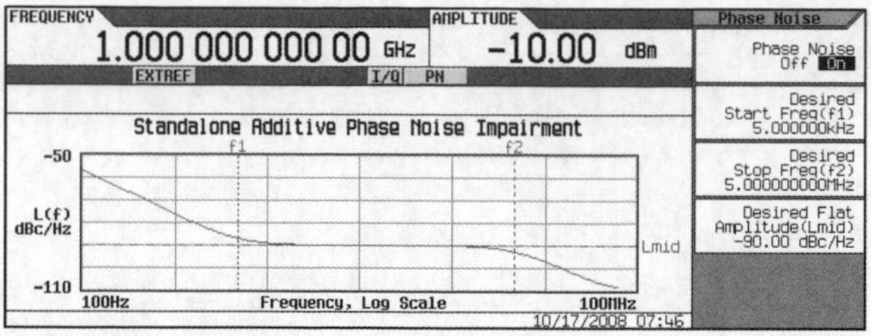

Figure 6.5-8. Agilent N5182A MXG vector signal generator showing phase noise profile for receiver evaluation

Figure 6.5-9 shows a phase noise plot of the MXG with and without additional phase noise added to the signal. Figure 6.5-10 shows the spectrum of two CW tones separated by 15 kHz, which is the normal subcarrier spacing (7.5 kHz is used only in the downlink for broadcast applications). Notice the two levels of phase noise when the pedestal region is varied from –125 dBc/Hz to –90 dBc/Hz. When modulation is applied to the subcarriers and the energy spreads in the frequency domain, the –90 dBc/Hz phase noise leads to significant inter-carrier interference. Phase noise can also be added directly to the signal that the receiver is trying to demodulate. This tests the ability of the receiver to demodulate signals from a transmitter in which the bulk of the EVM budget is represented by phase noise, an impairment more likely in the UE transmitter than eNB transmitter. Figure 6.5-11 shows the EVM performance of a downlink signal with phase noise at –90 dBc/Hz in the pedestal region. Note that the EVM performance has degraded from less than 0.5% to more than 6%. The upper figure is close to the entire 64QAM EVM requirement, which indicates that the –90 dBc/Hz phase noise level is above what can be used for this modulation depth.

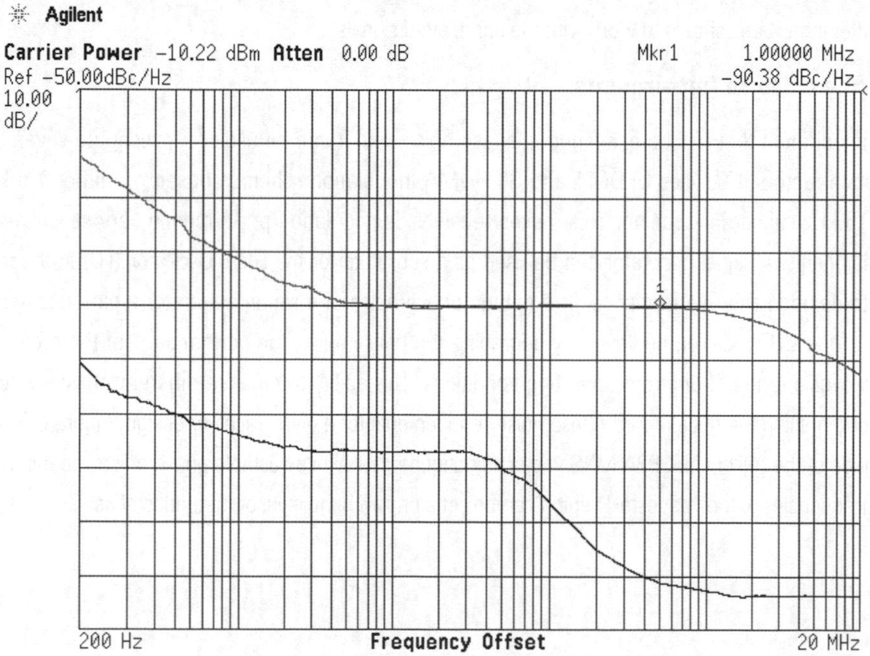

Figure 6.5-9. Agilent MXG phase noise with and without phase noise impairment

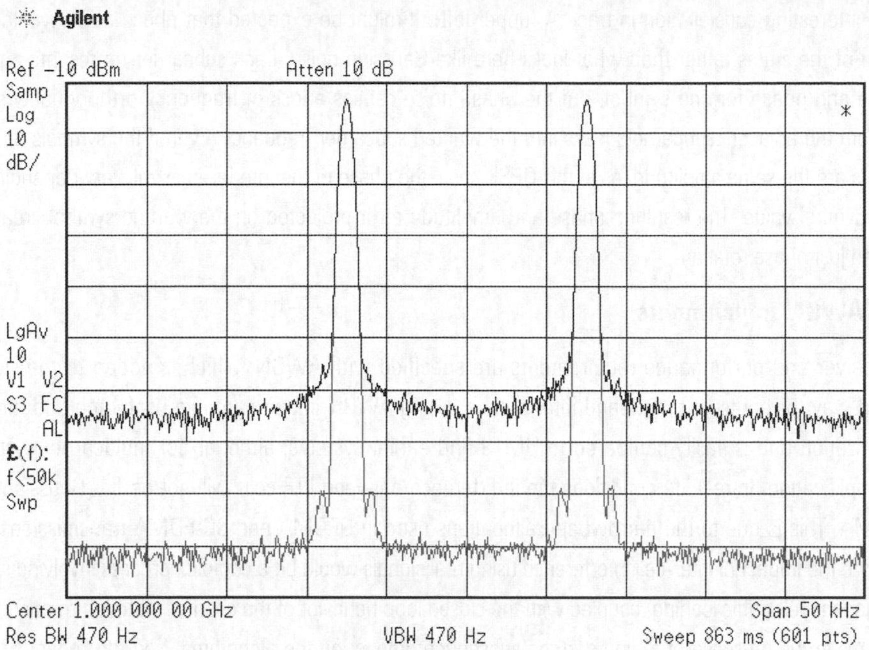

Figure 6.5-10. MXG with two tones spaced at 15 kHz with/without the phase noise impairment

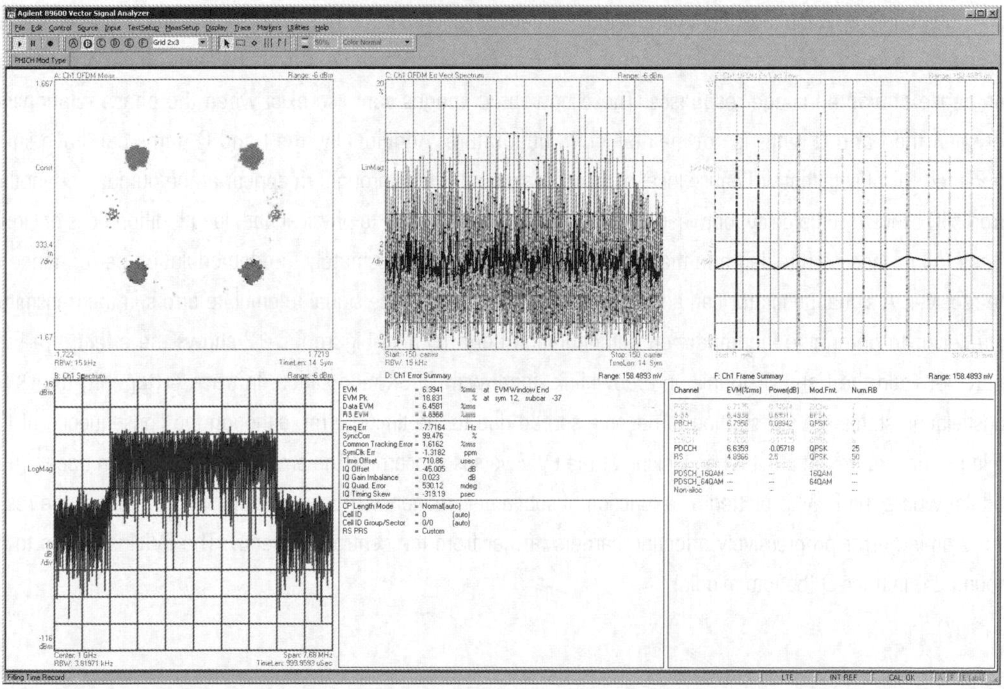

Figure 6.5-11. Modulation analysis of the MXG with phase noise at –90 dBc/Hz showing EVM performance around 6%

Note the interesting constellation in trace A (upper left). It might be expected that phase noise would produce a rotation of the states rather than what looks here like Gaussian noise. Each subcarrier represents a particular amplitude and phase for one symbol, but the phase noise causes a loss of frequency orthogonality such that energy from the adjacent subcarriers leaks into the wanted subcarrier frequency. Even if the symbols on adjacent subcarriers are the same amplitude, as in this QPSK case, the phase of the interference will vary depending on the adjacent symbol value. The resulting phase and amplitude error projected on the wanted symbol creates noise rather than just phase rotation.

6.5.4.2 AWGN Impairments

Most receiver and performance requirements are specified with AWGN, which is added to the signal in a controlled way to represent broadband interference. Using AWGN impairment is a useful method for receiver characterization and is easily compared to UMTS and earlier systems, although for multicarrier systems it is also a simplification. In real life conditions the interference between LTE cells will not be flat Gaussian noise as with CDMA. This is due to the narrowband allocations used in OFDMA and SC-FDMA transmissions. To fully characterize the impact of inter-cell interference using real signals would be a complex process involving simulation of the adjacent cell traffic loading, coupled with the closed loop behavior of the channel state information feedback mechanisms in the presence of fading and the subsequent impact on the algorithms used for frequency selective scheduling and power control.

6.5.4.3 IQ Impairments

An IQ demodulator is the most common method of demodulating data from the RF carrier. The demodulator can introduce a number of errors that the baseband will have to compensate for. Gain imbalances in the demodulator can cause unwanted image responses. These unwanted images can also exist when the phase relationship between the I and Q paths is not maintained in quadrature. Additionally, the I and Q paths can have small unwanted DC offsets that will cause local oscillator leakage (LO feedthrough) to appear at the output. Yet another error is IQ skew, or time delay, between the I and Q signals that is due to physical path length differences of circuit traces. All of these errors degrade the received signal quality and ultimately the demodulation performance of the receiver. A signal generator can add calibrated IQ distortions to the signal to emulate errors in the transmitter or receiver to determine the impact on demodulation performance. Figure 6.5-12 shows the effect of a 5 ns delay between the I and Q signals on a downlink signal with QPSK modulation. In trace A (top left) the QPSK constellation states are just starting to become spread due to the timing error, although the consequence of the timing error is more apparent when looking at the EVM versus subcarrier. The error is more evident in trace C (top middle) where the EVM is plotted as a function of subcarrier frequency. This characteristic "V" shape is the result of the timing error progressively affecting carriers farther from the central frequency. The EVM is shown to be around 2% in trace D (bottom middle).

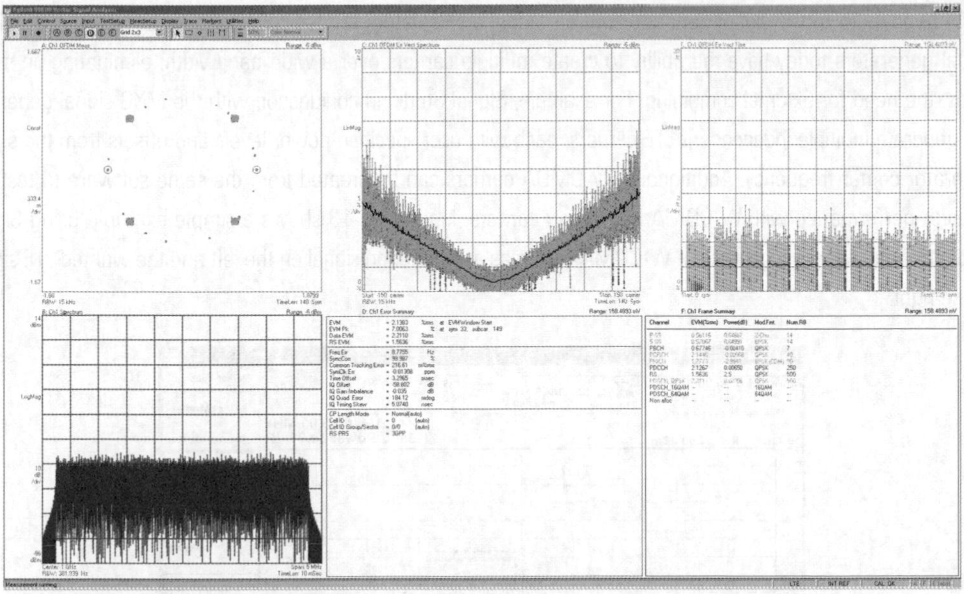

Figure 6.5-12. Modulation accuracy using 89601 VSA software for a 5 MHz downlink signal with 5 ns of timing skew between the I and Q paths

6.5.4.4 Interfering Signals

Interfering signals are required for testing the selectivity, blocking characteristics and intermodulation immunity of the receiver. These tests are important to determine the ability of a receiver to correctly demodulate the wanted signal in the presence of interfering signals in an adjacent channel or from another band. The receiver performance under these conditions needs to be verified because, for example, a UE handset will often communicate with a distant eNB in the presence of some nearby interfering transmitter.

The selectivity tests are performed by demodulating the wanted LTE signal in the presence of an interfering LTE signal on the adjacent channel. The configuration of the wanted and interfering signals is defined in the conformance test specifications and is complicated by the combination of different channel bandwidths.

The blocking tests are performed by demodulating the wanted LTE signal in the presence of an interfering LTE signal for in-band blocking or a CW signal for out-of-band blocking tests.

The intermodulation immunity tests are performed by demodulating the wanted signal in the presence of an interfering LTE signal and CW carriers. This procedure tests how the distortion products generated by non-linear elements in the receiver — for example, a mixer — can influence the system performance. The Third Order Intercept (TOI) of the analog stages should be checked if there are any issues with this test.

Traditionally, tests with interfering signals have been performed using multiple signal generators and power combiners for the wanted and interfering signals. However, when power combiners are used, the signal generators can intermodulate with each other if the generated signals are within the Automatic Loop Control

(ALC) bandwidth of the signal generator output amplifiers. Isolators are typically used to prevent this problem. Signal generators today have the ability to create multiple carriers over a wide bandwidth, eliminating, in many cases, the need for external combining. For example, Signal Studio in conjunction with the MXG signal generator can generate multiple independent LTE carriers, each with user specified power levels and offsets from the signal generator center frequency. Additionally, W-CMDA carriers can be created from the same software to test the receiver performance with W-CDMA interfering carriers. Figure 6.5-13 shows a simple example using Signal Studio to simultaneously generate a W-CDMA carrier as an interfering signal on the left and the wanted LTE signal on the right.

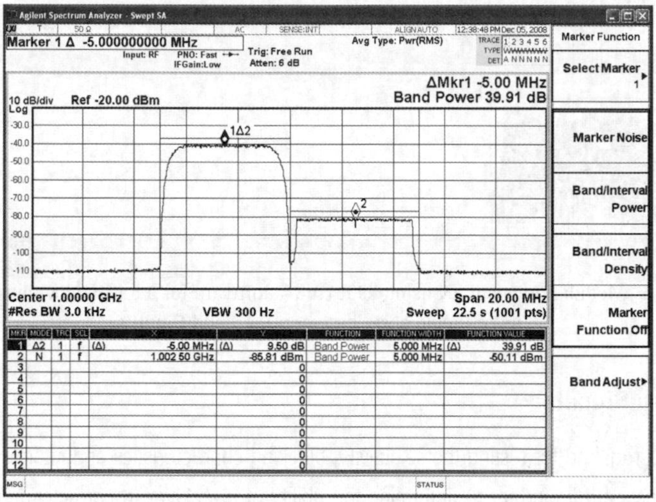

Figure 6.5-13. Example multicarrier signal from one MXG showing a W-CDMA carrier on the left and a LTE carrier on the right

6.5.4.5 Receiver Testing With Channel Propagation Impairments

Up to this point the distortions affecting receiver performance have been within the receiver itself or the result of interfering signals. In any real mobile radio environment, the dominant distortion mechanism that the receiver has to deal with is distortion of the wanted signal resulting from impairments in the radio channel propagation conditions. These distortions, commonly known by the more generic term fading, are the result of changing reflections and frequency shifts caused by fluctuations in the distance between the transmitter and receiver. The radio specifications define specific propagation conditions for use in the receiver performance tests, the general concepts of which are briefly introduced here.

In free space, objects in the environment such as mountains, buildings and vehicles can reflect, refract and block transmitted signals. These objects can be at different locations from the receiver with some objects close and some far away. As a result of this variation in distances, a large number of time delayed copies of the transmitted signal can arrive at the receiver antenna. These time delayed copies of the signal have different phase relationships that cause both constructive and destructive addition at the receiver.

Small variations in the phase relationships occur due to the movement of objects in the environment, such as pedestrians and vehicles. If the UE is moving, then the phase variations can be larger with the rate of change being a function of the UE speed. Empirical data shows that the received signal level fluctuates up and down; occasionally dropping to very low levels caused when there is nearly complete signal cancellation. Another effect of a moving transmitter or receiver is that the signal can undergo a Doppler (frequency) shift. Since the time delayed copies of the signal arrive from different directions relative to the direction of motion, some of the signals are shifted to higher frequencies and some are shifted to lower frequencies. This causes particular difficulty in OFDM systems since simple frequency shifting cannot be used to remove the inter-subcarrier interference.

As the number of paths increases, the superposition of multiple copies of the transmitted signal at different amplitudes, timings, frequencies and phases results in a stochastic (non-deterministic) signal that follows a Rayleigh distribution. This distribution is known to accurately represent the amplitude fluctuations and frequency variations (also known as Doppler spreading) typical in urban environments. This type of multipath propagation condition is used in specifying receiver performance requirements. For the LTE UE, propagation conditions are specified in 36.101 [10] Annex B, and a similar set of conditions is specified for the eNB in 36.104 [17] Annex B.9. Propagation conditions are made up of three components: a multipath delay profile, a Doppler spread and, for multi-antenna requirements, a set of correlation matrices defining the correlation between the transmitting and receiving antennas. An example of a delay profile for a typical pedestrian environment is given in Table 6.5-1.

Table 6.5-1. Extended Pedestrian A model (EPA) (36.101 [10] Table B.2.1-2)

Excess tap delay [ns]	Relative power [dB]
0	0.0
30	–1.0
70	–2.0
90	–3.0
110	–8.0
190	–17.2
410	–20.8

For LTE there are a total of three delay profiles defined: the one for pedestrian use defined in Table 6.5-1, one for vehicular use and a third for typical urban use. In addition to the delay profile — which defines the number of taps, the delay and the attenuation — the delay profile is further defined by a root mean square (rms) delay spread. The three delay profiles are shown in Table 6.5-2.

Table 6.5-2. Delay profiles for E-UTRA channel models (36.101 [10] Table B.2.1-1)

Model	Number of channel taps	Delay spread (rms)	Maximum excess tap delay (span)
Extended Pedestrian A (EPA)	7	45 ns	410 ns
Extended Vehicular A model (EVA)	9	357 ns	2510 ns
Extended Typical Urban model (ETU)	9	991 ns	5000 ns

With the delay profile defined, it is necessary to specify the maximum Doppler frequency shift also. Three different values are used, representing low, medium and high frequencies of 5 Hz, 70 Hz and 300 Hz, respectively. At 2 GHz these frequencies translate to UE velocities of 2.7 km/h, 37.8 km/h and 162 km/h. These Doppler frequencies are combined with the delay profiles to produce the combinations used for defining the performance requirements. Although there are three delay profiles and three Doppler frequencies, only five of the possible nine combinations are used. These are shown in Table 6.5-3.

Table 6.5-3. Channel model parameters (36.101 [10] Table B.2.2-1)

Model	Maximum Doppler frequency
EPA 5 Hz	5 Hz
EVA 5 Hz	5 Hz
EVA 70 Hz	70 Hz
ETU 70 Hz	70 Hz
ETU 300 Hz	300 Hz

The pedestrian profile is defined only for the low speed 5 Hz Doppler frequency; the vehicular profile is defined only for 5 Hz and 70 Hz; and the typical urban profile excludes the 5 Hz case.

One additional special delay profile has been defined for high speed trains. The definition of this profile is based on the velocity of a train and particular distances between base stations at a specified distance from the track. The result is a Doppler shift with a nearly square wave profile.

An important difference exists between the way LTE propagation conditions have been specified compared to UMTS. In UMTS, the delay profiles were specified for different UE velocities. This meant that the different frequency bands each required a different set of Doppler frequencies to test with. In the early days of UMTS, when only one band had been defined, this method of requirement was not a problem. Today, however, 25 bands are currently defined (23 by 3GPP and 2 by ETSI; see Section 2.1.1). This has created a huge growth in test configurations. To reduce the test burden, it was decided for LTE to fix the Doppler frequencies for the EPA, EVA, ETU and HST profiles and apply these to all frequency bands. As a result the effective UE velocity has now become variable as a function of the test frequency, and for the HST case, the inter-site distances have also become variable. This approach is not as pure as the fixed velocity approach from UMTS; nevertheless, fixing the Doppler frequencies is expected to provide sufficient test coverage with the benefit of significant test simplification.

Figure 6.5-14 shows amplitude fluctuations over a period of one second for one path of Rayleigh fading at a Doppler spread of 10 Hz (5.4 km/h at 2 GHz). The dynamic range of the signal is contained mainly within the top 10 dB although much deeper fades can be seen.

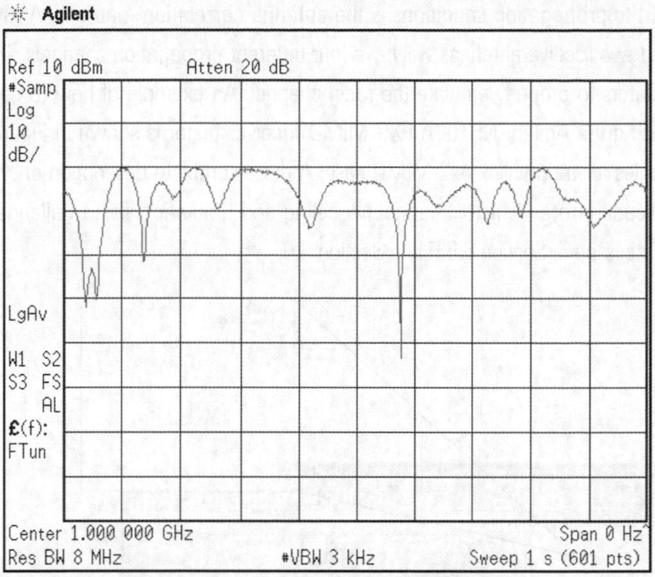

Figure 6.5-14. Time domain profile of one path of Rayleigh fading applied using the Agilent PXB MIMO receiver tester

The constellation diagram in Figure 6.5-15 shows how one path of Rayleigh fading affects a QPSK modulated signal. Although not an LTE signal with multi-carrier OFDMA or broadband SC-FDMA modulation, the signal in this simple example illustrates the problem that Rayleigh fading presents to the receiver and the need to properly verify the receiver under a variety of propagation conditions. The trajectory of the constellation can be seen to change in both amplitude and phase as is expected with Rayleigh fading. It is interesting to note that the constellation approaches the origin during deep fades and the Doppler spreading causes the trajectory to migrate from one quadrant to the next. The propagation conditions defined for LTE use up to nine paths, creating a much more complex signal than the ones shown in Figures 6.5-14 and 6.5-15.

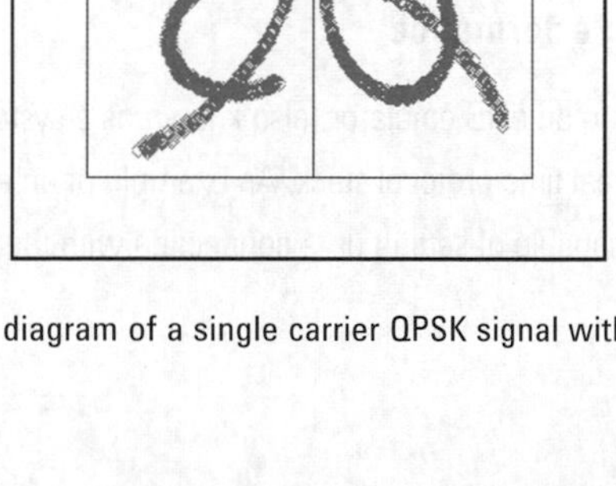

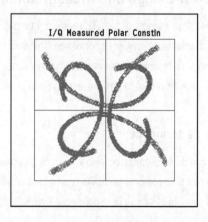

Figure 6.5-15. Constellation diagram of a single carrier QPSK signal with one path of Rayleigh fading

The third element of the propagation conditions is the antenna correlation matrices. A radio system with two transmit antennas and two receive antennas will have four different propagation channels. This then requires four separate fading simulators to properly emulate the radio channel. An example of how to generate multi-channel signals with fading using the Agilent N5106A PXB MIMO receiver tester is shown in Figure 6.5-16. This figure shows the fading profiles for a downlink 4x2 MIMO case. A more complete description of channel emulation can be found in the application note "MIMO Channel Modeling and Emulation Test Challenges" [17]. Correlation matrices are further discussed in Section 6.5.5 and Section 6.6.

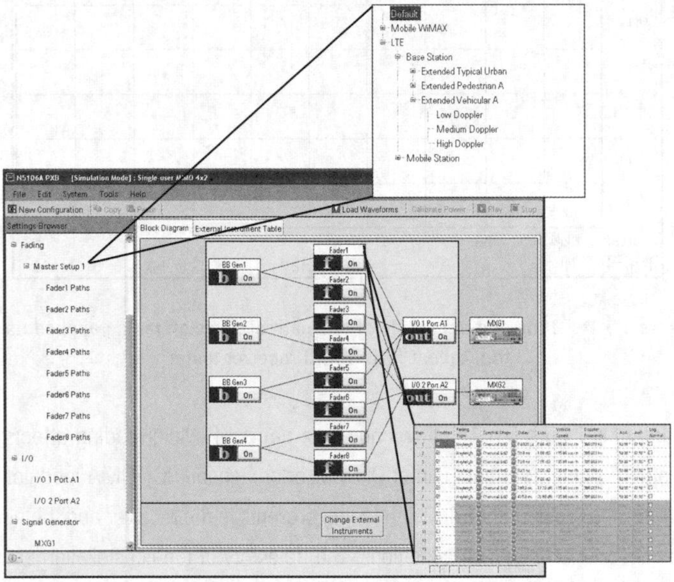

Figure 6.5-16. Agilent N5106A PXB MIMO receiver tester configured for 4x2 channel emulation showing the LTE downlink MIMO fading profiles

6.5.5 Closed Loop Receiver Design and Measurement Challenges

So far this section has covered open loop aspects of the LTE receiver; however, closed loop interactive testing is required in many instances to fully characterize receiver performance. This section examines some of the UE closed loop test requirements for such things as receiver performance, Channel State Information (CSI) and application layer throughput analysis. The eNB receiver requirements are less complex than those of the UE and are discussed in Section 7.2.9.

6.5.5.1 Testing Closed Loop Performance

Closed loop testing is performed using an eNB emulator (also known as a system simulator) consisting of a source and receiver under the control of a real time protocol stack. An example of an eNB emulator is the Agilent E6620A wireless test set. Such a product is capable of setting up a connection with the UE and maintaining and controlling that connection in real time. By accurately setting downlink power and noise conditions, and by using uplink UE reports such as the UE CSI and HARQ information to adapt to the downlink channel conditions, an eNB emulator is capable of closed loop UE receiver testing. For receiver performance testing, it is also necessary to add fading to the downlink for both single and multi-channel configurations (MIMO) to fully exercise the UE under a wide range of radio link conditions.

Closed Loop Receiver and Performance Requirements

In 36.101 [10] the minimum UE receiver and performance requirements are defined along with the signal configuration to which the requirements apply. The distinction between receiver requirements in 36.101 [10] subclause 7 and the performance requirements in subclause 8 is that the receiver requirements are simpler and performed in a static channel with only AWGN as a channel impairment. The performance requirements include the addition of a fading propagation channel.

The term fixed reference channel is used to describe the signal definition. An FRC implies that the underlying RMC does not include any of the dynamic parameters, such as coding rate or modulation depth, that are necessary if Adaptive Modulation and Coding (AMC) is applied. In real network operation AMC is active and the format of the signals varies constantly.

During the development of UMTS the possibility of defining requirements for using Variable Reference Channels (VRCs) was discussed but never implemented. These would have tested closed loop receiver performance with AMC enabled. At the time of this writing, the LTE requirements are defined only for FRC and hence the terms FRC and RMC may appear interchangeable. If VRCs were to be introduced, however, the underlying RMC definition would become more complex. Referring to a receiver test condition using the term FRC rather than RMC makes it clear that AMC is not enabled in this scenario.

The FRCs for the receiver requirements have no specific names, but those for the performance requirements are named numerically: R.3 FDD, R.4 FDD, R.7 TDD, etc. A discussion of all the many receiver and performance requirements is beyond the scope of this chapter, so one example is described in detail to show how the various elements including the FRC, channel propagation conditions and other parameters combine to create the right conditions for ensuring that the UE can deliver the required performance.

6.5.5.2 Throughput Performance Example with Spatial Multiplexing

The performance requirement chosen for discussion is for multi-layer spatial multiplexing (i.e., MIMO) as specified in 36.101 [10] subclause 8.2.1.4. This is a complex requirement involving many advanced features of LTE. The purpose of the requirement is to define the closed loop throughput performance for two spatial streams with wideband and frequency selective pre-coding. Table 6.5-4 defines the general parameters for the requirement. ("TBD" indicates that a parameter is still to be defined.)

Table 6.5-4. Test parameters for multi-layer spatial multiplexing (FRC) (36.101 [10] Table 8.2.1.4.2-1)

Parameter		Unit	Test [5.1]	Test [5.2]	Test [5.3]
Downlink power allocation	ρ_A	dB	–3	–3	–6
	ρ_B	dB	–3 (Note 1)	–3 (Note 1)	–6 (Note 1)
N_{oc} at antenna port		dBm/15 kHz	TBD	TBD	TBD
Precoding granularity		PRB	50	50	6
PMI delay (Note 2)		ms	6	6	6

Note 1: $\rho_B = 1$
Note 2: If the UE reports in an available uplink reporting instance at subframe *SF#n* based on PMI estimation at a downlink subframe not later than *SF#(n-4)*, this reported PMI cannot be applied at the eNB downlink before *SF#(n+2)*

Table 6.5-5 provides the specific performance requirements for several configurations of channel bandwidth, Modulation and Coding Scheme (MCS), reference channel, channel propagation conditions and MIMO channel correlation matrix for 2x2 and 4x2 antenna configurations.

Table 6.5-5. Minimum performance for multi-layer spatial multiplexing (FRC) (36.101 [10] Table 8.2.1.4.2-2)

Test number	Bandwidth and MCS	Reference channel	Propagation condition	Correlation matrix and antenna configuration	Reference value		UE category
					Fraction of maximum throughput (%)	SNR (dB)	
[5.1]	10 MHz 16QAM 1/2	[R.11 FDD]	EVA5	2x2 Low	70	12.9	
[5.2]	10 MHz 16QAM 1/2	[R.11 FDD]	ETU70	2x2 Low	70	14.3	
[5.3]	10 MHz 16QAM 1/2	[R.14 FDD]	EVA5	4x2 Low	70	TBD	

The performance requirement is the SNR at which 70% throughput is achieved. The SNR definition for the 2x2 MIMO case is

$$SNR = \frac{\hat{E}_s^{(1)} + \hat{E}_s^{(2)}}{N_{oc}^{(1)} + N_{oc}^{(2)}}$$

where $\hat{E}_s$ represents the received energy per Resource Element (RE) during the useful part of the symbol (excluding the cyclic prefix) averaged across all allocated RB and normalized to the subcarrier spacing. The denominator N_{oc} is the power spectral density of a white noise source, averaged per RE and normalized to the subcarrier spacing. The superscripts refer to the receiver antenna number.

There are two ways that a test based on the SNR requirement could be devised. The first would be to determine the SNR at which 70% throughput is reached, and the second is to fix the SNR and determine the throughput. For practical reasons the LTE conformance tests fix the SNR and measure the throughput. However, in an R&D environment the variable SNR method is useful in determining how many dB of margin the receiver has relative to the minimum requirement.

Table 6.5-6 shows the parameters for the required FRC, R.11 FDD.

Table 6.5-6. Fixed reference channel with two antenna ports (36.101 [10] Table A.3.3.2.1-1)

Parameter	Unit	Value	
Reference channel		[R.10 FDD]	[R.11 FDD]
Channel bandwidth	MHz	10	10
Allocated resource blocks		50	50
Allocated subframes per Radio Frame		10	10
Modulation		QPSK	16QAM
Target Coding Rate		1/3	1/2
Information Bit Payload			
For subframes 1,2,3,4,6,7,8,9	Bits	4392	12960
For subframes 5	Bits	4392	12960
For subframes 0	Bits	4392	12960
Number of Code Blocks per subframe		1	3
Binary Channel Bits per subframes			
For subframes 1,2,3,4,6,7,8,9	Bits	13200	26400
For subframes 5	Bits	12912	25824
For subframes 0	Bits	12384	24768
Max. Throughput averaged over 1 frame	Mbps	4.39	13.0

Note 1: 2 symbols allocated to PDCCH for 20 MHz, 15 MHz and 10 MHz channel BW; 3 symbols allocated to PDCCH for 5 MHz and 3 MHz; 4 symbols allocated to PDCCH for 1.4 MHz

Note 2: Reference signal, synchronization signals and PBCH allocated as per TS 36.211

The FRC definition provides all the parameters necessary to calculate the maximum throughput averaged across one 10 ms frame. The reason for the averaging is that within the frame structure the number of data symbols varies in each subframe, but over the length of one frame the number of data symbols is constant. See Section 3.2.6 for more details on the frame structure. R.11 FDD is used for the requirement being described. It is a fully allocated RMC (all available RB are used) giving a maximum throughput of 13 Mbps. The target performance for the configurations given in table 6.5-5 would be 70% of this figure. The other RMC defined in Table 6.5-6 is used for different requirements. It uses QPSK modulation rather than 16QAM (two bits rather than four bits per symbol) and uses a lower coding rate of 1/3 rather than 1/2. The coding rate refers to the amount of redundancy in the channel coding; the lower figures represent more repetition with corresponding lower throughput and better resilience to noise. The maximum throughput for R.11 FDD is three times that of R.10 FDD due to the use of higher order modulation and a higher coding rate. This indicates that R.10 FDD is a more robust signal and is used for requirements based on much lower SNR than requirements using R.11 FDD.

Table 6.5-5 specifies the required MIMO correlation matrix and antenna configuration. The details for these are shown in Table 6.5-7. The definition of the correlation matrices is given in terms of the parameters α and β defined in 36.101 [10] Annex B.2.3. For the 2x2 cases the channel correlation matrix R is defined for the eNB and UE as:

$$R_{eNB} = \begin{pmatrix} 1 & \alpha \\ \alpha^* & 1 \end{pmatrix} \quad R_{UE} = \begin{pmatrix} 1 & \beta \\ \beta^* & 1 \end{pmatrix}$$

When α and β are zero, the channel can be described as if it were two completely independent channels with no leakage from one to the other. As α and β approach 1, the channel starts to look like a Single Input Single Output (SISO) channel in which the transmitted signals add together in the channel and the signals at both receivers are identical, thus reducing any potential MIMO gain to zero. For further discussion of channel correlation refer to Sections 3.4 and 6.6.

Table 6.5-7 MIMO correlation matrices (36.101 [10] Table B.2.3.2-1)

Low correlation		**Medium correlation**		**High correlation**	
α	β	α	β	α	β
0	0	0.3	0.9	0.9	0.9

The low correlation scenario is essentially a perfect MIMO channel in which the paths are completely de-correlated. For the 2x2 case this means a potential doubling of throughput compared to that of a SISO channel. Low correlation is an impractical and unlikely real world scenario; however, it does enable like for like comparison with the equivalent performance requirements in UMTS, which are also based on full de-correlation. The medium correlation scenario represents a more likely real world channel situation, while the high correlation scenario describes a situation in which the paths are almost fully correlated — the point at which MIMO becomes ineffective. It can be seen from Table 6.5-5 that only the low (no) correlation case has been specified, thus the requirement can be mapped to a high SNR radio environment with a near perfect uncorrelated channel. The intention of specifying a performance requirement in such conditions is not meant to be indicative of typical MIMO performance in real life. Rather the intention is to determine if the UE is capable of reaching the maximum performance in ideal conditions.

To further characterize the UE it is necessary to supplement this ideal scenario with additional minimum requirements covering QPSK, 64QAM, additional propagation conditions and the medium and high correlation matrices.

6.5.5.3 Channel State Information Performance Testing

Channel State Information (CSI) consists of reports sent by the UE to the eNB to provide real time updates of the downlink channel conditions. CSI is introduced in Section 3.4.6 and includes the Pre-coding Matrix Indicator (PMI), Channel Quality Indicator (CQI) and Rank Indication (RI).

At the time of this writing, only one CQI requirement has been formally defined. The discussion of PMI and RI reporting requirements in this section represents only the likelihood of what may be specified. The CSI requirements are likely to follow the UMTS example and be defined without AMC. This means that the requirements will be based on FRCs (with and without fading) with a statistical analysis of the CSI reports. The alternative would be a fully closed loop condition in which the CSI performance is inferred from the throughput performance of the system acting upon the real time CSI feedback. The latter approach would give a better indication of real life performance; however, it requires the definition of quite complex AMC and scheduling behavior in the eNB emulator, and this is considered both very difficult and outside the scope of the specifications.

Because the scope of the minimum requirements is narrow, it will be valuable during the R&D phase to evaluate UE performance under closed loop conditions with AMC and dynamic scheduling, even though there are no formal requirements against which to assess performance. The differences between closed loop CQI performance of different designs was an issue for UMTS and will be even more so with LTE due to a much higher degree of flexibility in the definition of the CSI reports.

Wideband CQI Test With AWGN

The wideband CQI requirements specified in 36.101 [10] subclause 9 follow the precedent set by UMTS. The wideband CQI test is a two part requirement based on the conditions shown in Table 6.5-8.

Table 6.5-8. PUCCH 1-0 static test (36.101 [10] Table 9.2.1-1)

Parameter	Unit	Test 1	Test 2
Bandwidth	MHz	10	
PDSCH transmission mode		[2]	
Reference signal power E_{RS}/I_{or}	dB	3	
SNR	dB	[0]	[6]
$N_{oc}^{(j)}$	dB[mW/15 kHz]	[–102]	[–102]
$\hat{I}_{or}^{(j)}$	dB[mW/15 kHz]	[–102]	[–96]
Reporting period	ms	[2–20]	

Note: Reference measurement channel as per TS 36.213 [19] Section 7.2.3

This requirement represents the simplest case for CQI, being wideband (the full channel bandwidth) and having a static propagation channel with interference represented by AWGN. The wanted-signal and noise-signal powers per subcarrier are represented by

$$\hat{I}_{or}^{(j)} \text{ and } N_{oc}^{(j)}$$

with the SNR for the two test conditions of 0 dB and 6 dB derived from these two parameters. Each test is in two parts. The first part is used to determine the median value of the reported CQI and to determine that 90% of all CQI reports fall within ±1 of the median. The number of CQI samples that have to be captured to obtain the required statistical significance will be determined in the conformance test specifications and is likely to be around 2000 reports.

The second part of each test checks the accuracy of the CQI reports around the 10% BLER target. The median CQI calculated from the first part of the test is used to pick a downlink transport format that provides an SNR that matches the CQI report. The BLER using this median CQI transport format is then measured. If the BLER is at or below 10%, the BLER is measured using the transport format for median CQI +1. This BLER has to be greater than 10%. Similarly, if the BLER using the median CQI transport format is greater than 10%, the BLER measured using the median CQI – 1 transport format has to be 10% or less.

Wideband CQI Test With Fading

The requirements for wideband CQI with fading are likely to follow the UMTS precedent. This involves calculating the median CQI using a specified fading channel, and then using the transport format for the median CQI to capture the BLER statistics of individual blocks correlated with the CQI reported by the UE at the time the BLER was measured. BLER targets will be set for all blocks received for specific CQI reports. For UMTS the blocks received during the reporting of the median CQI must have a BLER of less than 15%. For those received during the period in which the CQI is reported as median +3, the BLER must be less than 60%.

It is likely that another requirement will be added to the specifications to ensure that the UE does not perform averaging of the CQI reports. The purpose of the CQI is to report instantaneous variations in the channel conditions, but the experience from UMTS is that the fading requirement just described is not particularly sensitive to the use of inappropriate averaging. To constrain the use of averaging, a further requirement was defined for UMTS based around a bi-stable condition in which the downlink conditions alternate between two different SNRs. The CQI reports are correlated with the known conditions on the downlink to generate two distinct distributions. Requirements for deviation around each distribution and the relative difference between the distributions can then be set.

Subband CQI Testing

The UE, as well as being configured to measure a single wideband CQI value, can be configured to provide reports on subbands to assist with frequency selective scheduling. This is discussed further in Section 3.4. Subband CQI reports are most useful when the channel conditions are not changing too quickly but also exhibit significant variation across the channel. Subband CQI is a differential report using only two bits of data referenced to the wideband CQI value. This coding places limits on the dynamic range of subband reports and is a compromise between fully describing the subband channel conditions with more bits versus the signalling overhead required to send a more accurate report. It is likely that subband CQI requirements will be based on the principles used for wideband CQI; however, the added dimension of needing to take into account the frequency domain could add significant complexity. It would be possible to analyze the statistics of the fading channel as a function of the configured subbands and then compare them to the reports received from the UE. The difficulty with this approach is that over time the statistics of any subband will average out to those of the whole channel and the value of subband CQI reports lies in the instantaneous accuracy of the report rather than any long-term average of the reports.

Subband CQI requirements are further complicated by the inclusion of a mode whereby the UE decides over which subbands it will report.

PMI Testing

Testing the correct PMI reporting will be important for LTE, particularly in environments with varying channel conditions. PMI testing is likely to be performed as a comparative throughput test with one part of the test conducted using a fixed pre-coder and the second part with UE reported PMI values. The test would pass or fail depending on this relative value, with test conditions including fading. Currently there are no such PMI requirements specified.

Rank Indication (RI) Testing

At the time of this writing no RI performance requirements have been defined. The definition of RI in the physical layer specifications is not as explicit as the definition of CQI, which adds a complicating factor. Ideally RI would be verified in a complex closed loop environment involving HARQ and AMC; however, no such closed loop requirements have been developed for CQI and it seems unlikely that they will be developed for RI either. An alternative to closed loop testing could be some form of open loop testing based on RI feedback in which the downlink alternates between single stream and dual stream transmission of an FRC, with an expectation of higher throughput as a result of correct RI feedback. Various forms of ad hoc testing with RI are possible but until performance requirements and the associated tests are developed, the significance of the results will remain open to interpretation.

6.5.5.4 Testing Real Time Throughput at the Application Layer in Real Life Conditions

Bringing together all of the considerations in this section provides a context for application layer throughput testing. The conditions for such testing and the results can vary considerably:

- Using static conditions with no noise, fading or interference, it is possible to establish the baseline throughput performance using data flooding.
- Real user data can be captured to establish the capability of the processing and memory management functions that cannot be fully tested with flooding data tests.
- Adding fading, noise or interference can be used to verify data recovery processes in the UE-HARQ operation, requesting or generating re-transmissions, etc., as well as testing correctly reported CQI.
- Using spatial multiplexing on the channel enables real world simulation and testing of the PMI and RI reporting aspects.

Throughput Test System

Testing the throughput of an IP-based packet switched data connection typically requires both a data source and a data sink. The requirements on the data source are usually straightforward and can often be summarized as "send data as fast as the air interface will allow." Most test environments use a generic PC or server connected to the LAN of an eNB emulator. The data sink is the UE itself or another PC, often referred to as the "client" PC connected to the UE and using the UE as a modem. Figure 6.5-17 shows a typical test system for evaluating application layer throughput.

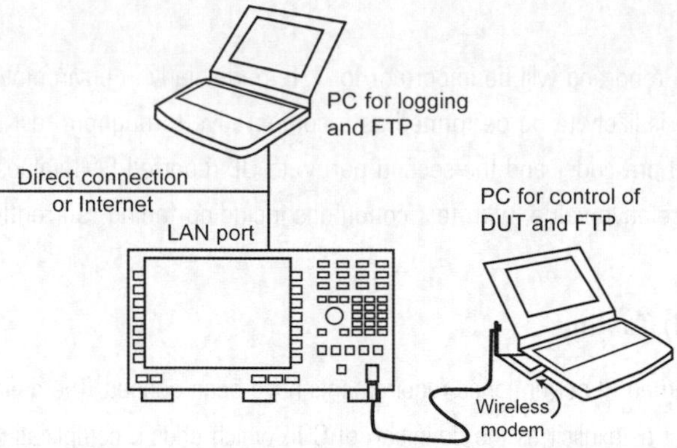

Figure 6.5-17. Test system for evaluating application layer throughput

The two standard use cases for throughput testing involve sending either User Datagram Protocol (UDP) or Transmission Control Protocol (TCP) data as fast as the air interface will allow.

UDP does not impose any throughput restrictions of its own and does not require any acknowledgements of the received data from the recipient of the transmission for retransmission of blocks with NACK. UDP is a good mechanism for testing the L1 data throughput capability of the UE to almost maximum theoretical limits; however, UDP throughput testing can never be completely representative of the end user experience.

TCP is used by common protocols such as Hypertext Transfer Protocol (HTTP) and File Transfer Protocol (FTP), so is a good choice for measuring throughput closer to what a real user will experience. However, end-to-end throughput can be restricted by TCP mechanisms in the server PC (such as receive window size and congestion control) that are not related to over-the-air capacity.

Once the physical layer baseline throughput has been established using static conditions, the UE should be stressed under adverse conditions. A highly variable channel for testing can be implemented by adding noise, interferers or a fading profile, and it may be useful to verify the UE's response to known conditions, which are more easily replicated. For example, by deliberately sending NACKs on the Physical Hybrid Indicator Channel (PHICH) even when the uplink data has been received correctly, a designer can assess the UE's capability to provide re-transmissions in a timely manner. Similarly, if some known portion of the downlink transmission is deliberately corrupted, it is possible to test whether the UE correctly requests retransmission of the corrupted data blocks. Such a test could be useful for repeatable testing of PMI and RI with a spatially multiplexed channel.

To assess how a UE will perform in the real world, data must be transmitted all the way up through the protocol stack, stressing all components and layers at the same time. This is commonly achieved on real networks; however, an eNB emulator can usually do such testing under repeatable conditions on the bench so that the test engineer doesn't have to leave the R&D laboratory. Using TCP allows data to be sent all the way up the protocol stack to the application layer and thus all layers, as well as the interactions between each layer, can be tested.

Note that for all these tests only one side of the channel can be tested at a time. For example, testing downlink throughput with a corrupted uplink will be meaningless if there is any uncertainty regarding the accuracy of the ACK/NACK information on the uplink. Therefore it is normal in UE receiver testing for the uplink to be free of any unwanted noise or interference and for the uplink power to be set at a level that ensures error-free reception of the control information.

6.6 Design and Verification Challenges of MIMO

6.6.1 Introduction

This section describes the design and verification challenges associated with spatial multiplexing and diversity-enabled radios for LTE. The impact of this technology on transmitter and receiver hardware and software will be considered as well as the effects of different antenna arrangements. Issues specific to closed loop operation are addressed in Section 6.7.

It has been said that MIMO is a baseband (digital coding) challenge. There is some truth to this belief, but not all situations are so straightforward. When designs become more compact, the isolation and performance of RF and analog circuits are not ideal. RF currents are notorious for leaking onto non-RF circuits, and the effects can be difficult to filter out. As a result, MIMO performance degrades. The transmit and receive antennas are key components in the signal chain. Their performance is not easy to model, and in the most complex beamforming cases it is necessary to use real-time calibration mechanisms to maintain performance. The receivers in the UE have a particularly demanding task, since they have to recover the MIMO signal using algorithms that balance performance with space in the Baseband IC (BBIC). Also, the UE has to report accurate real-time channel state information to the eNB.

There are other important factors that impact MIMO performance indirectly, such as battery power consumption in the UE. These factors are dealt with in Section 6.10 on battery drain testing.

To work in practice, spatial multiplexing needs better channel conditions and higher SNR than does equivalent SISO operation. The better conditions required for successful MIMO operation are achieved through a combination of diversity-enabled or beamforming cells, and the use of progressively smaller or isolated cells.

The issues in the downlink paths are considered first, starting with the eNB transmitters in Section 6.6.2. After noting potential problems such as unwanted signal coupling, this section is broken down to describe a variety of single and multiple input measurement techniques that are useful for isolating problems during development. These include a description of how to use a single input analyzer for MIMO measurements, the use of channel condition number, and insights into IQ impairments, which give effects such as the "constellation of constellations."

Section 6.6.3 describes the UE module and eNB receiver implementation issues and test methods. Section 6.6.4 is a description of the additional parameters needed for MIMO performance verification, including the use of fading channels and the use of channel emulation with configurable path correlation. The influence of variables such as antenna spacing, polarization and path correlation is described. This section also addresses the addition of noise to the signals used for receiver testing in a correlated channel, which relates both to performance assessment and to the measurement of the MIMO channel state information (CQI, PMI and RI) that the UE has to provide to the eNB for dynamic control of the link.

The final Section 6.6.5 deals with the question of phase coherence and its impact on design and measurement for the transmitter and receiver when precoding is applied.

6.6.2 Base Station (eNB) Transmitter MIMO Challenges

Figure 6.6-1 shows a simplified block diagram of an eNB showing separation of RF and digital processing circuits. The development tasks are often carried out separately by different teams or different companies, which requires that subsystem performance testing be done before the modules are brought together. The techniques for using test equipment to simulate SISO RF or baseband signals can be adapted for analyzing individual signal paths. For digitized signal interfaces, it is normal to begin by using repetitive arbitrary waveforms and batch-mode, post-processed measurements.

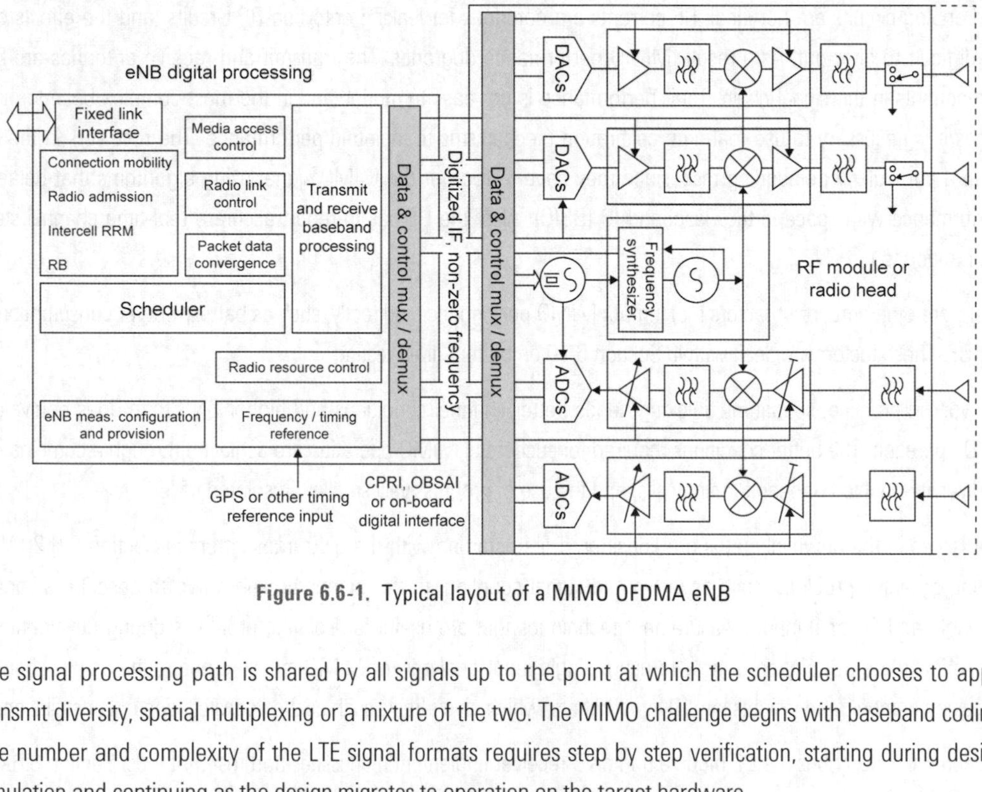

Figure 6.6-1. Typical layout of a MIMO OFDMA eNB

The signal processing path is shared by all signals up to the point at which the scheduler chooses to apply transmit diversity, spatial multiplexing or a mixture of the two. The MIMO challenge begins with baseband coding. The number and complexity of the LTE signal formats requires step by step verification, starting during design simulation and continuing as the design migrates to operation on the target hardware.

Another challenge for multi-channel operation is that of interconnection, whether between modules within the eNB or between the eNB and the test equipment. Digital interfaces such as CPRI and OBSAI are not sufficiently standardized to make it straightforward to plug and play with generic test equipment. However, when vendor-specific options are available, analyzing the signal as digitized IQ is a helpful step in early signal verification, particularly when the specifications are not final.

6.6.2.1 Baseband Coding Assessment Using Spectrogram Pattern Recognition

Software-based analysis using a vector signal analyzer such as the Agilent 89601A VSA is valuable for fault finding. To demonstrate how this works, Figure 6.6-2 shows the spectrograms of a four transmitter LTE signal. (Spectrograms are introduced in more detail in Section 6.4.5.3.) Each spectrogram shows time in the vertical axis, and spectral power is identified with white as highest and black as lowest power. There are patterns clearly visible and after a short time studying the traces, components in the LTE signal structure become readily recognizable. In this example, the different RS structures used for transmitters 2 and 3 on the top left and top right of Figure 6.6-2 are clearly visible and look as expected. However, what is not expected is the truncation of the data that starts in the second subframe. The transmission should have continued to the edge of the channel.

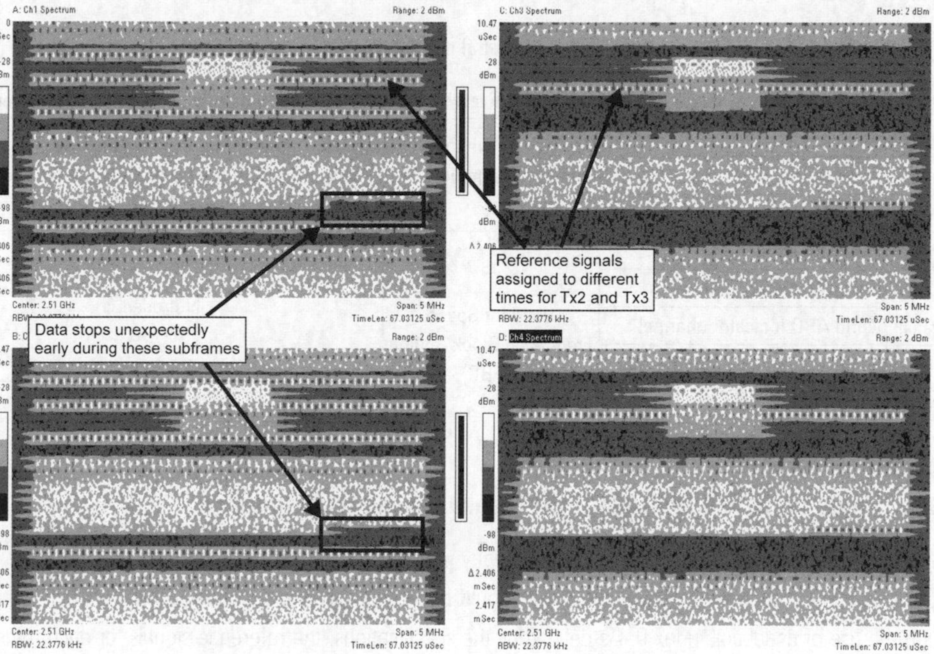

Figure 6.6-2. Using spectrograms for quick diagnosis of basic coding problems of a 4x4 MIMO signal

It can also be seen that the power on Tx1 (bottom left) is slightly higher than the power of the other transmitters. (This higher power is shown as lighter shades in the display, but in the software the spectrogram is displayed in color, giving more clarity to the patterns.) The spectrum gating period is matched to the OFDM symbol length of 66.7 μs, and a Hanning window is used for improved resolution in the frequency domain.

When RF connections are made between the DUT and signal analyzer, the number of available measurement ports determines how the signals can be analyzed. Figure 6.6-3 shows the connection options, starting with direct cable connections on the left and going through to a real or emulated channel on the right. For some measurements, power combiners can be used when only one analyzer input is available, as long as the signals from the transmitters contain some orthogonality in frequency or time.

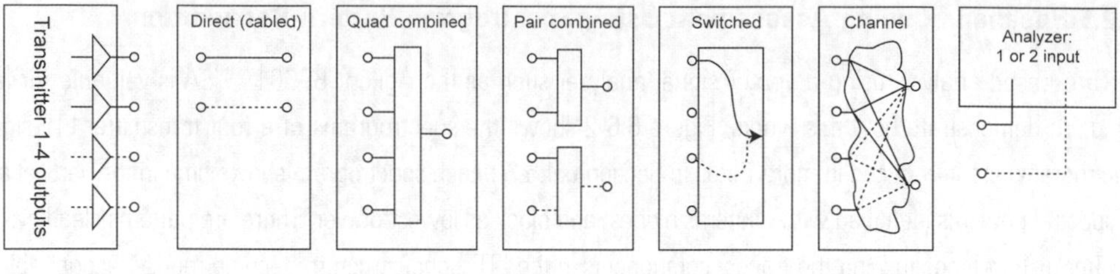

Figure 6.6-3. Connection options between an eNB and signal analyzer

Table 6.6-1 shows which physical signals and physical channels are coupled between the transmitters of the base station. The presence of coupling has an impact on some of the measurement techniques described here.

Table 6.6-1. Application of diversity and spatial multiplexing for different downlink signal types

<table>
<tr><th>Physical signal or physical channel</th><th>Transmit diversity</th><th>Spatial multiplexing</th><th>Cyclic delay diversity</th></tr>
<tr><td>Reference signal</td><td colspan="3" rowspan="3">Neither diversity nor spatial multiplexing is applied, but the assignment of the sync signals to the transmit antennas may vary (refer to 36.211 [2] subclause 6.11.1.2)</td></tr>
<tr><td>Primary synchronization signal</td></tr>
<tr><td>Secondary synchronization signal</td></tr>
<tr><td>Physical broadcast channel</td><td rowspan="6">Used for Space Frequency Block Coding (SFBC)</td><td colspan="2" rowspan="4">Not used</td></tr>
<tr><td>Physical downlink control channel</td></tr>
<tr><td>Physical hybrid ARQ indicator channel</td></tr>
<tr><td>Physical control format indicator channel</td></tr>
<tr><td>Physical multicast channel</td><td rowspan="2">Used</td><td>Not used</td></tr>
<tr><td>Physical downlink shared channel</td><td>Used (long)</td></tr>
</table>

6.6.2.2 Single Input and Multiple Input Measurement Techniques

If there is little or no coupling between channels, many measurements can be made on a multi-antenna signal using a single input analyzer. In development, it should be straightforward to achieve this signal configuration through the use of codebook index 0. As defined by the specifications, the reference signals for each transmitter are always orthogonal in frequency and time.

There are many possibilities for errors in signal generation in the eNB. Finding errors requires flexible signal analysis. The process of signal analysis for troubleshooting follows similar steps to those used for demodulation in a real receiver. Figure 6.6-4 shows a simplified block diagram of the analysis steps that relate to the signal analyzer user interface settings. It is normal to alternate between analyzer settings to explore what impairments are affecting the signal. An example of how switching between analysis blocks can be used is to distinguish distortion of a single transmitter (e.g., in a power amplifier) from that on a single layer (e.g., due to a mathematical processing error). Table 6.6-2 shows the range of MIMO measurements possible depending on the number of analyzer inputs.

Table 6.6-2. Measurement possibilities based on number of analyzer inputs

Measurement objective	**Number of measurement inputs required**		
	1	2	> 2
SISO and MISO errors due to phase noise, timing errors and amplitude clipping	Yes		
Spectrum mask, harmonics and spurious	Yes		
RF phase and baseband timing alignment, using RS-based measurements	Using a power combiner	No combiner needed but errors from the second analyzer input will contribute to result.	
Cross channel isolation using RS-based measurement	Yes	Similar measurements to single input. Can connect to two transmitters at the same time.	
Interference, grounding, transient settling	Yes		
Transmit diversity space time coding (control channel and PDSCH)	Yes		
MIMO spatial multiplexing (with unwanted coupling) and coding verification	Individual (direct mapped) layers	Yes	If > 2 layers

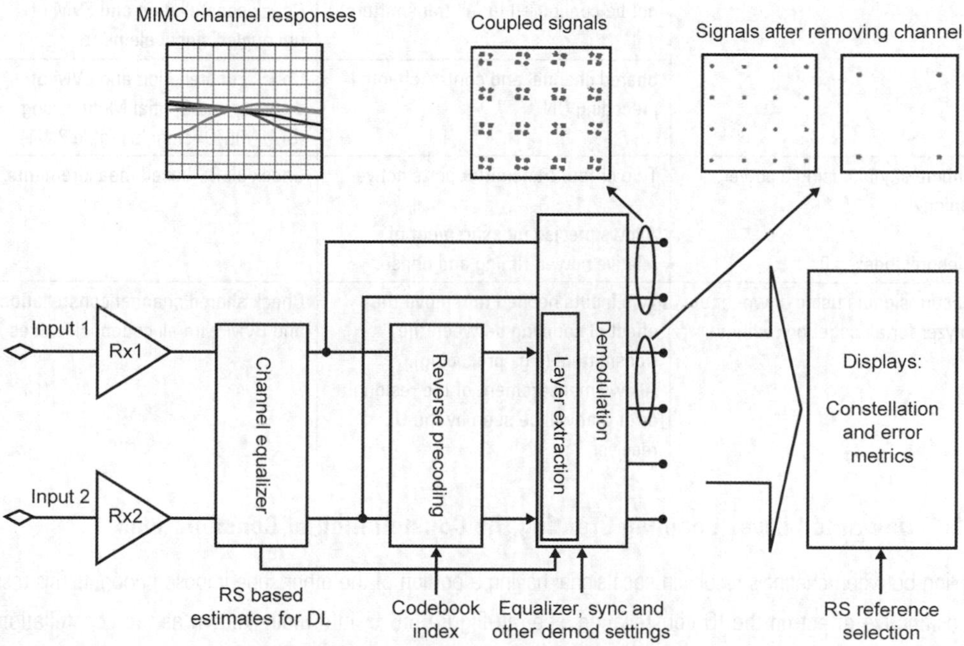

Figure 6.6-4. MIMO signal analysis processing

Figure 6.6-4 is drawn with two measurement inputs but could be extended to four. When cabled connections are used instead of a real or emulated radio channel, the reverse precoding block is required. This block removes the precoding that would have been removed by the radio channel.

6.6.2.3 An LTE MIMO Troubleshooting Process

When two or more layers are in operation, there are additional ways the signal can be impaired. As with a SISO signal, a systematic approach is needed to understand what errors are present. Table 6.6-3 summarizes such a method:

Table 6.6-3. A basic structure for diagnosing multi-transmitter signal impairments

Device configuration and analyzer connection	**Analyzer configuration**	**Measurement steps**
Single input measurement; connect to each transmitter output separately. TX Diversity or spatial multiplexing ON Codebook index = 0	Use the same analysis configuration steps as for SISO signal. Start with analyzer demodulator OFF. Use Hanning window with gate time = 1 symbol (66.7 μs).	Measure power vs. time and gated spectrum to ensure that each channel has the expected power level and structure. Record signal and use spectrogram.
	Turn demodulator ON. Display RS, primary and secondary synchronization signals (which may not be configured for all transmitters).	Synchronize to primary synchronization signal or RS Check constellation and EVM of uncoupled signal elements.
	Shared channel and control channel precoding ON.	Check constellation and EVM of diversity and Spatial Multiplexing (SM, MIMO) signals (Table 2.4-1).
Combine signals using a power coupler. Codebook index = 0	Two or four transmitter ports active. Allows precise measurement of relative power, timing and phase.	Check all RS-based measurements.
Measure signals using a two input analyzer for all codebook values.	Two inputs needed to remove the effect of coupling between the transmitters (e.g., precoding). Allows measurement of the residual error that will be seen by the UE receiver.	Check shared channel constellations and EVM with all codebook values.

6.6.2.4 Unwanted Layer Coupling Creating the Constellation of Constellations

Coupling between channels results in each signal having a portion of the other superimposed upon it. This results in a distinctive effect on the IQ constellation, seen in Figure 6.6-5, informally known as the constellation of constellations. The reason this effect occurs is that the coupled signals are highly correlated in time. Demodulation using the correct code index will remove the expected coupling but any unwanted coupling will remain. The way in which transmitter impairments result in channel coupling varies depending on the precoding.

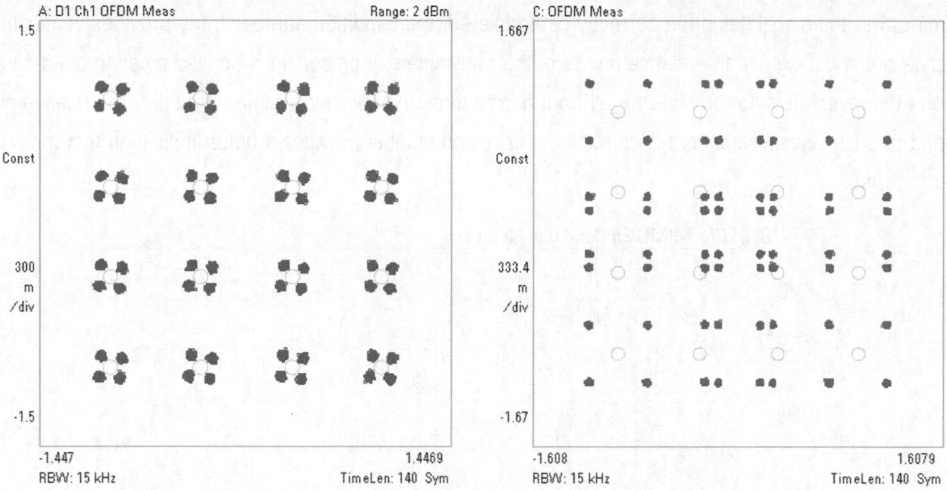

Figure 6.6-5. Constellation of constellations. Left: Unwanted QPSK has coupled into the 16QAM layer. Right: The wrong codebook index has been used.

To determine whether coupling is intentional (due to precoding) or unwanted, and to further understand the likely coupling mechanism, it is necessary to have as many measurement inputs to the signal analyzer as there are layers in the signal. Figure 6.6-4 showed the processing blocks used during analysis and indicated the paths used to produce results when different analysis functions, such as channel estimation and MIMO decoding, are applied.

6.6.2.5 Channel Training Signal Verification Using Equalizer Condition Number

As discussed in Section 2.4.2, the condition number of the matrix representing the channel can be used to show the improvement in SNR required to recover a spatially multiplexed signal. The additional SNR versus condition number is shown in Figure 6.6-6. The measurement and display of channel condition number can also provide a number of useful troubleshooting insights, even when the channel is just a simple cabled connection.

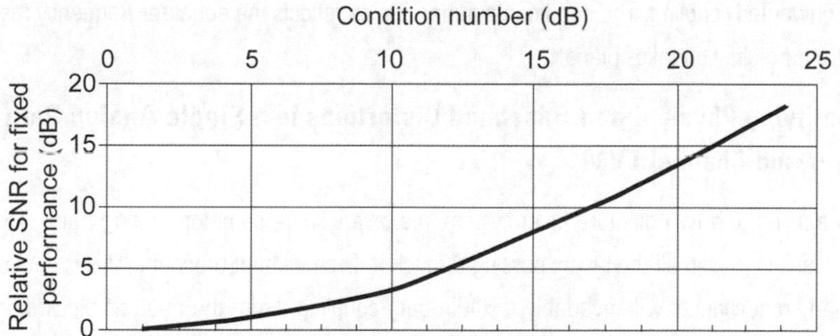

Figure 6.6-6. Additional SNR required versus channel condition number to maintain, constant demodulation performance

Assuming that the signal has been correctly demodulated, the condition number trace provides verification of reference signal coding and the relative power of the transmitters. If precoding is applied creating cross-coupling between the layers, it is not possible to tell from a broadband power measurement whether the relative power assigned to each signal component is correct. The condition number provides a better indication that the relative power is correct.

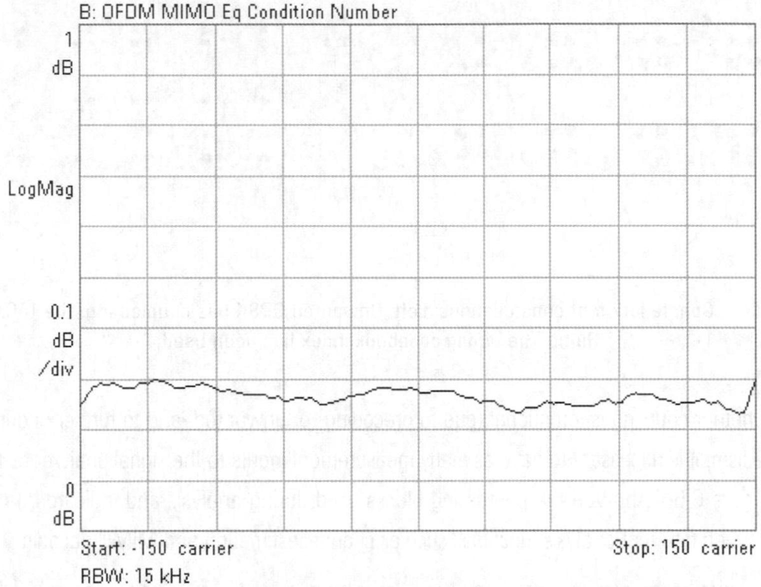

Figure 6.6-7. Matrix condition number trace for a well-behaved two transmitter eNB

The perfect condition number is 0 dB, which occurs when the diagonal values of the matrix representing the received signal are perfectly balanced. To achieve the near perfect performance of the trace in Figure 6.6-7, not only does the precoding have to be correct, but the power of each transmitter needs to be well matched and there has to be little unwanted coupling. The condition number display reflects the equalizer frequency response, since it uses data before normalization takes place.

6.6.2.6 Identifying Physical and Baseband Distortions in a Single Analog Path Using Layer and Channel EVM

If precoding is applied to a two or more layer system, the layers share common analog paths. Distortion in any single path will cause errors in all the layers passing through it. Even without precoding this is generally true at the receiver since any real channel will invariably result in path coupling. From the analysis block diagram in Figure 6.6-4, it can be seen that by turning off the layer extraction block, it is possible to demodulate the signal and measure the EVM of either the received signal or a specific layer encoded onto the signals.

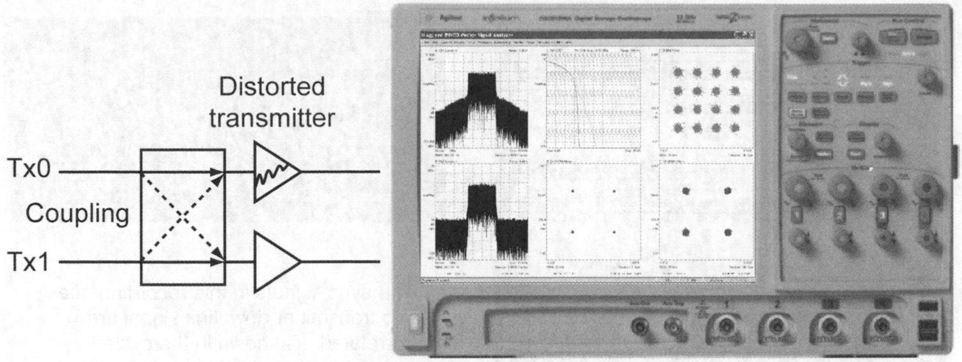

Figure 6.6-8. Distortion of a single transmitter causing impairment of both layers

In Figure 6.6-8, the upper amplifier has been deliberately set to clip, and precoding is applied so that each layer appears on both paths. The bottom left trace of the VSA running on the oscilloscope shows the undistorted spectrum of the lower amplifier. The top left trace shows the spectral regrowth caused by the distortion in the upper amplifier. The top center trace shows a CCDF, which indicates that the upper amplifier is in compression. The constellation trace in the bottom center shows what the unclipped signal looks like. The top right and bottom right constellations show distortion in both the original layers after decoding.

It is worth remembering that the level of distortion will depend strongly on the drive level, biasing and pre-distortion applied in the power amplifier relative to the signal power. In LTE, the signal power varies rapidly within each symbol at a rate determined by the number of subcarriers. As such, any distortion results in state spreading as discussed in Section 6.4.1.6. In addition the channel measurement made by the UE is also vulnerable to RF impairments and this in turn can create incorrect cross channel coupling due to selection of the wrong precoding matrix.

6.6.2.7 Identifying Unexpected Power Peaks Using Cross Channel Correlation

When two equal, power-correlated signals are combined, the power can increase by 6 dB rather than by 3 dB as occurs when the signals are uncorrelated. Combining correlated signals therefore will have serious consequences for all parts of the processing chain, from clipping at baseband to unexpected distortion by the power amplifiers.

Cross channel correlation measurements can be used to investigate whether the transmitter signals are orthogonal (uncorrelated). As noted in Table 6.6-1, how the RS and sync signals are transmitted on each antenna in terms of timing is undefined. Figure 6.6-9 is the result of a cross channel measurement to determine the correlation between the sync signals.

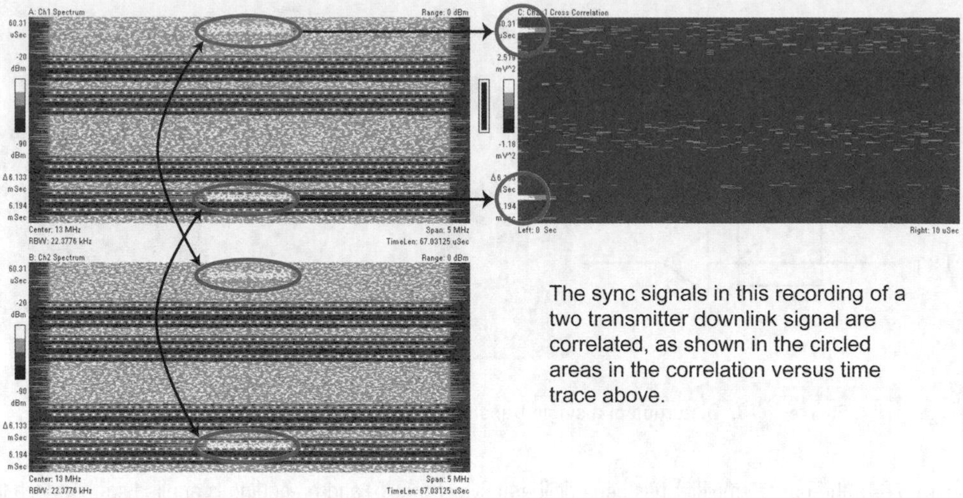

Figure 6.6-9. Using cross correlation to determine sync signal timing between different transmitters. The sync signals and correlation peaks are highlighted

On the left of Figure 6.6-9 are spectrograms of each signal. The vertical axis is time and the period shown is just over one 10 ms frame. The horizontal axis is frequency and the entire 5 MHz channel is shown. The top right trace shows the time correlation between the two signals. The vertical axis is time and it is aligned with the spectrograms. The horizontal axis is also time, but only 10 µs, a fraction of a symbol. The circled light-colored spots on the vertical axis of the top right trace show where correlation occurs between the signals. Since the correlation occurs for only a short period of time in the vertical axis, only that part of the signal is common. By reference to the spectrogram it can be concluded that it is the synchronization signals that are the common element. Since the correlation occurs on the Y-axis at 0 µs, it can be concluded that the sync signals were transmitted with no time offset.

6.6.2.8 Measurement of Antenna Signal Relative Timing and Phase

The LTE requirement for alignment between the antenna signals is ±65 ns, which is approximately 0.1% of the symbol period. The cross correlation measurement described in Section 6.6.2.7 does not have sufficient resolution to make this measurement. However, by demodulating the RS it is possible to make relative timing measurements with sub-ns accuracy. Furthermore, since the RS are orthogonal between the antennas, a power combiner can be used to measure the timing relationship using a single input rather than a dual input signal analyzer.

Figure 6.6-10 shows the result from such a measurement. Tx1 is 619 ps behind the reference on Tx0, with a –3.8 degree phase difference.

The same measurement technique involving the combining of signals into one analyzer input can be used to verify the calibration of signals used for phased array beamforming and to calibrate the timing of signals for receiver testing from multiple signal generators with associated RF cabling. The right hand part of Figure 6.6-10 shows the MXG signal generator user interface for adjusting RF phase and baseband timing.

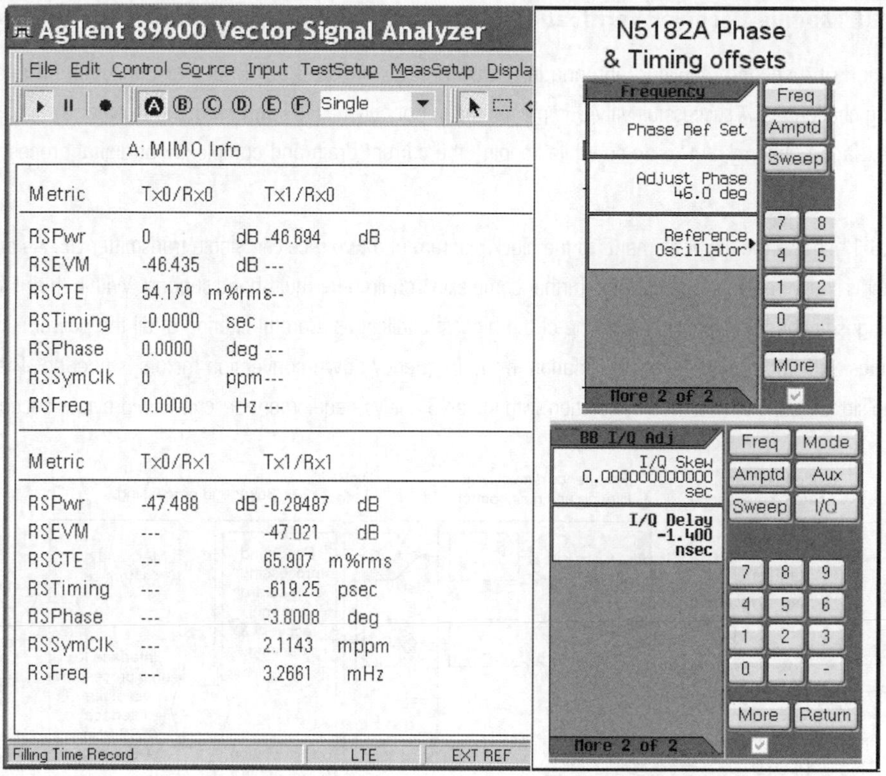

Figure 6.6-10. RS-based timing and phase measurements of a composite downlink 2x2 MIMO signal made using a single input analyzer

6.6.3 MIMO Receiver Design and Verification Challenges

The challenges for MIMO receiver design are similar to those for the transmitter, ranging from the need to ensure adequate analog circuit performance to verifying baseband coding implementation. Problems can be more difficult to isolate unless the system development environment is available to provide visibility to internal processing steps. The most obvious approach is to start with a SISO test signal to verify synchronization and then introduce a second receiver input. During the early phases of a new standard such as LTE, differences in interpretation or gaps in the specifications can lead to interoperability problems. It is essential to be clear which version of the specification is being used and to document any area not yet fully defined where an implementation choice was made. The analysis tools designed for the eNB transmitter can help isolate differences in interpretation. If the receiver designer has created a test harness with proprietary signals, these should be analyzed with the same independent tool.

This section contains short descriptions of the configurations for testing UE and eNB MIMO receivers. Also covered are the additional complexity of channel fading with a MIMO signal and the performance testing options that address the complexity. It is assumed that the individual input signal paths are already verified using normal SISO techniques as discussed in Section 6.5.

6.6.3.1 UE Module Receiver Verification Challenges

The addition of a second receiving antenna in the UE brings a mixture of RF, power consumption and digital processing challenges. A successful MIMO implementation not only has to interoperate with other devices through a complex faded channel, but to do so while keeping the current drain and complexity of digital processing to a minimum.

Figure 6.6-11 shows the major elements in the block diagram of a two receiver, single transmitter UE. An additional transmitter is shown as an example of the further complexity required for multi-band support. Within the RF circuitry, maintaining isolation between signals is one of the biggest challenges. Careful filtering of all the power supply and control lines and appropriate levels of isolation in the frequency down-conversion mixers is needed. The down-converted signals can be measured in isolation with the eNB analysis equipment described in previous sections.

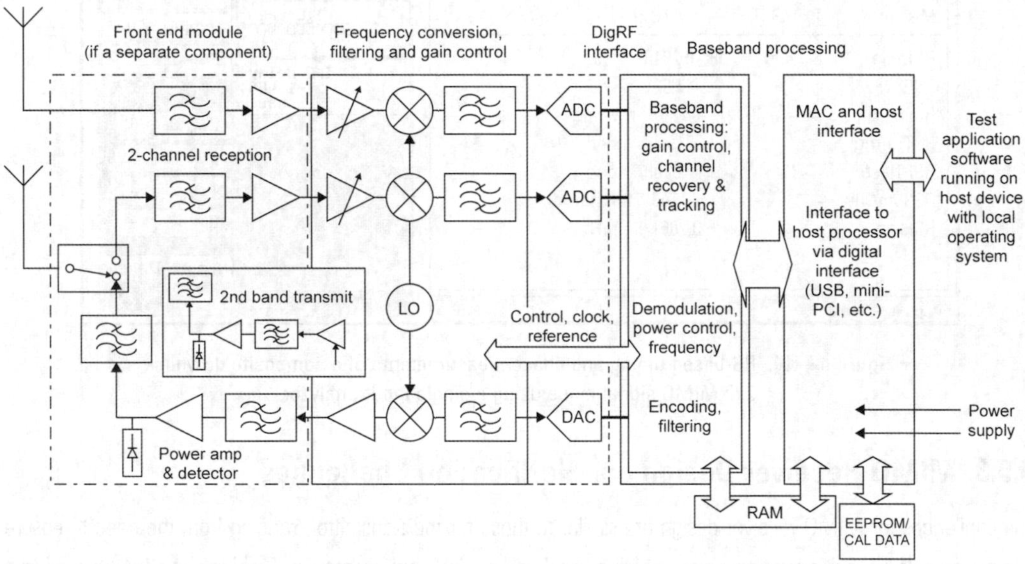

Figure 6.6-11. Simplified diagram of an LTE UE radio

If the RFIC has analog IQ outputs, these can be analyzed using an oscilloscope or MXA signal analyzer. If the RFIC interface uses DigRFv3 or v4, the signal can be captured with the Radio Digital Cross Domain (RDX) tester as described in Section 6.3. These digital or analog IQ signals can then be analyzed with the same 89601A VSA software. For the baseband developer, hardware probes are available for analog IQ and DigRF interfaces.

The VSA software provides numerical EVM performance measurements for verification as well as more detailed graphical information useful during product development to isolate the source of signal impairments. If Gaussian noise is added to the signal as the impairment, a relationship can be drawn between EVM and the raw bit error ratio. Alternatively, the captured IQ signals can be fed into a simulated receiver such as Agilent design software for LTE. The precise design of a receiver determines the performance, so the results may differ from any specific vendor's implementation.

As shown on the right side of Figure 6.6-11, during early development when the radio is in the form of an RFIC or BBIQ module, a host environment and test application software are needed for configuration and result display. At this stage open loop testing without signalling can be used to ensure design implementation margins meet expectations. It should also be possible to verify the accuracy of channel state information reports that will be transmitted back to the eNB.

It is not always possible or necessary to have a separate signal source to test each receiver input. Table 6.6-4 summarizes what can be achieved for single and dual signal cases. As a corollary to the phase and timing measurement of Section 6.6.2.8, a single source split between inputs removes the possibility of phase variation, although in a receiver test this means that the phase between them is not adjustable.

Table 6.6-4. Tests and fault finding using one or more signal sources

Verification task	Single source	Dual source
Input sensitivity (BER or BLER) due to noise floor, phase noise, RF signal Interference	Yes	
Signal path response matching Amplifier characterization	Yes	
Interference, grounding, transient settling, dynamic performance (e.g., AGC operation)	Yes	Yes
Cross channel isolation	Yes*	Yes
MIMO operation and interoperability Full channel model testing		Yes

*Requires that the receiver be able to distinguish between signals from different inputs

For dual source testing the standard RF phase and baseband timing alignment that can be achieved using a common frequency reference and frame synchronization signal is sufficient for most purposes unless the signals need to be precoded to match the channel, or beamsteering operation is being evaluated. In these cases special measures are required to provide the necessary phase alignment. See Section 6.6.5 for more information.

6.6.3.2 Base Station (eNB) Receiver Verification Challenges

The eNB receiver faces many of the same MIMO challenges that the UE receiver faces, but in addition has to simultaneously receive multiple users. From the point of view of Multi-User MIMO (MU-MIMO), each signal comes from a separate UE, so each signal therefore has a completely independent channel, somewhat different power levels and different timing. These characteristics can be emulated using the Agilent N5106A MIMO receiver tester (PXB) in conjunction with RF signal generators.

The receiver test configuration for the eNB is different from the configuration for the UE. The UE normally sends packet error reports on the uplink back to the test system, whereas the eNB hardware is more likely to make a suitable demodulated signal output available.

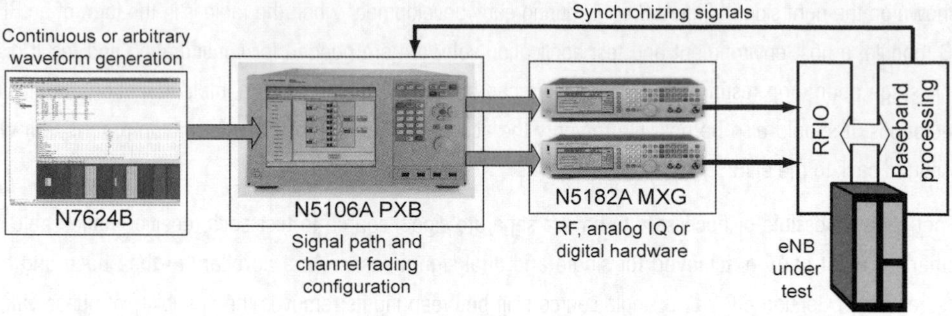

Figure 6.6-12. Continuous faded path receiver test configuration for RF, analog or digital interfaces using the N5106A (PXB) MIMO receiver tester

Figure 6.6-12 shows a typical configuration for eNB receiver test. The synchronization signals are required because it is the eNB that establishes frame timing in the system, and the eNB receiver relies on the UE adapting to the downlink reference.

Verification of UE coding can be achieved using the uplink signal routing configuration shown in Figure 6.6-13. The downlink may be configured as a separate cabled connection, using isolators from one of the eNB transmitters and UE receiver.

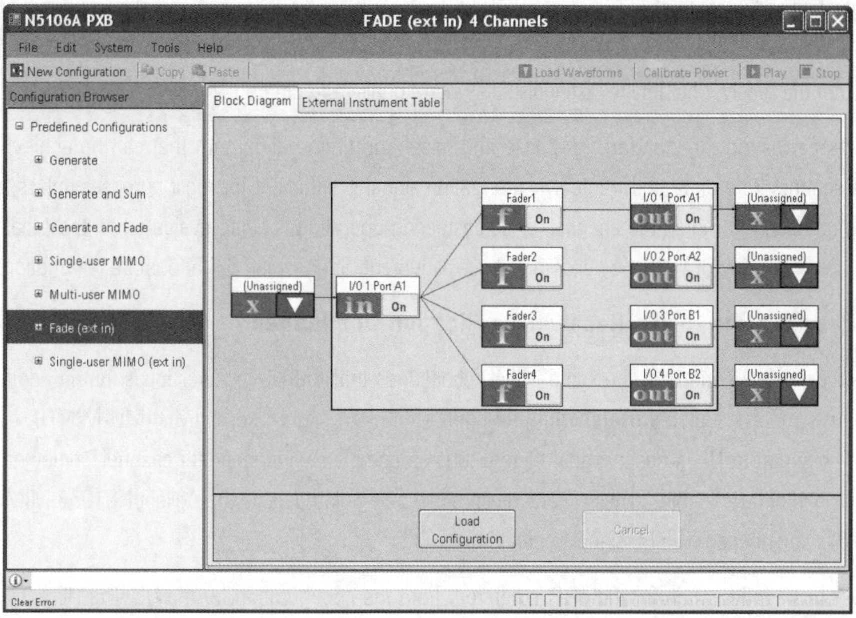

Figure 6.6-13. N5106A PXB user interface showing configuration for single RF input and four RF outputs

6.6.3.3 Verifying Interoperability Using Recorded Multi-channel RF Signals

One of the most troublesome aspects of receiver design is trying to predict what another designer has done to overcome a design constraint. A troubleshooting technique to speed up the understanding of how a third party signal interacts with a receiver is to capture the signal at RF and then replay it from a signal generator. This gives considerable flexibility in when and where the troubleshooting takes place. The recorded signals can also play a role in regression testing.

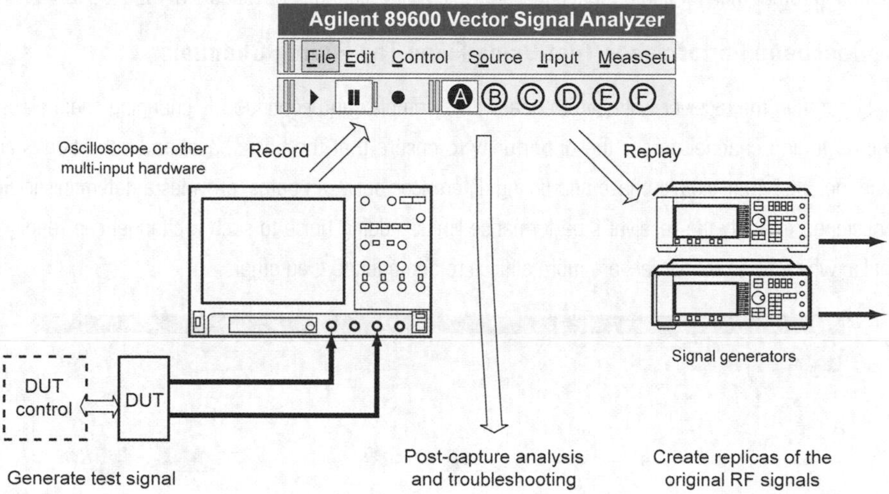

Figure 6.6-14. Dual input signal capture and replay using 89601A VSA, oscilloscope and MXG or ESG signal generators

Figure 6.6-14 shows one of the possible signal capture methods using an oscilloscope as part of the test setup. The oversampling rate may be reduced to increase the capture time when the carrier frequency is chosen to avoid sampling aliasing products.

6.6.4 Receiver Performance Testing Using Static and Continuously Faded Channels

Some general observations can be made about the antenna systems appropriate to MIMO systems for use in macro-cellular environments. Cross polarized antennas at the eNB outperform uniformly polarized antennas with equivalent characteristics. The normally wide angle of arrival at the UE antennas helps offset the close physical proximity, but in the lower frequency bands the wavelengths involved make it progressively more difficult to avoid interaction between the antennas.

To support the observations from real systems, many parameters are incorporated into the models used to emulate the physical transmission channel. The following sections assume some understanding of these parameters as they apply to a SISO channel. Described here are the additional considerations needed for MIMO channels.

MIMO channel recovery involves the separation of multiple signal components in the presence of noise and interference. When the signals are transmitted they are orthogonal, but by the time the signals reach the multiple receivers the coupling in the radiated path can reduce the difference between the signals.

Section 6.6.4.1 describes a method of using a fixed tap channel for MIMO receiver evaluation. The remainder of Section 6.6.4 addresses the parameters needed to more realistically represent the channel when a continuous fading test is used. The intention is to provide a test environment for performance testing and design troubleshooting rather than for conformance testing, which is described in Sections 6.5.4.2 and 7.2.7.2.

6.6.4.1 Baseband Performance Test Using Fixed Tap Fading Channels

In normal operation the receiver will have to deal with a complex and continuously changing channel, but testing using such a fading channel misses the opportunity to ensure that the basic baseband operation is correct. A fading channel, built from simple phase and timing differences between paths, provides a deterministic signal that can be designed to verify the receiver's performance limits. Adding noise to such a channel can readily create a test signal in which some subcarriers are more difficult to demodulate than others.

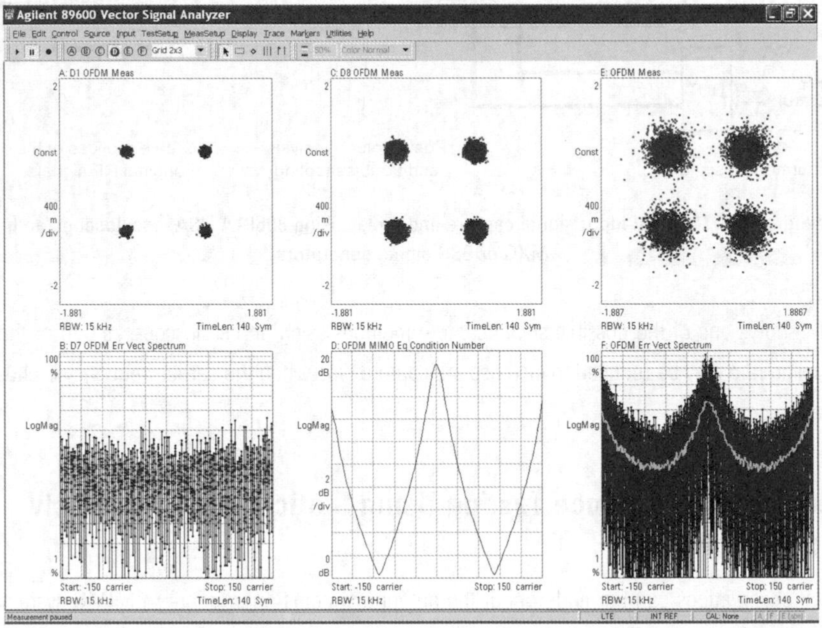

Figure 6.6-15. Example of cross-coupled, fixed tap fading channel for spatial multiplexing test

Figure 6.6-15 shows the results of a fixed tap fading channel. Trace A (top left) and Trace B (bottom left) show the SISO RS constellation and EVM spectrum, which are not affected by coupling through the channel. Trace C (top middle) is the uncoupled MIMO constellation prior to passing through the channel. Trace E (top right) shows one of the layers after passing through the channel, with the corresponding EVM spectrum shown in Trace F (bottom right). It can be seen how the EVM tracks the channel condition number shown in Trace D (bottom middle), which is the result of the 400 ns delay and –2 dB coupling parameters chosen for this example.

6.6.4.2 Spatial Correlation

MIMO systems require a rich multipath environment for optimum operation, and the spatial positions of the multiple transmit antennas, relative to each other and relative to their placement in the surrounding environment, will influence the fading correlation between the different MIMO channels. The same is true for the antenna positions at the receiver. It will be shown in this section that inadequate antenna spacing leads to spatial correlation, which limits MIMO performance gains.

The spatial correlation coefficient ρ_{12}, between two antenna elements, is a function of their spacing and the spatial power distribution of radiated or received signals; i.e., the Power Azimuth Spectrum (PAS) and the gain pattern of the individual elements. Here it is assumed that the antenna elements are identical with the same gain pattern. The correlation coefficient can be calculated using the following equation.

$$\rho_{12} = \frac{\int_{-\pi}^{\pi} e^{-j2\pi \frac{d}{\lambda}\sin(\theta)} PAS(\theta)G(\theta)\,d\theta}{\int_{-\pi}^{\pi} PAS(\theta)G(\theta)\,d\theta} \qquad (1)$$

$PAS(\theta)$ and $G(\theta)$ are calculated using one of the equations found in Agilent's application note 5989-8973EN [18]. $PAS(\theta)$ is dependent on the selection of the appropriate distribution; i.e., Laplacian, Gaussian or uniform, according to the physical environment. The parameter "d" is the distance between antenna elements. The gain pattern, $G(\theta)$, assumes that the far field assumption holds and that the two antennas have exactly the same radiation pattern and boresight direction.

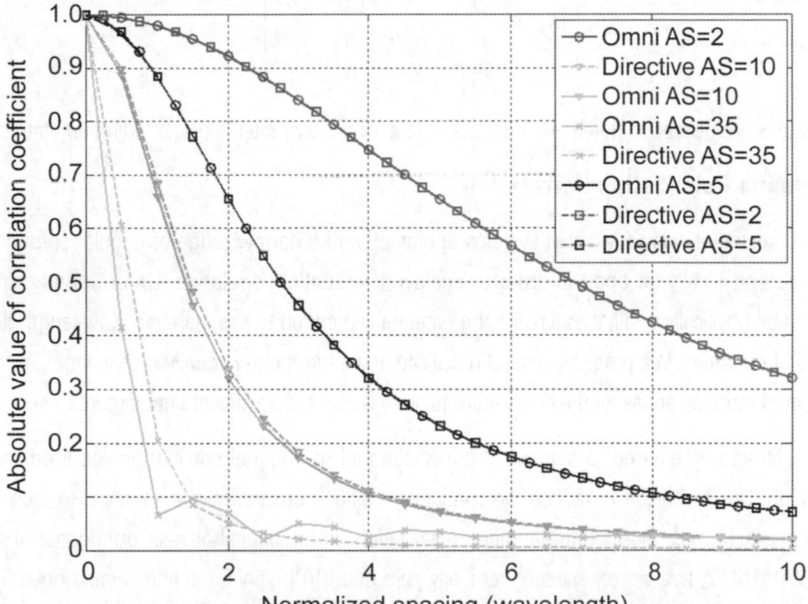

Figure 6.6-16. Relationship between antenna spacing and correlation coefficient using a Laplacian PAS with AoA=200 degrees and $\Delta\theta$ =180 degrees

Figure 6.6-16 shows the absolute value of the correlation coefficient as a function of antenna spacing for several examples of antenna type and Azimuth Spread (AS). The antenna type was varied between omni-directional and directive using a 3-sector antenna. Each curve represents a different value for AS covering 2, 5, 10 and 35 degrees. These curves assumed a single-modal Laplacian PAS with mean Angle of Arrival (AoA) of 200 degrees and $\Delta\theta$ of 180 degrees. The correlation coefficient decreases for increasing normalized spacing and for increasing AS. It is worth noting also that for a given antenna spacing and large AS=10 or 35, the directive antennas tend to be slightly more correlated than the omni-directional ones.

The spatial correlation matrix for the complete system can be calculated using equation (1) above and forming the individual spatial correlation matrices at the eNB and the UE. For example, given a 2x2 MIMO system, assume the factors α and β represent the correlation coefficients, calculated using (1), for the eNB and UE antenna pairs, respectively. The correlation matrices for eNB and the UE are represented as

$$R_{BS} = \begin{pmatrix} 1 & \alpha \\ \alpha^* & 1 \end{pmatrix}, \tag{2}$$

$$R_{MS} = \begin{pmatrix} 1 & \beta \\ \beta^* & 1 \end{pmatrix}. \tag{3}$$

The system spatial correlation matrix for the downlink channel can be calculated using the Kronecker product

$$R_S = R_{BS} \otimes R_{MS}, \tag{4}$$

$$R_S = \begin{pmatrix} 1 & \beta & \alpha & \alpha\beta \\ \beta^* & 1 & \alpha\beta^* & \alpha \\ \alpha^* & \alpha^*\beta & 1 & \beta \\ \alpha^*\beta^* & \alpha^* & \beta^* & 1 \end{pmatrix}. \tag{5}$$

These expressions are needed to determine the parameters for the user interface of a fading emulator.

6.6.4.3 Antenna Polarization Correlation

In the previous section it was shown that systems operating with a narrow range of angular spread may require antennas placed physically far apart in order to achieve low spatial correlation. Unfortunately some wireless devices tend to be physically small, thus limiting the antenna separation to less than one wavelength depending on the frequency of operation. In a practical case of a cell site, the issue is often equally prosaic: the cell tower cannot physically support more antennas, or the cost and regulatory issues are significant impediments.

An alternate solution is required to achieve the low channel-to-channel correlation required for successful MIMO operation. One technique to reduce the spatial correlation between two antennas is to cross polarize the antennas — in other words, position the antenna polarizations in orthogonal or near orthogonal orientations. As shown in Figure 6.6-17, two closely spaced, vertically polarized (0/0) dipole antennas would have a high spatial correlation while two orthogonally polarized (0/90) antennas, one vertical and one horizontal, would have a much lower correlation coefficient.

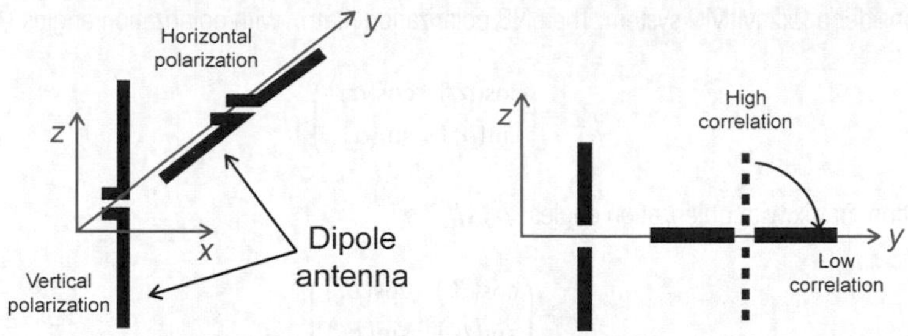

Figure 6.6-17. Diagram showing the effects of relative antenna polarization on correlation characteristics

The use of antennas with different polarizations at the transmitter or receiver may lead to power and correlation imbalances between the various MIMO channels. This implies that one layer of the transmission will have a better average performance than the others.

It is a common practice to derive the correlation matrices using the antenna configuration and angular information of the paths. The definition of channel correlation for LTE is in 36.101 [10] Subclause B.2.3. These correlation matrices are defined based on corner case conditions representing low, medium and high correlation, independent of the transmitting and receiving antenna configurations necessary to create such correlation. Developing performance requirements for MIMO operation at the corner case correlation conditions helps ensure that the underlying system behaves as expected. The next step, calculating nominal correlation matrices from actual antenna designs at specific frequencies, is outside the scope of the LTE specifications as defined by 3GPP.

Although LTE does not use the physical antenna characteristics to derive the correlation matrices, it is useful to see how this can be done to evaluate the nominal correlation for a particular design. The following example, which shows how to calculate a correlation matrix using nominal antenna configurations, is taken from the conformance test definition for WiMAX [20].

The WiMAX antenna polarization matrix at either the transmitter or receiver is given by

$$S = \begin{bmatrix} s_{vv} & s_{vh} \\ s_{hv} & s_{hh} \end{bmatrix}, \tag{6}$$

where the index v represents vertical polarization and h horizontal polarization. The first index denotes the polarization at the transmitter and the second denotes the polarization at the receiver. Correlation between polarized antennas can be quantified using the Cross Polarization Ratio (XPR). The XPR is the power ratio between a pair of cross polarized antennas (v-h or h-v) to that of a co-polarized (v-v or h-h) case. Assume that the XPR = –8 dB, then

$$\frac{|s_{vh}|^2}{|s_{vv}|^2} = \frac{|s_{vh}|^2}{|s_{hh}|^2} = -8\,\text{dB}\,(= 0.1585). \tag{7}$$

For example, consider a 2x2 MIMO system. The eNB polarization matrix with polarization angles α_1, α_2 is

$$P_{BS} = \begin{pmatrix} \cos(\alpha_1) & \cos(\alpha_2) \\ \sin(\alpha_1) & \sin(\alpha_2) \end{pmatrix}. \tag{8}$$

The UE polarization matrix with polarization angles β_1, β_2 is

$$P_{MS} = \begin{pmatrix} \cos(\beta_1) & \cos(\beta_2) \\ \sin(\beta_1) & \sin(\beta_2) \end{pmatrix}. \tag{9}$$

For the downlink case, the total channel polarization matrix is the matrix product of the eNB polarization, channel polarization and UE polarization:

$$Q = P_{MS}{}^{T} S P_{BS}. \tag{10}$$

Lastly, the polarization correlation matrix is defined as

$$\Gamma = E\left\{\mathrm{vec}(\mathrm{Q}) \cdot \mathrm{vec}(\mathrm{Q})^{H}\right\}. \tag{11}$$

For specified polarization angles, such as +45/−45, 0/90 and 0/0, the diagonal elements of Γ have the same value, which means there is no power imbalance between different channels. For arbitrary polarization angles, the diagonal elements of Γ are not equal, which means that polarization leads to an undesired power imbalance between the channels.

Normalization of Γ is required so that the diagonal elements reflect the channel power. In this case the correlation matrix then becomes

$$\Gamma^{R} = \frac{K}{\sum_{i=1}^{K} \Gamma_{i,j}} \Gamma. \tag{12}$$

This power normalization process is based on the assumption that the overall channel power is $K = N_{\gamma} N_{t}$ for a MIMO system with N_t transmit antennas and N_r receive antennas. The correlation matrix Γ^{R} will properly reflect the channel imbalance due to polarization, and the diagonal elements in Γ^{R} relate to the relative power in each channel.

Using a 2x2 MIMO channel as an example, assume that the XPR = −8 dB and the system uses cross-polarized UE antennas (0/90) and slant-polarized eNB antennas (+45/−45). The resulting polarization correlation matrix is

$$\Gamma^{R} = \begin{pmatrix} 1 & 0 & 0.7264 & 0 \\ 0 & 1 & 0 & -0.7264 \\ 0.7264 & 0 & 1 & 0 \\ 0 & -0.7264 & 0 & 1 \end{pmatrix}. \tag{13}$$

The diagonal elements of this polarization correlation matrix are all ones, which show that the selected polarization angles do not result in a power imbalance among the different MIMO channels. The other elements in the matrix relate to the correlation between different channels. For example, in the first row, this matrix shows that channel 1 is only correlated to channel 3 with a coefficient of 0.7264. The second row shows that channel 2 is only correlated with channel 4. It can be shown that the use of antennas with differing polarizations at the transmitter and receiver leads to polarization diversity, giving worthwhile performance improvements and enabling antenna designs that do not require the spatial separation otherwise expected.

As another example, consider a case in which the correlation matrix results in a power imbalance. Here, assume that the antenna polarization angles are −10/80 at UE antenna and +30/−60 at eNB. The resulting polarization correlation matrix is

$$\Gamma^R = \begin{pmatrix} 1.3413 & 0.1242 & 0.5911 & 0.2151 \\ 0.1242 & 0.6587 & 0.2151 & -0.5911 \\ 0.5911 & 0.2151 & 0.6587 & -0.1242 \\ 0.2151 & -0.5911 & -0.1242 & 1.3413 \end{pmatrix}. \quad (14)$$

For this matrix, the diagonal elements are not equal and therefore demonstrate that using this combination of polarization angles leads to a power imbalance among the different channels.

6.6.4.4 Combined Spatial and Antenna Polarization Correlation

Spatial and polarization correlation effects in compound antenna systems are independent and multiplicative. In this case, the corresponding spatial and polarization correlation matrices can be derived separately and combined by an element-wise matrix product. The combined spatial-polarization correlation matrix is then defined as

$$R = R_S \cdot \Gamma^R, \quad (15)$$

where R_S is the system spatial correlation matrix using equation (5) and Γ^R is the polarization correlation matrix calculated using equation (12).

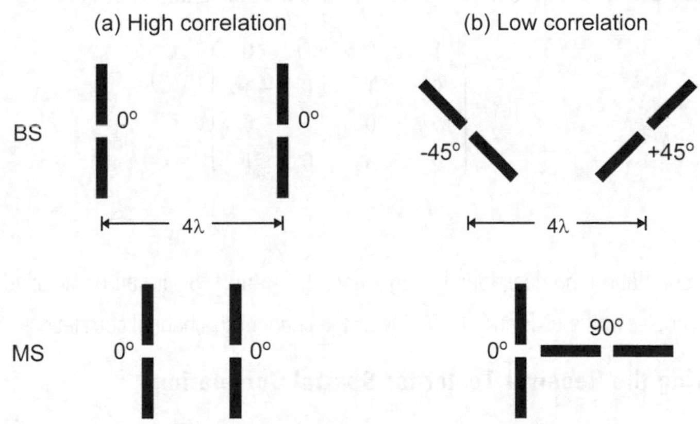

Figure 6.6-18. eNB and UE antenna configurations for (a) high and (b) low channel correlations

Orthogonal antenna positions (0/90) provide the lowest spatial correlation but may not always be required or practical under all conditions. For example, the diagrams in Figure 6.6-18 show two possible 2x2 MIMO configurations for the eNB and UE antenna positioning. In one case, as shown in Figure 6.6-18(a), all the antennas are vertically polarized resulting in a potentially high level of spatial correlation. To overcome this problem, the eNB antennas are spaced at 4λ to improve the correlation for this typically narrow angle spread condition. The spacing at the UE is fixed at λ/2. This first case is the reference antenna configuration for the high correlation channel model as specified in the WiMAX standard. For this high correlation condition, all the antennas have the same polarization angle, which does not provide any polarization diversity. Therefore the polarization matrix is defined as

$$\Gamma^R = \begin{pmatrix} 1 & 1 & 1 & 1 \\ 1 & 1 & 1 & 1 \\ 1 & 1 & 1 & 1 \\ 1 & 1 & 1 & 1 \end{pmatrix}. \qquad (16)$$

By applying equation (15) to this high correlation antenna configuration, the combined spatial-polarization correlation matrix is the same as the spatial correlation matrix previously defined in equation (5):

$$R = R_S \cdot \Gamma^R = \begin{pmatrix} 1 & \beta & \alpha & \alpha\beta \\ \beta^* & 1 & \alpha\beta^* & \alpha \\ \alpha^* & \alpha^*\beta & 1 & \beta \\ \alpha^*\beta^* & \alpha^* & \beta^* & 1 \end{pmatrix}. \qquad (17)$$

The second case, as shown in Figure 6.6-18(b), has the antennas at the eNB polarized at ±45 degree orientations while the UE uses orthogonal polarization (0/90). This second combination can greatly reduce channel-to-channel correlation, thus enabling better operation of the MIMO system. This combination is the reference antenna configuration for the low correlation channel model for WiMAX conformance testing. For this configuration, the polarization matrix was defined in equation (13) and the final correlation matrix is defined as

$$R = \begin{pmatrix} 1 & 0 & \gamma\alpha & 0 \\ 0 & 1 & 0 & -\gamma\alpha \\ \gamma\alpha^* & 0 & 1 & 0 \\ 0 & -\gamma\alpha^* & 0 & 1 \end{pmatrix}, \qquad (18)$$

where $\gamma = 0.7264$.

Comparing the two correlation matrices found in equations (17) and (18), it can be concluded that introducing different polarization angles at the eNB and UE will lower the channel-to-channel correlations.

6.6.4.5 Configuring the Receiver Tester for Spatial Correlation

It is possible to improve the process of entering the correlation matrices into a wireless channel emulator while minimizing the mathematical complexity and still be capable of modeling realistic wireless channels. The PXB MIMO receiver tester greatly improves the process of MIMO channel emulation by eliminating the need to calculate complex correlation matrices. Users can enter the physical antenna characteristics directly in the instrument. For example, Figure 6.6-19 shows the PXB user interface for entering the receive channel spatial parameters including antenna type, spacing and polarization. A similar table is used to enter the transmit antenna parameters. PXB uses this spatial information along with the AoA and AoD entries in the fading paths table to automatically calculate the spatial-polarization correlation matrix. This simple entry table eliminates the burden of calculating the correlation matrices and manually entering the coefficients into the emulator.

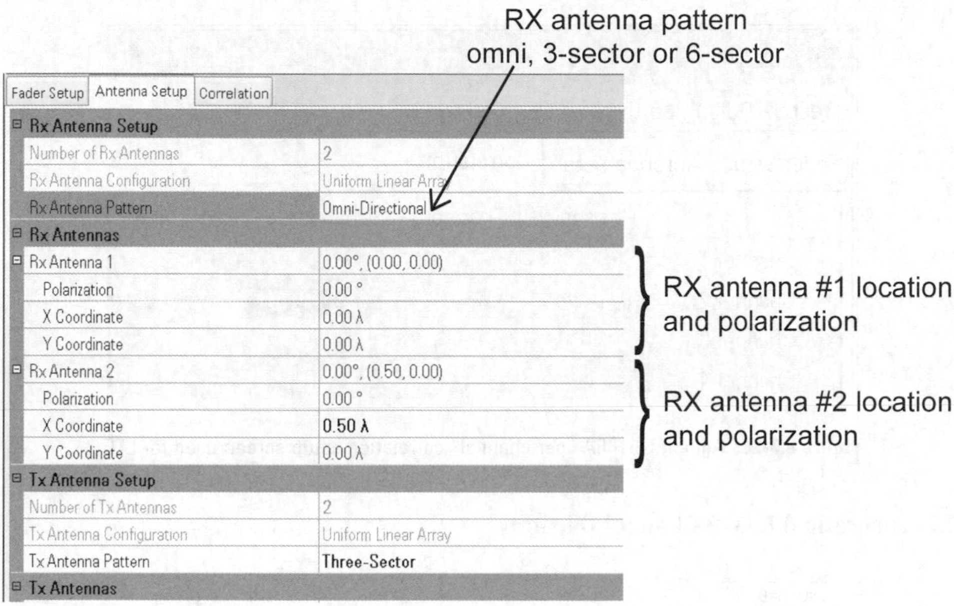

Figure 6.6-19. Agilent N5106A PXB antenna parameter setup screen

6.6.4.6 Per Path vs. Per Channel Correlation

When test conditions for emulating MIMO channels are standardized, the correlation properties can be "per-path" or "per-channel." Per-path correlation means that each tap uses a different correlation matrix, while per-channel correlation means that all the taps use same correlation matrix. As explained above, the spatial correlation coefficient between two antenna elements is a function of antenna spacing, the PAS, and the radiation pattern of the antenna elements. The PAS is a function of path AoA/AoD and path AS. In real-world conditions not all paths have the same AoA/AoD and AS values; therefore, different paths could have different correlation coefficients. The use of per-path correlation may improve the fidelity of the channel emulation process. In order to emulate this real-world scenario, the MIMO channel models used for Mobile WiMAX and the WLAN 802.11n standards use the per-path correlation based on different AoA/AoD for each path. While per-path spatial correlation can closely model a real wireless channel, it has a high level of computational complexity. The PXB has pre-defined channel models to automatically configure the instrument's path correlations.

The LTE requirements, in an effort to reduce MIMO complexity, recommend the per-channel correlation model without considering the path AoA/AoD information. When a MIMO system is tested against these specifications, the PXB can also provide per-channel correlations using pre-defined models, or, as shown in Figure 6.6-20, provide a simple table entry for custom per-channel emulation models.

When wireless channels are emulated, it is important to understand the test requirements in relation to spatial correlations. The PXB tester has flexibility to support both per-path correlation and per-channel correlation, either individually or at the same time.

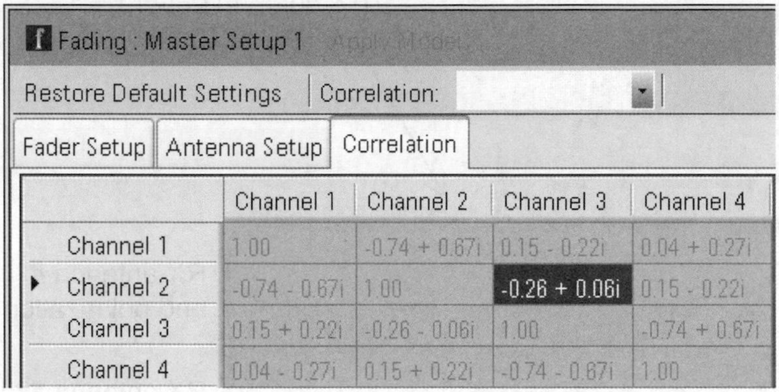

	Channel 1	Channel 2	Channel 3	Channel 4
Channel 1	1.00	-0.74 + 0.67i	0.15 - 0.22i	0.04 + 0.27i
Channel 2	-0.74 - 0.67i	1.00	-0.26 + 0.06i	0.15 - 0.22i
Channel 3	0.15 + 0.22i	-0.26 - 0.06i	1.00	-0.74 + 0.67i
Channel 4	0.04 - 0.27i	0.15 + 0.22i	-0.74 - 0.67i	1.00

Figure 6.6-20. Agilent N5106A "per-channel" correlation setup screen used for LTE

6.6.4.7 Theoretical MIMO Channel Capacity

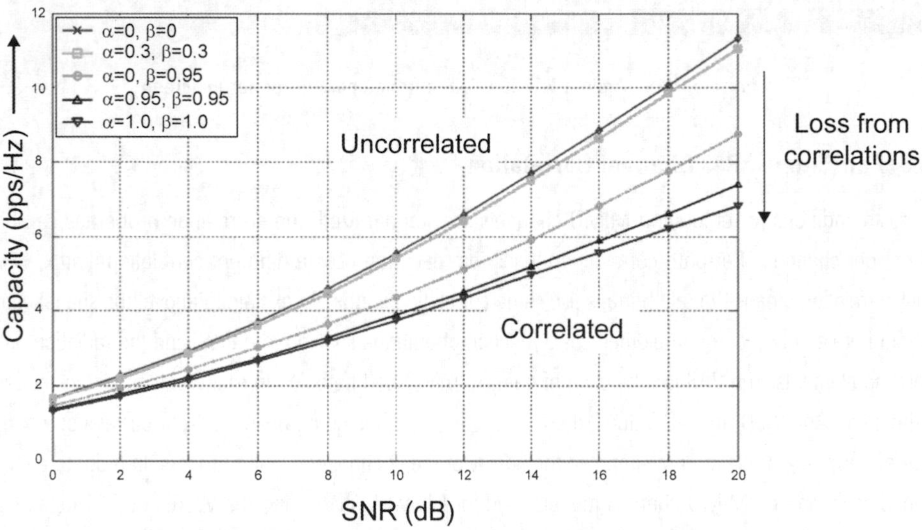

Figure 6.6-21. Ergodic (statistically representative) capacity for a 2x2 MIMO system with different transmit and receive correlation coefficients

To give a more intuitive impression of the channel capacity loss caused by fading correlation, Figure 6.6-21 compares the capacity as a function of SNR for a 2x2 MIMO system with different correlation coefficients at the transmitter (α) and the receiver (β). Compared with the completely independent MIMO channel ($\alpha = \beta = 0$), the figure shows that there is only a small capacity loss for the low correlated channels ($\alpha = \beta = 0.3$). For highly correlated channels ($\alpha = \beta = 0.95$) at high SNR, the capacity decreases by 3.9 bps/Hz compared to the ideal uncorrelated case. For completely correlated channels ($\alpha = \beta = 1.0$), the capacity decreases by 4.4 bps/Hz at high SNR. Note that even when the correlation coefficients are 1, there is still an increase in capacity relative to SISO, though the improvements are small, from the increase in number of antenna pairs. The largest improvements are achieved when the channels are independent. In this case the MIMO capacity is improvement by approximately the SISO capacity multiplied by min (N_t, N_r). See "Capacity scaling in MIMO wireless systems under correlated fading" [21]. Note that the median SNR in typical cells is less than 10 dB.

6.6.4.8 Using Condition Number to Understand the Performance Limitations of a MIMO Channel

An alternative way to view the impact of the MIMO channel is to use the channel condition number calculation. It provides an understanding of what takes place frame by frame, rather than using the statistical methods described earlier.

In Figure 6.6-22, two samples have been taken from a Pedestrian A channel. Although not primarily intended for faded channel measurements, the Agilent 89601A VSA is able to demodulate this relatively benign channel and display the results. The noise in the channel was set by adjusting the input level of the measurement system.

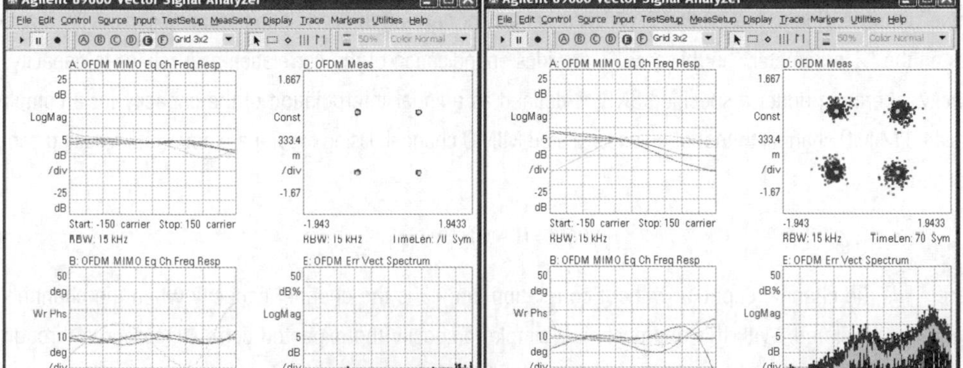

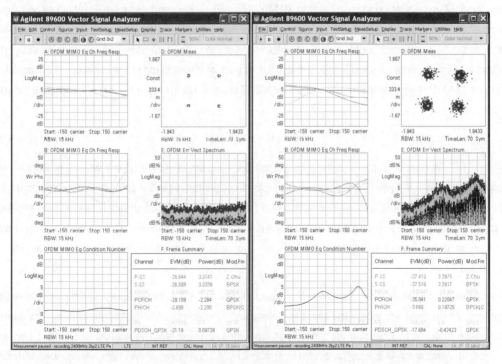

Figure 6.6-22. Measurements from a Pedestrian A faded channel showing channel frequency responses, condition number and effect on EVM versus subcarrier

The matrix condition number is calculated for each subcarrier frequency and plotted below the corresponding channel amplitude and phase responses. As expected, in the 2x2 system shown, four traces are used to represent each component of the channel. In the left half of Figure 6.6-22, the condition number response, shown in the bottom left trace, is approximately 10 dB. This value is typical of a good MIMO channel. The resultant EVM is about 3%. It is plotted in the center right trace on a logarithmic scale to allow a direct comparison with the condition number.

On the right half of Figure 6.6-22, a second sample shows a very different response. This is not unusual for a faded channel. The condition number trace shows several peaks, and a gradual increase in condition number from left to right — i.e. the upper subcarriers — have a poorer MIMO channel than the lower half. The EVM plot in the center right trace shows how the degradation in condition number points to worsening demodulation performance. In practice, this would imply using closed loop operation with frequency-selective scheduling to avoid transmitting the MIMO signal at the upper part of the channel. There is another aspect of the MIMO channel that is not immediately obvious: in any particular channel, the performance for different layers may not be the same. This is discussed further in Section 6.6.4.12.

6.6.4.9 Configuring the Channel Emulator to Achieve the Desired Correlation

Under ideal channel conditions, MIMO systems can provide dramatic channel capacity gain through increased spatial diversity. However, the capacity gain is reduced if the fading characteristic among various channels is correlated. Many wireless standards, such as WiMAX and LTE, recommend test scenarios that use correlated channel matrices. One approach that is widely accepted for defining the correlation properties of a MIMO channel relies on the "λ-parameter." In this case, λ provides an indication of the correlation as it relates to capacity. The capacity, operating under a specified SNR, is defined as a linear interpolation of the capacity for a completely correlated MIMO channel to that of an uncorrelated MIMO channel. Using the λ-parameter, the resulting capacity is defined as

$$C_\lambda = (1-\lambda)C_0 + \lambda C_1, \tag{19}$$

where C_0 is the channel capacity without correlation and C_l is the channel capacity when the channels are completely correlated. With this approach, it is simple to specify the expected correlation degree through the λ parameter. For example, in the LTE channel model for 2x2 antenna configurations, the medium and high correlation matrices are defined using values of $\lambda \approx 0.5$ and $\lambda \approx 0.9$, respectively. For a system operating with a target value for λ and under a specified SNR, the correlation matrix can be tuned to achieve the desired correlation.

The correlation matrix that can guarantee the expected capacity, C_λ, is not unique and different correlation matrices can be chosen to satisfy this capacity requirement. One very flexible method of achieving the desired correlation matrix is by adjusting the antenna configuration, such as element spacing and polarization. For example, the eNB antenna spacing is adjusted using a 2x2 MIMO configuration with vertically polarized antennas, as was shown in Figure 6.6-18(a), until the desired correlation is achieved. The antenna parameters for the UE are fixed with values shown in Table 6.6-5. The receiver correlation coefficient, β, is calculated using equation (1).

Table 6.6-5. UE (receiver) antenna configuration

	Antenna spacing in wavelength	Antenna type	AS (degrees)	AoA (degrees)	Correlation coefficient (β)
UE	0.5	Omni	35	67.5	−0.6905 + 0.3419i

For this example, the eNB uses a 3-sector antenna configuration with AS = 2 degrees and AoD = 50 degrees. The eNB correlation coefficient, α, changes when the spacing between the eNB antenna elements is adjusted. With this configuration, the combined spatial-polarization correlation matrix can be calculated using equation (17). If the calculated channel capacity is lower than the desired channel capacity, the antenna spacing is increased to reduce the correlation and thus increase the channel capacity. By iteratively adjusting the antenna spacing, the desired λ can be achieved. Table 6.6-6 shows correlation index λ as a function of eNB antenna spacing for this 2x2 MIMO example.

Table 6.6-6. Relationship between eNB antenna spacing, correlation coefficient and channel capacity under specified SNR values

Antenna spacing d	correlation coefficient α	λ SNR=10 dB	λ SNR=20 dB
0	1.0000	0.9060	0.9445
0.5	−0.7390 + 0.6700i	0.9004	0.9270
1.0	0.0969 − 0.9854i	0.8921	0.8806
1.5	0.5827 + 0.7857i	0.8543	0.8189
2.0	−0.9433 − 0.1881i	0.8252	0.7598
3.0	−0.2687 + 0.8779i	0.7591	0.6542
4.0	0.7955 + 0.3350i	0.6958	0.5636
5.0	0.3854 − 0.7028i	0.6246	0.4951
6.0	−0.6061 − 0.4196i	0.5704	0.4389
7.0	−0.4388 + 0.5106i	0.5232	0.3971

6.6.4.10 Adding Noise to a Multiple Input Receiver Test

Adding noise to SISO signals is necessary to allow the baseband developer to understand the performance limitations of the demodulator. When a multiple input receiver is verified, the correlation of the noise between channels becomes an important factor to address.

6.6.4.11 SNR for SISO and Uncorrelated MIMO Channels

A convenient place for setting the channel's SNR is typically at the receiver. The signal power can be accurately measured with a power meter and the channel emulator can generate the required noise according to the desired SNR. This technique is valid for SISO systems and for MIMO systems that have uncorrelated channels. When the MIMO channels are correlated, an alternate approach to measuring the signal power and generating noise is required.

For SISO systems, the received signal, Y, is defined as

$$Y = HX + N, \tag{20}$$

where X is the transmitted data, H is the channel coefficient and N is the noise. For a specified SNR, the signal power, S, is first measured at the output of the channel emulator in the absence of noise. The covariance of the noise, σ^2, being a random Gaussian process, can be calculated and added by the channel emulator to simulate the effect of applying noise to the SISO channel. As shown in Agilent application note 5989-8973EN appendix B [18], this technique is also valid for uncorrelated MIMO channels. In this case, the signal at the receiver can also be defined using equation (20) where X is now a vector of M_t transmitted signals, H is the channel coefficient matrix with M_r rows and M_t columns, and Y is a vector of M_r received signals. In the MIMO case, N is an M_r row of random Gaussian processes. It is also shown in the same reference that the signal power can be measured at either the receiver or the transmitter for the uncorrelated MIMO system.

6.6.4.12 SNR for Correlated MIMO Channels

When the MIMO channels are correlated, the measured signal power at the receiver side can be dependent on the correlation of the channels. This correlation dependency prevents a channel emulator from accurately configuring the MIMO system for a desired SNR using power measurements at the receiver. To overcome this difficulty, the channel emulator can use measurements of the signal power at the transmitter to appropriately set the required SNR. The following derivation shows a simplified example using a 2x1 MISO system to demonstrate an appropriate measurement technique for configuring the SNR in a channel emulator when the channels are correlated. The MISO pre-coding matrix is defined as

$$\frac{1}{\sqrt{2}}\begin{bmatrix} 1 \\ e^{j\theta} \end{bmatrix}. \tag{21}$$

The signal transmitted from antenna 1 is $X/\sqrt{2}$, the signal transmitted from antenna 2 is $Xe^{j\theta}/\sqrt{2}$ and the transmitted signal power from each antenna is S. The channel between transmit antenna 1 and the receive antenna is H_1. The channel between transmit antenna 2 and the receive antenna is H_2. Using equation (20), the received signal becomes

$$Y = \frac{X}{\sqrt{2}}H_1 + \frac{Xe^{j\theta}}{\sqrt{2}}H_2. \tag{22}$$

If H_1 is independent with H_2, the received signal power is

$$E(YY^*) = (\overline{H}_1 + \overline{H}_2)S, \tag{23}$$

where $\overline{H}_1$ and $\overline{H}_2$ represent average channel gains of H_1 and H_2 respectively. When $\overline{H}_1 = \overline{H}_2 = \overline{H}$ then $E(YY^*) = 2\overline{H}S$.

If $\overline{H}_1$ is completely correlated with $\overline{H}_2$, meaning that $\overline{H}_1 = \overline{H}_2 = \overline{H}$, then the received signal becomes

$$Y = \left(1 + e^{j\theta}\right) H \frac{X}{\sqrt{2}}, \qquad (24)$$

and the received signal power is

$$E\left(YY^*\right) = 2\left(1 + \cos(\theta)\right)\overline{H}S. \qquad (25)$$

When $\theta = \pi/4$, the received signal power becomes $2(1+\sqrt{2}/2)\,\overline{H}S$, which is different from the case with independent channel conditions. Therefore, if the measured signal power at the receiver is used to calculate the noise power required for a specific SNR, then the added noise power will vary according to the fading correlation property. Continually adjusting the noise power as a function of correlation property introduces unnecessary complexity into the measurement and may result in reduced accuracy when the required SNR is configured. To overcome this difficulty, the PXB tester defines the SNR relative to the transmitted signal power and uses the following SNR definition:

$$SNR = \frac{S_1\overline{H}_1 + S_2\overline{H}_2}{\sigma^2}, \qquad (26)$$

where S_1 and S_2 are the signal powers from each transmitter. With this definition, the PXB measures the signal power at the transmitters prior to fading and then adds the appropriate noise power to achieve the desired SNR. In this technique the noise contribution can be determined without considering the fading correlation property of the channel.

6.6.5 Requirements for Phase Coherence

This section describes the impact of phase coherence and potential solutions. For directly mapped, open loop MIMO testing, the phase relationship between the test signals does not affect the performance of the receiver because orthogonal signals have to be coupled twice for vector addition to take place. In closed loop systems, the phase between test signals needs to be constant during the period when the channel is sampled, allowing any coupling coefficients to be calculated and applied. This may require the system to be stable rather than phase-locked.

It was shown earlier that the channel condition number can be used to determine the SNR needed to achieve a specific performance at the demodulator. The condition number gives a measure of the composite channel performance. Each layer of the MIMO signal may actually have a different performance. The plots in Figure 6.6-23 show the demodulated signals from a single frame of an LTE signal. The channel was flat-faded (no frequency selectivity).

The two constellations at the top of the figure show the two layers of the MIMO signal. It is clear that the constellation on the left is tighter, which would result in a lower BER in a real receiver.

If the channel characteristics are known — e.g., by the UE sending channel state information to the eNB — the mismatch in performance can be dealt with in either of two ways. The layer with better performance can be loaded with a higher order modulation, or precoding can be applied to equalize the performance of the two layers.

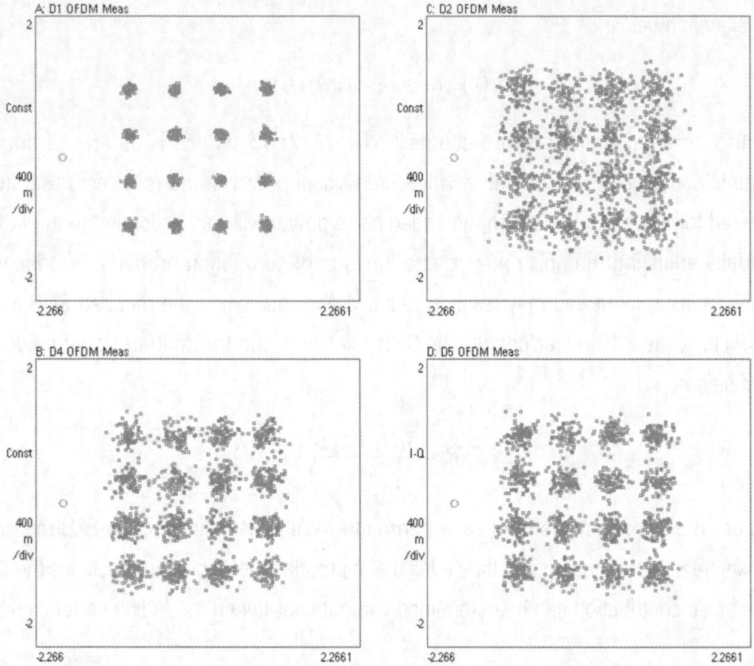

Figure 6.6-23. Spatial multiplexed signals without precoding (top) and with precoding (bottom) to match the channel

In LTE, the codebook index method is used to facilitate channel precoding, with a small number of codes used to minimize the system overhead in signalling. This means that the codebook index provides an approximation to the channel, implying some level of residual error. Figure 6.6-24 shows that once a codebook is chosen to equalize the EVM, the actual EVM still depends on the phase match between the transmitters.

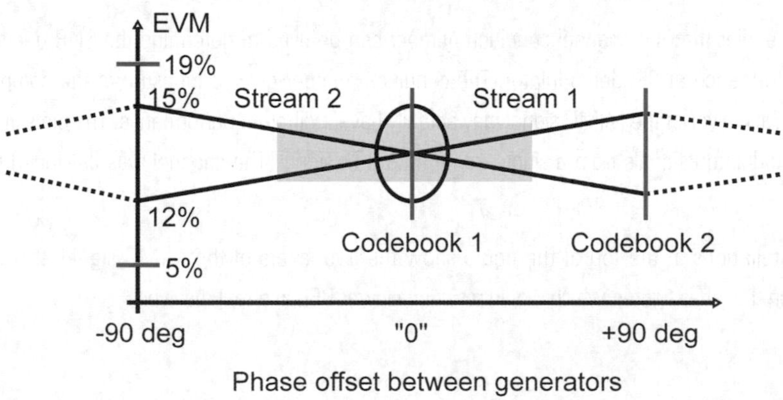

Figure 6.6-24. Impact of phase errors on precoding effectiveness, with example performance values

The rectangular block at the center of the figure represents the region in which codebook 1 would be chosen as the best fit. The diagonal lines show how the EVM of each stream varies with phase error. EVM is used as a performance metric, but BER could be also used. In the best circumstance, the codebook exactly fits the channel state and the performance of both layers is made the same. This is the case for the constellations in the lower half of Figure 6.6-23. As the phase between the transmitters varies — indicating that a mismatch in the codebook choice or variation in the channel occurred after the channel station information was provided — the layer performance separates. At extremes, the performance of the layers can be swapped.

For receiver measurements, the significance of precoding errors can be seen in the need for a fixed RF phase relationship at the output of the signal generators being used for a test. The term phase coherence is used to signify that the RF phase at the outputs of two or more generators is being maintained at a specified frequency.

When it is necessary to guarantee that phase will not change versus frequency, a test configuration such as that shown in Figure 6.6-25 can be used. Note that when two generators are used, the external Local Oscillator (LO) is not required.

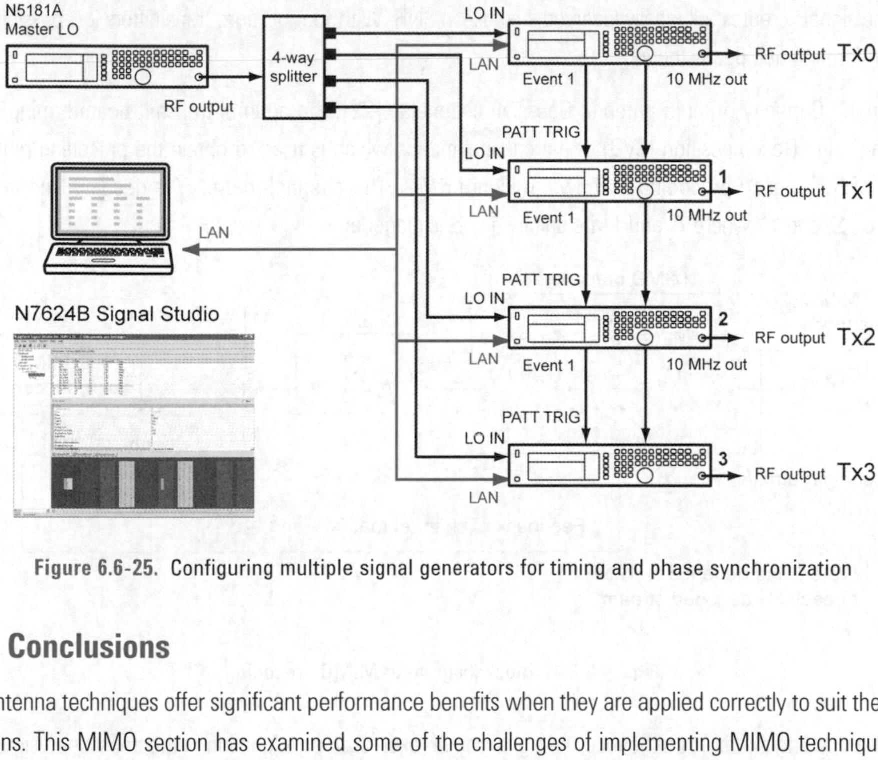

Figure 6.6-25. Configuring multiple signal generators for timing and phase synchronization

6.6.6 Conclusions

Multi-antenna techniques offer significant performance benefits when they are applied correctly to suit the channel conditions. This MIMO section has examined some of the challenges of implementing MIMO techniques in the transmitters and receivers of LTE eNBs and UEs. A number of measurement techniques have been identified that allow the impact of cross coupling, timing errors and distortion to be analyzed in the transmitter.

The issues for the receiver include the need to test performance with a wide variety of impaired signals. Impairments in this case include noise, interference and channel fading. The extensive features available in the N5106A PXB MIMO receiver tester provide the flexibility needed to make these tests.

6.7 MIMO Closed Loop Operation

6.7.1 Introduction

In LTE, closed loop MIMO is one of the key technologies for delivering the performance gains relative to the Release 6 HSPA baseline discussed in Chapter 1. The basics of MIMO operation are described in Section 2.4 and the open loop RF aspects are described in Section 6.6. This section focuses on closed loop operation and some of the performance tradeoffs inherent in the system design and implementation. Closed loop MIMO is a high performance system comprising four types of physical layer indicators: Channel Quality Indicator (CQI), Precoding Matrix Indicator (PMI), Rank Indication (RI) and Hybrid Automatic Repeat Request (HARQ) indicator as described in Section 2.4. This section focuses on the PMI.

The PMI is the feedback metric used for MIMO precoding. The precoding process is used to optimize the quality of the signal at the receiver. For multiple layer transmission, precoding takes the form of spatial beamforming with the goal of minimizing the coupling between the spatial streams. In the case of single layer transmission, precoding is used for beamsteering, which directs the energy from the different transmitters towards the receiver so that the sum of the signals creates a spatially localized increase in SNR. With four or more transmitters it is possible to mix both beamforming and beamsteering.

As shown in "Capacity of multi-antenna Gaussian channels" [22], the optimal transmit beamforming scheme is Singular Value Decomposition (SVD) of the channel matrix, which is used to obtain the precoding matrix. The principle of SVD-based precoding is shown in Figure 6.7-1. The channel matrix H is decomposed into three matrices U, Σ, and V' where U and V are unitary and Σ is diagonal.

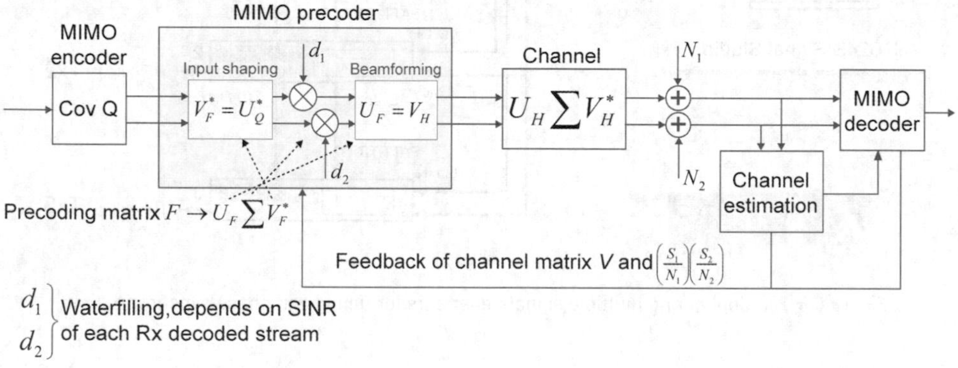

Figure 6.7-1. Block diagram of MIMO precoding

If F is the precoding matrix, then the received signal can be expressed as a function of the transmitted signal:

$$R = HFS + N \quad (1)$$

In the example of a 4x2 configuration, R and N are vectors with two entries, S is a vector with four entries, F is a 4x4 matrix and H is a 4x2 matrix.

If SVD is applied to both H and F, $U_H \Sigma V_H^*$ and $U_F \Sigma V_F^*$ are obtained and (1) becomes

$$R = U_H \Sigma_H V_H^* U_F \Sigma_F V_F^* S + N. \quad (2)$$

The goal of precoding for beamforming is to cancel as much of the interference among the spatial streams as possible, thus maximizing the SINR. The result of the product of the channel matrix and the precoding matrix should be a diagonal matrix. If the matrices Σ_F and V_F^* are left out, (2) can be rewritten as

$$U_H^* R = U_H^* U_H \Sigma_H V_H^* U_F S + U_H^* N. \quad (3)$$

If $U_F = V_H$, then (3) reduces to $U_H^* R = \Sigma_H S + N$, which is the desired result ($\widetilde{N}$ is still AWGN as U is unitary). The matrix Σ_H is a diagonal matrix with the eigenvalues of H. To achieve optimal performance, the different streams use different coding and modulation according to the eigenvalues.

From the above it can be concluded that SVD-based precoding is an attractive method, especially if adaptive modulation and coding is used for each codeword.

6.7.2 Optimizing PMI Feedback

In practical systems the information bandwidth available for channel feedback is limited and it is not efficient to transmit the full V beamforming matrix from the receiver back to the transmitter to achieve the optimal precoding. To illustrate this point consider the following example: user 1 (two antenna ports) is allocated five RBs by the eNB (four antenna ports) and uses closed loop spatial multiplexing with two layers. Theoretically, user 1 should feedback a channel matrix per subcarrier with zero delay. Practically, the smallest update interval is 1 TTI (one subframe, 1 ms) and a resource block is twelve subcarriers wide. Using a resolution of eight bits for the precoding matrix coefficients, the required information bandwidth of the feedback can be calculated as:

$$\frac{5 \times 12 \times 4 \times 2 \times 8 \text{ bits}}{1 \text{ ms}} = 3.84 \text{ Mbps},$$

where 5 is the number of RBs, 12 is the number of subcarriers, 4x2 is the channel coefficients, 8 bits is the quantization and 1 ms is the update interval.

In LTE, several mechanisms have been developed to reduce the amount of feedback to a reasonable level. These mechanisms include codebook based precoding, frequency clustering, and longer and variable feedback period.

6.7.2.1 Codebook-based Precoding

The principle of codebook-based precoding is to restrict the choice of precoding matrix (denoted W in LTE) to among a limited set of predefined matrices called the codebook (C). The codebook chosen for LTE contains Householder unitary matrices, maximizing the minimum chordal distance (performance close to the optimal random codebooks). The receiver, having estimated the channel realization, makes a decision on the optimal precoding matrix from the codebook to be used at the transmitter. The index of that matrix in C is then sent to the transmitter using the uplink channel. The selection process is implementation-specific but usually reduces to a simple optimization problem, as discussed in "Limited Feedback Unitary Precoding for Spatial Multiplexing Systems" [23].

For Minimum Mean Squared Error (MMSE) receivers, the output of the MIMO receiver is a function of the precoding matrix W where $W \in [C_1 \ldots C_L]$ used at the transmitter and the Minimum Squared Error (MSE) criterion can be expressed as

$$\overline{MSE}(W) = \frac{E_S}{N_0} tr\left\{\left(I_{M_{tx}} + \frac{E_S}{N_{rx}N_0} W^H H^H HW\right)^{-1}\right\}.$$

The receiver selects the best precoding matrix that minimizes the mean squared error:

$$W = \arg \min_{l \in \{1,2,\ldots,L\}} MSE(W_l),$$

where l is the index of the codebook matrix, L is the size of the codebook and $\log_2(L)$ is the number of bits required to encode the codebook index. The MSE computation can be further simplified by taking into account the Householder structure of the matrix.

The codebook size for LTE has sixteen entries for four antenna ports and four entries for two antenna ports.

6.7.2.2 Frequency Clustering

The second PMI compression mechanism in LTE is frequency clustering. When the channel does not contain significant frequency selectivity, adjacent subcarriers are likely to share the same choice for the precoding matrix. This is also true for adjacent resource blocks so the reporting is limited to one PMI per group of RBs. As explained in Section 3.4.2, one group of RBs sharing the same feedback indicators is called a subband. For lower rate feedback transmissions using the PUCCH rather than PUSCH, an additional layer of clustering is introduced, grouping the subbands into bandwidth parts.

6.7.2.3 Variable Feedback Reporting Period

The time domain counterpart of frequency clustering is the variable feedback reporting period. This parameter is closely linked to the coherence time of the channel: for high speeds a fast update is required as channel realizations become outdated quickly, while for low speeds a lower update rate can be used as the channel coherence time is longer.

6.7.3 Factors Impacting the Performance of Downlink Closed Loop MIMO

The PMI feedback compression schemes described in the previous section impact the performance of the link. This section discusses the ways in which the compression and other feedback impairments affect the overall closed loop MIMO performance.

The following different parameters will be discussed:

- Feedback period/rate
- Feedback granularity
- Feedback delay
- UE speed
- Feedback errors

The impact of each parameter will be assessed by simulation in terms of Block Error Ratio (BLER) versus the received signal to noise ratio (SNR) in a typical closed loop environment.

The following parameters are used in the simulations:

Table 6.7-1. Settings for PMI feedback simulation parameters

Parameter	Setting
Channel bandwidth	10 MHz (FFT size = 1024)
Sampling frequency	15.36 MHz
Channel model	SCME urban macro
Channel assignment	Localized
MIMO scheme	Closed Loop Spatial Multiplexing (CL-SM) 4x2 (2 layers)
Precoding	Codebook based, size 16
Modulation	Fixed to 16QAM (same for both codewords)
Channel coding	Turbo coding rate ½
MIMO receiver	LMMSE
CP length	Normal CP
Channel estimation	Perfect

If not specified, the following are applied by default:

Table 6.7-2. Default PMI feedback parameter settings

Parameter	Setting
Feedback delay	3 ms
Feedback period	1 ms
Feedback frequency granularity	1 report per subband (6 RBs)
UE speed	3 km/h – 30 km/h
Feedback errors	No errors

6.7.3.1 Effect of Feedback Period

The feedback period is defined as the number of subframes between two PMI reports. The periodic reporting mode (which is carried on the PUCCH) consists of a wideband PMI report together with a wideband CQI report with the period being a semi-static parameter (see Section 3.4.6.5). In the example in Figure 3.4-7, the PMI feedback period was set to 8 (slow). However, in the aperiodic mode (carried on the PUSCH), in which the reporting is triggered by the scheduling grant, finer periods are possible.

The simulation results for Closed Loop Spatial Multiplexing (CL-SM) feedback period are given in Figure 6.7-2 and show that for a pedestrian speed, the difference between 1 ms and 8 ms is small, on the order of 0.3 dB at 1% BLER.

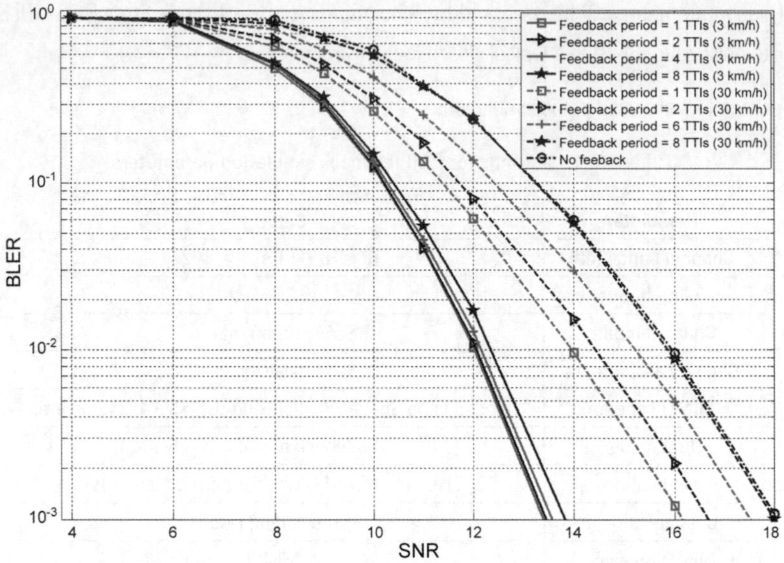

Figure 6.7-2. Effect of PMI feedback period on CL-SM 4x2 performance

At such low speeds, setting the period to 4 ms achieves a performance similar to that of the finest resolution of 1 ms. At a speed of 30 km/h, the performance impact increases and different periods result in very different results. The loss increases linearly with the feedback period. With a feedback period of 8 ms, the system performance does not perform better than the open loop case (no feedback, PMI cyclically rotated every subframe). A good scheduler would adapt the reporting period taking into account the velocity of the UE.

6.7.3.2 Effect of Feedback Delay

The feedback delay is defined as the number of subframes between the computation of the PMI at the receiver and the application of this information to a subsequent transmitted signal. The faster the channel changes, the more important the feedback delay becomes as the PMI gets quickly outdated. Figure 6.7-3 shows the simulation for feedback delay. It is clear that the delay has a significant impact on the performance, especially at higher speeds.

For low velocity (3 km/h), the impact is limited, on the order of 0.2 dB for a delay of nine TTIs at 1% BLER. For a speed of 30 km/h (regarded as the limit for practical closed loop operation), the impact is greater. As compared to a minimum delay of three TTIs, delays of six TTIs and nine TTIs show a degradation of 0.6 dB and 1.4 dB respectively.

It is therefore desirable that the delay be minimized. This is challenging for both the transmit and receive entities.

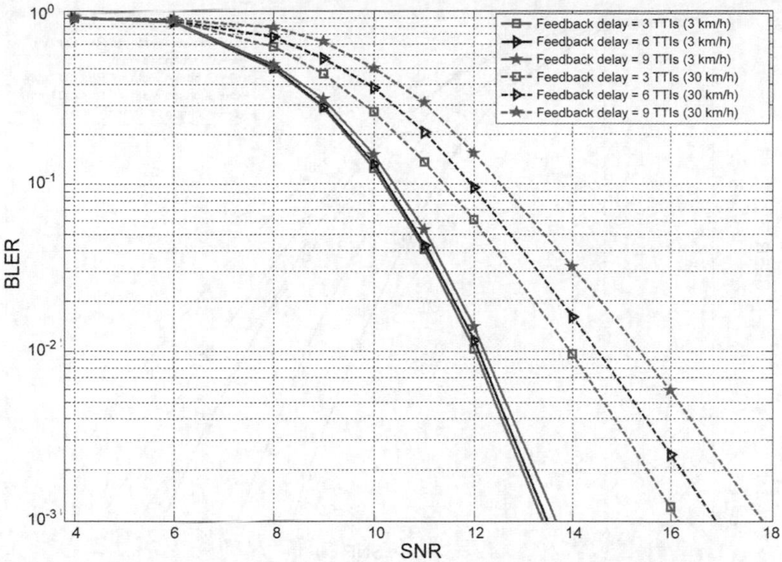

Figure 6.7-3. Effect of PMI feedback delay on CL-SM 4x2 performance

6.7.3.3 Effect of Feedback Frequency Granularity

When the transmitted signal is precoded, several options are available: precoding with a wideband PMI (using the same PMI for all allocated RBs/subbands), precoding with a per-subband PMI (frequency-selective mode) or precoding with a preferred subband PMI (PMI computed on the preferred subbands only). These three options relate to two different levels of granularity: a single PMI is applied to the complete band, or several subband-specific PMIs are applied separately on each subband.

In frequency selective channels the PMIs are likely to show low correlation between subbands. This type of channel benefits from different reports for the different subbands. Alternatively, in correlated fading channels or flat fading channels the correlation of PMIs among subbands is high and a wideband PMI report is sufficient.

Figure 6.7-4 shows the impact of the subband size on the performance for the urban macro scenario, which has significant frequency selectivity.

Unlike the feedback period and delay, the subband size has a large effect on performance even at low speeds. Compared to the finest resolution of one RB, the curves in Figure 6.7-4 show a large performance loss when reports of adjacent RBs are grouped. A subband size of 6 RBs loses almost 1 dB at 3 km/h while a wideband report (all RBs groups in a subband) loses more than 2 dB. This result demonstrates that great care should be taken when the PMI reporting mode is selected: in rich scattering environments such as the typical urban scenario, the gain from using frequency-selective PMI reports justifies the additional signalling overhead in the uplink.

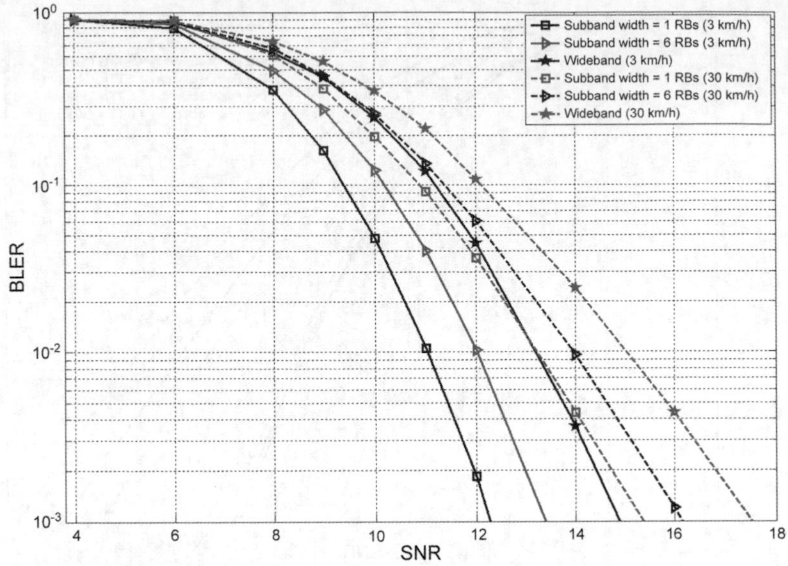

Figure 6.7-4. Effect of subband size on CL-SM 4x2 performance

6.7.3.4 Effect of UE Speed

The UE speed is another dominant factor that should be taken into account when the reporting mode is chosen. It is generally assumed that a high speed UE will not be able to benefit from closed loop MIMO since the rate of change in the channel is faster than the feedback mechanism. Figure 6.7-5 shows that UE speed has a significant impact on the performance of the closed loop system.

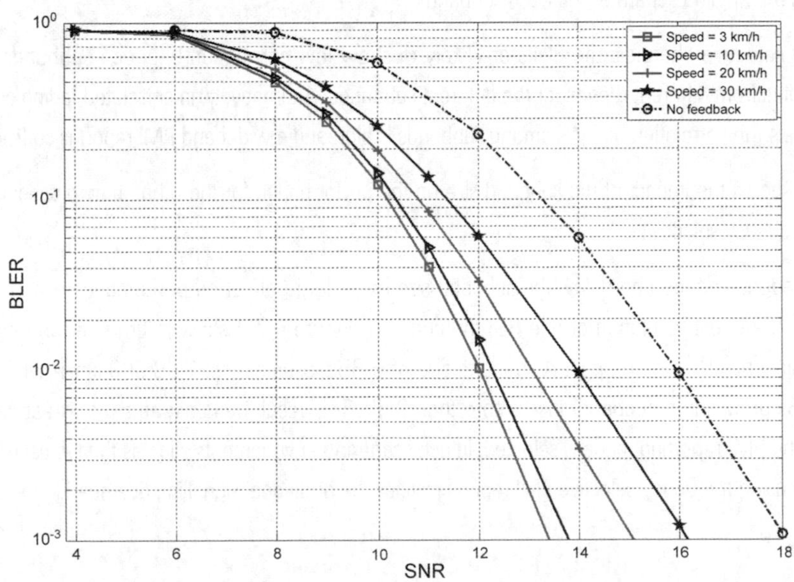

Figure 6.7-5. Effect of mobile speed on CL-SM 4x2 performance

Compared to the performance at 3 km/h, the performance degradation is 0.3 dB at 10 km/h, 1.1 dB at 20 km/h and 1.9 dB at 30 km/h (for a BLER of 1%). At 30 km/h, it becomes important to choose the shortest reporting period and the smallest frequency granularity as there is no other way to improve the open loop system performance.

6.7.3.5 Effect of PMI Decode Errors

Even though the PMI report is protected by strong channel coding, it is subject to block errors that affect closed loop performance. A value of 4% BLER is typically assumed as the control channel error rate. Figure 6.7-6 shows the impact of PMI decode errors (the report is ignored if the CRC is wrong).

Assuming a feedback period of 1 TTI, the results show that feedback errors have little impact on the performance. The extreme case of a feedback link BLER of 0.25 at 30 km/h is the only one in which some degradation is visible. At a target BLER of 4% for PMI decoding, the effect on closed loop performance is negligible.

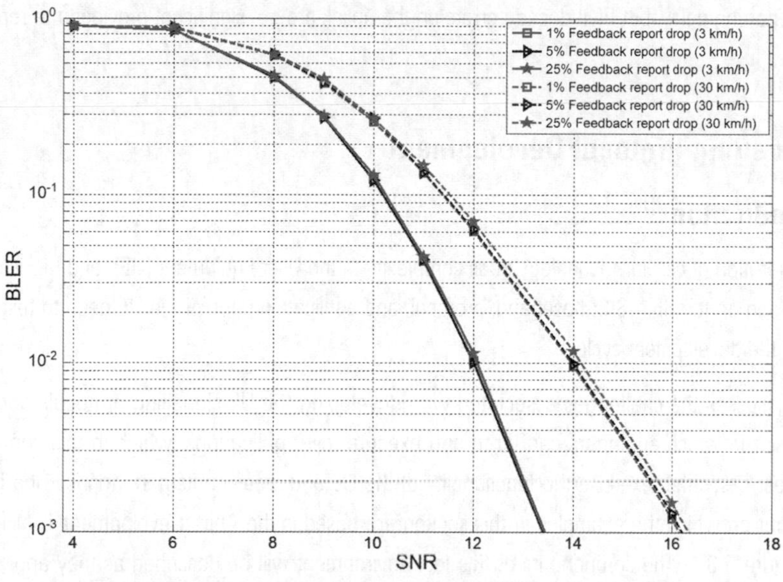

Figure 6.7-6. Effect of loss of PMI reports on CL-SM 4x2 performance

6.7.4 Conclusion

With closed loop spatial multiplexing, LTE specifies a complex and advanced system to enable high throughput while keeping acceptable hardware requirements. Compressing the feedback information is difficult since many factors have to be taken into account. The first factor reduced the channel matrix into a codebook in which only a few bits for the index are needed to characterize the channel. Ideally, such an index should be reported per subcarrier but in real-life conditions, the coherence bandwidth is low enough that the PMI can be reported once for a group of subcarriers.

The optimum reporting mode depends on the characteristics of the channel (frequency selectivity, line of sight, correlated fading, UE speed). The size of subband used has a big effect on the performance of frequency-selective channels. Frequency domain reporting can be compressed by using subbands, and time compression can be applied by using longer reporting periods. Channel variations are slow for low UE speeds so the feedback period can be reduced. In LTE, 30 km/h is a realistic maximum speed for closed loop operation. There is some sensitivity to increased reporting delay, but PMI decode errors on the uplink are not significant provided the reporting period is not long.

6.8 Signalling Protocol Development

6.8.1 Introduction

Every new generation of cellular technology adds complexity to the User Equipment (UE), and LTE is no exception. Engineers working on the RF, ASIC, baseband, protocol, and application parts of the UE need to test their devices at all stages of the development cycle.

This section discusses the challenges associated with developing the UE signalling protocols and describes a test environment in which engineers can write and execute test applications, which in this context comprise one or more test cases that exercise the functionality of the UE and measure its performance and behavior. The test environment on which the examples in this section are based is the Anite Development Toolkit (DT), which is shown is Figure 6.8-1. The components of this test environment will be described as they apply to signalling protocol development and testing.

To provide some background, this section first discusses the issues faced by mobile device developers and then discusses how test applications are developed and executed. The focus is on the creation of test applications for development testing in particular, which encompasses Inter-Operability Development Testing (IODT) and functional testing.

It is worth pointing out that in the case of the Anite system, additional applications can be added to address signalling conformance testing, RRM conformance testing and interoperability testing.

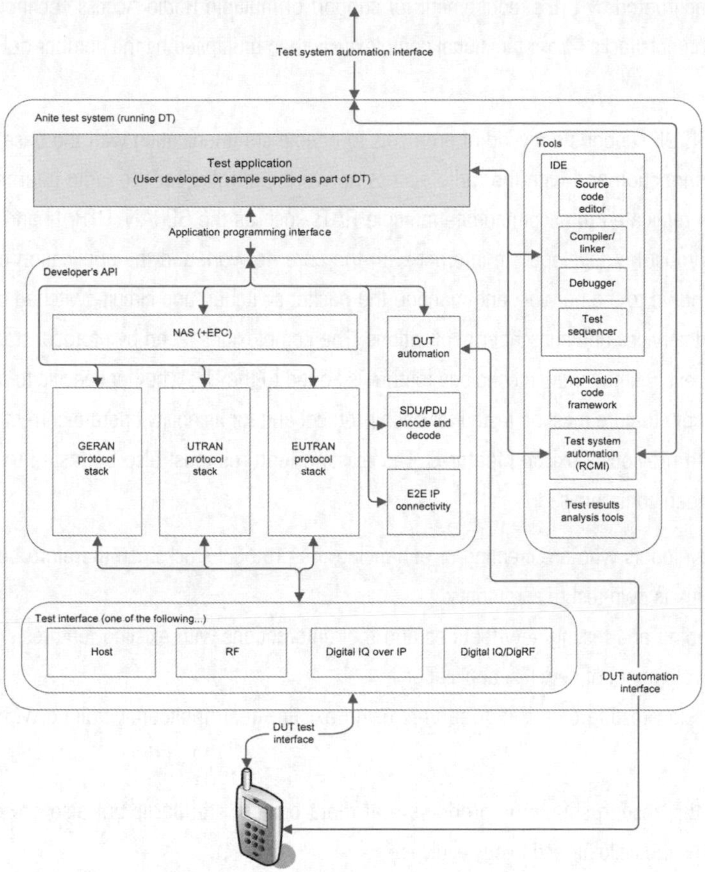

Figure 6.8-1. High level view of the Anite Development Toolset

6.8.2 Challenges of UE Development

6.8.2.1 Industry Issues

The process of producing the UE and components such as data cards and chipsets is extraordinarily complicated. To develop just the protocol stack and chipset requires technical teams with focused skill sets that include expertise in telecommunication standards and protocols, high level and embedded real time software, algorithms for propagating radio signals and maximizing data rates, and semiconductor design.

Because so much specialization is required, different teams (often in different locations) work on the development tasks such as Layer 1 and baseband design, RF development, protocol stack development, Layer 1 and RF integration, and system integration. The technical terminology and concepts used by these teams are usually understood only within the teams themselves. Therefore if the product being developed malfunctions in some way, differences in terminology, areas of understanding, and even the test equipment used contribute significantly to delay in identifying and isolating the defects.

This problem is exacerbated by LTE's requirement for support of multiple Radio Access Technologies (RATs) and their associated protocol stacks. Cross-functional complexity is then multiplied by the number of RATs supported in the UE.

By necessity the LTE UE supports a myriad of protocols to enable communication with the base station (eNB) for the air interface connection and with the radio access network controller for the radio bearers. In many cases these protocols are replicated to accommodate multiple RATs such as the GERAN, UTRAN and LTE E-UTRAN. In addition, protocols must be developed to interact with the core network and the application entities that make the UE's location known to the network and manage the packet-switched and circuit-switched connections along with the associated services and subscriber applications. The complexities faced by protocol stack developers are evident. Moreover, every time a new technology feature is added to the UE, whether specific to a RAT or spanning multiple RATs, the new feature must be tested for each protocol and for its ability operate correctly both in isolation and interacting with previously existing features. The existing features must also be tested to ensure that their operation has not been compromised.

The work of UE developers who are creating or enhancing the protocol stacks can therefore be divided into two categories, each with its own test requirements:

- Developing and testing new features and their interactions with existing features. This work requires the development of new test applications.
- Regression testing of existing features using existing test applications along with test automation functions.

The end result of this testing should be products that meet current standards but also are capable of being upgraded in future as the cellular technology evolves.

Development of the signalling protocol stacks involves several stages and is best done using a test system that links to both the UE host and target forms to maintain consistency between different product iterations. Test applications that were written earlier in the development process can be reused. The test cycle can be separated from the development cycle; however, consistent use of the test system from early development through final testing will facilitate the fastest possible identification of defects in the signalling protocol design.

6.8.2.2 Existing Test Approaches

A common test strategy pursued by manufacturers is one in which each team uses focused test equipment and tools, which may be sourced from the same or different test equipment vendors or developed in-house. This approach can hinder development when a team is unable to share log files or even tests with other teams in different locations or to recreate the test scenario that caused the fault to occur. Furthermore, while some initial development and testing may be performed using OPNET, MATLAB or internally developed software environments, manufacturers commonly test the UE protocol stacks in hardware, after integration with the baseband and RF.

Often test equipment is designed to test the Layer 3 (L3) procedures, again requiring that the UE protocol stack be tested as an integrated whole. In such cases different solutions are needed for L1 and integrated stack testing. This can cause difficulties in isolating the location of any faults encountered during testing. It is estimated that up to 80% of the time an engineer spends solving a fault is spent simply trying to locate it.

6.8.2.3 Solution Requirements

Describing the industry issues relating to UE development and testing uncovers some obvious shortcomings. It is worth noting the dramatically increased costs associated with late discovery of defects. A defect is on average 100 times cheaper to fix in the design phase than post release. Significant defects cost an unquantifiable amount more.

To effectively deliver defect-free protocol stacks for the LTE UE, a test system should encompass a range of integral components for L1 through L3 testing. The remainder of this section explores the key characteristics, facilities and tools needed to address the shortcomings of current test processes used in protocol development. Because test systems are highly individualized, the discussion is illustrated using the Anite Development Toolset (DT) shown in Figure 6.8-1 as part of the Anite SAT Test System.

6.8.3 Test System Overview

Whether a test system is being used for IODT, conformance testing or IOT, it provides the complete environment into which the DUT is placed to perform the desired test procedures. The test system typically emulates one or more networks employing one or more RATs via one or more cells. It therefore must provide a controlled environment with strict attention paid to the versions of all software (test application, Application Programming Interface (API) software, system software, etc.) and hardware required to test the UE. The reason for this is the need for test results to be reproducible.

The UE can be connected to the test system using any of a number of alternative interfaces. The following is a list of the most common ones, which will be discussed later in the section.

- Host
- RF
- Digital IQ
- IQ over Internet Protocol (IQoIP)

Depending on the test interface in use, the system will be made up of a combination of different units, such as a test system PC, cell generation hardware (such as base station emulators), baseband processors and an RF combiner.

The host interface may be a test system PC on which the test applications are executed, and which can optionally execute the protocol layers (from one or more protocol stacks in one or more RATs) of a DUT. This means that the DUT protocol stacks execute either locally on the test system PC or on a separate system communicating with the test system PC via Ethernet.

Figure 6.8-2 shows the layout of an Anite RF Test System consisting of four Agilent E6620 base station emulators, an Anite RF Combiner Unit and an Anite Test System PC.

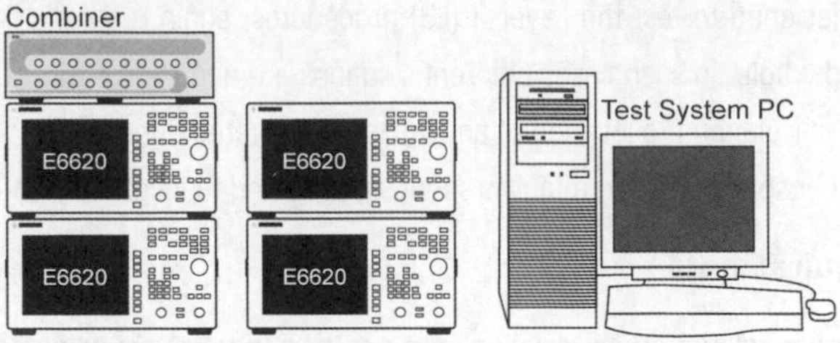

Figure 6.8-2. Example RF-based Anite Test System

This system has a considerable level of capability in terms of the number of cells and RATs that can be created by a test application. Test system configurations involving a greater or lesser number of base station emulators are also supported.

6.8.4 Test Application

The test application, defined in the Introduction to this section, is developed by the user or supplied with the test system. Test applications generally fall into two categories:

- "Continuous" applications in which test steps run continuously or are triggered by the user in an interactive manner — for example, the user determines when testing has completed and terminates the test application manually.
- "Sequential" applications in which a set of test steps runs in sequence from start to finish, and the test application terminates when the test sequence ends.

The test application uses facilities provided by the API to create the required network simulation for the test scenario. The network simulation may comprise multiple Public Land Mobile Networks (PLMNs), RATs and cells along with servers, applications and other elements. The test application uses these to communicate with and exercise the protocol stack, protocol layers, applications and services within the DUT.

Wherever possible it is desirable for the test application to be portable across the different test interfaces and this is achieved via the API.

The test application's purpose is to create a test scenario in which the DUT can be exercised to test the following:

- Correct protocol/stack operation
- Error condition handling
- Performance analysis such as data rates, protocol/stack latency, etc.

To enable the test application developer to get started as quickly as possible, example test applications are typically provided with the test system. These examples can be easily cloned by the developer — e.g. automatically copied to a new location, renamed and then delivered to the developer for easy modification.

As new versions of software and firmware for the test system become available to keep pace with evolution of the 3GPP standards, efficient management of test applications written using previous versions of the standard becomes critical. The ability to run old test applications is a key requirement for regression testing, reproducibility and traceability. These older versions need to run on either the original or later version of the test system software or firmware. This is achieved by providing the test system API in a form that supports backward compatibility. Backward compatibility also enables automatic switching of software/firmware versions. As a result the user eliminates many of the upgrade or downgrade steps required for version switching. Test applications from different versions of the test system software/firmware can then be mixed together at execution time to create powerful regression test plans. Test plans are explained further in the discussion of test application sequencing.

The continuous and sequential test applications mentioned earlier are discussed in more detail in the following sub-sections.

6.8.4.1 Continuous Test Applications

Continuous test applications are typically interactive; that is, the user decides which high level test(s) to run, for how long and with which parameters and configurations. The user interacts with the test application to make these settings typically via a Graphical User Interface (GUI). The user then executes the tests and monitors the results, which are the behavior of the DUT as seen by the test system. These results are fed back to the user via the GUI. The user may then choose to adjust the parameters of the test in real time while continuing to monitor the effects of the changes on the DUT.

6.8.4.2 Sequential Test Applications

Sequential test applications comprise a series of test steps that are to be executed in a certain sequence from start to finish. If the DUT behaves in such a way that the sequence is executed completely, then the test application has completed successfully.

The test application may have to support different execution paths depending on the complexity of the UE behavior being tested. The different execution paths can be executed optionally. Any departure from the correct sequence of test steps is considered to be a failure and execution can be stopped on the basis of this. In addition to supporting different execution paths, the test application may also be designed to execute loops of test steps.

6.8.5 Integrated Software Development Environment

For those who wish to develop their own test applications, an Integrated Development Environment (IDE) becomes the central interface through which they interact with the test system. The IDE allows them to perform the following activities:

- Code development
- Execution and monitoring of test application progress
- User interaction and control (where relevant)
- Online debugging of the test application and DUT
- Post execution analysis

Offline test application development also can be carried out via the IDE installed on the developer's workstation as opposed to the test system PC. When the host test interface and DUT protocol stack are run on the developer's workstation, the overall test environment is considered to be a test system in its own right. If the workstation is a laptop, the user can even develop DUT protocols and test applications while working from home or any other remote location. The IDE is common irrespective of the type of test system.

The screenshot in Figure 6.8-3 shows the Anite DT IDE viewing the source code of a test application currently under development.

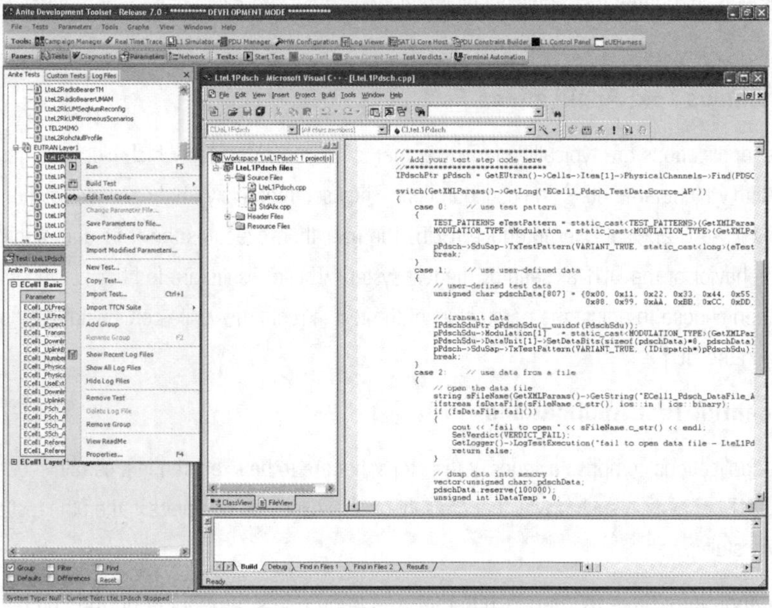

Figure 6.8-3. Anite DT IDE showing test application development

6.8.5.1 Source Code Editor

The IDE links to the source code development environment seamlessly so that the developer can carry out work on test applications without having to interact with a separate tool. This enables the developer to start up, open and otherwise manipulate the relevant software project and associated source code files of the test application from within the IDE.

6.8.5.2 Build Environment

The build environment, including the compiler and linker, is seamlessly integrated into the IDE so that the process of building test applications is performed without the user having to follow additional steps.

6.8.5.3 Debugger

In the Anite DT environment, executing test applications is a one click operation, and if the test application has been built for debugging, the source level debugger will be launched automatically. Breakpoints, stepping code execution and all the other normal software debugging activities are available.

When it comes to debugging the DUT, certain considerations must be given to the test application design. The test applications must allow for single-stepping of the DUT protocol layers. This typically involves ensuring that the test application and network protocol layers can handle delays in responses; timers must be suspended and resumed; and so forth. If an In-Circuit Emulator (ICE) or Background Debug Mode (BDM) is used to debug the DUT processors, then a certain level of execution can continue within the CPU of the DUT. The DUT's baseband, unless hosted in a simulation environment, is less tailored for interactive execution and therefore offline analysis of the DUT's trace logs and the test application's protocol and diagnostic log files is required.

One particular capability required for testing the DUT protocol layers is "protocol error injection" into the network side peer protocol layer in the test system. For example, to test an LTE device's handling of Over The Air (OTA) errors of the "HARQ ACK to NACK error" and "NACK to ACK error" sort, it is necessary to inject a HARQ NACK or ACK at the appropriate point. To control what message the DUT receives requires the test system's network side Medium Access Control (MAC) protocol layer to accept an instruction to convert a HARQ NACK into a HARQ ACK and vice versa at the appropriate timing.

6.8.5.4 Execution Monitoring

DUT performance is a key area of analysis when it comes to high data rate scenarios and operating conditions. The IDE's performance monitoring capabilities allow graphing capabilities of Key Performance Indicators (KPIs). This in turn allows real time monitoring of, for example, uplink data throughput, downlink data throughput, etc.

6.8.5.5 Test Application Sequencer

Once developed and debugged, large numbers of sequential type test applications can be sequenced together by including them in test plans. Test plans are then executed by the automated test sequencer, which executes each test application in turn and records the execution results. These results, including log files, are stored together to ensure that a complete picture of the test plan is retained for future reference.

The test sequencer can be used in conjunction with a DUT automation function (described in Section 6.8.9.2) to enable unattended execution of test applications. It is just as valid, however, to use the test sequencer without DUT automation, and control the DUT manually.

Figure 6.8-4 shows the Anite DT IDE with the test sequencer, called the Campaign Manager, running.

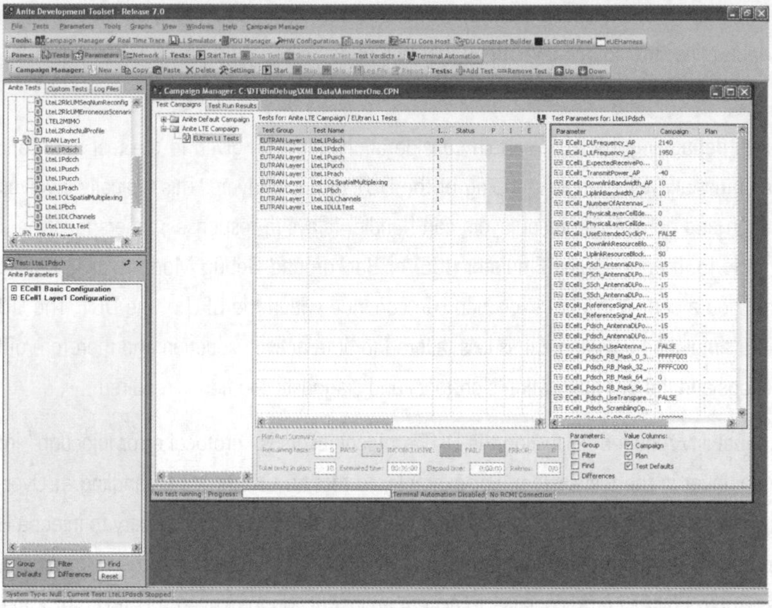

Figure 6.8-4. Anite DT IDE running Campaign Manager

6.8.6 Application Programming Interface

The API provides the test developer with a programmable interface to one or more network side protocol stacks on the test system. These protocol stacks make up the RATs that are required on the network side to fully test the DUT.

The ways in which APIs are used depends on the level of complexity of the network side protocol layers and how much control of these protocol layers is required. Control requirements are in turn determined by the level of testing required of the DUT protocol layers and stacks.

In general the easiest way to represent the API is through object oriented programming. In this format the API can support popular programming languages such as C++, C#, Java, and Visual BASIC, but can also be used with programming languages not specifically defined as object oriented such as C.

The API simulates the required RATs and their associated protocol stacks with a minimum representation of the core network architecture. This is done to keep the API as simple as possible for the test developer. The DUT requires a full representation of the Access Stratum (AS) — that is, the LTE physical layer (PHY), MAC, Radio Link Control (RLC), Packet Data Convergence Protocol (PDCP) and Radio Resource Control (RRC) protocol layers. The DUT doesn't require a representation of the Non Access Stratum (NAS) internal interfaces such as the LTE S1, X2 etc., since the DUT never interacts with these internal interfaces directly. The DUT does, however, need to interact with the NAS layer itself and therefore, again for the test developer's convenience, this layer is considered from a protocol stack perspective to be present immediately above the RRC layer. In other words, for LTE, the key interface for testing the DUT is the Uu (radio or air) interface and it is this interface that forms the basis for control via the API. In terms of the GERAN, UTRAN and other RATs, the corresponding equivalent air interfaces apply.

In simulating the real world, the API models all aspects of multiple PLMNs, which employ multiple RATs which in turn employ multiple cells, etc., with the corresponding object model being held within the API. The test developer can then navigate and configure the object model as required from within the test application.

6.8.6.1 Message (PDU/SDU) Handling

For ease of use, messages in the form of Protocol Data Units (PDUs) or Service Data Units (SDUs) are handled by the API as objects. This allows object based manipulation of the PDUs/SDUs by "walking" through the Information Elements (IEs), reading individual IEs in the application and setting individual IEs. The reading of IEs is typically performed on PDUs/SDUs received from the DUT and allows the test application to determine what information should be provided by the DUT; for example, the UE Category. The setting of IEs is typically performed on PDUs/SDUs before being sent to the DUT and allows the test application to send information to the DUT; for example, a paging cause in a paging message.

6.8.6.2 Asynchronous Event Handling

Asynchronous event handling and synchronization have always been areas of complexity for software development and this is particularly true for test application development. With this in mind the API supports a variety of mechanisms to provide different levels of flexibility versus complexity; e.g., the more powerful mechanisms are inevitably more complex whereas the simple mechanisms tend to provide a more restricted operation. These different mechanisms are provided to suit different requirements of test developers and their different levels of experience.

6.8.6.3 DUT and End User Applications

For the purposes of testing IP based applications that run in the DUT, the API provides "end-to-end IP" connectivity. An end-to-end IP pipe is available to the test application through the API and communicates with the peer IP layer in the DUT via the User Plane (UP). End-to-end IP capability is supported across handovers, whether intra- or inter-RAT.

This facility also provides the test developer with access to IP-based "servers" and "applications" running on the test system PC or out to the Internet. Testing with these servers and applications via the test system PC provides a controlled and repeatable test environment. Testing via the Internet provides a "real world" experience but is not controlled and therefore not a repeatable environment. Examples of end-user application type testing are web browsing, SMTP/POP3 e-mail and FTP.

With LTE employing IP Multimedia Subsystem (IMS) as the framework for IP based services such as Voice Over IMS (VoIMS), the need for application layer testing is critical. Other RATs are also set to employ IMS, and VoIMS will become more common, especially as part of the All IP Network (AIPN).

6.8.6.4 Utility Objects

Within the API, facilities commonly needed in the test application are provided by utility objects. Examples of these would be timers, error handlers, data sources and audio (end-to-end speech via the test system PC's sound card).

6.8.6.5 SDU/PDU Objects

Messages sent and received are referred to as SDUs and PDUs, respectively, depending on whether they are travelling into or out of the top of a protocol layer or travelling into or out of the bottom of a protocol layer.

For Control Plane (CP) communication, complex messages containing many IEs, each encoded using Abstract Syntax Notation number 1 (ASN.1), Concrete Syntax Notation number 1 (CSN.1) or other encoding notations are transferred between the network and the DUT. The SDU/PDU API objects wrap each message sent or received and they also provide mechanisms for easy manipulation of the message's contents from within the test application.

6.8.6.6 Constraints

When DUT behavior is tested, the ability to define constraints on messages received from the DUT is critical. Constraints, in the context of the API, are message objects that can compare themselves with the contents of received messages. The constraint can then determine whether the message received is the expected type of message and has the required data values in the IEs of the message (specific values, within a range of values, greater than, less than, not equal to, etc.).

Constraints can be used to change the path of execution through the test application and therefore control the test sequence as necessary for the DUT. Constraints can also verify correct operation of the DUT in terms of the DUT response to the expected message in sequence of message exchanges with the network.

6.8.6.7 Protocol and Diagnostic Logging

Logging is considered in two forms: protocol or diagnostics-based. Protocol logging is the logging of data as it passes down or up through a protocol layer within a protocol stack. Diagnostic data refers to data from within the test system as a whole (protocol layers, hardware units, processor cards, etc.). It concerns general operation and any unlikely operational issues that might occur under extreme circumstances.

Programmatic control is provided by the API to control the level of protocol and diagnostic logging generated by the protocol stacks and their protocol layers at run time. This control enables the test developer to define the key protocol layers, the points in the test execution where logging is required, and the level of detail to be logged. The level of detail has a direct bearing on the volume of data logged.

6.8.6.8 Signalling Message State Machines

Protocol layers such as the RRC and NAS are typically modeled as a set of state machines driven by the transmission and reception of CP messages, each signalling procedure with its own state machine.

So that test developers can avoid having to implement these state machines and the associated message and event handling, the API provides predefined default signalling procedures that a test developer can either use unmodified or customize for the purpose of testing the DUT. If a nonstandard signalling procedure is required, the test developer can also attach other procedures to those provided by the API.

For the purposes of monitoring and modifying the API-provided signalling procedures, the test developer can register for a complete signalling procedure or just specific messages. The level of interaction with the signalling procedure is entirely up to the test developer. Once the test application is registered for a signalling procedure or individual messages, it will be notified when that procedure is being performed or when messages have been received or a message is about to be sent.

6.8.7 Application Code Framework

The application code framework provides an environment on top of the API and wraps up common code solutions to further ease the test developer's job. The application code framework is typically language-specific and is provided in such a way that the test developer can easily modify and extend the functionality of the test application as required.

The framework also provides a means by which a consistent test application development approach can be implemented. It is particularly helpful in situations in which a number of test developers are exchanging test applications and test application code.

6.8.8 Test Interfaces

Different test interfaces between the test system and the DUT are available. In a number of cases the test interface can be changed without requiring significant reconfiguration by the developer although inevitably a different form of interconnection with the DUT will be required. Interchangeability of the test interface enables reuse of test equipment, and therefore a greater return on the investment.

6.8.8.1 Host

The host interface provides an interface for connecting the DUT at the bottom of Layer 2 via a simulated Layer 1. In the case of HARQ operation, which some consider to be part of PHY as opposed to the MAC, the simulation may optionally include or exclude the HARQ functionality. The connection of the DUT's Layer 2 to the test system includes multiple protocol stacks and multiple RATs. This allows the DUT's multiple RAT functionality to be tested, profiled and debugged in an entirely host-based environment.

Importantly, no specific DUT "target" hardware is required for protocol and test development to progress. In terms of making development activities parallel, this capability can prove very powerful. Indeed for business functions focused on delivering the protocol layers or protocol test applications, dependency on the "target hardware" can be significantly reduced.

As previously discussed there are alternative configuration options for the test system using a host interface:

- For Rapid Application Development (RAD) approaches, protocol and test developers have their workstation organized so that the IDE, test applications and DUT protocol stack all run together. This means that as protocol or test application development progresses, testing can be performed locally and quickly using the host testing environment.
- Alternatively the DUT protocol layers, protocol stacks and RATs can be executed on a workstation separate from that running the test development environment. The DUT and the test system communicate with each other via a high speed Ethernet interface.

6.8.8.2 RF

The RF interface enables direct connection to one or more DUT antennas depending on the configuration and capabilities of the DUT. With the RF interface it becomes straightforward to combine multiple transmitter and receiver based units to create complex multi-cell, multi-antenna scenarios for testing the DUT. In addition, the final combining with a DUT that has separate antennas for different RATs is also possible.

For test system configurations employing multiple RF base station emulators, the RF combining function introduces small path losses. The test system itself is configured with details of the path losses and adjusts for these automatically in both the uplink and downlink directions.

6.8.8.3 Digital IQ

The Digital IQ interface provides a parallel physical interface over which IQ samples are sent and received for one or more antenna IQ streams. The interface is intended for virtually direct connection to the baseband of the DUT (some physical connection handling, and in some cases signal modification, is necessary not least because of the high signal rates involved).

The interface is hardware based and typically provided by a single base station emulator due to the complexities of combining and splitting the signals from multiple base station emulators. Having said that, the capability to emulate two cells in a single base station emulator unit — for example, in the Agilent E6620 — means that it is possible to digitally combine the two cells at baseband.

DigRF is a standard for Digital IQ interfacing between the baseband and RFIC level; however, unless this standard interface is designed into the baseband from the start an alternative interface is typically required.

Whether the interface is DigRF or an alternative, the interface is typically based on the Low Voltage Differential Signalling (LVDS) electrical standard, although Transistor-to-Transistor Logic (TTL) is also used in some non-real-time applications. An example of TTL use is the interconnection with Application Specific Integrated Circuit (ASIC) emulator products such as the Cadence Palladium or Mentor Graphics VStation. The use of an ASIC emulator allows the testing of the DUT's baseband in early Field Programmable Gate Array (FPGA) simulation modes.

6.8.8.4 IQ over Internet Protocol

The IQ over Internet Protocol (IQoIP) interface provides IQ data for one or more antennas in the form of IP datagrams. The physical connection of the interface to the DUT is provided via high rate Ethernet, although not typically at real time rates due to the sheer volume of data involved.

6.8.9 Unattended DUT Testing

6.8.9.1 Test System Automation

The use of a test system to test the DUT does not have to be a manual process requiring the user to be present for the execution of test applications. It is worth noting that the sequential type of test application is better suited for test system automation as opposed to the continuous type. To fully automate unattended operation, the DUT as well as the test system must be automated. DUT automation is discussed in Section 6.8.9.2.

Test system automation enables a test system to be integrated into a company-wide automated testing environment potentially involving multiple test systems. For example, in large customer test laboratories using multiple test systems, centralized control of procedures such as testing and conformance certification is sometimes the norm. The controlled environment of test automation provides a high degree of test co-ordination in this case.

Anite's test system automation solution is referred to as Remote Control Management Interface (RCMI). RCMI provides a remote control interface to the test system so that the centralized test control system can issue commands to the test system instructing it, for example, to execute a test application, monitor progress as that test application executes, abort the execution (if required) and feed results back into the system.

With RCMI it is possible to create an overall integrated test environment employing multiple test systems executing tests in parallel for 24 hours, 7 days a week, unattended. This capability is particularly powerful when large numbers of regression tests must be run and test results recorded in a central location for analysis of test coverage, DUT failures, or the effects of new software or firmware versions being installed in the DUT.

For use with RCMI, the mechanism that triggers execution of the test application must be transparent to the test application. The test application also must be able to execute in an unattended manner; for example, it must not pause execution to wait for a user response. In addition the test system and DUT must both have recovery mechanisms to ensure their continued operation. The Anite test system is designed with an automated hardware reset mechanism and watchdog timer to enable a full reset in the unlikely event of a problem that causes test execution to stop.

Figure 6.8-5 shows Anite's test system automation solution.

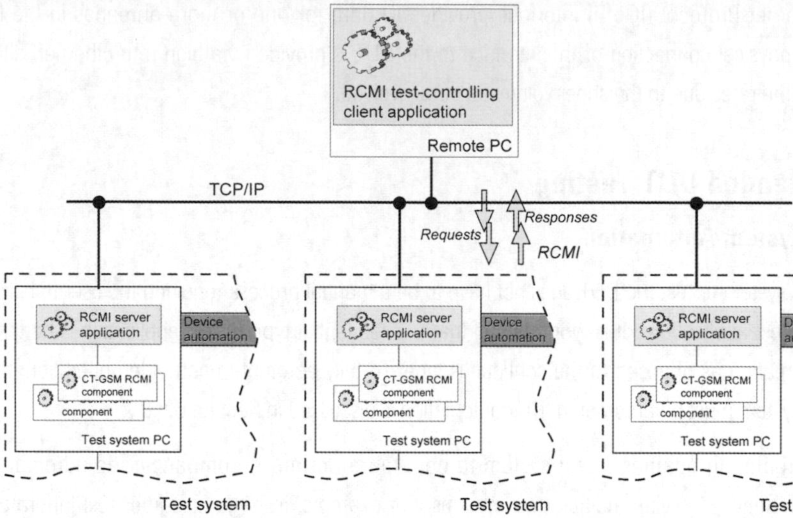

Figure 6.8-5. Test system automation with the Anite RCMI

6.8.9.2 DUT Automation

DUT automation, sometimes known as terminal or UE automation, is an interface provided between the test application and the DUT. By means of this interface the test application is able to transfer commands, receive data from the DUT and query the status of the DUT. This feature enables automatic control of the DUT as necessary for the successful execution of the test application without the need for the user to be present. Although DUT automation is required for test system automation to reach its full potential, DUT automation on its own can still prove useful.

When DUT automation is used but test applications are executed manually, the user does not need to know how to control the DUT. In situations requiring complex configuration of the DUT, this can prove beneficial and ensures consistent and repeatable testing.

In early DUT development when the DUT does not yet have an L3 implementation, DUT automation can be used to configure the DUT as required by the test application. Such configuration data would normally be acquired using CP signalling transferred via the test interface itself.

For mature DUT developments the commands are typically Attention (AT) commands from the protocol defined in 27.007 [24].

Figure 6.8-6 shows Anite's DUT Automation combined with RCMI.

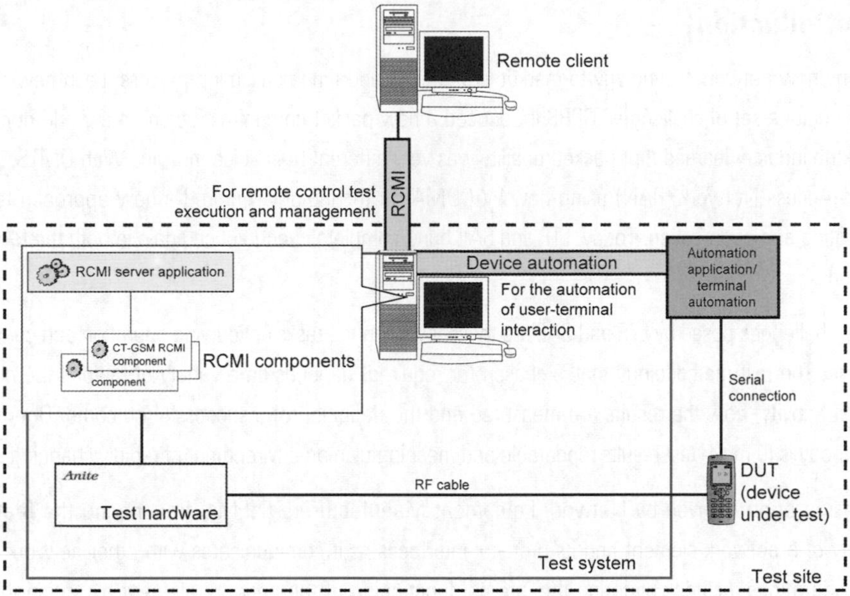

Figure 6.8-6. DUT Automation

6.8.10 Test Result Analysis Tools

The execution of tests generates results in the form of protocol log files and in some cases diagnostic log files. Depending on the success or failure of the test execution or the behavior of the DUT, the protocol and diagnostic log files may require analysis.

Analysis of these log files is achieved using log viewer tools that enable searching and comparison of timestamps in the log files with associated timestamps in the trace logs produced by the DUT. Note that timestamps are typically frame numbers although they can be the system time.

The log viewing tools for protocol log file analysis enable decoding of the SDUs and PDUs that have been transferred between peer protocol layer entities in both the uplink and downlink directions. For the CP signalling messages, the analysis includes the decode of the message IEs into human-readable form showing the value of each IE based on the corresponding 3GPP specification and version.

6.9 Network Troubleshooting

6.9.1 Introduction

Bringing any new network technology to market is a difficult and time consuming process. Each new technology has its own unique set of challenges. GPRS introduced a new packet core infrastructure in a world dominated by voice, and the industry learned that packet mobility was very different than voice mobility. With UMTS, an entirely new Radio Access Network (RAN) using new W-CDMA RF technology required a new approach to network troubleshooting and optimization. Today, LTE and SAE bring complete change once again in both the RAN and the core network.

Among the challenges posed by LTE and SAE are those involving the tasks of verifying operation and characterizing performance. The test methodology that is chosen (or required) depends on a variety of factors: the objective of a given test activity, how the results are measured and the definition of a successful outcome. One interesting challenge today is to make test results repeatable and meaningful in an environment of rapidly changing standards.

Much consideration is given by Network Equipment Manufacturers (NEMs) to verifying the features and functionality of a network element and its protocol interfaces as it communicates with other network elements. Other considerations include validating the internal functioning of the network element by optimizing internal management algorithms and verifying the internal measurements and reporting.

The concerns of Wireless Service Providers (WSPs) may differ from those of NEMs. For instance, when technology and vendor trials are held, will common measures be used? Will these measures be taken from the internal network element counters, or will they be independently monitored and verified? Will these measures be a part of the First Office Application (FOA)/deployment benchmarking activities?

This section examines some of the challenges that LTE/SAE brings to network monitoring and troubleshooting.

6.9.2 Overview of LTE Test Challenges

While some aspects of the LTE/SAE architecture simplify network configuration, they also create complexities for testing and optimization. As more intelligence moves to the edge of the network, key Radio Resource Management (RRM) functionality collapses into the eNB. In UMTS, the Iub interface offered visibility to key RRM procedures that are now hidden within the LTE eNB (see Figure 6.9-1). The challenge is to get visibility to these procedures. With only a few choices available — UE simulators, passive air probes and internal eNB debug logs — the focus has been on finding the most cost effective way to do this analysis and correlate it with other network interfaces.

With UMTS and GPRS, most of the analysis focus is on the control plane, and the IP user plane can be filtered out or selectively analyzed. This is due in large part to the separation of the Circuit Switched (CS) voice services from the Packet Switched (PS) services. The LTE/SAE architecture, however, eliminates the CS domain, combining all services, including voice, within the PS domain. This change requires the analysis focus to move into the user plane and up the stack into the application layers.

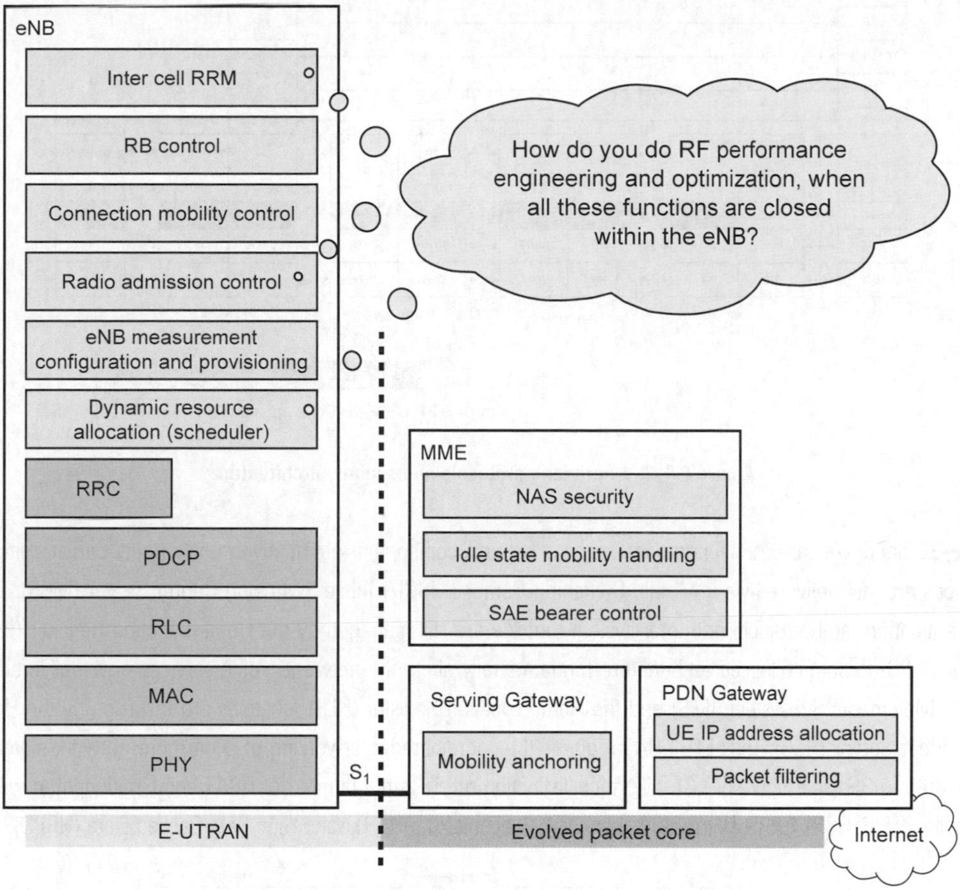

Figure 6.9-1. Key RRM functions closed within the eNB (Based on 36.300 [25] Figure 4.1-1)

All 3GPP networks, including LTE, provide ciphering algorithms to protect user information transmitted over the air. Therefore, monitoring network interfaces requires deciphering. In addition, LTE standardizes on the use of IPsec in both the transport network domains and in the user domain (IPsec AKA) as shown in Figure 6.9-2. Considering that IPsec is specifically designed to protect information between sender and receiver; network designers must consider how to build the test environment (or deployed network) for testability.

Even in well understood UMTS environments, there are still problems managing 2G-3G handovers. Managing Inter-Radio Access Technology (I-RAT) handover procedures is less about the functionality of individual network elements and more about the coordinated functioning of all the network elements. Numerous race conditions and timing variables need to be optimized to ensure high handover success rates. It is difficult to establish a test configuration to verify all the possible permutations of this functionality.

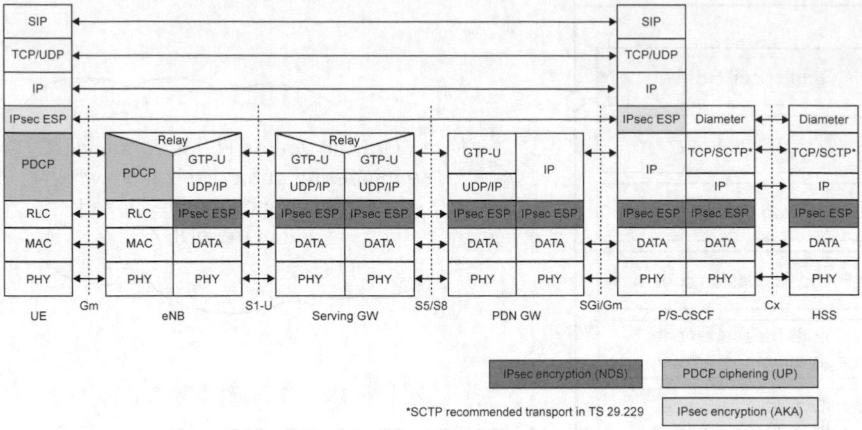

Figure 6.9-2. User plane protocols and security architecture

In 2G-3G handover cases, the fundamental serving network components are relatively unchanged. Circuit switched services are still delivered via a Mobile Switching Center (MSC)/Mobile Switching Center Server (MSS). User authentication, authorization, and inter-system mobility are still managed by the Home Location Register (HLR). LTE's all PS-domain collapsed architecture fundamentally alters the network. Voice services now delivered via the IP Multimedia Subsystem (IMS) and the Home Location Register (HLR) functions are taken on by the Home Subscriber Server (HSS). Thus LTE I-RAT requires the coordinated interworking of even more network elements compared to 3G (see Figure 6.9-3). A further distinction of LTE is the number of I-RAT combinations that will be possible: LTE to GSM/GPRS, UMTS and even 3GPP2's cdma2000 1xRTT and High Rate Packed Data (HRPD).

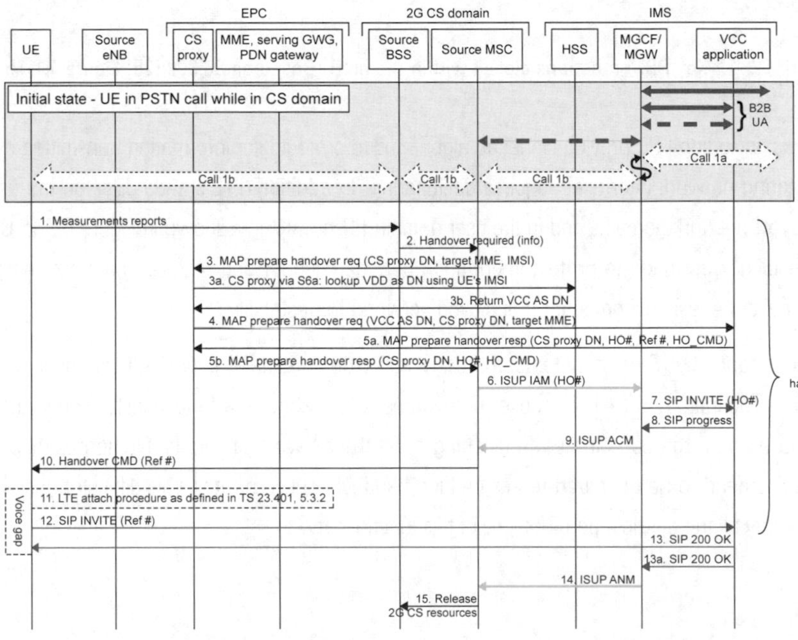

Figure 6.9-3. LTE CS I-RAT handover to 2G (Based on 23.401 [26] and IEEE 802.21 Media Independent Handover)

These aspects of LTE — the collapsed architecture, multiple layers of detailed user plane analysis and complex security architecture — increase the demands on the tools used during the test process.

6.9.3 KPIs vs. Measurements

One commonly misunderstood and misused term in network testing is Key Performance Indicator (KPI). At the most basic level, a KPI is nothing more than a statistic or a measurement. However, it is the test objective or market requirement for a given service that allows a particular statistic or measurement to be considered an indicator of performance.

Even the term "performance" can mean very different things depending on the testing context. For instance, service performance for Voice over IP (VoIP) may be measured in terms of jitter, latency and dropped packets. Network performance may be measured by the number of concurrent VoIP users that can be served with an acceptable level of jitter, latency and packet loss. Thus one of the test challenges when quality or performance is measured is how to agree on the definitions in order to interpret results consistently.

Properly identifying the source of the data needed to calculate KPIs further complicates the issue. Consider the example of a data throughput measurement. What is meant by the phrase "IP throughput of a given user on the S1 interface"? Is a throughput measurement an accurate indication of the end-user's perceived throughput? Does the measurement properly account for retransmissions? Is there even enough information available on the S1 interface to derive the end-user perceived throughput, or is it necessary to look somewhere else? If, for instance, throughput were instead measured on the radio bearer side by analyzing the RLC/MAC protocols, a clearer picture of end-user perceived or effective throughput could be obtained, because more information is available about the retransmissions sent over the radio bearer. That means in addition to the effective throughput, information about the efficiency of the radio bearer could also be learned. It is therefore important to understand that KPIs are a subset of all the measurements needed to achieve the desired test objectives.

6.9.4 LTE KPIs

According to 3GPP, KPIs can generally be categorized according to accessibility, retainability, integrity, availability and mobility. 3GPP KPI standardization efforts are focused on measurements related to the end-user perceived Quality of Service (QoS). These tend to be more operator-centric as they focus on measuring the end user ability to obtain, maintain and access a service connection to the network.

KPIs need be understood in the context of the actual object of measurement. Each part of the network has different responsibilities associated with delivering a single service. Therefore, LTE-specific KPIs focus on the E-UTRAN and, in many cases, rely on the eNB to measure its own performance. One challenge for an NEM, then, is how to verify that KPIs calculated by the eNB are correct, especially when the eNB is running at high load or full capacity. Another challenge for both NEMs and WSPs is how to translate KPIs into troubleshooting activities needed to identify root cause of errors. KPIs are defined in 32.450 [27] and 32.451 [28].

For each KPI category, each service may have a different QoS profile or QoS Class Identifier (QCI) label. KPI measurements will need to be on a per QCI basis to identify performance for each type of service being accessed. Beyond the 3GPP-defined KPIs additional measurements in each of these categories must be considered to evaluate the whole end-to-end service Quality of Experience (QoE).

6.9.4.1 Accessibility: Obtaining a Connection to the Network

The accessibility KPI measures the UE's ability to obtain the necessary connection to the network in order to access the requested service. The accessibility KPI provides no QoS information.

In the LTE/SAE case, the eNB manages the radio resources and is responsible for serving the radio bearers. Thus, the accessibility of the eNB can generally be measured by counting the RRC messages used to request and establish a radio bearer:

$$\text{RRC connection success rate} = \frac{\#\,\text{RRC connection setup complete}}{\#\,\text{RRC connection request}}.$$

In many cases, a service will require multiple radio bearers. For instance, the default radio bearer is needed first to request a specific service that then requires a dedicated radio bearer. The actual service accessibility of the eNB is therefore a combination of the success rates of both the default and the dedicated radio bearers. This is generally shown as:

$$\begin{aligned}&\text{Service specific radio bearer accessibility}[\%]\\&\quad = \text{default RRC connection success rate} * \text{dedicated RRC connection success rate} * 100.\end{aligned}$$

The E-UTRAN has a similar set of accessibility measures that look at messages on the S1 interface related to the Evolved Radio Access Bearer (E-RAB) establishment success rates (also called SAE bearer rates). This calculation is also straightforward and, as was shown in the RRC case, the service-specific accessibility needs to combine the default and service specific bearers.

$$\text{E-RAB success rate} = \frac{\#\,\text{E-RAB setup success}}{\#\,\text{E-RAB setup request}}.$$

$$\text{Service specific E-RAB accessibility}[\%] = \text{default E-RAB success rate} * \text{dedicated E-RAB success rate} * 100.$$

It is interesting to note that E-RAB procedures are not successful without the successful completion of the RRC procedures. Thus, to measure service accessibility, only E-RAB success rates need to be computed. However, for root cause isolation — for example, in the case of high E-RAB failures rates — and for overall optimization, RRC connection success rates are important to measure.

The discussion above is focused on the accessibility of the E-UTRAN, which is insufficient by itself to actually measure the accessibility of a given service from a whole network perspective. If voice call establishment is taken as an example, once a UE has obtained a connection to the access network, it must then be able to reach a specific Application Server (AS) within the IMS. This can generally be calculated as:

$$\text{SIP session success rate} = \frac{\#\,\text{SIP OK (voice)}}{\#\,\text{SIP invites (voice)}}.$$

where SIP is the Session Internet Protocol.

The success rate for voice call establishment then depends on the E-UTRAN accessibility and the IMS voice AS accessibility. This discussion takes the example of voice services; however, the same general principles apply to any service that is delivered to the end user.

Additional measurements related to accessibility can also be considered:

- E-RAB setup time
- Attach success/failure ratios and setup times
- Paging success/failure ratios
- UE context setup success/failure ratios and setup times

6.9.4.2 Retainability: Maintaining a Connection to the Network

Retainability KPI's are intended to measure the ability of the UE to maintain a connection to the network once that connection has been established. These types of measurements are often generalized as the drop call ratio. A "call" in this context refers to all types of session establishments (voice, video and data). Typically, drop call ratios are calculated by counting the number of abnormally released connections against the total number of established connections.

As discussed for accessibility in the E-UTRAN, the E-RAB is used also as the basis for the retainability measurement. It represents the connection to the network carrying a given service. Thus, the dropped call/session ratio is defined as:

$$\text{Dropped call or session ratio}[\%] = \frac{\#\,\text{E - RAB release command (abnormal cause)}}{\#\,\text{Total E - RAB release command}} * 100.$$

There is an additional consideration in evaluating retainability. In LTE, it is likely that the E-RAB will remain active even when it is not currently in use. Since evaluating retainability means measuring the actual impact of service interruptions on the end user, the dropped call ratio is insufficient by itself as a measure of retainability.

In order for a dropped call/session to be considered service-affecting and relevant to the measurement of retainability, the E-RAB must be considered active. 3GPP defines an E-RAB to be active only if data has recently been sent over it. Further, 3GPP defines a release to be abnormal only if there is un-transmitted data in any of the eNB buffers.

The retainability KPI is thus defined as the rate of abnormal release events over the active session time.

$$\text{Retainability rate}\left[\frac{\#\,\text{drops}}{\text{session time}}\right] = \frac{\#\,\text{E - RAB release command (abnormal cause)}}{\text{active E - RAB time}}.$$

But how can an external monitoring device determine the buffer status of the eNB? One algorithmic approach, when monitoring from the S1 interface, is to determine if the eNB buffer is likely to be empty. However, at best, this is an estimate since no information is available about congestion, ARQ/HARQ failures, RLC block errors, and corresponding retransmission. So it will be impossible to explicitly measure and verify in the absence of trace information being available from the eNB itself.

Additional measurements related to retainability can also be considered.

- UE context drop rates
- E-RAB modification success and failure rates

6.9.4.3 Integrity: Measuring the Quality of the Connection

So far, the KPI categories of accessibility and retainability have dealt specifically with obtaining and maintaining a connection to the network. Integrity KPIs seek to measure the quality of the service connection. Since LTE supports only the PS domain, these measurements revolve around IP throughput and latency.

Generally, throughput is the volume of IP traffic measured over a specific interval of time (e.g., bytes/sec). An important consideration is where to measure throughput. Because LTE integrity KPI definitions look at this from the E-UTRAN perspective over the Uu interface, these KPIs must be measured at the eNB or UE, or via a passive air interface probe.

A consideration of throughput on the Uu interface (from the eNB) should take into account the characteristics of that interface. The goal is to evaluate the performance of the E-UTRAN in delivering IP packets. Thus, the measurements need to be independent of the size of the transmitted data set and unaffected by the bursty nature of the traffic itself.

In order to achieve size-independent results, the data must be transmitted in discrete data blocks sent at specific intervals. Transmitted data sets will not always fill exactly 100% of the data blocks (see Figure 6.9-4.) In such cases, some data will overflow, partially filling another data block. Furthermore, some retransmissions may occur and the volume of these retransmissions cannot be counted as throughput in integrity measurements, but the time spent on retransmissions must be counted.

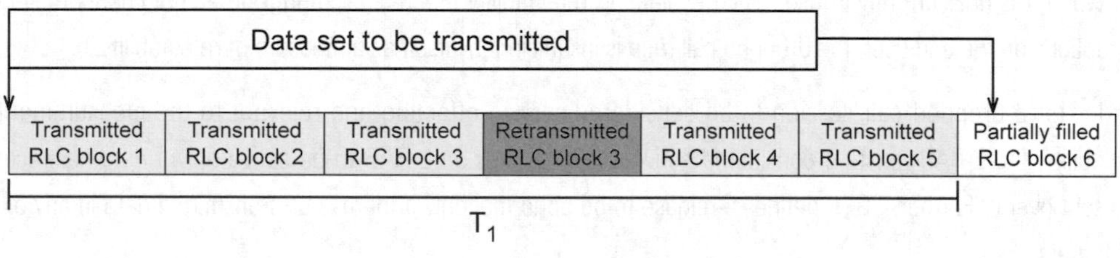

Figure 6.9-4. How data is organized for transmission on the Uu interface

This yields the following calculation for each data set transmitted:

$$\text{Uu throughout IP1}\left[\frac{\text{bytes}}{\text{sec}}\right] = \frac{V_{IP1}}{T_1} = \frac{V_{RLC1} + V_{RLC2} + V_{RLC3} + V_{RLC4} + V_{RLC5}}{T_1}.$$

In typical bursty traffic scenarios, there are idle times in which no data is transmitted, as shown in Figure 6.9-5. These idle times should not be counted in the calculation of throughput.

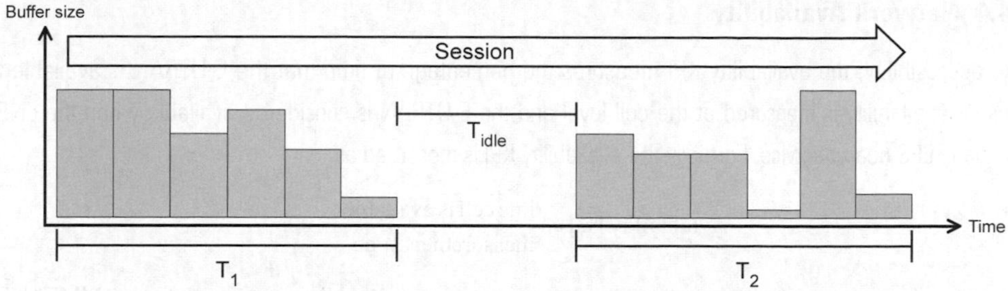

Figure 6.9-5. Bursty traffic profile during session (32.450 [27] Figure 2)

Thus, the calculation of integrity throughput yields the sum of the total volume of data transmitted against the sum of the time to transmit each set of data.

$$\text{Uu session throughput}\left[\frac{\text{bytes}}{\text{sec}}\right]=\frac{V_{IP1}+V_{IP2}}{T_1+T_2}.$$

An interesting outcome of these measurements is that if the IP throughput is measured for a given user on the S1 interface (and X2 for the inter-eNB handover case), the end user perceived throughput may differ because no information is available on the S1 interface about retransmission times, active/idle times or RLC block sizes.

In determining integrity, additional measurements related to throughput can also be considered:

- Variations in throughput during mobility
- RLC block acknowledge ratios
- Block error ratios
- HARQ failures

Latency

The focus of the LTE integrity latency KPI is measuring the time it takes the eNB to receive a packet on the S1 interface and send on to the Uu interface. Latency is also known as delay.

As has been discussed, one IP packet can be split into multiple data blocks for transmission over the air (see Figure 6.9-4). To avoid latency measurements being dependent on packet size, LTE latency is defined as the time difference between when the data enters the eNB buffer from the S1, and when the first data block is transmitted over the air.

Additional measurements related to latency can also be considered:

- Packet jitter and how to compare the jitter introduced by each part of the network
- IP packet loss ratios
- Mean opinion score (for voice)

6.9.4.4 Network Availability

Unlike accessibility, the availability KPI measures the percentage of time that the E-UTRAN is available to be accessed. Availability is measured at the cell level and the E-UTRAN is considered available when the eNB can provide any EPS bearer service. Formally the availability KPI is measured as:

$$\text{Availability}\,[\%] = \frac{\text{time cell is available}}{\text{measurement time}} * 100.$$

It can generally be assumed that once the cell setup is complete and the eNB is registered to an MME/UPE, it is available. The challenge then becomes how to measure the time when the cell is unavailable. Generally this will happen either in cell overload/blocking conditions or during maintenance periods.

6.9.4.5 Mobility

The mobility KPI is identified as a key measurement category on which to standardize and is defined in terms of handovers from one cell to the next. UMTS introduced the concept of macro-diversity and soft and softer handovers. These concepts allow for some tolerance in initial handover failures in overlapping cell areas. LTE, similar to GSM, has no macro-diversity and therefore all handovers are hard handovers. Understanding handover performance is essential, both in terms of success rates and in interruption times during handover.

When considering LTE mobility there are three basic scenarios that need to be evaluated: inter-cell, inter-eNB, and inter-routing area technology handovers. Generally, the LTE mobility KPI of handover success rate is defined as:

$$\text{Handover success rate}\,[\%] = \frac{\#\,\text{successful handovers}}{\#\,\text{handover preparations}} * 100.$$

There are two key scenarios that identify when the handover preparation phase begins. In the case of intra-frequency handovers, the eNB determines that a new target cell is preferred over the current source or serving cell. For inter-frequency handovers, the eNB determines that the current cell coverage is inadequate and thus additional measurements are required to identify a new neighbour cell in which to make the handover.

From the Uu interface (or eNB trace feed) the intra-LTE handover success rate can then be measured as:

$$\text{Uu intra-LTE handover success rate}\,[\%] = \frac{\text{RRC connection reconfiguration complete}}{\text{RRC connection reconfiguration (cause = mobility control information)}}.$$

Perhaps a more interesting metric in the intra-LTE handover case is the failure rate, measured as:

$$\text{Uu intra-LTE handover failure rate}\,[\%] = \frac{\text{RRC connection re-establishment request (cause = handover failure)}}{\text{RRC connection reconfiguration (cause = mobility control information)}}.$$

Similarly in the I-RAT handover case, the failure rate is measured as:

$$\text{Uu I-RAT handover failure rate}\,[\%] = \frac{\text{RRC connection re-establishment request (cause = handover failure)}}{\text{mobility from E-UTRA command (target RAT type)}}.$$

From the S1 interface the mobility KPI can then be defined as:

$$\text{S1 handover rate}\,[\%] = \frac{\text{UE context release command (cause = successful HO) + HO request acknowledge}}{\text{handover required + handover request + UL CDMA2K tunneling(CDMA2K HO required indication)}}.$$

When mobility is evaluated, it is important to know and understand not only the overall mobility KPI measurements but which type of mobility procedures are failing. For instance, if the handover success rate is 98.3%, it is important to determine the distribution of the 1.7% of failures between inter and intra LTE handovers. What may not be readily apparent from the calculations above is that the signalling contains enough information to identify inbound versus outbound handover success rates and, additionally, the I-RAT handover type distributions.

Some additional measurements related to mobility that can also be considered:

- Handover success/failure rate distribution by I-RAT type
- Tracking area update
- Handover interruption time in U-plane
- Interruption time (HO cases) on MAC layer

6.9.4.6 Additional Measurements for LTE

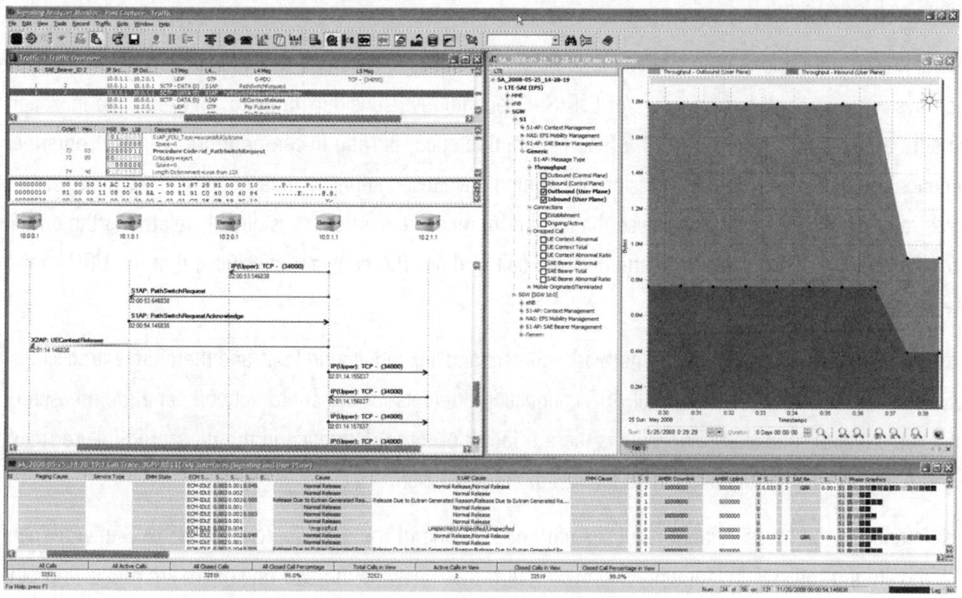

Figure 6.9-6. Agilent Signaling Analyzer aids in troubleshooting, benchmarking and optimization of mobile networks

As mentioned earlier, the 3GPP KPI definitions tend to be operator-centric measurements that evaluate overall network and service performance. However, when it comes to node and network characterization, additional measurements should be considered.

- Transition times
- Call setup time
- VoIP calls/cell/MHz
- Traffic volume
- Peak/mean key processor usage
- Peak/mean transmit power
- Peak/mean simultaneous RRC connections
- Peak/mean simultaneous SAE bearer connections

Which of these additional measurements are needed or useful will depend on the measurement purpose — troubleshooting, performance optimization, benchmarking, etc.

6.9.5 Monitoring Points and Data Sources

6.9.5.1 A Useful Example

A well designed end-to-end LTE/SAE network test system must take into account the data sources and possible monitoring points. Efforts in this area are being made by 3GPP, ETSI and other industry groups and will likely continue well into the future.

Fundamental to the topic of data sources and monitoring points is the need to understand measurement theory, basic physical laws, and the workings of LTE/SAE technology. Consider the following example in which two engineers are required to measure the RRC connection success ratio in the network. The first engineer has experience using drive test and commissions a targeted drive test campaign, measuring the RRC connection setup success ratio for a wide area. In this case the number of measurement points is directly related to the duration of the testing and the number of actual attempts per unit of time. The engineer concludes that the RRC connection success ratio is 98.5%.

The second engineer is accustomed to network counters and link monitoring tools and therefore extracts logs from the system. This provides a report of all RRC connection attempts for the entire network, and the measured RRC connection success ratio is 99.5%. Why is there a factor of three difference in the measured failure ratio? The answer to this question is fundamental to the rest of this discussion.

The difference in the measurement results is not because one of the data sources (drive test, network counters or link monitoring tools) is fundamentally flawed, but rather because the two engineers are measuring different network procedures, using different approaches:

- The drive test method analyzes network performance as seen from a specific handset at specific physical points in the network at specific points in time.
- The network counters and link monitoring tools record all of the network traffic and occurrences of signalling that the tools are designed to monitor. But this method analyzes network performance as seen on the network and at the network monitoring points.

This means that if drive test measurements are made outside the actual (and, potentially, intended) network coverage area, RRC connection requests at these locations will be recorded by the drive test system but not by network counters or link monitoring solutions operating only within the coverage area. Therefore, an extensive drive test campaign provides additional information beyond what network counters or link monitoring tools are able to provide. To make use of these data sources, test engineers must understand the range and limitations of the methods they are using.

In the optimization community, it is generally agreed that KPIs should be compared to each other only when they are derived from the same data source, or when they are normalized to remove any bias due to method or source. This is particularly true if comparisons show unexpected results. The lack of proper comparison is one of the largest contributors to unsound optimization decisions in the wireless industry today.

6.9.5.2 Different KPIs for Different Phases

Engineers will have several possible strategies from which to choose when they develop test plans for LTE, whether they are engaged in R&D or network optimization. Selecting the strategy that is most cost-effective and produces acceptable results is one of the most important decisions made early in each phase of the work. Once a strategy has been selected, the boundaries of its applicability must be established. A strategy that is appropriate for one phase of the work probably has significant shortcomings in later phases. It may not be a good idea to use the same fundamental KPIs for all phases of a network's deployment and maintenance, or to expect the data sources to provide the same types of measurement throughout. The reason can be illustrated with an example that contrasts Quality of Service (QoS) with Quality of Experience (QoE).

Monitoring the end-user IP traffic on a mobile network provides a full and detailed understanding of the traffic flows (TCP or UDP), the applications (voice, video, HTTP, email, etc.), and, potentially, the performance of the applications. A test engineer may believe that by monitoring just the UDP or TCP flows it will be possible to gather enough information about the end-user QoS to make a good approximation of the end-user QoE.

However, consider a user watching streaming video on his handset when the radio is not able to deliver the full bandwidth required over the air interface. When the RTP-UDP stream is measured in the core network, no degradation of the RTP-UDP stream is observed. Rather, the network monitoring tool in the core network reports a high and stable bit rate indicating good QoS. Nevertheless, the user reports a poor QoE. In this case, a better place to look for the degradation would be on the air interface, on the user's handset or between the two end points of the RLC entity — that is, in the UTRAN between the UE and the Radio Network Controller (RNC), and in the E-UTRAN between the UE and the eNB.

Consider now that the end user's application is quality-aware and, due to the poor radio conditions, the UE signals the network that a change of bit rate of the codec should be performed in the video streaming server. When this new RTP-UDP bit stream appears on the network, the network monitoring tool associates the change with a lower QoS because the stream has a lower bit rate. On the other hand, the radio conditions are now good enough to deliver the adapted bit stream, and the end user QoE increases.

This scenario shows that the crucial element of QoE is not the bit rate measured in the core network, but rather the ability of the entire end-to-end system to deliver a specific service to the end user. The application domain will, in this case, ensure that the best possible QoE is achieved. Therefore, the monitoring tool must be application-aware so that it can deliver the QoS measurements that lead to a correct estimation of end-user QoE.

Many similar examples can be found in almost all areas of test and monitoring. Test engineers have to understand clearly the extent to which their chosen test methods depend on the available data sources and the limitations imposed by this dependency.

6.9.5.3 Characteristics of Data Sources and Monitoring Points

The previous section provides a background for discussing the different data sources and their inherent characteristics.

Some examples of data sources and monitoring points are shown in Figure 6.9-7. Other examples include:

- Drive test
- Passive air probing
- eNB tracing
- Network interface tracing
- Signalling element counters, such as network counters
- Transport network statistics, such as Remote Network Monitoring (RMON) logs

Each data source or monitoring point has different inherent characteristics and will deliver information about different aspects of the network or service. Some of these sources require a substantial investment if deployed across the network and would almost certainly give a poor Return On Investment (ROI). But when these sources are used as point solutions in specific monitoring and test applications, they can prove quite valuable. A good example is a passive air interface probe, which is an important tool in Inter-Operability (Development) Testing (IOT/IODT) but, considering its cost, would not likely be a candidate for permanent deployment across the network.

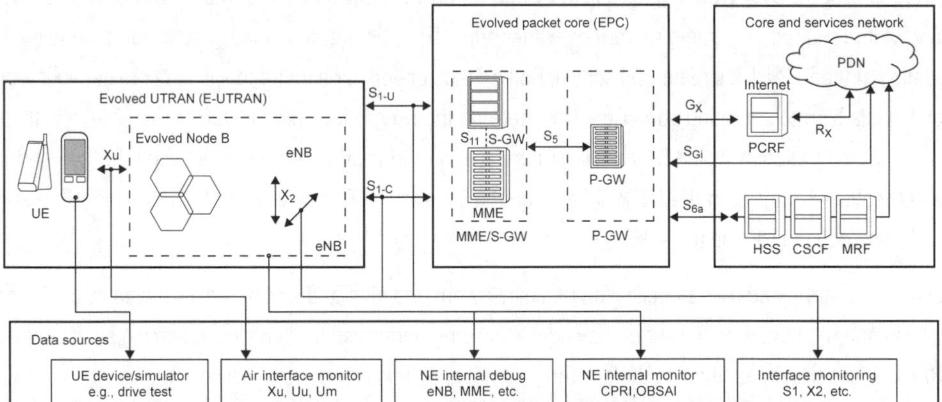

Figure 6.9-7. Monitoring points and data sources in LTE

Drive Test

Drive test is a familiar type of network testing that uses dedicated RF tools such as a scanner and receiver to gather data from the cellular network, and a commercial or dedicated test engineering phone to execute test calls and transactions. A drive test system logs RF characteristics, physical location (GPS coordinates), and events and transactions including protocol and message logs, application and IP performance results and voice quality Mean Opinion Score (MOS). Drive test provides an end-user view of the network and offers deep insight into network coverage and location-based issues. However, because drive test typically is performed by individuals driving a vehicle or walking, significant operational costs are associated with it. Drive test phones and scanners are sometimes installed in public transportation systems such as buses or taxis as an alternative, less expensive method of data collection. The importance of drive test and techniques for getting the most from this investment are covered in Section 6.9.6.

Passive Air Interface Probing

In some test scenarios — for example, IOT and IODT — it is crucial to have full, network-independent insight into the air interface. The logging capability of a test engineering phone records only what was processed and managed by the baseband unit in the UE. Similarly, eNB tracing logs typically contain information about only what has been processed by the eNB baseband processing entity. In contrast, a passive air interface monitor is designed to provide a fully independent view of all of the air interface protocols. This means that the passive monitor must contain an independent baseband demodulator for both the uplink and the downlink, and it must contain a message and protocol decoding entity with access to the content on the relevant baseband frequencies.

In terms of today's technology, passive air interface probing represents a significant structural cost. Therefore, because these tools are so expensive, they are typically used in low numbers in those environments in which full visibility is most important.

eNB Tracing

In an E-UTRAN, much of the system complexity has been removed or reduced because the UTRAN architecture, which consists of an RNC and a NodeB, has been collapsed into an eNB. This means that all of the highly valuable information previously available on the Iub or Iur interfaces is now contained inside the eNB and is less readily available to monitoring and test systems. The industry has identified the lack of access as a problem and work is ongoing in 3GPP to standardize an eNB trace interface.

An eNB trace interface will provide deep insight into not only the actual signalling messages terminated in the eNB (RRC messages, etc.) but also information related to the overall system and node performance over time. Remember that the eNB's primary function is to be a network node and not a measurement device. Thus, in an overload situation, the eNB will focus its resources on the primary task of relaying data and maintaining end-user QoS according to the agreed-upon parameters.

The high value of an eNB trace is its potential to provide, apart from certain overload scenarios, reliable and relevant data for KPIs and overall troubleshooting. Moreover, this will be done at a relatively low structural cost, because the hardware is already in place. Adding logging capabilities to the eNB with software should not increase the structural cost per unit substantially, particularly in high-volume deployments.

It is important to note that an eNB trace interface normally provides only statistics and information about procedures terminating in the node. This means that for a more complete network view, combining eNB tracing with network interface probing is desirable.

Passive Network Probing

The traditional approach of using passive, network-based probing is still valid in the LTE and SAE framework. A network-based probe can gather data on all of the traffic on the interface, provide a means to either store it in a log file or process it, and generate measurement results (such as call and session tracing, statistics, KPIs). The network can generally be monitored on all physical links. In light of the security and integrity protection in the Evolved Packet Core (see Chapter 5) the passive probing solution must be able to manage the deciphering and decryption of various security methods and algorithms.

One of the key benefits of a passive probing system is its ability to gather, filter and analyze data independent of any call processing in a network node. This ability allows the probing system to show the traffic and the resulting network behavior, even under certain transport overload scenarios that would be impossible to depict by any other means. It is this independent view that makes the system invaluable for root cause analysis and for providing reliable KPIs.

Crucial to an investment in a passive monitoring probe system is the system's ability to deliver a high ROI, which in turn depends on its ability to be customized and scaled. Passive monitoring solutions typically provide an ample set of standardized statistics and KPIs, but the ability of the network operator to customize the measurement and tailor the output of these systems is key to maximizing their value. In addition, a highly scalable and stable multi-user architecture allows concurrent access to the monitored data feeds. This multiplies the value of the passive probing system compared to a single user instrument solution.

Signalling Element Counters

All network elements, as they switch and forward traffic, provide some type of performance counters. In some cases this is an extensive set of functionality fully managed by a separate processing entity in the network element, but more often it is a by-product of the network element's primary capability — for example, switching.

Network element counters can be a rich source of data. They are not always stable, but when they are able to deliver statistics, they provide an inexpensive and relatively easily integrated source of network performance data. It is always important to understand what the various network element statistics actually show. In general, a network node can only provide details on the messages and procedures that terminate in the node or provide flow measurements (such as the number of IP packets that have been sent in the uplink and downlink). To fully understand end-user QoS or to attempt an assessment of end-user QoE, information and statistics from several network elements must be combined. However, it is outside the scope of this book to provide a detailed explanation of QoS and QoE analysis from KPIs and how the various data sources are used.

Both network element counters and passive probe-based monitoring systems report only on the traffic and procedures that take place in the area of coverage. Neither system can report when a user is out of coverage range and loses service capability.

Transport Network Statistics

Transport network statistics provide relevant data on the utilization of transport resources, the number of transport network issues and the overall transport network performance. One relevant issue is that in many cases these statistics are directly related to a physical link between two end points rather than the logical link between two network elements. The logical link may be built from several different physical links, and in some cases may include the passive standby links that cover link breakage, etc. It can be difficult to extract the logical link or transport level QoS from the physical transport network statistics.

One piece of information that transport network statistics can add to the overall view is the number of resources used in comparison to what is available. This information is not directly available from any other monitoring source. Once again, though, the data must be considered carefully as the transport network itself can have certain rate or traffic limiting aspects, and so analysis cannot be based solely on the possible bandwidth available from a given type of network interface. For example, a Gigabit Ethernet (GbE) interface connection on one network element might be carried over a Digital Subscriber Line (DSL) interface somewhere in the transport path, or even more likely this GbE interface may have several different Virtual Local Area Networks (VLANs) carried on the same link.

6.9.6 Drive Testing LTE

6.9.6.1 Why Bother With Drive Test?

In LTE as with other cellular technologies, drive testing will be a part of the network deployment and management life cycle from early on. Drive testing provides an accurate real-world capture of the RF environment under a particular set of network and environmental conditions. The main benefit of drive testing is that it measures the actual network coverage and performance that would be experienced by a user on the route of the drive. It is argued that in modern networks with modern simulations, network engineers can mathematically model how a network will perform. While this is true to a certain extent, it is also essential to do drive testing as network parameter settings alter how the UEs interact and deal with the network environment. Such interactions cannot be wholly predicted through mathematical modeling. Figure 6.9-8 shows how drive test is used in the network planning lifecycle.

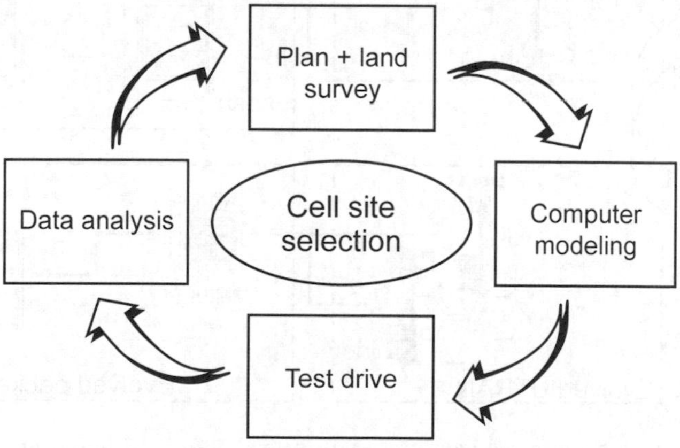

Figure 6.9-8. Network planning cycle

6.9.6.2 Components of a Drive Test System

Drive test systems are generally built around two measurement components, instrumented mobile phones (test engineering phones) and measurement receivers. Each has its own characteristics with associated benefits and drawbacks. Phone-based systems can respond to problems within network-controlled constraints. Receiver-based systems give a complete overview of RF activity but cannot duplicate network-related problems.

The measurements carried out during drive testing have evolved over time, from the early days when the focus was purely on parametric RF measurements, to the wide variety of application-based data performance measurements integrated into modern drive test systems. Many of these changes have been driven by the change in services provided from a simple voice carrier to the multi-service, data-centric wireless networks that LTE intends to enable. Network operators have shifted their focus from purely measuring RF performance to measuring customer experience, and this has driven the integration of many data application tests such as video streaming and VoIP into drive test systems so that engineers can correlate end-user application performance with detailed RF measurements.

Another evolution is the move from single-band single-technology networks to multi-band multi-technology networks. LTE is not going to exist as an island technology, but will be overlaid and integrated with the existing UMTS/HSPA and cdma2000 1xRTT and HRPD (1xEV-DO) networks. Drive test tools need to embrace this multi-technology multi-band environment. An area of key interest to cellular operators will be the interaction of LTE with their existing infrastructure and in particular the crossover points where handovers take place.

6.9.6.3 Importance of Drive Test for LTE

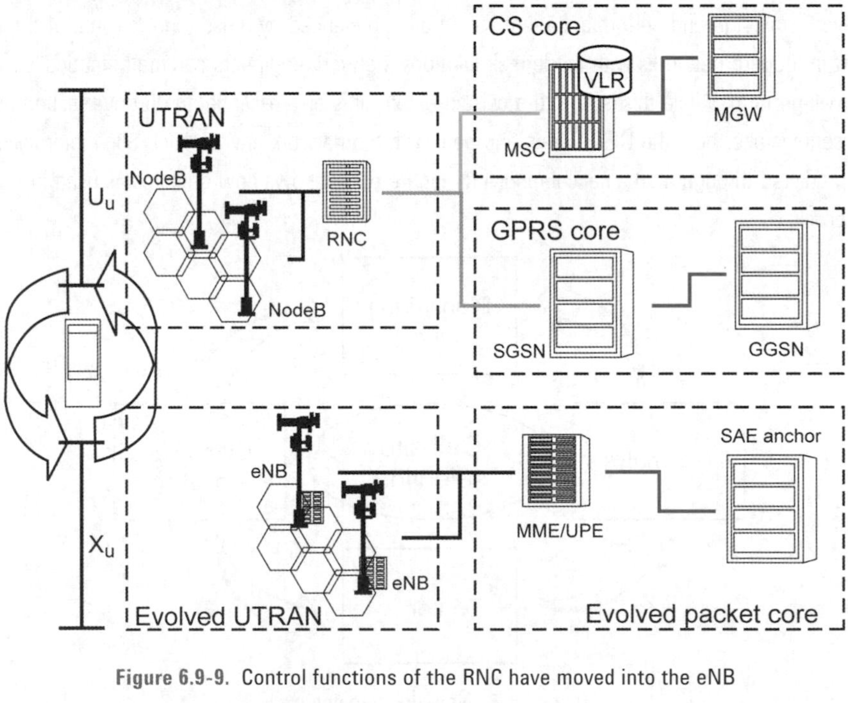

Figure 6.9-9. Control functions of the RNC have moved into the eNB

Many different strategies and methods to monitor network performance have been described. Network "probing" in which the signalling traffic is monitored at control points and then centrally analyzed can provide valuable insights into the overall network health. This strategy works well where, as in GSM and UMTS networks, much of the control traffic is consolidated through RNCs or Base Station Controllers (BSCs) so that by monitoring relatively few major interfaces, a good view of a wide range of base station end-points can be obtained.

As the industry has moved ahead with HSPA and now LTE technologies, more and more of the network intelligence has moved out from the core to the edge of the network and into the eNBs, taking the traffic management also towards the network edge (see Figure 6.9-9). This means that much of the control and decision making is now deployed within the eNBs, and interaction between the UE and base stations can be most effectively monitored by instrumented phones involved in the actual transactions.

6.9.6.4 Phone-Based Drive Test for LTE

Phone-based drive test systems are useful for evaluating basic network performance and are essential to characterize what the end user is experiencing while using the network. Phone-based systems address the need to verify network settings such as cell selection and re-selection boundaries, and to measure the voice and data application performance in the live network. With radio resource management taking place in the eNB, suitably instrumented phones can be used to monitor the performance of the physical layer including modulation schemes, access procedures, synchronization and power control. Instrumented phones can also report the measured channel state information (CQI, PMI, RI) and Hybrid ARQ (HARQ) interaction with the scheduler in the eNB. If the network is not achieving the expected data performance, it is important to be able to analyze the signalling performance and settings at each signalling layer including the RRC, RLC and MAC. Monitoring the resources allocated to a UE together with the measured network conditions, available neighbour cells and power levels will allow troubleshooting and optimization of network settings.

6.9.6.5 Receiver-Based Drive Test for LTE

Receiver-based systems are used to obtain a "raw" view of the RF environment. They can measure the entire spectrum and are not constrained by network operator settings. These systems are useful for activities such as band clearing and general coverage estimation but they cannot give a true measure of customer experience as they do not physically interact with the network under test.

Modern drive test receivers include specialist measurements targeted at specific technologies. To be useful, it is necessary to identify which signals are contributing positively to the mobile environment and which are negative influences. For LTE, identification of the reference signals and synchronization signals which the UEs use to lock onto the network are key measurements. The ability to extract the LTE cell ID allows the next level of identification of the cell in the same way that the scrambling code would be used to identify a UMTS cell or a Base Station Identity Code (BSIC) would identify a GSM cell.

6.9.6.6 Benefits of Combining Phone and Receiver Based Test

While both phone-based and receiver-based systems have their place, the real advantages come when the measurements from both systems are combined to allow troubleshooting that either cannot be done or is difficult to do when only one type of system is used. A solution such as the Agilent E6474A Drive Test system software creates links between the test engineering phones and receivers in the system so that the receivers can dynamically track and measure the channels being used by the UE.

In all network technologies, identifying missing neighbour cells is a classic problem that can be addressed by the use of a combined phone and receiver based system. The phone reports and measures how the network has set the neighbour list while the receiver reports the actual impartial neighbour list. Combining the results of these two independent measures allows optimization of the network settings for the current RF environment.

Identifying interference where it matters is also facilitated by the use of a combined receiver and phone solution. The phone part of the system is able to establish network connection and report application performance, and the receiver part of the system is able to monitor any external RF sources that may be adversely affecting the on-going connection. Thus network-dependent application performance and independent RF measurements are combined to provide information to solve customer application problems. A typical RF network optimization cycle is shown in Figure 6.9-10. The data collected automatically by the Operation and Maintenance Center (OMC) is used with drive test data from both phone and receiver-base systems to optimize the network.

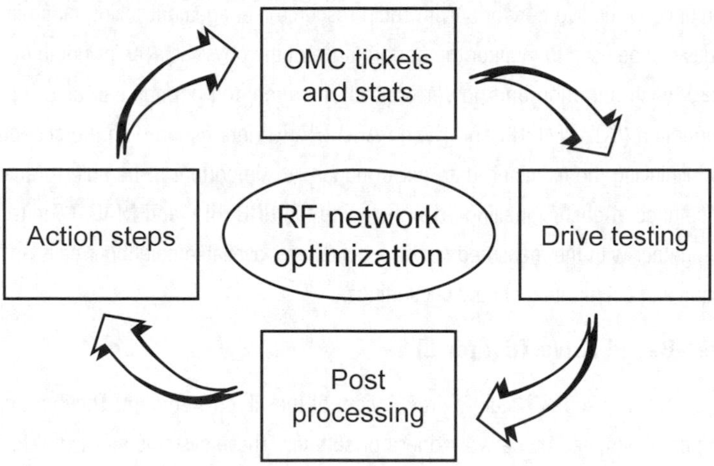

Figure 6.9-10. RF network optimization cycle

6.9.6.7 Verifying LTE Application Performance using Drive Test

Delivering user data rates of 100 Mbps and above is one of the key challenges for LTE. Therefore, in addition to RF measurements, data application testing will be a critical activity during network deployment. LTE moves wireless communications to an all-IP network. Bridging the gap between RF performance and end-user IP services such as VoIP, video telephony and video streaming, is a challenge for network operators who need to be able to ensure that these new offerings can be added to their infrastructure without affecting the quality of existing services.

Drive test solutions need to include a broad portfolio of instrumented data test applications including video streaming, video telephony, HTTP, FTP, e-mail, SMS, MMS and WAP. These are essential to allow network engineering departments to measure the performance of the applications in conjunction with the RF environment. If a service is not performing as expected, the RF performance and network configuration information is available alongside application performance data. GPS provides precise geographic location to allow troubleshooting and problems to be identified. Figure 6.9-11 shows a typical network troubleshooting cycle involving analysis of data on site.

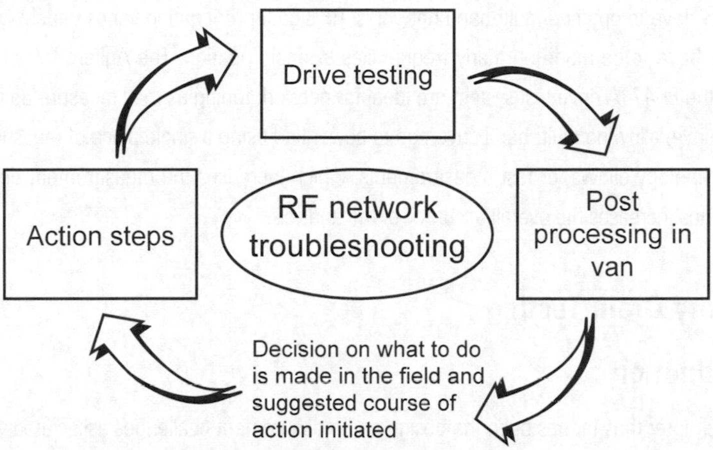

Figure 6.9-11. RF network troubleshooting cycle

6.9.6.8 Drive Test Solutions for LTE

Comprehensive drive test systems such as the Agilent E6474A Wireless Network Optimization Platform address the challenges of optimizing LTE network performance by quickly and accurately identifying problems. The E6474A system shown in Figure 6.9-12 can be used in site evaluation, base station commissioning, system acceptance, and ongoing optimization and troubleshooting. The system can be scaled from a single phone-based solution to a multi-phone, multi-technology receiver and phone combined system covering the major technologies that are deployed in wireless networks worldwide: LTE, HSPA, UMTS, GSM, GPRS, EDGE, 1xEV DO, cdma2000, TD-SCDMA, iDEN and WiMAX. The system also encompasses a wide range of application tests including messaging, analog and VoIP testing, web oriented and video streaming components.

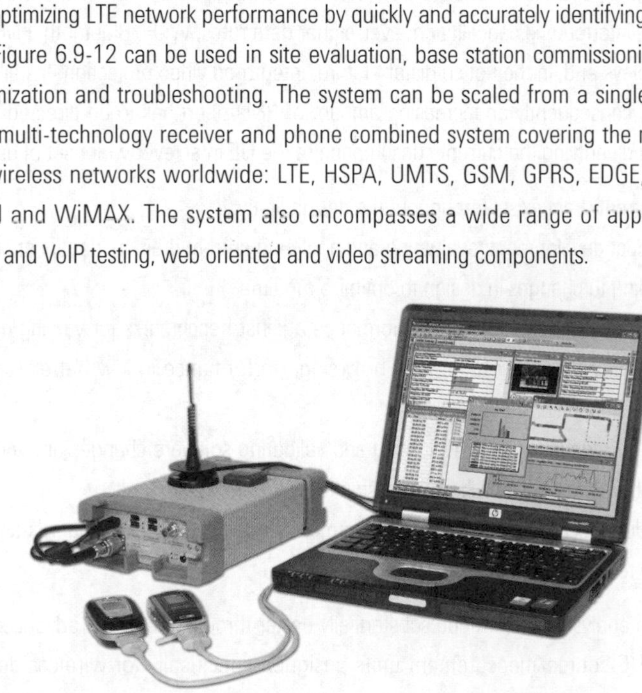

Figure 6.9-12. Agilent E6474A drive test system for network planning, deployment and maintenance

With the flexibility to combine multiple receivers and multiple phones, the drive test system allows multiple technologies to be measured simultaneously with a single computer. A broad range of data collection and analysis functions are available to aid network optimization and determine quality of service from the customer perspective.

Network operators have to optimize multi-band networks. RF signal propagation varies widely with frequency and so measurements have to be made on many frequencies at each location. The Agilent W1314A measurement receivers used in the E6474A drive test system are ideal for network tuning as they measure up to eight frequency bands in a single drive, allowing multi-band coverage to be verified using a single piece of measurement hardware. Powerful DSP technology allows for fast measurements, which increases the measurement density at any drive test speed and hence increases the overall accuracy of the analysis.

6.10 Battery Drain Testing

6.10.1 Introduction

The focus of this chapter thus far has been the design and measurement challenges associated with the radio and network aspects of LTE/SAE. However, one topic remains that is crucial to bringing successful products to market, and that is the humble battery. Indeed, it was primarily concern with battery performance that led 3GPP to define SC-FDMA for the LTE uplink rather than the more power hungry OFDMA used for the downlink.

Although advances in battery capacity continue to be made, they are being outpaced by the demands of modern UE. It is not just the primary radio that requires power; power is required by the multi-band multi-RAT support, receive diversity, MIMO, interference cancellation, ever-higher data rates, Wi-Fi, Bluetooth, FM Radio, MP3, MP4, GPS, larger brighter displays and, in the not so distant future, integrated video projection. Installing a larger battery is usually not an option; consequently an increasing amount of R&D effort has to be directed towards designing, measuring, optimizing and verifying the current consumption of the UE in an ever wider set of use cases.

The need to measure current drain exists throughout the design lifecycle.

- During product development: evaluating and analyzing current drain to identify anomalies and the root causes leading to changes in design to optimize run time.
- During design validation: checking performance against benchmarks for varying operating conditions such as standby time, talk time, web browsing, performance in low battery conditions, extreme environmental conditions, etc.
- During software development: evaluating and validating software changes and the impact on current drain though a suite of established regression tests.
- During product acceptance: validating performance against industry standards and operator-specific acceptance tests.

The task of current drain analysis can be made substantially easier through the use of advanced tools. The Agilent 66319D/66321D are DC source/measurement units designed specifically for wireless device current drain testing. The DC sources can be used as battery emulators or in a special zero voltage configuration to measure the performance of the mobile device battery, commonly called battery run down testing. The DC sources are used in conjunction with the Agilent 14565B battery drain analysis software, enabling the designer to carry out advanced current drain analysis either manually or with full automation at all stages of the product design lifecycle. Three basic measurement modes are supported:

- Waveform mode provides an oscilloscope-like capability for capturing and analyzing current drain signals from tenths of milliseconds to seconds in duration.
- Data logging mode provides extended current drain measurement and analysis for up to 1,000 hours of testing.
- Complementary Cumulative Distribution Function (CCDF) mode provides statistical profiling to display current drain performance for up to 1,000 hours operation.

The following sections give examples of the measurement process and examples of waveform and CCDF current drain measurements and how they are used to carry out essential battery performance measurements.

6.10.2 Measurement Process

A typical battery run down test and measurement setup is shown in Figure 6.10-1.

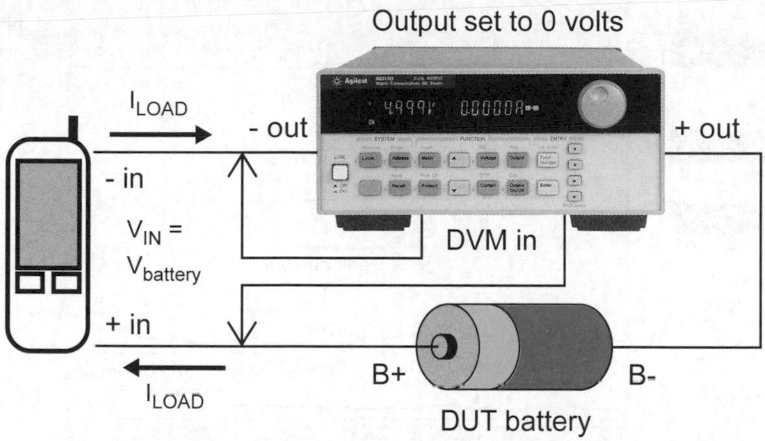

Figure 6.10-1. Typical DUT battery drain measurement setup

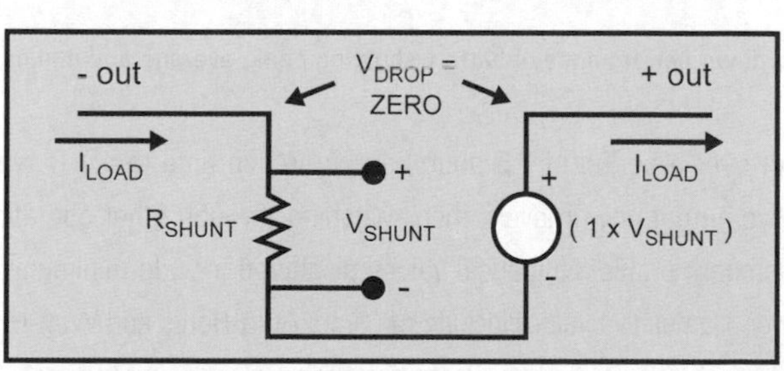

Figure 6.10-2. Schematic for zero-burden active shunt concept

The DC source can be used just as a battery emulator, but in the configuration of Figure 6.10-1 it is connected in series with the real Device Under Test (DUT) battery in what is known as a zero-burden active shunt mode. In this mode the DC source acts as a logging ammeter utilizing the built-in basic Digital Volt Meter (DVM) input to measure the voltage. Figure 6.10-2 shows a conceptual schematic of the DC source operating as a zero-burden shunt.

A zero-burden shunt in combination with an active opposing voltage source cancels the voltage drop across the shunt resistor. The benefit of doing this is that the DUT sees the full voltage from the battery or source powering the DUT. In addition, since the voltage drop across the shunt resistor is no longer an issue, a larger value of shunt resistor can be used to improve the dynamic range and resolution of measurements. The current and voltage of the battery can then be measured and logged at 64 kHz for periods of 10 seconds to 1,000 hours.

6.10.3 Waveform Measurements

Figure 6.10-3 shows a typical voltage and current waveform profile created as part of a test to analyze the run down performance of the battery.

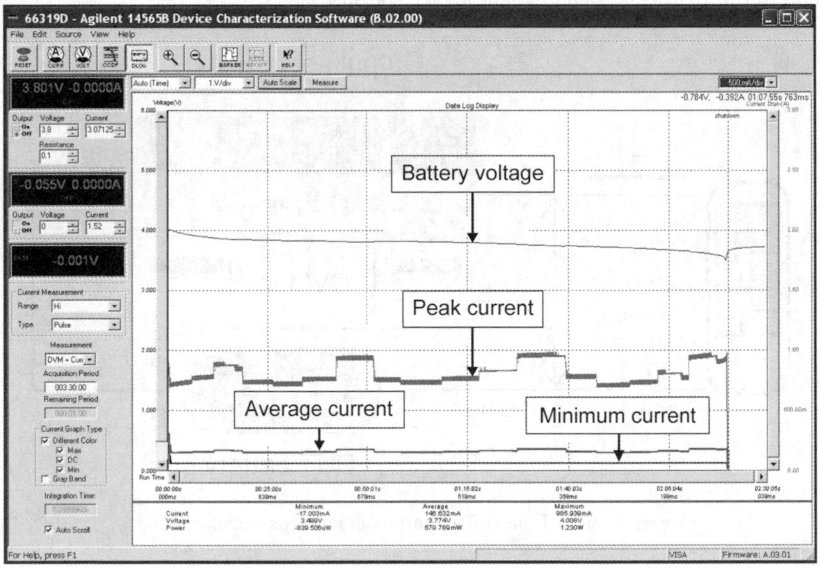

Figure 6.10-3. Run down performance of battery showing peak, average and minimum current profiles

The test was carried out over a period of 2.5 hours, during which time the DUT was executing a dynamic sequence: changing active output power levels, then switching through other operating modes (standby, off, active) as part of a benchmark profile. Numerical values displayed include minimum, maximum and average current, voltage and power. Cumulative values include run time, Amp-Hours and Watt-Hours actually delivered to the DUT. It can be seen from the figure that the device switched off after approximately 2 hours and 20 minutes. This type of measurement is essential to ensure correct operation of the circuits and software responsible for shutting down the UE at the appropriate time, before the radio performance begins to degrade. In the trace, vertical markers have been placed at the start point and at the end point where the phone shut off, indicated by the current dropping to zero and the battery voltage recovering due to removal of the load. The numeric values are recalculated based on the markers and show that the UE ran for 2.3 hours and consumed 382 mA-Hours and 1.442 Watt-Hours. This integrating feature of the software enables the large quantity of results to be reduced to a meaningful set of critical figures that enable a fuller understanding of the battery and DUT performance. Zoom and marker controls allow closer analysis of subsections of the data log.

In addition to all the peripheral features on modern phones that have relatively simple current demands from the battery, the underlying primary radio function has a complex relationship with current drain. The talk time (or data connect time) as well as the standby time of the radio is a function of the radio conditions and network parameters. To control all the variables that have an impact on current drain, a base station emulator such as the Agilent E5515C or E6620A is required. These emulators can provide a controlled radio and network environment in which the designer can experiment with the many parameters that impact performance. Testing in such environments can be challenging and so the Agilent N5970A Interactive Functional Test Software has been created to automate current drain testing using the base station emulator. See application note 5989-9153EN [29] for more details.

The standby time of the same UE in different networks can be vastly different, and it is therefore essential that the designer understand the underlying capabilities of the product independent of any specific network implementation. To set guidelines for the process of battery drain performance testing, industry standards have been developed such as the "Battery Life Measurement Technique" produced by the European Conference on Technology-Enhanced Learning (ECTEL) and the GSM Association [30], which defines the essential parameters that affect current drain so that products can be fairly compared.

The waveform example in Figure 6.10-3 demonstrates what can be done over long periods of time, but the sampler within the DC source runs at 64 kHz and is capable of measuring current profiles over very short durations. The RF designer can use this level of resolution to monitor the profile of current drain over periods shorter than a single SC-FDMA symbol. Examples in which this technique may be useful is in the profiling of the uplink Sounding Reference Signal (SRS), which is a pulse lasting just over 70 μs used to train the eNB receiver. This signal needs to have an accurate power profile, be flat in the frequency domain, and have low Error Vector Magnitude (EVM). Problems with supplying sufficient current from the off state to full power in perhaps 20 μs could contribute to signal impairments.

6.10.4 Statistical Measurements

Figure 6.10-4 shows an example of how the underlying data logged by the DC source can be displayed in the form of a CCDF profile. This is a powerful technique that enables the designer to see the probability of a particular current drain and then link to particular activity factors such as talk time, standby, etc.

The figure shows three different user profiles: idle time, talk time and typical PC data use. The CCDF is using a double log scale with probability of occurrence on the vertical scale and current on the horizontal scale. Any point on the graph represents the probability that the measured current over the duration of the measurement period will exceed the value shown. The idle time trace shows the lowest current drain. The near flat line at 100% extending out to the inflection at 45 mA and 20% indicates that for 80% of the time the UE is drawing almost no current. This figure should align with the design goals of the UE and will reflect the operating parameters in the network. From the inflection at 45 mA and 20% there is a near constant decline to 200 mA at 3% before the curve decreases rapidly to around 350 mA at 0%, which is the maximum current observed during idle mode.

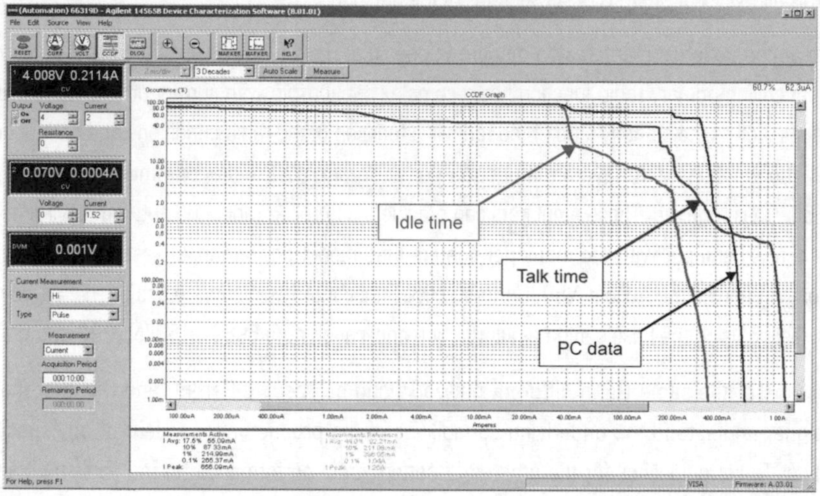

Figure 6.10-4. CCDF current profile for three different use cases

The talk time curve shows that for 50% of the time the current is below 3 mA. This is to be expected and indicates that the voice activity factor for speech is less than 50% transmit. The large increase out to 170 mA at 20% represents the bulk of the current drain. The current continues to rise out to 900 mA at 0.6 % before reaching a maximum of around 1.2 A. The reason for the peak current being over five times the average during the transmit periods is not obvious. It may be due to other background factors such as backlighting or to peaks in the audio currents driving the speaker. Correlating the peak current with specific activity on the UE would lead to an understanding of whether this is an expected or unexpected result.

The PC data curve is a hybrid of the two previous curves. The curve starts out like the idle time curve, showing little current drain for 80% of the time, as would be expected during the periods when no data is being transmitted or received. The first inflection occurs at 200 mA and 70%, with a slow decline to 300 mA at 60% and then a sharp decline to 400 mA at 1.5% indicating the effective peak current. The trace trails off to a maximum current of 600 mA. It is interesting that the peaks of data current are much lower than voice peaks. This may be due to not having to drive the audio circuits.

For further reading see application note 5989-6016EN, "Battery Drain Analysis Improves Mobile-Device Operating Time" [31] and application note 1427, "Evaluating Battery Run-down Performance" [32].

6.11 References

[1] 3GPP TS 36.212 V8.5.0 (2008-12) Multiplexing and Channel Coding

[2] 3GPP TS 36.211 V8.5.0 (2008-12) Physical Channels and Modulation

[3] Voelker, Ken, "Vector Modulation Analysis and Troubleshooting for OFDM Systems." Paper presented at 2002 Wireless Systems Design Conference.

[4] Cutler, Bob, "Effects of Physical Layer Impairments on OFDM Systems." RF Design, May 2002. Available from http://rfdesign.com/images/archive/0502Cutler36.pdf.

[5] Wright, Tom and Gorin, Joe and Zarlingo, Ben, "Bringing New Power and Precision to Gated Spectrum Measurements," High Frequency Electronics, August 2007, www.highfrequencyelectronics.com/Archives/Aug07/HFE0807_Zarlingo.pdf.

[6] "Spectrum Analyzer Basics," Application Note 150. Agilent Technologies, Literature Number 5952-0292.

[7] "Spectrum Analyzer Measurements and Noise," Application Note 1303. Agilent Technologies, Literature Number 5966-4008EN.

[8] Matsuoka, H., and Zarlingo, B., "Analysis of Baseband IQ Signals." Paper presented at IMS2008. Available from www.agilent.com/find/IMS2008-MicroApps.

[9] Zarlingo, B., and Gorin, J., "Spectrum Analyzer Detectors and Averaging for Wireless Measurements." Proceedings of the Wireless and Portable by Design Symposium, Spring 2001.

[10] 3GPP TS 36.101 V8.4.0 (2008-12) UE Radio Transmission and Reception

[11] Rumney, Moray, "3GPP LTE: Introducing Single-Carrier FDMA, "Agilent Measurement Journal, Issue 4 2008, p 18-27, Literature Number 5989-7680EN.

[12] Rumney, Moray, "Understanding Single Carrier FDMA — The New LTE Uplink." Webcast March 20, 2008, at TechOnline, www.techonline.com.

[13] Zemede, Martha, "RF Measurements for LTE." Webcast August 7, 2008, at TechOnline, www.techonline.com

[14] "N9080A LTE Measurement Application Technical Overview with Self-Guided Demonstration." Agilent Technologies, Literature Number 5989-6537EN.

[15] 3GPP TR 36.942 V8.1.0 (2008-12) Radio Frequency (RF) system scenarios

[16] 3GPP TS 36.141 V8.1.0 (2008-12) Base Station (BS) conformance testing

[17] 3GPP TS 36.104 V8.4.0 (2008-12) Base Station (BS) radio transmission and reception

[18] "MIMO Channel Modeling and Emulation Test Challenges," Application Note. Agilent Technologies, Literature Number 5989-8973EN, October 2008.

[19] 3GPP TS 36.213 V8.5.0 (2008-12) Physical Layer Procedures

[20] MIMO channel model for TWG RCT Ad-Hoc Proposal, V16, pp. 6-8

[21] Chen-Nee Chuah et.al., "Capacity scaling in MIMO wireless systems under correlated fading." IEEE Transactions on Information Theory, Volume 48, Issue 3, Mar 2002, pp 637-650.

[22] Telatar, I. Emre, "Capacity of multi-antenna Gaussian channels." European Transactions on Telecommunications, Vol. 10, No. 6, pp. 585-595, Nov/Dec 1999. Available from http://mars.bell-labs.com/papers/proof/proof.pdf

[23] Love, D.J., and Heath, R.W., "Limited Feedback Unitary Precoding for Spatial Multiplexing Systems." IEEE Transactions on Information Theory, Volume 51, Issue 8, Aug. 2005, pp 2967-2976.

[24] 3GPP TS 27.007 V8.6.0 (2008-12) AT command set for User Equipment (UE)

[25] 3GPP TS 36.300 V8.7.0 (2008-12) Evolved Universal Terrestrial Radio Access (E-UTRA) and Evolved Universal Terrestrial Radio Access Network (E-UTRAN); Overall description; Stage 2

[26] 3GPP TS 23.401 V8.4.1 (2008-12) GPRS enhancements for E-UTRAN access

[27] 3GPP TS 32.450 V1.0.0 (2008-12) Telecommunication management; Key Performance Indicators (KPI) for Evolved Universal Terrestrial Radio Access Network (E-UTRAN): Definitions

[28] 3GPP TS 32.451 V1.0.0 (2008-12) Telecommunication management; Key Performance Indicators (KPI) for Evolved Universal Terrestrial Radio Access Network (E-UTRAN): Requirements

[29] "Agilent N5970A Interactive Functional Software," Application Note. Agilent Technologies, Literature Number 5989-9153EN, July 2008.

[30] ECTEL/GSM Association, "Battery Life Measurement Technique," October 1998.

[31] Brorein, Edward, "Battery Drain Analysis Improves Mobile-Device Operating Time," Application Note. Agilent Technologies, Literature Number 5989-6016EN, February 2007.

[32] "Evaluating Battery Run-down Performance," Application Note 1427. Agilent Technologies, Literature Number 5988-8157EN, December 2006.

Links to all reference documents can be found at www.agilent.com/find/ltebook

Chapter 7

Conformance Testing

This chapter covers User Equipment (UE) and evolved Node B (eNB) conformance testing. The role of certification bodies in UE certification such as the Global Certification Forum (GCF) and PCS Type Certification Review Board (PTCRB) is also explained.

7.1 Introduction to Conformance Testing

The goal of the LTE conformance tests is to ensure a minimum level of performance. Although the list of tests can seem very large, it should be understood that passing all the conformance tests represents a minimum level of performance and there are many other kinds of testing that equipment vendors will need to carry out. This includes a more thorough investigation of performance margins since conformance testing is a pass/fail result and gives no indication of how close the product is to a particular limit. At a higher level there is a need to test applications since the conformance tests are very much aimed at a lower level of capability, ensuring that the underlying transport mechanisms are in place to carry end-user services. Operator acceptance testing is another step in the process to market and will include additional user-centric tests not otherwise covered. Thus conformance testing is an important and essential step towards the successful deployment of a new system, but it is by no means the beginning or end of the test process.

For the UE, conformance testing is in three parts: Radio Frequency (RF), Radio Resource Management (RRM) and signalling. For the evolved Node B (eNB or Base Station) only RF conformance tests are defined.

7.1.1 Common Conformance Test Specifications

Table 7.1-1 shows two important specifications common to the UE conformance tests.

3GPP test specification 36.508 [1] aims to define the typical operating conditions of a real network and is developed based on the input received from network operators. It describes the following features:

- Reference conditions
- The test frequencies to use for each of the defined frequency bands
- Test signals
- The default parameters for the system information blocks and all signalling messages. It also describes the network simulation for Intra LTE, LTE-UTRAN, LTE-GERAN and LTE-cdma2000 networks.

- Reference radio bearer configurations used in radio bearer interoperability testing.
- Common radio bearer configurations for other test purposes.
- Generic setup procedures for use in UE conformance tests. These procedures describe the sequence to bring the UE into a stable state before starting the test sequence.

Table 7.1-1. Common UE conformance test specifications

Specification	Title	Purpose
36.508 [1]	Evolved Universal Terrestrial Radio Access (E-UTRA) and Evolved Packet Core (EPC); Common Test Environments for User Equipment (UE) Conformance Testing	Provides the call setup and bearer definitions used for testing
36.509 [2]	Evolved Universal Terrestrial Radio Access (E-UTRA) and Evolved Packet Core (EPC); Special Conformance Testing Functions for User Equipment (UE)	Defines test-specific functionality in the UE not otherwise defined in the core specifications

3GPP test specification 36.509 [2] defines any special functions needed for testing that are not otherwise defined in the core specifications. The most important of these functions is the UE loopback capability, which enables signals sent on the downlink to be returned on the uplink for analysis by the test system.

7.2 RF Conformance Testing

This section describes the RF conformance tests as they apply to the UE and eNB. Comparison is made where appropriate to the UMTS conformance test specifications. Because of space limitations, it is not possible to go through all the tests in detail; they can be read directly from the specifications. Rather, the intent is to provide the overall context within which the RF tests exist.

7.2.1 Conformance Test Specifications

The key specifications relating to UE RF conformance test are defined in Table 7.2-1.

Table 7.2-1. UE RF FDD and TDD conformance test specifications

Specification	Title	Purpose
36.124 [3]	Electromagnetic Compatibility (EMC) Requirements for Mobile Terminals and Ancillary Equipment	Tests for EMC emissions and immunity
36.521-1 [4]	User Equipment (UE) Conformance Specification; Radio Transmission and Reception Part 1: Conformance Testing (FDD/TDD)	The RF conformance tests primarily based on 36.101 [5]
36.521-2 [6]	User Equipment (UE) Conformance Specification; Radio Transmission and Reception Part 2: Implementation Conformance Statement (ICS)	Definition of applicability of tests for different UE capabilities
36.521-3 [7]	User Equipment (UE) Conformance Specification; Radio Transmission and Reception Part 3: Radio Resource Management Conformance Testing	The RRM conformance tests based on 36.133 [8]

Base station RF FDD and TDD conformance test documents are listed in Table 7.2-2.

Table 7.2-2. Base Station (eNB) RF FDD and TDD conformance test documents

Specification	Title	Purpose
36.113 [9]	Evolved Universal Terrestrial Radio Access (E-UTRA); Base Station (BS) and Repeater Electromagnetic Compatibility (EMC)	Tests for EMC emissions and immunity
36.141 [10]	Evolved Universal Terrestrial Radio Access (E-UTRA); Base Station (BS) Conformance Testing	The RF conformance tests primarily based on 36.104 [11]
36.143 [12]	Evolved Universal Terrestrial Radio Access (E-UTRA); FDD Repeater Conformance Testing	The repeater conformance tests primarily based on 36.106 [13]

The UE and eNB EMC tests in 36.124 [3] and 36.113 [9] are largely independent of the radio system and are not discussed further here.

7.2.2 Scope of RF Conformance Tests

The complexity of the air interface continues to grow from one cellular system to the next. One of the system design goals for LTE was to reduce this complexity in the UE. Seen from the baseband, it can be argued that OFDM is indeed simpler to implement than CDMA. Nevertheless, the complexity seen from a test perspective is defined by the number of permutations of the RF configuration that can impact performance. LTE introduces more degrees of freedom than any previous radio standard, and these degrees of freedom have a direct impact on the number of tests that could be carried out. LTE inherits some of the degrees of freedom from UMTS, including the three modulation formats (QPSK, 16QAM and 64QAM), but many more variables have been added.

When UMTS was first specified it had only one FDD frequency band, but more were added over the years. At the outset LTE will have 17 possible FDD frequency bands and 8 possible TDD bands. No one product is likely to ever implement all these options, but the wide range of choices adds to the complexity of specifications since many requirements become a function of the band and position within the band. Furthermore, all UE have to support six different channel bandwidths. The use of OFDMA and SC-FDMA rather than CDMA introduces more variability since the transmission and reception requirements of OFDMA and SC-FDMA are a function of the allocation bandwidth, which can range anywhere from 180 kHz to 18 MHz. The position of the allocation within the channel can also affect performance since allocations towards the edge of the channel are influenced by the roll-off of channel and duplex filters aimed at meeting out-of-channel and out-of-band requirements.

When all the flexibility of the LTE air interface is considered, it quickly becomes apparent that the number of permutations that could be tested is enormous. Moreover, the list of possible tests needs to include those already defined for other Radio Access Technologies (RAT) supported by the UE, as well as any new inter-RAT tests required by the addition of LTE.

In selecting the configurations for the LTE RF conformance tests, considerable effort was made by 3GPP to identify those combinations of parameters that represent the most difficult operating conditions so that when a UE or eNB passes the tests, the design engineer can be reasonably confident that the device will perform satisfactorily in many more combinations than those explicitly tested. Prior to reaching conformance testing, a wider set of testing will have been carried out during product development. Chapter 6 of this book explores such testing in greater detail. The remainder of this chapter focuses on those tests that are mandatory to obtain conformance certification.

7.2.3 Generic Structure of RF Conformance Tests

The structure of the UE RF conformance test follows a set pattern that comprises the following steps:

- Test purpose
- Test applicability
- Minimum conformance requirements
- Test description:
  - Initial conditions
  - Test procedure
  - Message contents
- Test requirements

The eNB RF conformance tests cover the same list in a slightly different order, and the message contents are not required since the eNB tests are done without signalling. Each step will now be described.

7.2.3.1 Test Purpose

Every test case starts with a description of the test purpose. Although the purpose of a test may seem obvious from its title, in some cases a test may appear to fail for reasons that have nothing to do with the test purpose. Some tests may generate intermediate results that could be meaningful to other tests, but it is only the specific items listed in the test purpose that actually determine the pass/fail result. A clearly written test purpose helps clarify what is and what is not important, especially when additional minimum requirements that are not to be tested get copied from the core specifications to the minimum conformance requirements subclause.

7.2.3.2 Test Applicability

This subclause is generally used to identify the specification release to which a test applies, although it may also identify particular UE capabilities such as support of FDD or TDD that are required for the test. Because FDD and TDD modes are more closely integrated in LTE than in UMTS, an important goal of LTE conformance test development has been to make as many tests as possible applicable to both FDD and TDD modes. Only when necessary are independent FDD and TDD test cases being drafted.

7.2.3.3 Minimum Conformance Requirements

The term "minimum requirements" is used in the RF specifications to define the lowest level of performance that the UE should meet. The subclause defining the minimum requirements is typically a direct copy of the minimum requirements listed in one of the so-called "core" specifications. In the case of RF and RRM tests, this document will be either 36.101 [5] or 36.133 [8], respectively. To avoid any doubt should a conflict arise between what is written in the test specification and what is written in the core specification, the core specification always takes precedence. Usually the subclause on minimum conformance requirements ends with a statement such as "The normative reference for this requirement is TS 36.101 subclause A.B.C." The use of "normative" is intended to stress that the test subclause contains information that is subservient to the core requirement.

7.2.3.4 Initial Conditions

The initial conditions define the test environment, which will be normal or extreme as defined in 36.508 [1] subclause 4.1. The initial conditions may specify the temperature range and battery voltages as well as the bands, channel frequencies and channel bandwidths that need to be tested. When test cases are developed, great care must be taken to ensure that the list of initial conditions is no longer than necessary, as every binary variable added to the list can double the number of times the test needs to be executed. For example, a quad band UMTS phone may take up to 1600 hours to execute a complete set of conformance tests.

In addition to defining the starting conditions for the test, the initial conditions subclause also defines the procedure for getting the UE into the correct state to start the test. Connection diagrams are usually included that show how the UE should be connected to the test system. Once the physical connections are made, the test will usually require that the UE be put into a specific state according to generic procedures in 36.508 [1]. For some tests the initial conditions may include reference to test-specific message contents not defined in 36.508.

In UMTS the wording of the initial conditions subclause mandated that a particular setup procedure be followed every time the test was executed. In LTE, however, the emphasis is on reaching the desired initial state rather than the procedure used to get there. Each test is written as a standalone procedure, but in the interest of saving time it is acceptable to bypass those parts of the initial condition procedures that do not change the state of the UE prior to the test. For example, a test system may concatenate two tests to save time, in which case it may not be necessary to switch the UE off at the end of the first test and on again at the start of the second. If a bearer of the correct type is already established, it may not even be necessary to end the call from the previous test.

7.2.3.5 Test Procedure

This subclause contains the main substance of the test case, which will include the collection of the measurement results used to determine pass or fail.

7.2.3.6 Message Contents

This subclause defines any additional test-specific message contents not already covered in the initial conditions.

7.2.3.7 Test Requirements

The final subclause of the test case provides the limits, known as test requirements, against which the results acquired during the test procedure are compared to determine a pass/fail verdict. The verdict is determined only for those results that support the purpose of the test. The test requirements are usually a copy of the minimum requirements from the earlier subclause of the same name, but modified by test tolerances to take into account the test system uncertainty. Test tolerances are discussed fully in the next section.

7.2.4 Test System Uncertainty and Test Tolerances

The concept of test tolerances first introduced in UMTS has been adopted for LTE also. The principle behind test tolerances is to relax the minimum requirements by an allowance based on the expected uncertainty of measurement in the conformance test system. The minimum requirements for UMTS and LTE were developed with an implementation margin to take into account practicalities such as component tolerances in the UE or eNB, but no further allowance was made for uncertainty in the measurement process. Since conformance testing is performed on a single sample of a product, it was decided that the probability of passing a good UE or eNB should not be reduced on account of uncertainty in the test system. For that reason the minimum requirements for most parametric tests are relaxed by a test tolerance to produce a test requirement against which any pass/fail criteria are compared.

The shared risk principle defined in ETR 273 [14] applies to UMTS and LTE. The principle comprises three parts:

- An agreed method of calculating measurement uncertainty
- A maximum acceptable value of measurement uncertainty (stated in the standard)
- An agreement to use the numerical value of a measurement as the pass/fail criteria

The principle states that allowances for measurement uncertainty should not be used to modify the measurement result since the uncertainty is uncorrelated with the DUT performance and is as likely to increase the chance of a pass as to decrease it – hence the risk from the verdict is shared between the DUT and the overall system. However, strict interpretation of the shared risk principle states that measurement results shall not be modified by measurement uncertainty. UMTS and LTE both employ a mechanism in which the minimum requirements are first modified by a test tolerance to create a test requirement against which unmodified measurements are then directly compared to generate a pass/fail verdict. The practice of modifying the requirement by the measurement uncertainty before measurement avoids having to later modify the measurement result by the uncertainty. This reflects technical adherence to the shared risk principle. However, the effect is more like having adopted the principle "never fail a good DUT" since it shifts the balance of performance in favor of the DUT at the expense of the system. The consequences of this on the system are considered minimal and hard to assess. The more important point is that measurement uncertainty is minimized and constrained within the specifications

7.2.4.1 Calculation of Conformance Test System Uncertainty

In many cases, the measurement uncertainty for a test is a direct function of a single parameter of the test system. Examples include power measurement accuracy and EVM accuracy. There are, however, some tests that involve more complex interactions between many variables. The most complex of these are often the tests in support of RRM, which can include many different stimuli, each with its own uncertainty influencing the behavior of the UE. However, if the uncertainty of every variable were stacked end to end to create a worst case uncertainty, the test requirement would then be so relaxed that the test would no longer have any value. Even a bad UE implementation would have no trouble passing the relaxed limit.

In fact most errors in the test system are uncorrelated and therefore to calculate a realistic uncertainty, the individual components are added using a Root Sum Square (RSS) approach to better predict the distribution of likely performance. The application of linear (worst case) addition or RSS addition varies depending on the test case, and each has to be analyzed in its own right to fairly represent a more probable uncertainty than that predicted by worst case analysis.

7.2.4.2 Test System Uncertainty Confidence Levels

The test system uncertainty, once defined, might appear to be a hard limit. In practice the uncertainty of any measurement can be expressed statistically, often as a normal distribution with a standard deviation σ. Within the 3GPP specifications, the norm for defining test system uncertainty is to adopt a 2 σ figure, which for a normal distribution represents approximately 95% of the population. This approach allows a tighter limit to be specified for the test system but it does mean that 5% of results are expected to have an accuracy outside of the specified limit. This consequence is accepted in the conformance test regime because the required confidence level for the test result is also 95%. In most cases the results of performance testing fall well inside the test requirements, and in these cases the test equipment confidence level is assumed to have little effect on the confidence level of the results. Only when the DUT is on the very limit of the test tolerance would the test system confidence level fully impact the confidence of the pass/fail verdict.

It is important to note that warranted specifications for test equipment are often derived for confidence levels higher than the 95% required for conformance testing. For example, Agilent Technologies usually specifies a 3 σ figure representing approximately 99% of the population of results. Regardless of the confidence level, any specification falling outside of a warranted limit would be considered a warranty failure and corrected accordingly. If test equipment warranted specifications based on 3 σ fall within the 3GPP requirements for 2 σ, then there can be no doubt that the test equipment will provide superior performance during conformance testing and reduce the chance of a good DUT being failed or a bad one being passed. Sometimes the specifications for test equipment provide 2 σ uncertainty figures that will look better than 3 σ figures, but which simply represent a smaller population of the test equipment performance. To correctly compare specifications it is important to know the confidence level that each represents.

7.2.4.3 Application of Measurement Uncertainty to Test Tolerances

In some regulatory tests with requirements that come from outside of 3GPP, test tolerances are set to zero despite the non-zero measurement uncertainty involved. Perhaps the most familiar example is the –36 dBm spurious emissions limit from ITU-R SM 329-10 [15]. This limit is non-negotiable and therefore must be used in the test requirement without relaxation. However, not relaxing the test requirement by of the measurement uncertainty does not mean that the DUT is then vulnerable to unlimited measurement uncertainty. Even though the test tolerance is set to zero, for such tests there is still a defined limit on the allowed test system uncertainty, which constrains the test system performance and impact on the DUT.

The sequence for determining the limits that apply for a particular test follow these steps. First the uncertainty of the test system is analyzed and limits set. In most cases this limit is then adopted as the test tolerance for that test and the minimum requirements are relaxed accordingly. For a few tests, the test tolerance must be set to zero, meaning no relaxation, but the uncertainty of the test system is still defined and thus constrained.

7.2.4.4 Excess Test System Uncertainty

One further provision is made for the case in which a test system does not meet the requirement for test system uncertainty. In this case it is allowable to use a less accurate system provided the test tolerance is reduced by the amount of the excess uncertainty. This narrows the range over which the DUT can pass the test, but if the DUT does pass the test under these conditions, it clearly would also pass if a more accurate test system were used. The choice of whether or not to use the excess uncertainty provision is entirely up to the test house. If the excess test system uncertainty principle is used, the test system can safely pass a good DUT, but a fail verdict does not prove that the DUT is bad. If the DUT performance is just inside the test requirements, a test system meeting the test system accuracy requirements would correctly pass the DUT.

7.2.5 Statistical Testing

The majority of minimum requirements are expressed as absolute limits that have to be measured with 95% confidence as already discussed. This is straightforward for cases in which the uncertainty can be linked directly to the test system error. There are two other scenarios that require special treatment. These are (1) tests with requirements that rely on error ratios, such as receiver tests, and (2) tests with requirements that are expected to be met only a percentage of the time, such as most RRM tests.

7.2.5.1 Statistical Receiver Testing

Receiver minimum requirements are expressed in terms of a percentage of a maximum throughput, typically 95%, which can be directly mapped to a Block Error Ratio (BLER). This ratio will by default be measured using a 95% confidence level, which should not be confused with the throughput requirement. The two variables are independent and just happen to have the same value. The 95% confidence level creates a difficulty for the test design because while it is straightforward to deal with the uncertainties associated with setting the signal levels that define performance, the actual BLER measurement involves a binomial statistical phenomenon that does not exhibit the continuous variation associated with analog results. To put this another way, when the test system reports the status of an individual block there is no uncertainty; the block is either received correctly or it has an error. In order to assess a throughput or BLER, many blocks must be observed before an error ratio can be calculated.

Given that the verdict needs to be assessed with a 95% confidence level, a determination must be made regarding how many blocks to measure to achieve the desired confidence before declaring a pass or fail verdict. The answer is not obvious. For instance, if 100 blocks are measured and 5% of them are in error, does this indicate a pass or a fail with 95% confidence? Or, if only 50 blocks are measured and two are in error, does this indicate a pass? What is the maximum length of time that the test should be run? The mathematics behind this determination are complex but the measurement period has been explicitly defined for each test in the specifications.

For the receiver conformance tests, in addition to the 95% confidence level and the minimum requirement (which is >95% throughput of the reference measurement channel), two other factors must be taken into account in calculating how long to run the test. The first is the possibility of early decision. It can be shown that when a receiver test is run, based on continuous analysis of interim results, the test can sometimes be stopped early with a pass or a fail verdict and this verdict will still meet the criteria for 95% confidence. The conditions under which this can happen occur when the DUT produces either very good or very bad results. Consider the example of early failure: if the criterion for a pass is defined as >95% throughput and, after running the test for more than 5% of the defined maximum time, the analysis indicates continued failure, the test can be aborted early with a fail verdict since nothing that happens after that point can change the verdict. The principle of early decision is illustrated graphically in 36.521-1 [4] Annex G. It is a powerful technique for speeding up throughput tests that get repeated hundreds of times; for example, blocking tests.

The second factor that must be taken into account in calculating the minimum test time is known as the "bad DUT" factor. Consider the case in which a DUT is right at the limit of the test requirement. How long should the measurement continue to ensure 95% confidence? The answer is that the test would have to run forever. Obviously this is not possible, so to prevent such an asymptotic situation from occurring, the fail limit is raised by the bad DUT factor such that if the higher limit is reached, the test can be stopped.

7.2.5.2 Statistical Performance Testing

The same concepts used for statistical testing of the receiver are applied to the performance tests as well. An important difference is that performance tests use fading channels (rather than white noise, which is used in the receiver tests), so the statistics of the fading profile must be considered and the test times adjusted accordingly. This impact on the minimum test duration is most noticeable for the slow fading profiles at 3 km/h, which can take tens of seconds to repeat. Another difference is that the performance tests are based on 30% and 70% throughput targets of the RMC maximum throughput. For these reasons the minimum test time calculations and early pass/fail criteria are calculated separately from the receiver tests.

7.2.5.3 Statistical Radio Resource Management Testing

The other major use of statistical testing is for Radio Resource Management (RRM) testing. The RRM requirements generally have to be met more than 90% of the time. An example is the cell re-selection delay requirement. System integrity does not rest on every single cell re-selection occurring within the target value, and the variables that can influence the re-selection time are numerous. For this reason the best approach is to set a tighter limit to be met 90% of the time and not put constraints on the remaining 10%. From a testing perspective this again means that calculations have to be done to determine how many times the test must be run to reach 95% confidence. Since some RRM tests take a long time to run, it is desirable to repeat them as few times as possible.

7.2.6 Typical RF Test System Configuration

The configuration of an RF conformance test system varies depending on the complexity of the tests. Some tests can be performed with just an eNB emulator (sometimes referred to as a System Simulator (SS) or one box tester). Other tests require additional equipment including an additional eNB emulator to provide multi-cell test capability for the RRM tests, interference sources for blocking tests and spectrum analyzers for spurious emissions tests. Figure 7.2-1 shows how some of these pieces of equipment might be used in an RF conformance test system.

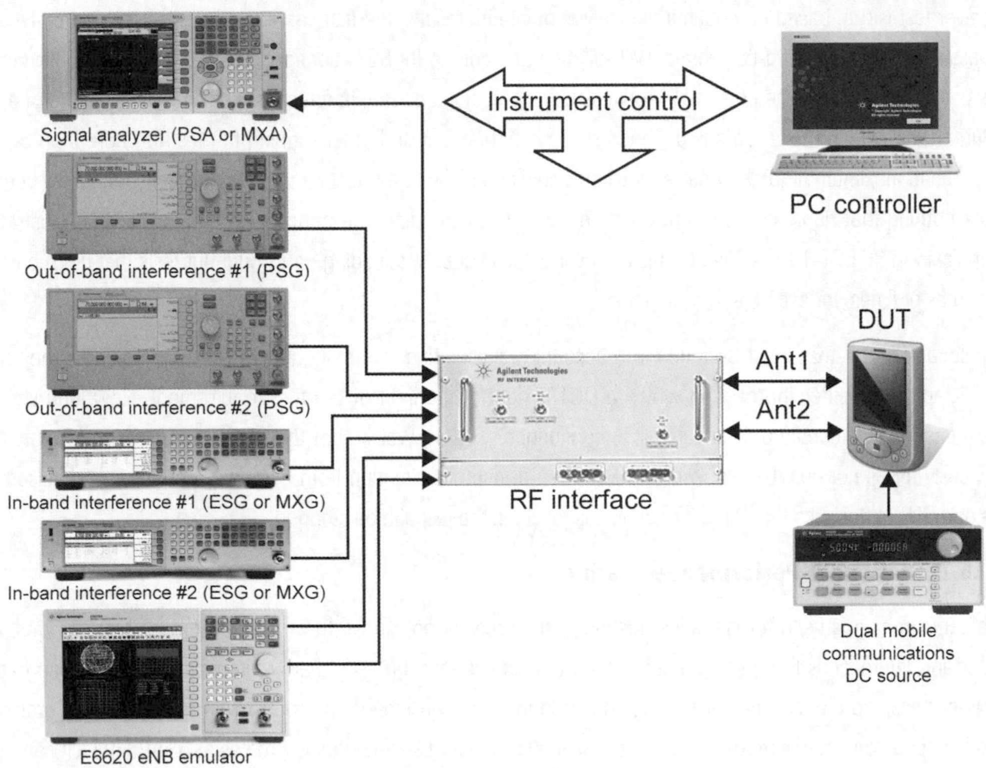

Figure 7.2-1. Components of a typical RF conformance test system

The RF interface module provides the essential connectivity between the test equipment and the UE under test. It contains the necessary switching required to enable the tests to be run automatically, as well as essential filtering to ensure that the correct RF conditions can be achieved. One essential component not explicitly shown is the channel emulator (sometimes known as a fading simulator). This emulates the channel conditions necessary for many of the performance and RRM tests. In the example shown in Figure 7.2-1 the functionality of the channel emulator is built into the E6620 eNB emulator. This significantly reduces the complexity and cost of the system as well as simplifying its calibration.

7.2.7 UE RF Conformance Test Case Overview

The UE RF conformance tests defined in 36.521-1 [4] are split into four main sections: RF transmitter characteristics, RF receiver characteristics, RF performance characteristics and reporting of Channel Quality Indicator (CQI) and Precoding Matrix Indicator (PMI). At the time of this writing the RF conformance tests are very much in development and in some areas the level of detail in the specifications is quite limited. The intention here is to provide an overview of the overall scope with some LTE-specific discussion rather than to go through every test in detail. Because the UE RF conformance tests are incomplete, the references provided are to the 36.101 [5] minimum requirements subclauses rather than the 36.521-1 [4] test subclauses.

Most UE requirements are defined relative to uplink and downlink Reference Measurement Channels (RMCs). These are defined in 36.101 [5] and are described in Section 2.1.7 and 2.1.8 respectively.

7.2.7.1 UE RF Transmitter Characteristics

Table 7.2-2 lists the transmitter test cases defined in TS 36.521-1 [4] with the reference to the 36.101 [5] core specification subclause and references to further information in this book.

Table 7.2-2. UE RF transmitter test cases

36.101 [5] Subclause	Test case	Sections in this book with further information
6.2.2	UE Maximum Output Power	2.1.3
6.2.3	Maximum Power Reduction (MPR)	2.1.3
6.3.5	Power Control	2.1.3
6.3.2	Minimum Output Power	2.1.4
6.3.3	Transmit ON/OFF Power	2.1.4
6.4.1	Out-of Synchronization Handling of Output Power	3.6.3.4
6.5.1	Frequency Error	2.1.5, 6.4
6.5.2	Transmit Modulation — EVM, IQ, In-Band, Flatness	2.1.5, 6.4
6.6.1	Occupied Bandwidth	6.4
6.6.2.1	Spectrum Emission Mask	6.4
6.6.2.2	Additional Spectrum Emission Mask	2.1.3, 6.4
6.6.2.3	Adjacent Channel Leakage Power Ratio (ACLR)	6.4
6.6.2.4	Additional ACLR Requirements	2.1.3, 6.4
6.6.3.1	Transmitter Spurious Emissions	6.4
6.6.3.2	Spurious Emission Band UE Co-existence	
6.6.3.3	Additional Spurious Emissions	2.1.3
6.7	Transmit Intermodulation	

The scope of these RF transmitter tests will be familiar from UMTS and are modified only in the details as they pertain to LTE and the SC-FDMA uplink modulation format. The main points worth noting are the additional tests for Spectrum Emission Mask (SEM) and Adjacent Channel Leakage ratio (ACLR). The concept of "additional" tests is new to LTE and comes from the need to control out of band emissions for certain combinations of bands. To achieve the desired performance the concept of network signalling has been introduced to indicate to the UE that dynamic requirements have to be applied. This is discussed more fully in Section 2.1.3. In essence, when the network sends a particular network signalling value, the UE has to meet additional emission requirements for co-existence with adjacent bands.

The transmitter tests are carried out using uplink Reference Measurement Channels (RMCs), which are discussed in Section 2.1.7. The RMCs fall into three main categories — fully allocated, partially allocated and single RB — and were defined based on the simulation assumptions used to derive the requirements. The number of different RMC configurations defined for testing is a balance between thoroughness and excessive test time.

7.2.7.2 UE RF Receiver Characteristics

Table 7.2-3 lists the UE receiver test cases defined in TS 36.521-1 [4] with reference to the 36.101 [5] core specification subclause. Further discussion of receiver testing is provided in Section 6.5.

Table 7.2-3. UE RF receiver test cases

36.101 [5] subclause	Test case
7.3	Reference Sensitivity Level
7.4	Maximum Input Level
7.5	Adjacent Channel Selectivity
7.6.1	In-Band Blocking
7.6.2	Out-of-band Blocking
7.6.3	Narrow Band Blocking
7.7	Spurious Response
7.8.1	Wide Band Intermodulation
7.8.2	Narrow Band Intermodulation
7.9	Spurious Emissions

The test cases above are similar to the equivalent UMTS test cases. One difference worth noting is that the receiver minimum requirements for UMTS were typically specified in terms of a Bit Error Ratio (BER) that was distinct from the BLER used in the UMTS performance tests. This difference was due to somewhat arbitrary choices made during the early development of UMTS when some requirements simulation work was done using BER and others using BLER. Because a verifiable BER result requires the transmitted data to be looped back to the test system, it is a more difficult measure to make than simply counting the UE's ACK and NACK reports necessary for calculating BLER. That said, BER is more subtle in its ability to pick up small variations in performance compared to BLER and remains a useful measure during product development. For LTE the receiver minimum requirements are expressed in terms of a percentage throughput (>95%) of the RMC used in the test. Since BLER can be mapped directly to throughput, the LTE receiver tests are brought in line with the performance tests that have always been based on BLER and throughput.

7.2.7.3 UE RF Performance Requirements

At the time of writing the 36.521-1 [4] performance requirements section is very much incomplete. Table 7.2-4 lists the UE performance test cases defined in TS 36.521-1 [4] with the reference to the 36.101 [5] core specification subclause.

Table 7.2-4. UE RF performance test cases

36.101 [5] subclause		Test case
FDD	TDD	
8.2.1.1	8.2.2.1	PDSCH Single Antenna Port Performance
8.2.1.2	8.2.2.2	PDSCH Transmit Diversity Performance
8.2.1.3	8.2.2.3	PDSCH Open Loop Spatial Multiplexing Performance
8.2.1.4	8.2.2.4	PDSCH Closed Loop Spatial Multiplexing Performance
	8.2.2.5	MU-MIMO
	8.2.2.6	Control Channel Performance D-BCH PCH
8.3		Demodulation of PDSCH (User-Specific Reference Symbols)
8.4.1.1	8.4.2.1	PCFICH/PDCCH Single-antenna Port Performance
8.4.1.2	8.4.2.2	PCFICH/PDCCH Transmit Diversity Performance
8.5		Demodulation of PHICH
8.6		Demodulation of PBCH

The performance requirements are written around the baseline UE capability, which has two receivers. It is still open to debate whether UE implementations meeting the dual receiver requirements with only one receiver will be allowed.

7.2.8 UE RRM Conformance Test Case Overview

The RRM requirements are defined in the core specification 36.133 [8] and the conformance tests are in 36.521-3 [7]. As a result of the complexity of the RRM requirements in terms of the number of variables that can affect performance, the core specification includes Annex A, which provides guidance on test case configuration for conformance testing. The RRM conformance tests are based on this annex rather than referencing the core requirements directly as is the case with the RF conformance tests and 36.101 [5]. Because the UE RRM conformance tests are incomplete, the references provided are to the 36.133 [8] core specification test annex rather than the 36.521-3 [7] test subclauses.

The RRM requirements from 36.133 [8] are discussed in Section 3.6.3. They are divided into six main areas and the annex follows the same six-part structure. The work to complete the RRM conformance tests has been split into two phases. The first phase is included in the December 2008 version of 36.133 [8] and covers the mobility aspects of E-UTRA including tests from A4, A5, A8 and A9. Table 7.2-5 lists the RRM test cases defined in TS 36.521-3 [7] with reference to the 36.133 [8] core specification subclause.

Table 7.2-5. UE RRM test cases

36.133 [8] subclause	Category of test
A.4.1	Cell selection in E-UTRAN RRC_Idle state
A.4.2	Cell re-selection in E-UTRAN RRC_Idle state
A.4.3	E-UTRAN to UTRAN cell re-selection
A.4.4	E-UTRAN to GSM cell re-selection
A.5.1	Handover delay in E-UTRAN RRC_Connected state
A.6	RRC connection control
A.7	Timing and signalling characteristics
A.8.1	E-UTRAN FDD intra-frequency measurements
A.8.2	E-UTRAN TDD intra-frequency measurements
A.8.3	E-UTRAN FDD inter-frequency measurements
A.8.4	E-UTRAN TDD inter-frequency measurements
A.9.1	RSRP measurements
A.9.2	RSRQ measurements

7.2.9 Base Station RF Conformance Test Overview

Base station (eNB) conformance testing for LTE is similar to UMTS except for those areas of testing affected by the change to using an OFDMA modulation scheme. The eNB RF conformance tests based on the core specification 36.104 [11] are defined in 36.141 [10]. There are three main sections: RF transmitter characteristics, RF receiver characteristics and RF performance characteristics. These tests are listed in the following sections with comments highlighting differences from UMTS.

7.2.9.1 BS RF Transmitter Characteristics

Table 7.2-6 lists the eNB RF transmitter characteristics test cases defined in 36.141 [10].

Table 7.2-6. eNB RF transmitter characteristics tests

36.141 [10] subclause	Test case
6.2	Base station output power
6.3.1	Resource Element (RE) Power control dynamic range
6.3.2	Total power dynamic range
6.4	Transmit ON/OFF power
6.5.1	Frequency error
6.5.2	Error Vector Magnitude (EVM)
6.5.3	Time alignment between transmitter branches
6.5.4	Downlink reference signal power

6.6.1	Occupied bandwidth
6.6.2	Adjacent Channel Leakage Power Ratio (ACLR)
6.6.3	Operating band unwanted emissions
6.6.4	Transmitter spurious emissions
6.7	Transmitter intermodulation

The eNB transmitter characteristics tests follow very closely the pattern from UMTS with differences mainly due to the use of OFDMA. The test for time alignment between the transmitter branches is particularly important to LTE because of the widespread use of transmit diversity, spatial multiplexing and beamsteering. The requirement is for a time alignment of 65 ns. This requirement is the same as that in UMTS, which was ¼ of a chip (65 ns).

The downlink RS power test is the equivalent of the primary Common Pilot Channel (CPICH) power accuracy test from UMTS.

7.2.9.2 BS RF Receiver Characteristics

Table 7.2-7 lists the eNB RF receiver characteristics test cases defined in 36.141 [10].

Table 7.2-7. eNB RF receiver characteristics tests

36.141 [10] subclause	Test case
7.2	Reference sensitivity level
7.3	Dynamic range
7.4	In-channel selectivity
7.5	Adjacent Channel Selectivity (ACS) and narrow-band blocking
7.6	Blocking
7.7	Receiver spurious emissions
7.8	Receiver intermodulation

Of note is the in-channel selectivity test. This is unique to OFDMA and is a test of the receiver's ability to maintain a particular throughput on an allocation on one side of the DC subcarrier when a larger signal is present on the opposite side. This test checks for IQ distortion in the receiver and is the reverse of the UE transmitter IQ image requirement for in-band emissions.

7.2.9.3 BS RF Performance Requirement

At the time of writing the eNB performance tests are still in development with the list in Table 7.2-8 representing only some of the requirements currently defined in 36.104 [11] subclause 8.

Table 7.2-8 lists the eNB RF performance test cases defined in 36.141 [10].

Table 7.2-8. eNB RF performance tests

36.141 [10] subclause	Test case
8.2.1	Demodulation of PUSCH in multipath fading conditions
8.2.2	Performance requirements for UL timing adjustment
8.2.3	Performance requirements for HARQ-ACK multiplexed on PUSCH
8.2.4	Performance requirements for High Speed Train conditions
8.3.1	ACK missed detection requirements for PUCCH format 1a
8.3.2	CQI missed detection for PUCCH format 2
8.3.3	ACK missed detection for multi-user PUCCH format 1a
8.4.1	PRACH false alarm probability and missed detection

7.2.10 Base Station Test Signals

7.2.10.1 Downlink Test Models

The eNB transmitter conformance tests are carried out using downlink configurations known as E-UTRA Test Models (E-TM). This concept has been inherited from UMTS although any similarity stops there. The highly flexible nature of the downlink OFDMA modulation scheme means that a large number of parameters are required to fully define any signal. An inspection of the definition of the E-TM in 36.141 [10] subclause 6.1.1 clearly shows how much more complex the signal structure is compared to UMTS. There are three distinct classes of test model defined, known as E-TM1, E-TM2 and E-TM3. The first and third classes have further subclasses. All test models share the following attributes:

- Defined for a single antenna port, single codeword, single layer with no precoding.
- Duration of one frame (10 ms)
- Normal cyclic prefix
- Localized virtual resource blocks, no intra-subframe hopping for PDSCH.
- Cell-specific reference signals only - no use of UE-specific reference signals.

The data content of the PDSCH is generated from a sequence of zeros scrambled using a length-31 Gold code according to 36.211 [16]. The reference signals and the primary and secondary synchronization signals are also defined according to 36.211 [16]. The physical channels PBCH, PCFICH, PHICH and PDCCH all have detailed definitions. For each E-TM every physical signal and physical channel is allocated into the channel at a specific power relative to the RS power. There are six different mappings for each E-TM to take account of the six different channel bandwidths. For E-TM employing power boosting or de-boosting of specific RBs there is an additional table defining for which RB this applies as a function of the channel bandwidth. Each E-TM is defined for specific use according to Table 7.2-9.

Table 7.2-9. Evolved Test Model mapping to test cases

E-TM	Notes	Test case
E-TM1.1	Maximum power tests	Output power, occupied bandwidth, ACLR, operating band unwanted emissions, transmitter spurious emissions, transmitter intermodulation, reference signal absolute accuracy
E-TM1.2	Includes power boosting and de-boosting	ACLR, operating band unwanted emissions
E-TM2	Minimum power tests	Total power dynamic range (lower OFDM symbol power limit at min power, EVM of single 64QAM PRB allocation (at min power), frequency error (at min power)
E-TM3.1		Total power dynamic range (upper OFDM symbol power limit at max power with all 64QAM PRBs allocated), frequency error, EVM for 64QAM (at max power)
E-TM3.2	Includes power boosting and de-boosting	Frequency error, EVM for 16QAM
E-TM3.3	Includes power boosting and de-boosting	Frequency error, EVM for QPSK

An example of a 5 MHz E-TM3.3 configuration using the Agilent Signal Studio signal creation software is shown in Figure 7.2-2.

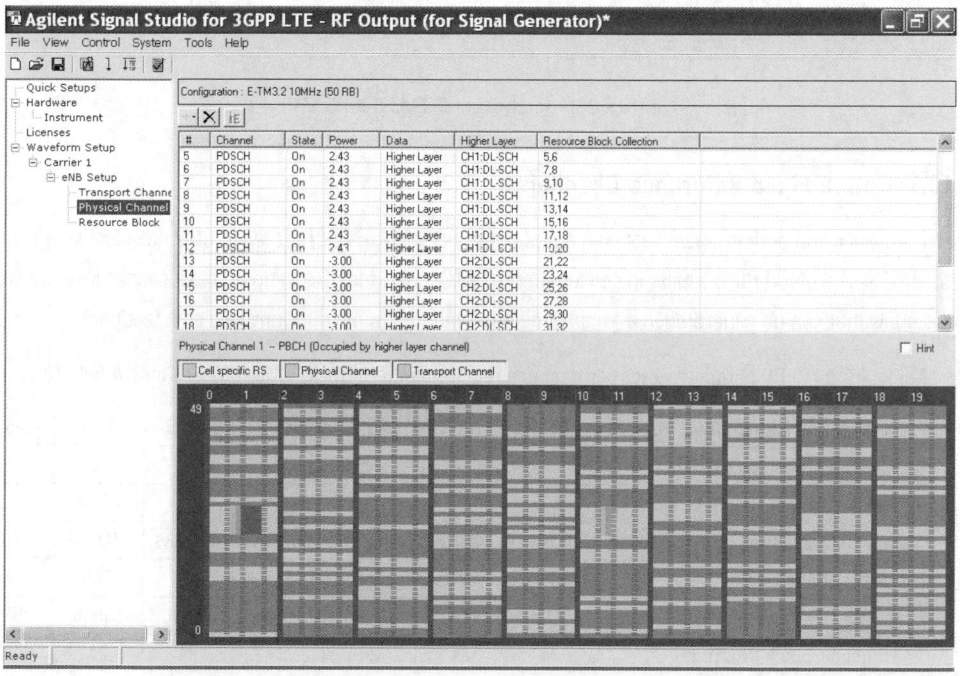

Figure 7.2-2. E-TM3.3 for 5 MHz

This particular signal has had amplitude clipping added to emphasize the impact this type of distortion has on EVM vs. time across the subframe. A measurement of this signal using the Agilent 89601A Vector Signal Analyzer software can be seen in Figure 7.2-3. The variation in EVM versus time is seen in the top right trace.

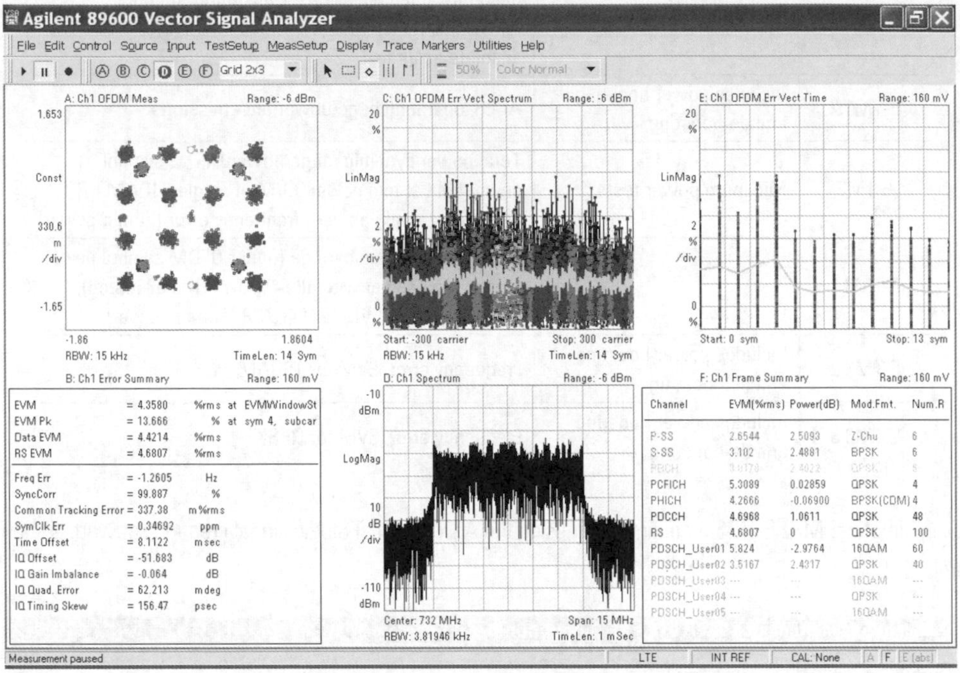

Figure 7.2-3. Analysis of E-TM3.3 for 5 MHz

7.2.10.1 Uplink Fixed Reference Channels

The eNB receiver and performance tests are carried out using uplink Fixed Reference Channels (FRCs) in a similar way to UMTS. The eNB FRC is similar in concept to the RMCs used for UE testing. In most cases these are single-ended signals that can be generated in a signal generator without the need for any real time feedback.

Table 7.2-10. FRC parameters for performance requirements (64QAM 5/6) (36.141 Table A.5-1 [10])

Reference channel	A5-1	A5-2	A5-3	A5-4	A5-5	A5-6	A5-7
Allocated resource blocks	1	6	15	25	50	75	100
DFT-OFDM Symbols per subframe	12	12	12	12	12	12	12
Modulation	64QAM	64QAM	64QAM	64QAM	64QAM	64QAM	64QAM
Code rate	5/6	5/6	5/6	5/6	5/6	5/6	5/6
Payload size (bits)	712	4392	11064	18336	36696	55056	75376
Transport block CRC (bits)	24	24	24	24	24	24	24
Code block CRC size (bits)	0	0	24	24	24	24	24
Number of code blocks – C	1	1	2	3	6	9	13

Coded block size including 12 bits trellis termination (bits)	2220	13260	16716	18444	18444	18444	17484
Total number of bits per subframe	864	5184	12960	21600	43200	64800	86400
Total symbols per subframe	144	864	2160	3600	7200	10800	14400

This example in Table 7.2-10 uses a code rate of 5/6, which is intended for testing the highest throughput requirements. For the 100 RB case of A5-7, there are 86,400 bits per 1 ms subframe indicating a maximum throughput of 86.4 Mbps. The eNB performance requirements measured under fading conditions will be based on reaching a percentage of the maximum throughput under particular conditions. An example from 36.141 [10] Table 8.2.1.5-6 shows that a two channel eNB receiver operating in a pedestrian A channel with 5 Hz Doppler is required to reach 70% of the A5-7 FRC maximum throughput when the SNR is above 19.7 dB.

7.3 UE Signalling Conformance Testing

Section 6.9 discussed the development of signalling protocols and a typical test environment. This section covers the formal UE signalling conformance tests that would be carried out on such systems. Due to the number of signalling conformance tests, it is not possible to go into detail. The intent here is to explain the scope of the testing and the role of each functional area.

7.3.1 Signalling Conformance Test Specifications

Table 7.3-1 shows the specifications that define the signalling conformance tests.

Table 7.3-1. Signalling conformance test specifications

Specification	Title	Purpose
36.523-1 [17]	User Equipment (UE) conformance specification; Part 1; Protocol conformance specification	Defines the overall test structure, the test configurations, the conformance requirements and reference to the core specifications, the test purposes and a brief description of the test procedure, the specific test requirements and short message exchange table.
36.523-2 [18]	User Equipment (UE) conformance specification; Part 2; Implementation Conformance Statement (ICS) Proforma Specification	Based on UE implemented features, provides the ICS proforma in compliance with the relevant EPS requirements and a recommended applicability statement for the 36.523-1 test cases.
36.523-3 [19]	User Equipment (UE) conformance specification; Part 3; Abstract Test Suite (ATS)	Provides a detailed and executable description of the test cases written in the test language TTCN-3.

7.3.2 Signalling Conformance Test Categories

The signalling conformance test cases for LTE are very similar to the UMTS signalling test cases with respect to design and methodology. However the LTE test cases are written in the newer Tree and Tabular Combined Notation version 3 (TTCN-3) rather than the TTCN-2 used for UMTS.

The test cases are organized based on the layer of the stack being tested. The number of test cases by function is shown in Table 7.3-2.

Table 7.3-2. Signalling conformance test cases by layer

Functional area	Number of tests
Idle Mode	47
Layer 2 (MAC/RLC/PDCP)	96
RRC	106
EMM	151
ESM	18
General Tests	4
Radio Bearer	For future study
Combined procedures	32
ETWS	2
Non-3GPP	2
Total	**458**

Due to the large number of signalling conformance tests, test development and implementation has been split into three batches based on priorities defined by the network operators. Table 7.3-3 shows the number of test cases in each batch. The test cases within each batch are designed to cover the high priority and medium priority features identified for LTE Release 8.

Table 7.3-3. Signalling conformance test cases by layer

Batch	Segment	Tests	Total	Segment description
1	1-Idle	6		Minimal idle mode cases/pure LTE, intra-frequency
	1-Proc	13		Minimal procedures for MO/MT connection
	1-L2	62		Minimal layer 2 cases
	1-HO	7		Minimal handover cases/pure LTE, intra-frequency
	1-RB	2		Minimal combinations of bearers for single service
	1-NAS	47		NAS procedures 1st priority
	1-Security	6		Ciphering and integrity protection
	1-ComProc	7		Combined procedures 1st priority
			150	Batch 1A 73, Batch 1B 77

2	2-Interfreq	4		Basic inter-frequency cases
	2-InterRAT	25		Basic Inter-RAT cases/GSM, GPRS, UMTS
	2-InterRAT-3GPP2	14		Basic Inter-RAT cases/3GPP2
	2-Idle	2		Increased coverage of idle mode cases
	2-Proc	10		Increased coverage of procedures for MO/MT connection
	2-L2	12		Increased coverage of layer 2 cases
	2-HO	13		Increased coverage of handover cases
	2-RB	2		Increased coverage of combinations of bearers
	2-CSG	4		Basic CSG cases
	2-NAS	87		NAS procedures 2nd priority
	2-ComProc	9		Combined procedures 2nd priority
			182	
3	3-Failure	6		Failure cases
	3-Performance	6		Latency and throughput test cases
	3-RoHC	6		RoHC Cases
	3-SMS	4		SMS cases (if C-plane services are defined)
	3-NAS	44		NAS procedures 3rd priority
	3-Variety	62		Other variety cases
	3-ComProc	16		Combined procedures 3rd priority
	3-Other-Non3GPP	0		Non-3GPP support
			144	
?	Test cases without assignment		1	Batch level assignment still under investigation
Total			**477**	

Note: The total number of 477 is not identical to Table 7.3-2 due to the ongoing development of the test specifications and these lists coming from different sources.

7.3.3 Signalling Conformance Test Overview

The following sections describe each functional area of the test cases outlined in Table 7.3-2.

7.3.3.1 RRC Idle State

The RRC idle state test cases shown in Table 7.3-4 are split into three subgroups.

Table 7.3-4. RRC idle state tests

Subgroup	**Description**
Pure E-UTRAN environment	Used to test UE cell reselection and PLMN selection in a pure E-UTRAN environment
Multimode environment	Used to test UE inter-RAT PLMN selection, cell selection/reselection in an environment consisting of ETRAN, UTRAN and GERAN cells
Closed subscriber group cells	Used to test UE in closed subscriber group cells

7.3.3.2 Layer 2

The layer 2 test cases shown in Table 7.3-5. are split into three subgroups.

Table 7.3-5. Layer 2 tests

Subgroup	Description
MAC	Mapping between logical channels and transport channels
	RACH
	DL-SCH data transfer
	UL-SCH data transfer
	MAC reconfiguration
	DRX Operation
	Transport block size support
RLC	Unacknowledged mode
	Acknowledged mode
PDCP	Maintenance of PDCP sequence numbers for radio bearers
	Robust header compression testing
	PDCP ciphering
	PDCP integrity protection
	PDCP — handover
	PDCP — others
	U-plane latency performance

7.3.3.3 RRC Connected State

The RRC connected state test cases shown in Table 7.3-6 are split into five subgroups.

Table 7.3-6. RRC connected state tests

Subgroup	Description
RRC connection management procedures	Paging, RRC connection establishment and RRC connection release procedures
RRC connection reconfiguration	Bearer setup, radio resource reconfiguration, radio bearer release and Intra LTE cell handover procedures
Measurement configuration control and reporting	Intra LTE measurements, Inter RAT measurements (GERAN, UTRAN, HPRD, 1XRTT cells) and self optimized networks
Inter-RAT handover	E-UTRA to UTRA
	UTRA to E-UTRA
	E-UTRA to GERAN
	E-UTRA to HRPD
	HRPD to E-UTRA
	E-UTRA to 1xRTT
Other	Radio link Failure, DL direct transfer, UL direct transfer and UE capability transfer

7.3.3.4 EPS Mobility Management

The EPS Mobility Management (EMM) test cases shown in Table 7.3-7 are split into five subgroups.

Table 7.3-7. EMM test cases

Subgroup	Description
EMM common procedures	GUTI reallocation procedure, authentication, security mode control procedure, identification, EMM information procedures
EMM specific procedures	Attach, detach and tracking area update procedures
EMM connection management procedures	Service request and paging procedures
NAS Security	NAS ciphering and integrity protection
Other	Radio link failure, DL direct transfer, UL direct transfer and UE capability transfer

Both success and failure scenarios are tested for these procedures.

7.3.3.5 EPS Session Management

The EPS Session Management (ESM) test cases are shown in Table 7.3-8.

Table 7.3-8. ESM test cases

Functional area	Tests
EPS Session Management	Dedicated EPS bearer context activation
	EPS bearer context modification
	EPS bearer context deactivation
	UE requested PDN connectivity
	UE requested PDN disconnect
	UE requested bearer resource allocation
	UE requested bearer resource release

Both success and failure scenarios are tested for these procedures.

7.3.3.6 General Tests

The general tests cover Mobile Terminated (MT) and Mobile Originated (MO) SMS with Circuit Switched (CS) fallback procedures in idle and connected states.

7.3.3.7 Radio Bearer

The radio bearer tests cover radio bearer interoperability under various conditions. A generic radio bearer test case verifies all the possible combinations of Unacknowledged Mode (UM) and Acknowledged Mode (AM) data radio bearers for each UE capability. This test case is based on the generic radio bearer SRB1 and SRB2 for

$$\text{DCCH} + n * \text{AM DRB} + m * \text{UM DRB, where } n=1..N \text{ and } m=0..M.$$

7.3.3.8 Combined Procedures

This section covers intra-system mobility within E-UTRAN and inter-system mobility between E-UTRAN (FDD and TDD) and UTRAN (UMTS), GPRS, cdma2000 and GSM. Table 7.3-9 lists the tests.

Table 7.3-9. Combined procedures

Functional area	Tests
Combined procedures	E-UTRA call setup and activation/deactivation of additional radio bearers
	E-UTRA connection re-establishment after link failure
	Inter-system packet connection re-establishment, E-UTRAN FDD and TDD to UTRAN, GPRS and cdma2000
	Intra- and inter-frequency mobility, E-UTRA FDD and TDD
	Inter-system mobility for packet data, E-UTRA FDD and TDD to UTRA, GPRS and cdma2000
	Inter-system mobility for voice, E-UTRA FDD and TDD to UTRA, cdma2000 and GSM CS

7.3.3.9 Earthquake and Tsunami Warning System

The Earthquake and Tsunami Warning System (ETWS) is designed to broadcast emergency warning messages to UE in both idle and connected states.

7.3.3.10 Non-3GPP

The non-3GPP tests cover interworking with WLAN and 802.16 systems.

7.4 UE Certification Process (GCF and PTCRB)

7.4.1 Introduction

The 3GPP core specifications are necessary to design the UE, and the 3GPP conformance tests define how to measure compliance against the core specifications. The last step of the sequence is to deliver certified devices to the market. This step involves the validation of the test systems used to carry out conformance testing and then the execution of the conformance test suites under controlled conditions. For UMTS and LTE, these two final steps are carried out under the management of certification bodies.

There are two main certification bodies involved with LTE. The first certification body is the Global Certification Forum (GCF). This organization was established in 1999 under the umbrella of the GSM Association (GSMA), the industry body representing GSM and UMTS operators worldwide. The GCF was formed in 1999, two years before the European Radio and Telecommunications Terminal Equipment (R&TTE) directive superseded the previous Terminal Directive of 1991. The new directive significantly reduced the scope of the tests required for type approval to just those tests essential to ensure efficient use of the spectrum and no harm to the network. The wider performance requirements that previously formed the bulk of the type approval tests in the 1991 directive were dropped. To fill the vacuum left by this change in European regulations the GCF was formed to promote an industry-backed certification scheme with a remit closer to the scope of the original Terminal Directive. This scheme is non-binding but GSMA members are encouraged to promote only UEs that have achieved GCF certification. In 2008, GCF became a private company.

Although GCF is not responsible for providing type approval certification — that remains the responsibility of accredited test laboratories — GCF is, in effect, managing the entire testing process, which incorporates those tests required for type approval. Type approval tests are the only tests that the UE must pass in order to be operated within the European Union.

The second major certification body was formed in the United States in 1997 at the introduction of the Personal Communications System (PCS), which was a variation of GSM for the 1900 MHz band. This body is known as the PCS Type Certification Review Board (PTCRB). The PTCRB provides UE certification services for North American operators.

There are other industry certification bodies such as the CDMA Certification Forum (CCF) that provides certification of performance for products designed to the 3GPP2 CDMA standards.

The roles of GCF and PTCRB are largely similar although they focus on those frequency bands and specific test lists appropriate to their markets. Over the years the co-operation between GCF and PTCRB has grown.

Figure 7.4-1 shows the two routes that a UE takes to reach the market. The regulatory certification under the administration of national and regional authorities such as the Federal Communications Commission (FCC) in the US and the CE mark administered by the European Commission are mandatory to get to market. The industry certification provided by GCF, PTCRB and others is optional but very much encouraged to reach a minimum performance level and enable stable international roaming.

Initially GCF and PTCRB started with certification of products based on the GSM standard. Their scope was expanded to GPRS, EGPRS, W-CDMA, HSDPA and now HSUPA, with LTE being the next standard covered.

For more information about GCF and PTCRB, refer to the following websites: for GCF, http://www.globalcertificationforum.org; for PTCRB, http://www.ptcrb.com.

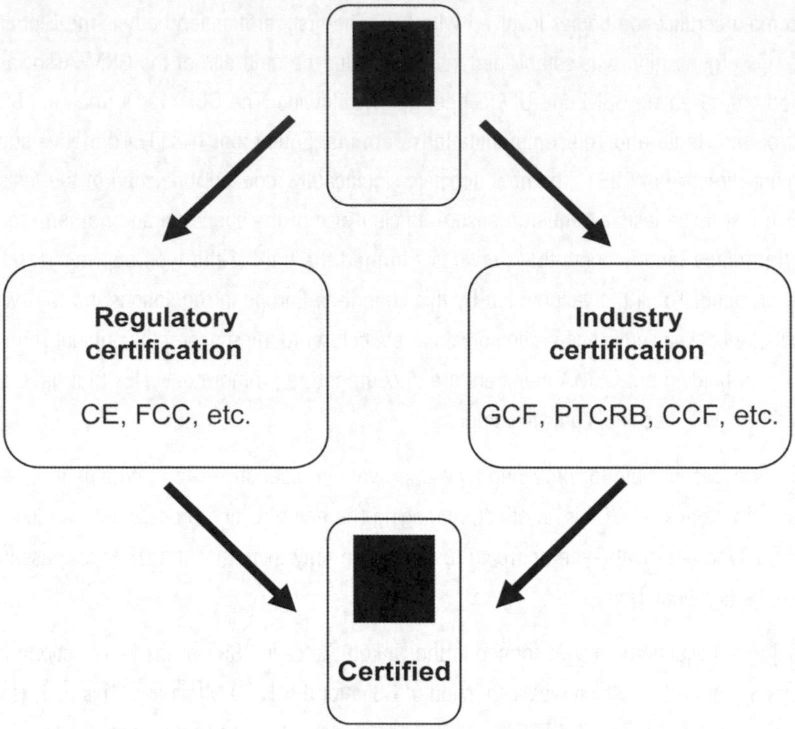

Figure 7.4-1. Regulatory certification and industry certification

7.4.2 Preparation Process for Mobile Handset Certification

Figure 7.4-2 shows the relationship between the standards development body, certification bodies, mobile phone manufacturers and test industry. Test industry here refers to the test system vendors and the certified test laboratories that validate the test systems and carry out the conformance tests.

The certification bodies do not automatically adopt the entire 3GPP conformance test specifications. Each certification body selects a group of test cases (called a work item) and defines its priority based on operators' deployment plans. In previous systems such as UMTS there were far more conformance tests defined than adopted by GCF, but in more recent times there is more coordination between the operators, GCF and 3GPP to ensure that only those tests likely to be implemented and used for certification are developed in detail within 3GPP.

Once a work item is clearly defined, test system vendors develop the test cases required by this work item on their test platforms. Each test system vendor selects a certified test laboratory to validate their test cases on the test platform using reference UEs that support required features for the designated work item.

The test laboratory submits a validation report to the relevant certification body for approval, which then enables the test system to be used to certify any UE. When sufficient tests in a work item have been validated (usually 80%), the certification body declares the work item active and UE certification can start.

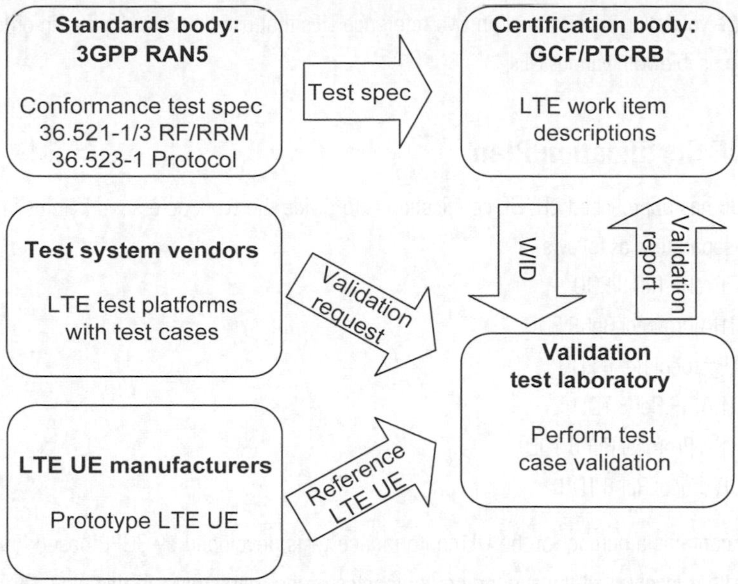

Figure 7.4-2. Development and validation of conformance test cases

7.4.3 Test Case Validation Process

Figure 7.4-3 illustrates in more detail the process of test case validation in accordance with 3GPP conformance test specifications. The test system vendor provides a measurement uncertainty analysis document for the test laboratory to review. This document is then used to validate conformance with 3GPP requirements for test system uncertainty.

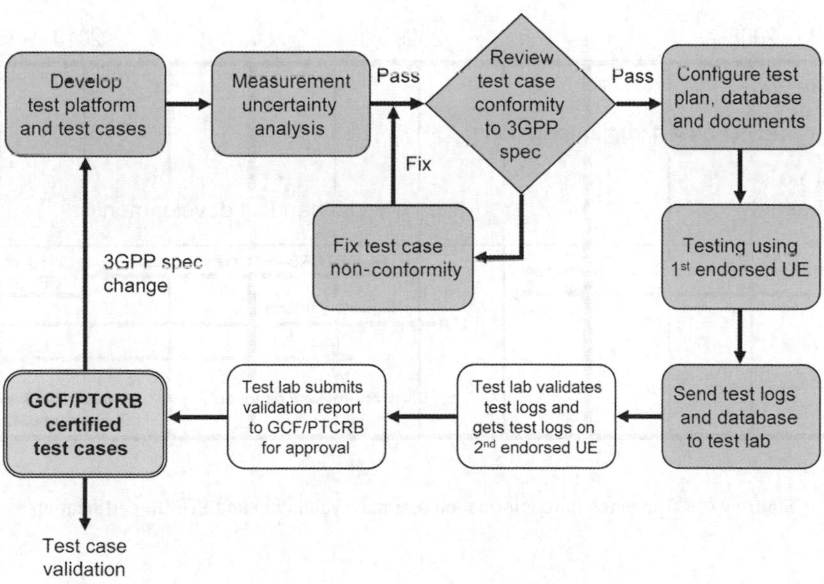

Figure 7.4-3 Test case validation process

Normally test case validation is performed on two reference UEs that use different chipsets in order to ensure that the test cases are usable with various UEs.

7.4.4 LTE UE Certification Plan

The way that GCF has approached LTE UE certification is to divide the work across work items in which FDD and TDD are treated separately, as follows:

- E-UTRA RF Rel-8 FDD
- E-UTRA Protocol Rel-8 FDD
- EPC Protocol Rel-8 FDD
- E-UTRA RF Rel-8 TDD
- E-UTRA Protocol Rel-8 TDD
- EPC Protocol Rel-8 TDD

Each work item contains a number of the UE conformance tests developed by 3GPP based on pre-determined selection criteria that involves all the supporting companies of the work items. In this way, GCF reflects market priorities for the first LTE devices. A minimum set of tests needs to be validated from each work item before UE certification can start. This ensures that a wide spread of tests must be passed for a device to be certified.

PTCRB focuses on the FDD mode, which corresponds to the first three of the GCF work items.

Test laboratories will start validation of the test cases during 2009 and continue until test coverage reaches the required coverage. The target date for completion is the middle of 2010, at which point UE certification can begin.

Figure 7.4-4 shows the timelines for conformance test case validation and LTE UE certification, along with LTE UE development and introduction timelines.

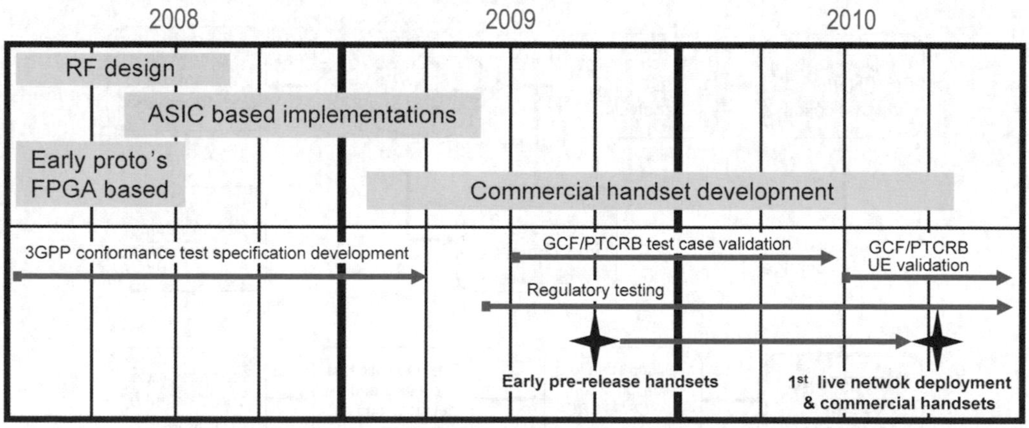

Figure 7.4-4 Timelines for conformance test case validation and LTE UE certification

7.5 References

[1] 3GPP TS 36.508 V8.0.1 (2008-12) Common Test Environments for User Equipment (UE) Conformance Testing

[2] 3GPP TS 36.509 V8.0.1 (2008-12) Special Conformance Testing Functions for User Equipment (UE)

[3] 3GPP TS 36.124 V8.0.0 (2008-09) Electromagnetic Compatibility (EMC) Requirements for Mobile Terminals and Ancillary Equipment

[4] 3GPP TS 36.521-1 V8.0.1 (2008-12) User Equipment (UE) Conformance Specification; Radio Transmission and Reception Part 1: Conformance Testing (FDD/TDD)

[5] 3GPP TS 36.101 V8.4.0 (2008-12) UE Radio Transmission and Reception

[6] 3GPP TS 36.521-2 V8.0.1 (2008-12) User Equipment (UE) Conformance Specification; Radio Transmission and Reception Part 2: ICS

[7] 3GPP TS 36.521-3 V0.6.0 (2009-01) User Equipment (UE) Conformance Specification; Radio Transmission and Reception Part 3: Radio Resource Management Conformance Testing

[8] 3GPP TS 36.133 V8.4.0 (2008-12) Requirements for support of Radio Resource Management

[9] 3GPP TS 36.113 V8.1.0 (2008-05) Base Station (BS) and Repeater Electromagnetic Compatibility (EMC)

[10] 3GPP TS 36.141 V8.1.0 (2008-12) Base Station (BS) Conformance Testing

[11] 3GPP TS 36.104 8.4.0 (2008-12) Base Station Radio Transmission and Reception

[12] 3GPP TS 36.143 V1.0.0 (2008-11) FDD Repeater Conformance Testing

[13] 3GPP TS 36.106 V8.0.0 (2008-12) Repeater Radio Transmission and Reception

[14] ETR 273 (1998-02) Uncertainties in the Measurement of Mobile Radio Equipment Characteristics, Part 1, sub-part 2, subclause 6.5

[15] ITU-R SM.329-10 (Feb 2003) Unwanted emissions in the spurious domain

[16] 3GPP TS 36.211 V8.5.0 (2008-12) Physical Channels and Modulation

[17] 3GPP TS 36.523-1 V2.0.0 (2008-11) User Equipment (UE) conformance specification; Part 1; Protocol conformance specification

[18] 3GPP TS 36.523-2 V1.1.0 (2008-10) Implementation Conformance Statement (ICS) Proforma Specification

[19] 3GPP TS 36.523-3 V0.1.0 (2008-05) User Equipment (UE) conformance specification; Part 3: Abstract Test Suites (ATS)

Links to all reference documents can be found at www.agilent.com/find/ltebook

Chapter 8

Looking Towards 4G: LTE-Advanced

8.1 Introduction

Fourth generation (4G) wireless has been anticipated for quite some time. To explain the evolution to 4G it is helpful to take a brief look at what came before. The third generation (3G) was defined by the International Telecommunications Union Radiocommunication Sector (ITU-R) through the International Mobile Telecommunications 2000 project (IMT-2000). The requirements for IMT-2000, defined in 1997, were quite simple, being expressed in terms of peak user data rates:

- 2048 kbps for indoor office
- 384 kbps for outdoor to indoor and pedestrian
- 144 kbps for vehicular
- 9.6 kbps for satellite

Early 3G systems, of which there were five, did not immediately meet the high peak data rate targets in practical deployment although they did in theory. However, there have been improvements to the standards since then that have brought deployed systems closer to and now even beyond the original 3G targets. From a 3GPP perspective, the addition of High Speed Downlink Packet Access (HSDPA) to UMTS ushered in the informally named 3.5G, and the subsequent addition of the Enhanced Dedicated Channel (E-DCH), better known as High Speed Uplink Packet Access (HSUPA), completed 3.5G. The combination of HSDPA and HSUPA is now referred to as High Speed Packet Access (HSPA).

At the time the IEEE 802.16e standard (Mobile WiMAX) was being developed, and later 3GPP's LTE/SAE, the ITU-R framework for 4G was not in place. For this reason the term 3.9G has been widely used to describe these technologies with the expectation of their evolving towards official 4G status in due course.

8.2 IMT-Advanced: The Real 4G

The formal definition of 4G wireless is being developed by Working Party 5D of the ITU-R. A timeline for their IMT-Advanced program and the parallel activities of 3GPP for LTE-Advanced is shown in Figure 8.2-1.

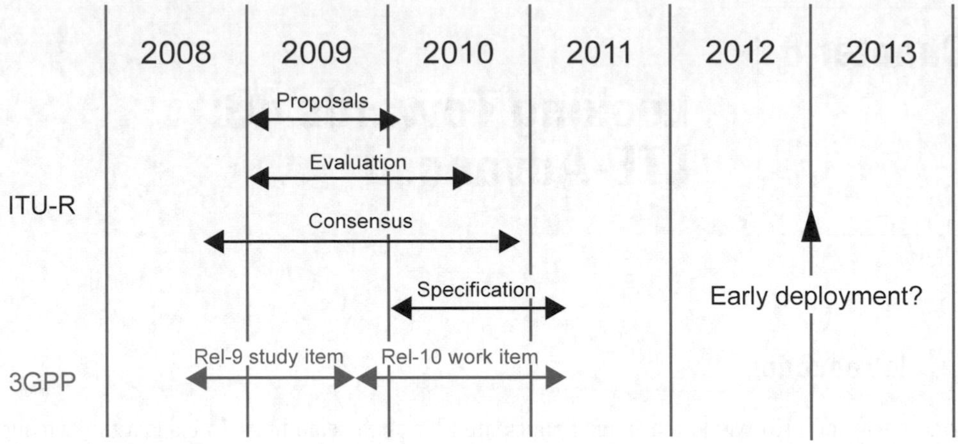

Figure 8.2-1. Overall IMT-Advanced and LTE-Advanced timeline

In naming its 4G initiative IMT-Advanced, the ITU has consciously reused the first part "IMT" (International Mobile Telecommunications) from the 3G IMT-2000 program. This naming is significant because it has been agreed that spectrum currently allocated for exclusive use by IMT-2000 technologies will now be known as just "IMT" spectrum and will be available to any approved IMT-Advanced technology. At the 2007 World Radio Conference (WRC-07), new IMT spectrum was identified in the following bands: 450 MHz, 698 – 960 MHz, 2.3 GHz and 3.4 – 4.2 GHz. Crucially, there are no plans for exclusive IMT-Advanced spectrum. This is pragmatic since spectrum is scarce and largely occupied. The late addition in 2008 of 802.16e to the list of approved IMT-2000 technologies is also noteworthy as it opens up the entire IMT spectrum to access by 802.16e prior to the possibility of 802.16m gaining the same access via the IMT-Advanced route. 802.16m is a planned enhancement to 802.16e, which may become a future IMT-Advanced submission to ITU-R.

The ITU's goal is to approve candidate 4G technologies by the end of 2009 with standards development and implementation to follow. This puts 4G about two years behind Release 8 LTE/SAE, suggesting that 4G commercial service will appear certainly no earlier than 2012. By any standard, and particularly by 3G standards, this is an aggressive timeline. It is made possible, however, because the two most likely 4G candidate technologies (evolutions of IEEE's 802.16e and 3GPP's LTE/SAE) are based on already specified technologies. The enhancements required to these technologies to meet 4G's requirements are not considered major. This is a significant point: Unlike 3G, 4G is not going to require a major rethinking of existing air-interface technologies.

The IMT-2000 project led the development of the 3G standards; however, in the intervening years the 3G standards have been considerably enhanced up to and including the so-called 3.9G standards such that the step to IMT-Advanced is actually relatively small compared to the jump from 2G to 3G. 3GPP's Radio Interface Technology (RIT) submission to the ITU, planned for September 2009, will be a backward-compatible enhancement of LTE Release 8, to be known generally as LTE-Advanced, and will be fully specified in 3GPP release 10. For the IEEE, any submission is likely to be based on the 802.16m standard.

8.3 IMT-Advanced High Level Requirements

The high level requirements for IMT-Advanced defined by ITU-R in [1] are the following:

- A high degree of common functionality worldwide while retaining the flexibility to support a wide range of local services and applications in a cost efficient manner.
- Compatibility of services within IMT and with fixed networks
- Capability of interworking with other radio access systems
- High quality mobile services
- User equipment suitable for worldwide use
- User-friendly applications, services and equipment
- Worldwide roaming capability
- Enhanced downlink peak data rates to support advanced services and applications (100 Mbps for high mobility and 1 Gbps for low mobility were established as targets for research.)

The first seven of the eight requirements are "soft" and are largely being pursued by the industry already. However, the eighth requirement, for 100 Mbps high mobility and 1 Gbps low mobility, is quite a different matter and has fundamental repercussions on system design. The 1 Gbps peak target for 4G is akin to the 2 Mbps target for 3G set some ten years earlier. Like its 3G predecessor, the 1 Gbps peak figure is not without qualification since it applies only for low mobility in excellent radio conditions and typically requires up to 100 MHz of spectrum. Nevertheless, if publicity focuses on the peak rates without taking account of the caveats, expectations of 4G may outstrip practical reality for what could be a long time.

The work by 3GPP to define a candidate RIT is starting in Release 9 with a study phase of LTE-Advanced. The requirements for LTE-Advanced have been captured in a new Technical Report 36.913 "Requirements for Further Advancements for E-UTRA (LTE-Advanced)" [2]. These requirements are defined based on the ITU-R requirements for IMT-Advanced as well as on 3GPP operators' own requirements for advancing LTE. Key elements include the following:

- Continual improvement to the LTE radio technology and architecture.
- Scenarios and performance requirements for interworking with legacy Radio Access Technologies (RATs).
- Backward compatibility of LTE-Advanced with LTE; i.e., an LTE terminal can work in an LTE-Advanced network, and an LTE-Advanced terminal can work in an LTE network. Any exceptions will be considered by 3GPP.
- Account to be taken of recent WRC-07 decisions for new IMT spectrum as well as existing frequency bands to ensure that LTE-Advanced accommodates geographically available spectrum for channel allocations above 20 MHz. Also, requirements must recognize those parts of the world in which wideband channels will not be available.

8.4 IMT-Advanced Detailed Requirements

When IMT-2000 was defined, the only requirements were for peak data rates with no targets for the more important average or cell edge performance, which define the experience for the typical user. Fortunately, this requirement gap has been addressed and more recent systems, starting with LTE, have been given explicit targets for average and cell edge performance. The link between LTE's targets and the retrospective performance derived for UMTS Release 6 is given in the introduction to this book in Tables 1.4-3 and 1.4-4. Looking forward, the relationship between a few of the LTE targets and those for LTE-Advanced and IMT-Advanced is given in Table 8.4-1. The cell and cell edge spectral efficiency figures are for Intersite Distance (ISD) of 500 m.

Table 8.4-1. LTE, LTE-Advanced and IMT-Advanced performance targets

Item	Sub-category	LTE (3.9G) target [3]	LTE-Advanced (4G) target [2]	IMT-Advanced (4G) requirement [1]
Peak spectral efficiency (b/s/Hz)	Downlink	16.3 (4x4 MIMO)	30 (up to 8x8 MIMO)	15 (4x4 MIMO)
	Uplink	4.32 (64QAM SISO)	15 (up to 4x4 MIMO)	6.75 (2x4 MIMO)
Downlink cell spectral efficiency b/s/Hz/user Microcellular 3 km/h, 500 m ISD	(2x2 MIMO)	1.69	2.4	
	(4x2 MIMO)	1.87	2.6	2.6
	(4x4 MIMO)	2.67	3.7	
Downlink cell-edge user spectral efficiency (b/s/Hz/user) (5 percentile, 10 users), 500m ISD	(2x2 MIMO)	0.05	0.07	
	(4x2 MIMO)	0.06	0.09	0.075
	(4x4 MIMO)	0.08	0.12	

The first point of note is that the peak efficiency targets for LTE-Advanced are substantially higher than the IMT-Advanced requirements — thus the desire to drive up peak performance is maintained despite the average targets and requirements being very similar. However, 36.913 [1] states: "The target for average spectrum efficiency and the cell edge user throughput efficiency should be given a higher priority than the target for peak spectrum efficiency and VoIP capacity." Most of this chapter will focus on the challenge of raising the average and cell edge performance.

8.5 Improving the Average and Cell-edge Spectral Efficiency

As discussed in Chapter 1, the LTE targets for average and cell edge spectrum efficiency are based on 2x to 4x improvements to Release 6 HSPA. The reference HSPA configuration is a single transmitter for both the NodeB and UE (SISO) with a diversity UE receiver with no equalizer (25.913 [4] Subclause 7.1). This reference configuration was analyzed during the LTE study phase to provide an average downlink cell spectral efficiency of around 0.53 b/s/Hz/cell using a 500 m ISD [3].

Increasing peak data rates by using more spectrum or higher order modulation in a good radio environment is a well-understood process that has been in use for years. However, improving the targets for average and cell edge performance is a much harder task due to radio propagation and interference issues, which are independent of the air interface technology. Many of the UMTS enhancements in Release 7 and Release 8 as well as LTE have addressed the challenge of increasing average efficiency. LTE-Advanced takes this challenge to the next level.

The underlying problem of interference is illustrated in Figure 8.5-1, which shows a cumulative distribution function plot of the geometry factor within a typical urban cell.

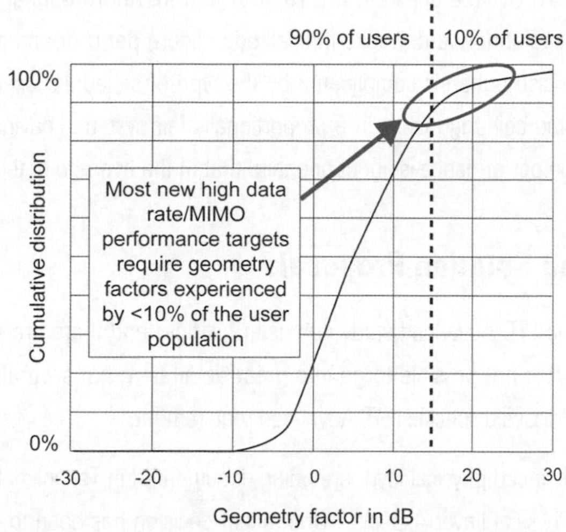

Figure 8.5-1. Geometry factor distribution in a typical urban cell with frequency reuse 1

The geometry factor is the term used in UMTS to indicate the ratio of the wanted signal to the interference plus noise. It is equivalent to Signal to Interference plus Noise Ratio (SINR). From the figure it can be seen that 10% of users experience a better than 15 dB geometry factor but 50% of users experience worse than 5 dB. The exact shape of the curve varies significantly depending primarily on the frequency reuse factor followed by the cell size. An isolated cell (e.g., a hotspot) would exhibit a shift to the right, indicating that most users are experiencing very good signal conditions. A cell in an urban area with significant co-channel inter-cell interference would shift to the left. Building penetration loss, as experienced when indoor coverage is provided from an external cell, would also cause a shift to the left. However, on the assumption that the deployment in a particular area has resulted in a certain geometry factor distribution, the challenge then becomes how to deal with the interference to improve average and cell edge performance.

In 2G systems, performance was obtained through interference avoidance through the use of high frequency reuse factors of up to 21. In 3G systems the frequency reuse was optimized at 1 and methods such as scrambling and spreading were used to minimize the impact of interference with resulting gains in average spectral efficiency. Later systems employed receive diversity, equalizers, transmit diversity and limited spatial multiplexing (MIMO). For LTE-Advanced, the planned performance enhancement techniques will take further steps by using more advanced MIMO and beamsteering, interference cancellation, fractional frequency reuse and other advanced methods.

It is worth explaining how the cell edge performance targets used by ITU-R and 3GPP were developed based on simulated geometry factor distributions for the target deployment environments. Ten users were randomly distributed within each cell and the resulting geometry factor was calculated for each UE. This information was converted into a data throughput rate that was in turn used to plot a distribution of throughput. The process was repeated many times in a multi-drop simulation to create a smooth throughput distribution. The cell edge performance was then defined as the fifth percentile of the throughput distribution. Because the simulation was carried out using groups of 10 UE, the units are b/s/Hz/user and therefore appear to be 10 times lower than might be expected. It is not straightforward to take the cell edge figure per user and multiply by 10 to predict the cell edge average since the distribution is complicated by the type of scheduler used. The scheduler may have allocated more resource to the cell edge users in a proportionally fair system. Leaving this complication aside, it can be seen that the cell edge performance is about one third that of the average of the cell.

8.6 LTE-Advanced Solution Proposals

At the time of this writing the LTE-Advanced study item is in full flow and there are a large number of solutions being considered by 3GPP. It is not possible to go into great detail here but several categories of research are worth highlighting. Each addresses a specific IMT-Advanced requirement.

The decisions for the LTE-Advanced physical layer are being documented in Technical Report 36.814 [5], "Further Advancements for E-UTRA Physical Layer Aspects." One recent decision has been to enhance the uplink multiple access scheme by adopting clustered Discrete Fourier Transform Spread OFDM (DFT-S-OFDM). This scheme is similar to SC-FDMA but has the advantage that it allows non-contiguous (clustered) groups of subcarriers to be allocated for transmission by a single UE, thus increasing the flexibility available for frequency-selective scheduling. This scheme was chosen in preference to pure OFDM in order to avoid a large increase in Peak-to-Average Power Ratio (PAPR). In addition, it has been decided to allow simultaneous transmission of control and data on the uplink.

8.6.1 Bandwidth Aggregation

This solution is aimed at addressing the LTE-Advanced requirements for peak data rates. Today's spectrum allocations do not offer much opportunity for finding 100 MHz of contiguous spectrum needed for 1 Gbps peak data rates. Some new IMT spectrum was identified at the World Radio Conference in 2007 (WRC-07), but there are still only a few places where continuous blocks of 100 MHz might be found (e.g., at 2.6 GHz or 3.5 GHz). One possibility to increase available bandwidths would be to encourage network sharing, which reduces fragmentation caused by splitting one band between several operators. However, sharing the spectrum, as opposed to just the sites and towers, is a considerable step up in difficulty. The ITU-R recognizes the challenge that wide-bandwidth channels present and so expects that the required 100 MHz will be created by the aggregation of non-contiguous channels from different bands in a multi-transceiver mobile device.

The beginnings of such aggregation techniques are already showing up in established technologies — first with EDGE Evolution, for which standards are being written to aggregate two non-adjacent 200 kHz channels to potentially double the single-user data rates that are possible with standard EDGE. Along similar lines, there are 3GPP specifications for dual-carrier HSDPA that try to close the bandwidth gap between 5 MHz UMTS and 20 MHz LTE. Contiguous multi-carrier cdma2000 (3xRTT) has also been defined, which avoids the need for multiple transceivers.

Bandwidth aggregation is clearly not a new idea; however, the proposal to extend aggregation up to 100 MHz in multiple bands raises questions about the viability of solutions due to the added cost and complexity to the UE. Although it is possible to conceive of applications for 1 Gbps data rates to a single mobile device the commercial viability has yet to be understood. It should also be noted that bandwidth-aggregation does not increase spectral efficiency (or network capacity) per se, although wider channels do offer better trunking efficiency. Taking all these factors into account suggests an uncertain future for 100 MHz multi-transceiver bandwidth aggregation as a means of delivering extreme single-user peak data rates. Aggregation of two contiguous 20 MHz channels is a more achievable goal provided the spectrum can be found.

8.6.2 Higher Order MIMO and Beamsteering

The Release 8 LTE specifications support up to four transmitters and receivers on the eNB with up to two transmitters and four receivers for the UE. The potential reception gains from MIMO systems and from beamsteering are a function of the number of antennas, and proposals are being considered that would increase this number for systems up to 8x8 for the eNB and 4x4 for the UE. Although the theoretical potential of such systems can be simulated, practical considerations make commercial deployment more challenging. At the eNB, compact 4x antenna systems are already in use. Increasing this to 8x to maximize the potential for MIMO and beamsteering may require the use of tower-mounted radio heads to avoid the need to run 8 sets of expensive and lossy cables up the tower. The increased power consumption of MIMO systems is also a factor that cannot be overlooked. There is a trade-off between number of antennas per sector and the number of sectors per cell. It may be preferable to use a six sector cell with four antennas per sector rather than a three-sector cell with eight antennas per sector.

At the UE, the main issue with higher order MIMO is the physical space required for the antennas. Laptop data-only systems clearly have an advantage over handheld devices in terms of size, power handling and throughput requirements. In addition, it is very hard in a small device to achieve the necessary spatial separation of the antennas in order to exploit the spatial beamforming in the channel. Cross polarizing the antennas can help.

8.6.3 Co-operative MIMO

Section 2.4.7 briefly introduced the concept of co-operative MIMO, which also goes by the name of network MIMO or Coordinated Multi-Point (CoMP). Figure 8.6-1 compares standard MIMO with co-operative MIMO.

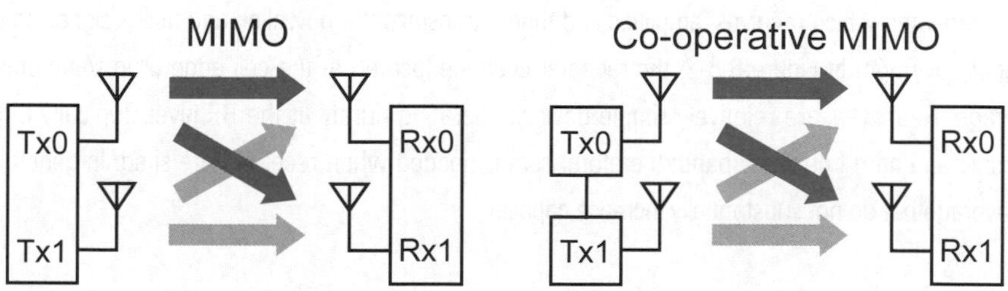

Figure 8.6-1. Standard MIMO versus co-operative MIMO

The most obvious difference between standard and co-operative MIMO is that for the latter, the transmitters are not physically co-located. Multi-User MIMO (MU-MIMO) in the uplink (described in Section 2.4.6.2) also has physically separate transmitters belonging to different UEs but there is no possibility of sharing payload data between the UEs for the purposes of co-operative precoding. In co-operative MIMO the transmitters are linked and can share payload data to allow the full benefit of closed loop performance using precoding. This scenario is possible in the downlink only since it is not yet practical to share baseband data between physically separate UEs. Even though downlink co-operative MIMO is possible, it does present new challenges for inter-eNB communication (X2 interface). In some ways co-operative MIMO is a more advanced form of the downlink macro diversity used to enable soft handovers. In the latter case the same payload data is transmitted from two physically separate sites. To get the full benefit of co-operative MIMO, each site transmits a different data stream and if precoding is implemented, payload data is shared between the sites. This sharing requires high bandwidth, low latency backhaul between the sites, which is likely to be expensive in terms of both initial capital expenditure (capex) and operational expenditure (opex). The need for some level of inter-eNB connectivity is, however, mandatory in LTE due to the new X2 interface in the E–UTRAN, which runs between the eNBs forming a mesh network between the base stations in a way that did not exist in the UTRAN.

The advantage of co-operative MIMO over soft handover is that the transmission of two streams over what is likely to be uncorrelated channel conditions will lead to a higher probability of increased data rates for cell edge users. Both techniques, however, reduce overall system capacity due to the scheduling of downlink resources in more than one cell. For every cell involved in soft handover there is an equivalent loss of capacity, but co-operative MIMO will be more efficient. If the MIMO gain approaches the theoretical limit then the system capacity would return to that seen if independent UEs had been served with single streams.

In summary, co-operative MIMO is a fairness technique that can improve the quality of service at the cell edge at the cost of additional inter-cell backhaul. The impact of co-operative MIMO on system capacity is more complex and may result in some rise or fall in system capacity depending on the fairness criteria of the scheduler.

8.6.4 In-Channel Relay

Another method of improving coverage in difficult conditions is the use of relaying. Figure 8.6-2 shows a typical scenario.

The concept of relaying is not new but the level of sophistication continues to grow. The most basic relay method is the use of a repeater, which receives, amplifies and then retransmits the downlink and uplink signals to overcome areas of poor coverage. In Figure 8.6-2, the repeater could be located at the cell edge or in some other area of poor coverage. Repeaters are relatively simple devices operating purely at the RF level. Typically they receive and retransmit an entire frequency band; therefore, care is needed when receivers are sited. In general they can improve coverage but do not substantially increase capacity.

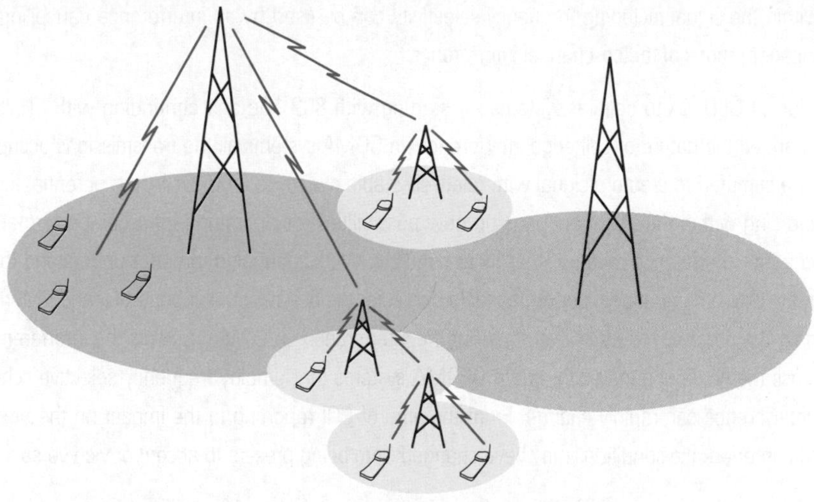

Figure 8.6-2. In-channel relay

More advanced relays can in principle decode transmissions before retransmitting them. This gives the ability to selectively forward traffic to and from the UE local to the relay station thus minimizing interference. Depending on the level at which the protocol stack is terminated in the relay node, such types of relay may require the development of relay-specific standards. This can be largely avoided by extending the protocol stack of the relay node up to Layer 3 to create a wireless router that operates in the same way as a normal eNB, using standard air interface protocols and performing its own resource allocation and scheduling. The distinguishing feature of such relays compared to normal eNBs is that the X2 interface connecting the relays to the other eNBs operates as an in-band LTE radio link.

The concept of the relay station can also be applied in low density deployments where a lack of suitable backhaul would otherwise preclude use of a cellular network. The use of in band or in-channel backhaul can be optimized using narrow point-to-point connections to avoid creating unnecessary interference in the rest of the network. Multi-hop relaying is also possible as shown in Figure 8.6-2. Extending the relay concept to direct transmission between UEs is a topic that has been studied since the early days of UMTS but remains a significant technical challenge.

8.6.5 Cell Edge Interference Coordination and Cancellation

In the CDMA systems that dominate 3G, cell edge interference is now a well-understood phenomenon and techniques for dealing with it continue to advance. This was not always the case and early CDMA systems were dogged with unexpected issues such as "cell breathing" caused by power control problems and by excessive soft handover activity factors. Cell breathing can now be used with care as a tool for inter-cell load balancing. UMTS Release 7 introduced the HSDPA Type 3i receiver, which incorporated diversity reception, an equalizer and dual input interference cancellation capability. The nature of a CDMA cell-edge interferer has considerably more structure than Additive White Gaussian Nose (AWGN). The use of cell-specific scrambling codes and the presence of patterns within the signal including frequency selectivity can be used by an interference cancelling receiver to remove significant portions of the co-channel interference.

The introduction of OFDMA to cellular systems — starting with 802.16e and continuing with LTE/SAE — has significantly changed the nature of cell edge interference. In CDMA systems all the transmissions occupy the entire channel and are summed to create a signal with relatively stable dynamics. In OFDMA the potential for frequency-selective scheduling within the channel opens up new possibilities for optimizing intra-cell performance, but the inter-cell co-channel interference created is far more dynamic. Work is ongoing to better understand the effect this interference may have on operational performance. In particular the behavior of subband CQI and PMI reporting will be influenced by the narrowband statistical nature of the interference. In CDMA systems the interference is largely consistent across the channel bandwidth, but in OFDMA systems that employ frequency-selective scheduling, the existence of interference can rapidly change. From the time of CQI reporting to the impact on the next scheduled transmission the interference conditions may have changed from being present to absent or vice versa.

The interference protection between CDMA cells offered by whitening of noise due to the use of scrambling codes is not available in narrowband OFDMA transmissions, which increases the vulnerability of narrowband signals to narrowband interference. Techniques to overcome such interference include making transmissions more robust by repeating (spreading) information across a wider allocation. This starts to introduce CDMA principles back into the system.

Other methods for controlling interference are still being researched. See "Binary Power Control for Sum Rate Maximization over Multiple Interfering Links" [6].

8.6.6 Self Optimizing Networks

Today's cellular systems are very much centrally planned and the addition of new nodes to the network involves expensive and time-consuming work, site visits for optimization, etc. One of the enhancements being considered for LTE-Advanced is the concept of the Self Optimizing Network (SON). The intent is to substantially reduce the effort required to introduce new nodes to the network. There are implications for radio planning as well as for the Operations and Maintenance (O&M) interface to the eNB. Some limited SON capability will be introduced in Release 8 and will be further elaborated in Release 9 and Release 10. See 36.902 [7].

8.6.7 Femtocells

The final category of network enhancement is the femtocell or Home — Home Node B (HNB) or Home eNB. 3GPP work on femtocell inclusion in UMTS has been ongoing during Release 8, and this work continues in Release 9 for the Home eNB. The femtocell concept is not unique to LTE or LTE-Advanced, but an opportunity exists for LTE to incorporate this technology from the start rather than retrospectively designing it into legacy systems such as UMTS and GSM. Figure 8.6-3 shows the topology of a femtocell deployment.

From a radio deployment perspective the femtocell operates over a small area within a larger cell. The radio channel could be the same as the larger cell (known as co-channel deployment) or on a dedicated channel. The femtocell concept is fundamentally different from relaying since the femtocell connection back into the core network is provided locally by an existing DSL internet connection rather than over the air back to the macrocell.

Most femtocell deployments will be indoors which helps provide isolation between the femtocell and macrocell. Also shown in Figure 8.6-3 is a femtocell outside the coverage area. This could be an example of how local cellular coverage can be provided in rural areas where DSL exists but not the coverage of the preferred cellular operator.

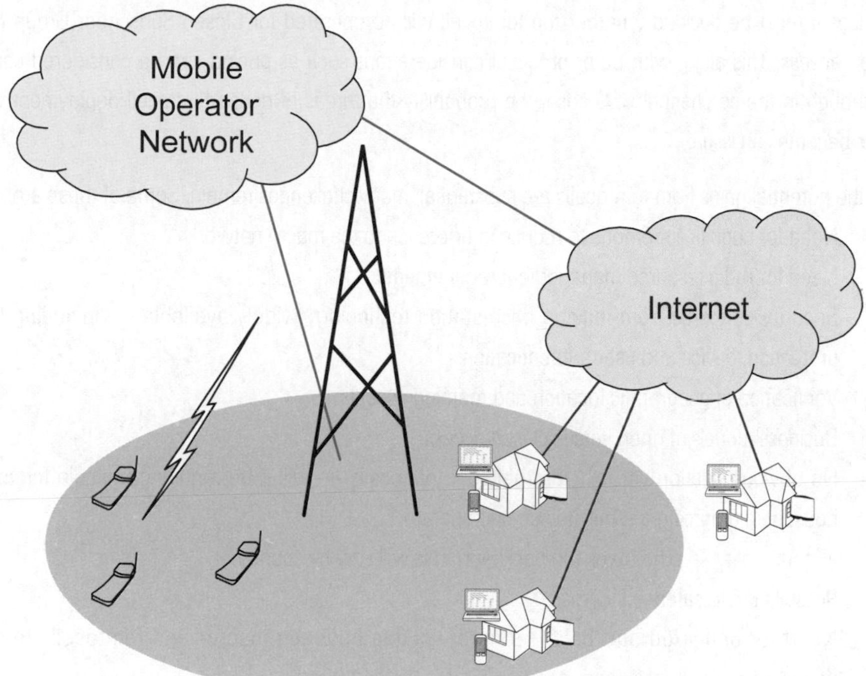

Figure 8.6-3. Femtocell (Home eNB)

Although the name femtocell suggests that the major difference from existing systems is one of coverage area, the defining attributes of femtocells are actually far more significant than coverage area alone. The key attributes of traditional macro-, micro- and picocell systems and femtocells is shown in Table 8.6-1:

Table 8.6-1. Traditional cellular versus femtocellular technology

Attribute	Traditional cellular	Femtocellular
Infrastructure cost	$10,000 – 100,000	$100 – 200
Infrastructure finance	Operator	End user
Backhaul	Expensive leased E1/T1 lines	Existing end-user DSL or cable broadband
Planning	Operator	End-user (no central planning)
Deployment	Operator truck roll	End user one touch provisioning
Quality of Service (QoS)	Operator controlled	Best effort
Control	Operator via O&M	Operator via Internet
Mobility	Good/excellent	Nomadic/best effort
Data throughput	Limited	Excellent

The two main deployment scenarios for femtocells are as follows:

- In rural areas with poor or no (indoor) coverage, probably using co-channel deployment.
- In dense areas to provide high data rates and capacity.

In both cases it must be decided whether the femtocell will be operated for Closed Subscriber Group (CSG) UE or for open access. This along with other practical considerations such as pricing can be considered commercial issues, although in the co-channel CSG case, the probability that areas of dense femtocell deployment will block macrocells becomes an issue.

Although the potential gains from femtocells are substantial, many challenges remain. Some of these are:

- Need for cognitive methods to reduce interference to the macro network.
- Need for radio resource management requirements.
- Security concerns from making base station technology widely available — including backhaul protection, device and user authentication.
- Verification of geographic location and roaming aspects.
- Business models of open versus closed access.
- No obvious solution yet for cross-network femtocells — will it be requiring multiple femtocells per household or forcing a family to use one operator?
- Net neutrality — who owns the backhaul? This will vary by country.
- Possible public safety concerns.
- Need for optimized and balanced interworking between macro- and femtocells to minimize unnecessary handovers (ping pong).
- Potential bottleneck over fixed broadband backhaul (such as DSL or cable) connection, especially on the uplink for services requiring symmetric bandwidths, prioritization and congestion management.
- QoS control for real-time services and applications requiring guaranteed bit rates, such as voice, with all the other traffic types on the broadband access network.
- Access control providing Closed Subscriber Group (CSG) local and roaming access.
- Self-configuration (plug and play), self-organization and self-optimization, including fault management and failure recovery (self-healing).

Despite these issues, studies have shown that increases in average data rates and capacity of some 100x are possible with femtocells over what can be achieved from the macro network. On the other hand, femtocells do not provide the mobility of macrocellular systems, and differences exist in the use models of these systems, as shown in Table 8.6-2.

Table 8.6-2. Comparison of macro- and microcellular with femtocellular use models

Macro/micro cellular	Femtocell/hotspot
Ubiquitous mobile data and voice	Opportunistic nomadic data
Mobility and continuous coverage	Hotspot coverage
Ability to control QoS	Limited QoS for lower value data
Limited capacity and data rates	Distributed cost (not low cost)

High costs, acceptable for high value traffic	Free or charged
Often outdoors and moving	Sitting down indoors

For these reasons, femtocellular and hotspot deployments should be considered as complementary rather than competitive with the macro/microcellular systems.

8.7 Proving LTE-Advanced

The targets that have been set for LTE-Advanced are very challenging. At 2.6 b/s/Hz/cell for a downlink 4x2 configuration, the average downlink cell spectral efficiency targets are around five times higher than Release 6 HSDPA. The intermediate target for LTE of 1.87 b/s/Hz/cell is also a major challenge. Delivering this with cost-effective technology is going to require a great deal of effort.

Proving that targets have been met will not be trivial. The 3GPP requirements are largely written from the perspective of individual UE performance and are based on link-level simulations. The conformance test requirements are based on spot measurement of performance in largely open-loop, single-UE environments. This is done for reasons of simplicity and repeatability. Performance in a real, loaded network is considerably more difficult to measure since there are hundreds of factors to take into account. The targets for LTE and LTE-Advanced were set using system level simulations far more complex than the link level simulations used to derive the UE requirements for conformance testing. From the perspective of the end user, the system-level simulations come a lot closer to predicting the potential performance of the system; however, this presents a challenge for the industry since conformance testing of the UE alone cannot prove that the system design targets have been met.

In order to address this complex issue LTE-Advanced test beds have been set up; for instance, in Japan and Germany. The intention is to test under real life conditions many of the technologies being considered for LTE-Advanced. This work is complementary to the work of LSTI discussed in the introductory chapter of this book.

8.8 References

[1] ITU-R M.[IMT-TECH] "Requirements related to technical performance for IMT-Advanced radio interface(s)," August 2008

[2] 3GPP TR 36.913 V8.0.0 (2008-6) Requirements for Further Advancements of E-UTRA (LTE-Advanced)

[3] 3GPP TSG RAN Tdoc RP-070466

[4] 3GPP TR 25.913 V8.0.0 (2008-12) Requirements for E-UTRA and E-UTRAN

[5] 3GPP TR 814 V0.3.1 Further Advancements for E-UTRA Physical Layer Aspects

[6] A. Gjendemsjoe, D. Gesbert, G. Oien and S. Kiani, "Binary Power Control for Sum Rate Maximization over Multiple Interfering Links." IEEE Trans. Wireless Communications, August 2008

[7] 3GPP 36.902 V1.0.1 (2008-09) Self-configuring and self-optimizing network use cases and solutions

Links to all reference documents can be found at www.agilent.com/find/ltebook.

List of Acronyms

1xRTT	Single-channel (1x) Radio Transmission Technology
1xEV-DO	1xRTT Evolution - Data Only
2G	2nd Generation
3G	3rd Generation
3GPP	3rd Generation Partnership Project

A

ACK	Acknowledgement
ACK/NACK	Acknowledgement/Negative Acknowledgement
ACLR	Adjacent Channel Leakage Ratio
ACS	Adjacent Channel Selectivity
ADC	Analog-to-Digital Converter
ADS	Advanced Design System
AF	Authentication Framework
AGC	Automatic Gain Control
AICH	Acquisition Indictor Channel
AIPN	All Internet Protocol Network
AKA	Authentication and Key Agreement
ALC	Automatic Loop Control
AM	Acknowledge Mode Amplitude Modulation
AMBR	Aggregate Maximum Bit Rate
AMC	Adaptive Modulation and Coding
AMD	Acknowledged Mode Data
A-MPR	Additional Maximum Power Reduction
AMR	Adaptive Multi-Rate
AMR-WB	AMR-Wideband
AN	Access Network
ANR	Automatic Neighbour Relation
AoA	Angle of Arrival
AoD	Angle of Departure
AP	Application Part Application Protocol
API	Application Programming Interface
APN	Access Point Name
ARIB	Association of Radio Industries and Businesses (Japan)
ARP	Allocation and Retention Priority
ARQ	Automatic Repeat Request
AS	Access Stratum Application Server Azimuth Spread
ASIC	Application Specific Integrated Circuit
ASN.1	Abstract Syntax Notation number 1
AT	Attention
ATC	Air Traffic Control
ATIS	Alliance for Telecommunications Industry Solutions (USA)
ATS	Abstract Test Suite
AWGN	Additive White Gaussian Nose

B

BBIC	Baseband IC
BBIQ	Baseband IQ
BCCH	Broadcast Control Channel
BCH	Broadcast Channel

BDM Background Debug Mode
BER Bit Error Ratio
BERT Bit Error Ratio Tester
BLER Block Error Ratio
BO Buffer Occupancy
BP Bandwidth Parts
BPSK Binary Phase-Shift Keying
BS Bearer Service
BSIC Base Station Identity Code
BSC Base Station Controller
BTS Base Transceiver Station
BW Bandwidth

C

CBC Cell Broadcast Center
CCCH Common Control Channel
CCDF Complementary Cumulative Distribution Function
CCE Control Channel Element
CCF CDMA Certification Forum
CCSA China Communications Standards Association
CDD Cyclic Delay Diversity
CDMA Code Division Multiple Access
CFI Control Format Indicator
CFR Crest Factor Reduction
CI Codebook Index
CK Ciphering Key
CL-SM Closed Loop Spatial Multiplexing
CMOS Complementary Metal Oxide Semiconductor
CN Core Network
Co-MIMO Cooperative MIMO
CoMP Coordinated Multi-Point
CP Cyclic Prefix
Control Plane
CPICH Common Pilot Channel
CPRI Common Public Radio Interface
CPT Control PDU Type
CQI Channel Quality Indicator
CR Change Request
CRC Cyclic Redundancy Check
C-RNTI Cell Radio Network Temporary Identity
CS Circuit Switched
CSFB Circuit Switched Fall Back
CSG Closed Subscriber Group
CSI Channel State Information
CSI 2 Camera Serial Interface 2
CSN.1 Concrete Syntax Notation number 1
CW Code Word
Continuous Wave

D

DAC Digital-to-Analog Converter
DAS Distributed Antenna System
DC Direct Current
DCCH Dedicated Control Channel
DCI Downlink Control Information
DCS Display Command Set
DFT Discrete Fourier Transform
DFT-S-OFDM Discrete Fourier Transform Spread OFDM
DHCP Dynamic Host Configuration Protocol
DL Downlink (base station to subscriber transmission)
DL-SCH Downlink Shared Channel
DMRS Demodulation Reference Signal
DNS Directory Name Service
D-PHY 500 Mbps Physical Layer
DRB Data Radio Bearer
DRX Discontinuous Reception
DSI Display Serial Interface
DSIM Digital Signal Interface Module
DSL Digital Subscriber Line
DSP Digital Signal Processing

DT	Development Toolset
DTCH	Dedicated Traffic Channel
DTM	Dual Transfer Mode
DTX	Discontinuous Transmission
DUT	Device Under Test
DVB-T	Digital Video Broadcast-Terrestrial
DVM	Digital Volt Meter
DwPTS	Downlink Pilot Time Slot

E

E	Extension
ECGI	E-UTRAN Cell Global Id
ECM	EPS Connection Management
ECTEL	European Conference on Technology-Enhanced Learning
ED	Error Detecting
EDA	Electronic Design Automation
E-DCH	Enhanced Dedicated Channel
EDGE	Enhanced Data rates for GSM Evolution
EMC	Electromagnetic Compatibility
EMM	EPS Mobility Management
eNB	Evolved Node B
EPA	Extended Pedestrian A
EPC	Evolved Packet Core
ePDG	Evolved Packet Data Gateway
EPS	Evolved Packet System
E-RAB	Evolved Radio Access Bearer
ESM	EPS Session Management
ESP	Encapsulating Security Payload
E-TM	E-UTRA Test Model
ETSI	European Telecommunications Standards Institute
ETU	Extended Typical Urban
ETWS	Earthquake and Tsunami Warning System
E-UTRA	Evolved Universal Terrestrial Radio Access
E-UTRAN	Evolved Universal Terrestrial Radio Access Network
EVA	Extended Vehicular A
EVM	Error Vector Magnitude

F

FCC	Federal Communications Commission
FDD	Frequency Division Duplex
FEC	Forward Error Correction
FFT	Fast Fourier Transform
FI	Framing Indicator
FIR	Finite Impulse Response
FPGA	Field Programmable Gate Array
FRC	Fixed Reference Channel
FS1	Frame structure type 1
FS2	Frame structure type 2
FTP	File Transfer Protocol

G

GAN	Generic Access Network
GANC	GAN Controller
GbE	Gigabit Ethernet
Gbps	Gigabit per second
GBR	Guaranteed Bit Rate
GCF	Global Certification Forum
GERAN	GSM Enhanced Radio Access Network
GP	Guard Period
G-PDU	GTP-U non-signalling PDU
GPRS	General Packet Radio Service
GRE	Generic Routing Encapsulation
GSM	Global System for Mobile Communication
GSMA	GSM Association
GTP	GPRS Tunneling Protocol
GTP-C	GTP Control
GTP-U	GTP User

GUI Graphical User Interface
GUMMEI Globally Unique MME Identity
GUTI Globally Unique Temporary Identity
GW Gateway

H

HARQ Hybrid Automatic Repeat Request
HDL Hardware Description Language
HeNB Home eNB
HFN Hyper Frame Number
HI HARQ Indicator
HLR Home Location Register
HO Handover
HPLMN Home Public Land Mobile Network
HRPD High Rate Packet Data
HSDPA High Speed Downlink Packet Access
HSPA High Speed Packet Access
HSS Home Subscriber Server
HSUPA High Speed Uplink Packet Access
HTTP Hypertext Transfer Protocol

I

IC Integrated Circuit
ICE In-Circuit Emulator
ICI Inter-Carrier Interference
ICIC Inter-Cell Interference Coordination
ICS Implementation Conformance Statement
Id Identity
IDE Integrated Development Environment
IDFT Inverse Discrete Fourier Transform
IE Information Element
IETF Internet Engineering Task Force
IF Intermediate Frequency
IFFT Inverse FFT
IM IP Multimedia
IMCS Index Modulation and Coding Scheme
IMEI International Mobile Equipment Identity
IMS IP Multimedia Subsystem
IMN CN SS IMS Core Network Subsystem
IMSI International Mobile Subscriber Identity
IMT International Mobile Telecommunications
IODT Interoperability Development Testing
IOT Interoperability Testing
IP Internet Protocol
IPv4 Internet Protocol version 4
IPv6 Internet Protocol version 6
IQ In-phase Quadrature
IQoIP IQ over Internet Protocol
I-RAT Inter-Radio Access Technology
ISD Inter-Site Distance
ISDN Integrated Services Digital Network
ISI Inter Symbol Interference
ISR Idle-mode Signal Reduction
ISUP ISDN User Part
ITU International Telecommunications Union
ITU-R International Telecommunications Union Radiocommunication Sector
ITU-T International Telecommunications Union Telecommunication Standardization Sect
IWS Interworking Solution

K

KPI Key Performance Indicator
KSI Key Set Identifier

L

L1 Layer 1
L2 Layer 2
L3 Layer 3

LA	Location Area
LAI	Location Area Identity
LAU	Location Area Update
LBI	Linked EPS Bearer Identity
LCR	Low Chip Rate
LCS	Location Service
LI	Length Indicator
LMMSE	Linear Minimum Mean Square Error
LO	Local Oscillator
LSF	Last Segment Field
LSTI	LTE/SAE Trial Initiative
LTE	Long Term Evolution
LVDS	Low Voltage Differential Signalling

M

MAC	Medium Access Control
MAC-I	Message Authentication Code
Mbps	Megabits per second
MBR	Maximum Bit Rate
MBSFN	Multicast/Broadcast over Single Frequency Network
MCC	Mobile Country Code
M-commerce	Mobile-commerce
Mcps	Mega-chips per second
MCE	MAC Control Element
MCH	Multicast Channel
MCS	Modulation and Coding Scheme
MIB	Master Information Block
MIMO	Multiple Input Multiple Output
MIPI	Mobile Industry Processor Interface
MISO	Multiple Input Single Output
MME	Mobility Management Entity
MMSE	Minimum Mean Squared Error
MNC	Mobile Network Code
MO	Mobile Originated
MOC	Mobile Originating Call
MOP	Maximum Output Power
MPR	Maximum Power Reduction
MSC	Mobile Switching Center
MSD	Maximum Sensitivity Degradation
MSE	Minimum Squared Error
Msps	Mega-samples per second
MSS	Mobile Switching Center Server
MT	Mobile Terminated
MU-MIMO	Multi-User MIMO

N

NACK	Negative Acknowledgement
NAS	Non-Access Stratum
NB	Node B
NDI	New Data Indication
NDS	Network Domain Security
NE	Network Element
NEM	Network Equipment Manufacturer
NGMN	Next Generation Mobile Networks
NNSF	NAS Node Selection Function
NRT	Non-Real Time

O

O&M	Operations and Maintenance
OBSAI	Open Base Station Architecture Interface
OBW	Occupied Bandwidth
OFDM	Orthogonal Frequency Division Multiplexing
OFDMA	Orthogonal Frequency Division Multiple Access
OMC	Operation and Maintenance Center
OTA	Over The Air

P

P	Polling
PA	Power Amplifier
PAPR	Peak-to-Average Power Ratio
PAR	Peak-to-Average Ratio
PAS	Power Azimuth Spectrum

PBCH	Physical Broadcast Channel
PBR	Prioritized Bit Rate
PCC	Policy and Charging Control
PCCC	Parallel Concatenated Convolutional Code
PCCH	Paging Control Channel
P-CCPCH	Primary Common Control Physical Channel
PCFICH	Physical Control Format Indicator Channel
PCH	Paging Channel
PCRF	Policy and Charging Rules Function
PCS	Personal Communication System
PDCCH	Physical Downlink Control Channel
PDCP	Packet Data Control Plane
	Packet Data Convergence Protocol
PDN	Packet Data Network
PDN-GW	Packet Data Network Gateway
PDSCH	Physical Downlink Shared Channel
PDU	Protocol Data Unit
PECF	Policy Enforcement and Charging Function
PHICH	Physical Hybrid ARQ Indicator Channel
PHY	Physical layer
PI	Paging Information
PLMN	Public Land Mobile Network
PMCH	Physical Multicast Channel
PM	Phase Modulation
PMI	Precoding Matrix Indicator
PMIP	Proxy Mobile Internet Protocol
PRACH	Physical Random Access Channel
P-RNTI	Paging Radio Network Temporary Identity
PS	Packet Switched
P-SS	Packet Switched Service
	Primary Synchronization Signal
PTCRB	PCS Type Certification Review Board
PUCCH	Physical Uplink Control Channel
PUSCH	Physical Uplink Shared Channel
PVT	Power Versus Time

Q

QAM	Quadrature Amplitude Modulation
QCI	QoS Class Identifier
QoE	Quality of Experience
QoS	Quality of Service
QPSK	Quadrature Phase-Shift Keying

R

R&TTE	Radio and Telecommunications Terminal Equipment
RA	Routing Area
RAB	Radio Access Bearer
RACH	Random Access Channel
RAD	Rapid Application Development
RAN	Radio Access Network
RA-RNTI	Random Access Radio Network Temporary Identity
RAT	Radio Access Technology
RAU	Routing Area Update
RB	Resource Block
RBW	Resolution Bandwidth
RCLP	Relative Carrier Leakage Power
RCMI	Remote Control Management Interface
RDX	Radio Digital Cross Domain
RE	Resource Element
RES	Response
RF	Radio Frequency
	Re-segmentation Flag
RI	Rank Indication
RIM	RAN Information Management
RIT	Radio Interface Technology
RLC	Radio Link Control
RMC	Reference Measurement Channel
RNC	Radio Network Controller

RNTI	Radio Network Temporary Identifier
RoHC	Robust Header Compression
ROI	Return on Investment
RR	Radio Resource
RRC	Radio Resource Control
	Root Raised Cosine
RRM	Radio Resource Management
RS	Reference Signal
RSCP	Received Signal Code Power
RSRP	Reference Signal Received Power
RSRQ	Reference Signal Received Quality
RSS	Root Sum Square
RSSI	Received Signal Strength Indicator
RT	Real Time
RV	Redundancy Version
RX	Receiver

S

SAE	System Architecture Evolution
SAES	System Architecture Evolution Specification
SAP	Service Access Point
SC-FDMA	Single Carrier Frequency Division Multiple Access
SCH	Synchronization Channel
SCTP	S Common Transport Protocol
SDF	Service Data Flow
SDO	Standards Development Organization
SDU	Service Data Unit
SEM	Spectrum Emission Mask
SFBC	Space-Frequency Block Coding
SFN	Single Frequency Network
SG	Security Gateway
SGSN	Serving GPRS Support Node
S-GW	Serving Gateway
SI	System Information
SIB	System Information Block
SIMO	Single Input Multiple Output
SINR	Signal to Interference plus Noise Ratio
SIP	Session Initiation Protocol
SI-RNTI	System Information Radio Network Temporary Identity
SISO	Single Input Single Output
SMS	Short Message Service
SN	Sequence Number
	Serving Network
SNid	Serving Network Identity
SNR	Signal-to-Noise Ratio
SO	Segment Offset
SON	Self Optimizing Network
SPID	Subscriber Profile ID
SPMI	System Power Management Interface
SPS	Semi-Persistent Scheduling
SR	Scheduling Request
SRB	Signalling Radio Bearer
SRS	Sounding Reference Signal
SRVCC	Single Radio Voice Call Continuity
SS	Subsystem
	System Simulator
S-SS	Secondary Synchronization Signal
STBC	Space Time Block Coding
SU-MIMO	Single User MIMO
SVD	Singular Value Decomposition

T

TA	Timing Advance
	Tracking Area
TAC	Tracking Area Code
TAI	Tracking Area Identity
TAS	Time Accurate Strobe
TAU	Tracking Area Update
TCP	Transmission Control Protocol
TDD	Time Division Duplex
TDMA	Time Division Multiple Access

TD-SCDMA Time Domain Synchronous Code Division Multiple Access
TEI Terminal Endpoint Identifier
TEID Tunnel Endpoint Identifier
TF Transport Format
TFT Traffic Flow Template
TM Transparent Mode
TOI Third Order Intercept
TPC Transmit Power Control
TR Technical Report
TrCH Transport Channel
TS Technical Specification
TSG Technical Specification Group
TTA Telecommunications Technology Association (Korea)
TTC Telecommunications Technology Committee (Japan)
TTCN-2 Tree and Tabular Combined Notation version 2
TTCN-3 Tree and Tabular Combined Notation version 3
TTI Transmission Time Interval
TTL Transistor to Transistor Logic
TX Transmitter

U

UCI Uplink Control Information
UDP User Datagram Protocol
UE User Equipment
UE-AMBR UE Aggregate Maximum Bit Rate
UL Uplink (subscriber to base station transmission)
UL-SCH Uplink Shared Channel
UM Unacknowledged Mode
UMB Ultra-Mobile Broadband
UMD Unacknowledged Mode Data
UMTS Universal Mobile Telecommunications System
UP User Plane
UPE User Plane Entity
UpPTS Uplink Pilot Time Slot
USIM Universal Subscriber Identity Module
UTRA Universal Terrestrial Radio Access
UTRAN Universal Terrestrial Radio Access Network

V

VLAN Virtual Local Area Network
VLR Visitor Location Register
VoIMS Voice over IP Multimedia Subsystem
VoIP Voice over Internet Protocol
VRB Virtual Resource Block
VRC Variable Reference Channel
VSA Vector Signal Analyzer

W

WAP Wireless Application Protocol
W-CDMA Wideband Code Division Multiple Access
WF Weight Factor
WG Working Group
WLAN Wireless Local Area Network
WSP Wireless Service Provider

X

XOR Exclusive Or
XPR Cross Polarization Ratio

Index

B

C

F

G

T

U

V

W

X

Z